P9-DGQ-040

THE PSYCHOANALYTIC FORUM

Volume One

THE PSYCHOANALYTIC FORUM

Volume One

INTERNATIONAL UNIVERSITIES PRESS, INC.

239 PARK AVENUE SOUTH · NEW YORK, N.Y. 10003

First edition in book form, 1972

Library of Congress Catalog Card Number: 66-9929
ISBN: 0-8236-4421-9

Manufactured in the United States of America

The Psychoanalytic

FORUM

Table of Contents Vol. 1, No. 1, 1966

The Forum

Title — **The New Technology and Our Ageless Unconscious**

Author — **Martin Grotjahn, M.D.**

Clinical Professor of Psychiatry at the University of Southern California and Training Analyst at the Southern California Institute of Psychoanalysis. He is the author of *Beyond Laughter*, *Psychoanalysis and the Family Neurosis*, co-editor of *Pioneers of Psychoanalysis*, Editor of "The Psychoanalytic Forum." He is on uneasy terms with the machine and does not drive a car.

Discussants

Richard F. Sterba, M.D.

Clinical Professor of Psychiatry at Wayne State University and a practicing analyst in Detroit, Michigan. He received his medical and psychoanalytic training in Vienna, and is the author of seventy psychoanalytic papers, many of them in the field of applied psychoanalysis. He has written *Introduction to the Psychoanalytic Theory of the Libido* and *Beethoven and His Nephew*, written in collaboration with Editha Sterba.

William L. Langer, PH.D., LLD., PHIL.DR., L.H.D., LITT.D.

Coolidge Professor of History, Emeritus, Harvard University. As president of the American Historical Association he delivered an address in 1957 urging the historical profession to study and make use of the findings of modern psychology, pointing out in concrete instances the value of new insights.

Jules H. Masserman, M.D.

States in his own words: "that he was trained at Wayne, Hopkins, Stanford and Chicago Universities—and worse, at the Chicago Psychoanalytic Institute—for his current nefarious trade of being Professor and Co-Chairman of Neurology and Psychiatry at Northwestern University. To confess further, he has published over three hundred articles, edited twenty-seven books and authored six, but hopes none may do permanent harm. He has been taught psychoanalysis by friends, patients, students and wife."

Thomas Szasz, M.D.

Professor of Psychiatry at the State University of New York's Upstate Medical Center in Syracuse. His two most recent books are *The Ethics of Psychoanalysis* and *Psychiatric Justice*.

John Wilkinson, PH.D.

Currently a Fellow of the Center for the Study of Democratic Institutions, Santa Barbara, California. He has taught physics and philosophy at Chicago, Istanbul, Vienna and California universities for twenty years. He has published many papers in physical chemistry, philosophy, logic and communication theory. He has translated, introduced and annotated several books from German and French on logic, technology and culture and has published a translation from Greek of the pre-Socratic philosophers. His next book is tentatively entitled *The Meaningless Society*.

The New Technology and Our Ageless Unconscious

Martin Grotjahn, M.D.

Beverly Hills, California

The Greek man of antiquity accepted proudly, happily and joyfully, his body and his mind. It did not occur to him, in spite of his great scientific knowledge, to project parts of his body or mind upon lifeless machines—which he used only sparingly, if at all. A schizophrenic person of modern times suffers under the weight and guilt of his narcissistic involvement, which the Greek accepted so gracefully. To solve his problem the schizophrenic patient projects parts of his internalized tensions and anxiety onto the outer world, where he then feels persecuted by hellish machines.

In between stands the prototype of the contemporary man—the engineer. He has lost the happy narcissism of antiquity. He has also freed himself from excessive medieval Christian repression of his body and the pleasure he receives from it. The engineer, therefore, feels ready to project parts of his human functions onto his environment and he finds delight in delegating a great part of body and mind upon the outer world, where he calls it the machine. Most recently, he does not especially mind delegating the proudest function of being human, his intelligence, upon the new thinking machine. It can think better than any human brain, no matter how mathematically gifted the human may be.

Modern man has projected and recreated the images of his body and of his unconscious onto the machine. He has done this with ease and grace—until the machine began to threaten him, his dominance and his master position.

Modern man created around himself inventions of his conscious and unconscious mind and gets great satisfaction from his machines. Where the vision of his eyes comes to an end, he invented the electronic eye and called it television. When he came to the limits of his hearing, he invented the radio and the telephone. His energy assumed the power of any god in antiquity, and no demon of Greek mythology could match the destructive power of the atomic age. What the proud person of antiquity tried to achieve with his body and soul, the modern engineer accomplishes with his machines. They are to a certain extent well equipped to re-establish the dreams of omnipotence as dreamed by the child. The Greek was satisfied in his love for beauty, truth and goodness. To reach for more was punished by the gods whose function it was to keep man from becoming divine.

Modern technology is based on the repression of primary narcissism which then returns in the inventions of the engineer to fulfill the original dreams once removed. Modern man has lost his narcissistic orientation and has to re-establish his childhood dreams by technical means. Modern man can no longer depend on his mother or on himself to become omnipotent again. He now tries a new variation of omnipotence with a new mother: his machine. His achievement has by far outdistanced anything previously dreamed in history.

The technology of modern times repeats the bliss of early existence, but also its powerful destructive elements. The dream of early infantile omnipotency comes to an end when the child realizes that he is not his mother and that he is not even in command of his mother and that she may leave him. No magic-mystical hallucinations can force the world to obey the infant's wishes. Then comes a time of frustration, of rage, of hostility, of destructive fantasies followed by guilt.

Modern man is now in a similar relation to his machines which turn against him. The robot is the dream of the modern engineer which is turning into a nightmare. The early infantile mother which has so much power over her dependent, helpless child is re-created in the self-sufficient machine which can turn her face from the engineer-child and may follow her own laws, like a bad mother who deserted her child. The man who kicks in desperate rage his stalled car reacts as if he understands the unconscious meaning of his machine which is called "she" when it fails him.

Life is becoming a mechanized nightmare, like Disneyland, and may end in atomic holocaust. The Greeks symbolized the bad mother in the Erynians; the Hindus in Kali; Pre-Columbian myth in the Eater of Filth; and we today project the image of the bad mother into reality and call it The Bomb. We adore it and we fear it, quite as intensely as a believer in demons of ancient times.

In our dreams, we can re-create our good and bad mothers. We can even become mothers ourselves, which still is the great unconscious hope of all babies. Modern man may become mother to his machine-children. This would make him both: man and woman, which would make him truly divine since it combines the creativity of both sexes. This in a modern scientific form is a re-creation of early primitive dreams of magic-mystic fulfillment. Mythology was to the Greeks a projection and embellishment of their narcissism. We can experience in our machines something similar, on different levels and with different means.

We could even—and do—invent machines which replace us. This would be the final and total victory of projecting human narcissism into the outer world. The Greek way led to freedom—to freedom even from the machines. Our time is full of examples showing that freedom can be sacrificed in the service of the machine. We invented the car to be free from our cities and to be free in our movements, and we end up in surrendering our culture to the call of the car. California is an excellent example. Californians live today as the rest of the world will live tomorrow. The technical utopia of tomorrow will not have any more cities, only complicated freeway systems. There will be no more orange trees for they are only in the way. Cars will be traveling easily and with great speed from nowhere to nowhere. A movie has already been made which convincingly shows that there are actually no more people living in California, only cars. This "documentary" movie shows that people do not go to church anymore; cars go. They also go to movies, banks, supermarkets, and liquor stores. The one place they cannot go is—to bed.

It is an assignment for the future to extend the idea of freedom to the machine which must not replace the dictatorial mother of early infancy. This is the assignment for the next generation. The juvenile delinquents of today will have the atomic bomb in their hands tomorrow. We can only hope that they turn this destructive energy to peaceful, life-giving power. Submission of nuclear energy is a life-and-death question. It can be done. The past generation invented the machine. The coming generation must interpret and understand this symbol which is called "machine." From there it must progress to the integration of the symbol.

The use of the machine can enhance a person's pride and can even re-establish something vaguely akin to the Greek narcissism. One need only look at an adolescent driving his auto: youthful, healthy, happy, carefree behind the wheel of his sportscar, roaring down the freeway. The Greeks with their admiration of the Olympian hero probably would have accepted such young men. Here, the car, as originally intended, serves narcissistic enjoyment. The individual is again in power and in charge. His body and mind are extended and projected into the world and enjoy mastery to the fullest. This young man moves like Apollo who traveled over the sky in his glorious sun-chariot drawn by the Divine Horses. Where the older generation has failed, the adolescent has succeeded again in fitting the sportscar into his body-scheme, gladly risking his life while playing "chicken," hair flying like Absalom's, roaring with anal impertinence noisily and aggressively down the road, departing from nowhere and arriving nowhere. He is the picture of individual dominance and of narcissistic bliss. He has succeeded in integrating the symbolic meaning of the car back into his body scheme out of which it developed in the first place. The sportscar again became his feet, his legs, his phallus, his power, his speed, his aggression. This is rebellion and glorious, youthful victory. Oedipus is back in the arms of his comfortable seat and he feels like the divine, omnipotent baby pushed in his cradle by his loving mother, Jocasta. If the speedy cradle goes kaput, slaves will fix it.

There is a peculiar perversion of our attitude towards the machine which is of special delight to the analyst: this is the gadgeteer whose true love is the gadget, to which he is addicted, as an addict to his drug.

The gadget is closely related to the fetish with which it has its phallic character in common. It is also close to the toy, since it strives only for perfect function but not for useful performance. Any purpose is of secondary importance and serves only as an excuse, not as a reason for the gadget's existence.

Men have to be seen in shops for stationery and office supplies, sporting goods, cameras, or in hardware stores in order to believe the full impact of a man's passion for a truly beloved gadget. Men must be seen with their shining eyes, their utter fascination, their absorption, their devotion, their minds being closed to the world around them, their sleepwalking in a dream-world of a Santa Claus wonderland and searching for the perfect gadget.

Men look and act as though they were buying themselves a mechanized, desexualized, perfectly functioning, always potent phallus. Gadgeteers have succeeded in projecting phallic enjoyment on a tool. I have seen men in ecstasy about a "voice-controlled" dictaphone, a more and more complicated hi-fi set with three dimensional sound that requires constant and loving attendance by modern troubadors praising the machine's virtues and ready to die for them—without ever having really enjoyed them in the true style of the troubador.

Similar addicts will stand in silent reverie watching heroes excavating the ground for a new office building as if they were witnessing an enormous curettage. They will watch with the same awe the wrecking of a house or the growth of a building into the sky. They almost forget their own bodies while watching the ease and grace with which mountains may be moved by heroic giants of machines.

It is never the purpose nor the function which characterizes the beautiful gadget or the powerful machine. It is only the perfection of function which counts, just as a joke is judged according to the perfection in the disguise of the unconscious aggression. The perfection which the Greek man sought to see in the performance of a victorious hero at an Olympian Game, the gadgeteer wants to see in a car that races faster or a rocket that will reach the moon, or in a tape recorder which records perfectly things we didn't want to hear in the first place. The modern man's narcissistic enjoyment is different from the more direct pleasure of the Grecian person in his body.

The mature woman of today is closer to the Grecian narcissism. She is not unduly impressed by any gadget which she instinctively distrusts. Even in the kitchen women prefer simple, and easily handled time and labor saving devices. The fancy, electrically controlled kitchen is dreamt up by her male partner, who must show the woman his masculine mechanized superiority even here in her domain. A fancy kitchen with electronic gadgets is greeted by the woman with suspicion and resistance. She cannot really understand the joy of the man for perfect performance which is the trademark of the gadgeteer.

The truly female counterpart of the gadgeteer is the spinster who finds it impossible to throw away any box and collects them, whether they be large or small, wide or narrow, flat or high, for hats or for gloves, gift-wrapped or simple cardboard. She will store them, defend her collection with her life against a male intruder who may need a box in which to store his gadgets. She will also hope to find an occasion to use her treasure, but no object is good enough to fill any one of her beloved boxes.

The test-ground of the good woman is her bed: there she is at her best, and there she knows she cannot be replaced by a machine— and her man cannot offer her a gadget.

There is no reason to be afraid of the machine, there is no reason to submit to it or to be against it. We must consider the machine as an extension of the human body and our unconscious. The machine should serve us and not dominate us.

Our next assignment is the integration of the machine as a symbol. Only when this is accomplished, can man develop full confidence in the machine, or better, we will have reached a new state of man's development— toward mastery of his inner and outer world. We will have turned the machine into a loyal, faithful friend of man. From there we really could proceed to enter the Millennium of an analytic Utopia.

Summary

The invention and development of the machine is related to the history of man's narcissism. The development proceeds from the person in Greek antiquity who was unwilling and incapable of projecting libido from his own body and mind upon mechanized objects in the outer world— to the Christian person of the Renaissance who recuperated from having experienced his body as sinful, and learned to project body functions on inanimate objects, as, i.e., the machine.

Finally the person of the modern engineer emerged. Joyfully and happily he accepted the machine as an extension of his body image. He does not even feel threatened by computers which compete with human intelligence.

Future progress in man's development to establish peace between his never aging unconscious and the future of technology is the final integration of technology (from which the machine is only a part) into man's conscious and unconscious. Only such "*symbolic integration*" will safeguard the future of mankind which is physically and spiritually threatened by technological progress. How this can be done is illustrated here with the analysis of the gadgeteer.

Without psychoanalytic insight, knowledge and application, such development is difficult to envisage.

Bibliography

1. Ellul, J. *The Technological Society*. Introduction and translation by John Wilkinson, New York, Alfred Knopf, 1964.
2. Freud, S. (1914) "On Narcissism: An Introduction." In *Standard Edition*, London, Hogarth Press, Vol. 14, 1957, pp. 67-102.
3. Grotjahn, M. "About the Representation of Death in the Art of Antiquity and in the Unconscious of Modern Men." In Wilbur, G., *Psychoanalysis and Culture*. New York, Int. Univ. Press, 1951, pp. 410-424.
4. ———. "The Recognition of the Oedipus Complex in Greek Antiquity: Two Quotations from Aristophanes." Samiksa, Journal of Indian Psychoanalytic Society, Bose Number, 1955, pp. 28-34.
5. ———. *Beyond Laughter*. New York, McGraw-Hill, 1957.
6. ———. "On Bullfighting and the Future of Tragedy." Int. J. Psa. Vol. 11, 1959, pp. 238-239.
7. ———. "Some Dynamics of Unconscious and Symbolic Communication in Present-Day Television." In *The Psychoanalytic Study of Society*, Vol. 3, 1963, pp. 356-359.
8. ———. "The Ancient Greeks' Awareness of Their Unconscious," Bulletin of the Philadelphia Ass'n for Psa., Vol. 14, 1964, pp. 43-44.
9. ———. *The Symbol in History and Today*. To be published.
10. Langer, W. "The Next Assignment." Amer. Imago, Vol. 15, 1958, pp. 235-266.
11. Masserman, J. (Ed.) *Psychoanalysis and Social Process. Science and Psychoanalysis Series. Vol. 4*. New York, Grune & Stratton, 1961.
12. Reik, T. *Myth and Guilt*. New York, George Braziller, Inc., 1957.
13. Sachs, H. "The Delay of the Machine Age," Psa. Quart. Vol. 2, 1933, pp. 404-424.
14. Sterba, R. "Comment on Dr. Hacker's Paper" (about "The Reality of Myth") Int. J. Psa. Vol. 45, 1964, pp. 444-446.
15. Szasz, T. S. "Ethics of Psychoanalysis." In *The Theory and Method of Autonomous Psychotherapy*. New York, 1965, p. 226.

416 North Bedford Drive
Beverly Hills, California 90210

Discussant

Richard Sterba, M.D.

Detroit, Michigan

Martin Grotjahn's paper, although written in a light vein and in an amusing, apercu-like fashion, deals with the matter of greatest importance in the present human situation and of deep disturbance to all people who care about the physical as well as the spiritual future of mankind. We are constantly reading about the unsavory influence of the machines on our culture, and hearing lamentations about the loss of spiritual values due to the second technical revolution. One cannot escape the impression that these are voices crying in the wilderness; the machine age progresses irresistably and the West and the great Eastern powers get more and more drunk with their technical success. Their competitive struggle for superiority and "firsts" in both constructive as well as destructive uses, keeps all of us in breathtaking suspense of expected triumph and anxiety of annihilation.

This nervewracking anguish, all man-made, should make us aware how irrational, nonsensical, nay utterly foolish the machines have made us. However, we have to realize that our own unconscious irrationality stares into our face when we are awed by the uncanny threat of the machines. It is the destructive urges within ourselves which have been externalized and taken material shape and power in the form of our technical creations.

Here the psychoanalyst feels called upon to raise his voice. He is familiar with the irrational in man, equipped to understand it and cognizant of its powerful, often overpowering influence on man's behavior. But, alas, this very familiarity makes him feel that his also will be but another cry in the wilderness. However, some hope lies in bringing the irrational under conscious control by recognizing its motor forces which ascend from repressed infantile sources and thus making it accessible to the rationality of intellect and reason.

Grotjahn tries to uncover some of the unconscious dynamic motivations for our inebriation with our technical creations. I find his interpretation of the machine as the projective materialization and dynamization of the early infantile mother image new and stimulating. However, I would like to add my own interpretation to his. The first machines were undoubtedly means to enlarge our sensory and muscular faculties. In "Civilization and Its Discontents" Freud speaks of this significance of our technical inventions. He says: ". . . man has almost become a god himself. Only, it is true, in the fashion in which ideals are usually attained according to the general judgment of humanity. Not completely; in some respects not at all, in others only half way. Man has, as it were, become a kind of prosthetic god. When he puts on all his auxiliary organs he is truly magnificent; but those organs have not grown on to him and they still give him much trouble at times. Nevertheless, he is entitled to console himself with the thought that this development will not come to an end precisely with the year 1930 A.D. [the year of publication of Freud's treatise]. Future ages will bring with them new and probably unimaginably great advances in this field of civilization and will increase man's likeness to God still more. But in the interests of our investigations, we will not forget that present-day man does not feel happy in his Godlike character."

It is my impression that the speedily increasing technological advances in our age, which were unimaginable even at the time Freud wrote these sentences, indicate and lead to a "Bedeutungswandel" (a change of significance) of our technical creations, in that a change of the unconscious significance of the machine from "self-god" to "object-god" has taken place. The immensely powerful and self-steering, self-controlling supermachines of our time remind one of the image of the omnipotent, terrifying godhead.—In the beginning the machines served man. Now, not only the gadgeteer but a great part of humanity—and I do not exclude mature women—have made a cult of the machine.

In this connection I am reminded of the first sentence in the Catholic catechism which I had to learn by heart in grade school: "Gott hat den Menschen erschaffen, damit er ihm diene und ihn anbete." (God has created man that he should serve Him and adore Him.) Nothing demonstrates better the projective investment of God with infantile narcissism than this dogmatic statement. For it is the baby who acts according to and lives by the conviction that everybody should wait on him and adore him,—and under favorable family circumstances, he is supported in this conviction by his surroundings.

In our age, the god of religion has been gradually destroyed by science. It has been replaced by the god of technique, the machine. This makes the worship of the machine deep and consuming. But this shift seems to imply a regression. The projective displacement from self to the technical object is of a more primitive character and goes along with a sharper ambivalence and a return to a more cruel and revengeful concept of the supreme power. "Ce Dieu aussi a soif" (This God is also thirsty), and his demand for blood is greater than any religious god had ever thirsted for. His high priests, the military technicians of the great powers, do not talk only of hecatombs, they figure on decades of millions of human sacrifices.

Grotjahn considers it the assignment of the next generation to gain control over this dictatorial power of the machine. But the voice of the intellect is so soft—and so slow in its effect, —and the machine-God grows so rapidly to inconceivable might and power that one shudders to think of the gigantic task that lies before us. Sigmund Freud himself considered mere reason not sufficient to stem the flood of destructive dynamism with which we invested our mechanized weapons. He had to base his hope for the survival of mankind on the instinctual antagonist of the destructive impulse, on the love instinct, and he finds the outcome of the struggle uncertain.

We in our present time of thousandfold increased destructive technical power and rapid disintegration of the human community read the last words of *Civilization and Its Discontents* with gowing apprehension: "The fateful question for the human species seems to me to be whether and to what extent their cultural development will succeed in mastering the disturbance of their communal life by the human instinct of aggression and self-destruction. It may be that in this respect precisely the present time deserves a special interest.

"Men have gained control over the forces of nature to such an extent that with their help they would have no difficulty in exterminating one another to the last man. They know this, and hence comes a large part of their current unrest, their unhappiness and their mood of anxiety. And now it is to be expected that the other of the two 'Heavenly Powers,' eternal Eros, will make an effort to assert himself in the struggle with his equally immortal adversary. But who can foresee with what success and with what result?"

Discussant

William L. Langer, PH.D., LLD., PHIL.DR., L.H.D., LITT.D.
Annisquam, Massachusetts

I find it difficult to comment constructively on Dr. Grotjahn's essay "The New Technology and Our Ageless Unconscious" because his approach is not at all historical and I lack the competence to judge of his thesis on the basis of psychoanalysis by itself.

I do see some danger, though, in broad generalizations about the Greek mind or kindred phenomena. We know what the views and attitudes of some select figures were, but we are certainly entitled to doubt whether the average, aggressive and businesslike Greek of ancient times would come near meeting the specifications of the philosophers. Furthermore, it must be remembered that that entire civilization rested upon slavery and that man need have no interest in gadgets or machines if he can exploit others for his purposes.

It strikes me that man has at all times had a keen curiosity about all kinds of contraptions and that, in cases of necessity, he could invent machines (building and war machinery, clocks, mill-wheels, harness, etc.) for which he could not enlist human power. After all, we know that animals, too, share this basic curiosity.

Finally, I think I have less animus against the machine than Dr. Grotjahn. From my own researches I can only conclude that the machine has saved humanity from untold misery. I recognize the dangers that the machine may run away with us and I see that the machine age has confronted us with a host of psychological problems. But I would feel better if the entire, broad question could be viewed a little more in its historical context.

Discussant

Jules H. Masserman, M.D.
Chicago, Illinois

Permit me first to offer a sincere testimonial to psychoanalysis. Before my own analysis, I did not believe in "the Unconscious" (used as a noun). After my ordeal, I now know the term to be a highly useful concept, exquisitely designed to hide fuzzily panchrestic thinking. Since this utility, being indispensable to human comfort, is "ageless," I am in thorough agreement with the title chosen for his paper by Dr. Grotjahn—who, as I tell him and everyone else, has long been my good, great and egregious friend. But as to his main theses:

I am not among the "we who have recognized two different personality types," other than that perhaps there *are* two types of persons, one of which recognizes "two different personality types."

I no longer even think I know what abstrusely arcane analytic aphorisms mean, e.g.:

"repression of narcissism" (what thought or act is not self-assertive?—and when Narcissus deserted his appropriately named Mistress Echo, was it for "love of himself"—irritating tautology—or of his self-reflective *image*?); or

"anal impertinence" (unless poet Grotjahn literally means auto-exhaust flatus)—and so on *ad nepentham*.

But I *do* know this: as a musician who likes to muse and be amused, I admire Dr. Grotjahn's felicitous phonemes, rhythmic rhetoric and homiletic harmonics—so herewith my applause, in hopes for a responsive encore.

Discussant

Thomas Szasz, M.D.

Syracuse, New York

Dr. Grotjahn addresses himself to an immense subject: man's effort to control his environment, both human and nonhuman. He tackles it with imagination, learning, and a humanistic commitment to individualism. Because of the vast scope of the subject and the brevity of the paper, inevitably the presentation is somewhat impressionistic.

I shall confine my comments to one aspect of the essay—the man-machine relationship. In some ways, man's relationship to the machine parallels man's relationship to man. In the past, man dominated his fellow man by enslaving him: the historical precursor of the machine is the slave. Now, man dominates his nonhuman slave: the machine is a mechanical "slave" (the robot).

How does the slave threaten the freeman, or the machine, man? The slave threatens his master in two basic ways: first, by revolt and direct aggression; second, by offering himself as a human *object*, rather than *subject*. I am not certain which of these threats was the greater in the past history of mankind; it might well have been the latter, as only now we begin to realize.

The machine threatens man in somewhat different ways: first, by providing the means whereby man can injure and destroy his fellow man with unparalleled ease and effectiveness; second, by rendering much human labor socially unnecessary and hence existentially meaningless, thus liquidating many persons' reason for being. Here also the latter may be the greater threat.

It is easier to state these problems than to solve them. This is especially so because just as man is indispensable to his fellow man, so the machine is indispensable to man. Though human aggression threatens mankind, it is only through human cooperation that culture—and hence the flowering of the individual *in* society—is possible. Similarly, though the machine may dehumanize and destroy man, it is only through the use of tools—that is, of machines—that man rises above the level of the animal. In the final analysis, the problem of man's relation to the machine turns on the same axis as his relation to his fellow man: the need to curb, to limit the human passion for control, mastery, and domination.

Psychoanalytic understanding can contribute to the amelioration as well as to the aggravation of the man-machine relationship. Like any knowledge, "psychoanalytic understanding" may be used for the humanization of man, or for his dehumanization.

Discussant

John Wilkinson, PH.D.

Santa Barbara, California

There is a notable parallelism between the Greeks' own account (insofar as it can be reconstructed) of the mature, responsible person, and Grotjahn's, which proceeds in terms of psychoanalytic theory. Since Grotjahn takes the ancient Greeks to represent a model of maturity, it is imperative that this should be so; entirely apart from the fact that the existence of such a parallel, amounting almost to an isomorphism, is the most convincing "proof" of the warranted assertibility of *both* accounts. The two indeed differ, but principally in the way a map differs from the terrain it represents.

Specifically, the Greeks lacked, or seemed to lack, an adequate account of the role played by the dynamic unconscious in the development of the psyche, which, according to many, was Freud's most important contribution. This lacuna, however, does not invalidate the truth of the Greek view; it merely requires that it be supplemented. In other words, the Greeks identified successfully the formal, final, and material "causes" of psychic development, but lacked what Grotjahn has given in Freudian terms, that is, an account of the efficient cause, much in the way Newton specified the efficient cause of Kepler's laws by introducing the concept of "force-at-a-distance."

There is only one thing which Grotjahn says that, I believe, requires explication. To his statement that the Greeks were "unwilling and incapable" to project their libido onto mechanized objects in the external world, I would add the stipulation: "and to let it remain there." The Greek libido had to proceed in every conceivable way outwards in experience; but it then had to return inwards upon itself in order that fullness of experience of the phenomenal world should be converted into symbolic awareness of the noumenal world. For example, we know that the Greeks constructed innumerable mechanical gadgets—and then destroyed them, not from fear of the autonomous technological society that is so wide-spread today, but because it just was not in the Greek character to have any traffic at all with the mechanical appurtenances of slaves or of the slave mentality.

Before giving concrete evidence for what I take to be the Greek attitude, it seems necessary to point out that Grotjahn has given a masterful account of what is in general lacking in discussions of technology and culture, i.e., what philosophers have termed the principium individuationis. We do not lack (and, in fact, we are overwhelmed by) macro-analyses of the technological phenomenon, sociological, political and philosophical. The question remains how the technological society at once refers to the individual person and to the larger social framework of which our knowledge is impersonal and statistical, and which limits but does not determine human activities.

To find the principle of individuation is inter alia to raise the moral problem, perhaps the most difficult problem of philosophy, the very name of which, "casuistry," indicates how contemptible are most of the proposed "solutions." The problem of the individual is an important one for physical realms like that of the subatomic particles or the extra-galactic island universes; but it is transcendently so for the human person. In the past this problem has most often been solved by the elaboration of a religious structure which related the person simultaneously to his culture and to whatever supreme value he descried in his universe, a value at once universal and personal. Many persons prefer this method yet, but others have turned to various versions of existentialism, most of which have the grave defect of explaining things by explaining them away, since they effectively deny the role of and need for symbolic resolution. Many educated persons today prefer some variant of the psychoanalysis of Freud, which is both a philosophy of life and a method of therapy, and perhaps more important in the former aspect than in the latter.

It is Grotjahn's great merit to have found the principle of individuation using the Freudian conceptual apparatus but at the same time making that historical sense which Freud himself most often did not make, perhaps from too great a fondness for paradox. It is, I think, historically sound, to seek, as Grotjahn does, the Greeks' solution in their resolution of that state of mind which is necessary to one who would harmoniously retain his individuality and live as a good citizen in the polis, that is, as the higher narcissism.

It is to be expected almost a priori that the most speculative and self-analytic people of history should have left behind them enough traces in their language and literature to enable us to test the merits of Grotjahn's contentions. I am convinced this is not possible with the aid of their explicit and perhaps overrational philosophies, which insufficiently describe the dynamism of their psychic development. It is clear that here only a beginning can be made in such an enterprise designed to support Grotjahn's analysis.

In the first place, the Greeks, without waiting for Sir James Frazer, were well aware that the myth of Narcissus was connected with their practice of deeming ominous the beholding of one's own reflection in a mirror. We call this abhorrence today a "superstition"; but this pejoration comes ill from people whose only apparent guide in political and social life consists in projecting images by mechanical means which have next to no connection with any possible reality.

The eidolon (or image) was primarily a deception to the Greeks, because it was material, unstable, and superficial; and anyone who took it as more than this could never attain to wisdom (sophia). To mistake the phenomenal for the noumenal was deservedly to bring upon one's head the fate of Narcissus. No possible image could serve as a basis for the fullest and most complete happiness, eudaimonia, or philosophic insight, in which matter falls away, and which, through the medium of dialogue, or dialectic, makes the world symbolic and universal. Here one might note the great similarity between the Freudian dialogue between analyst and analysand, and the dialectic, say, of Plato.

To return from the observation of the world to the contemplation of reality was to experience the highest happiness and to grasp the true nature of things. The individual who remained mired in externalities suffered paranoia, literally a derangement of the highest faculties by being distracted. Most men, even among the Greeks, were not true lovers of wisdom; but they were, nevertheless, capable of an intermediate condition of practical self-containment, euphoria or dysphoria, in which they remained partially wise and partially stuck in mere externalities. These two terms always referred to persons who were in a state of content, or discontent, with those material things which the true philosopher would despise. As intermediate conditions of mind they correspond, respectively, remarkably well to Grotjahn's engineer, the technological euphoriac who has not achieved the higher eudemonic narcissism even though he has lost his mediaeval crankiness about guilt and sin, and to the man who is discontented with the modern world because he feels threatened by the machine as a result of his inability to understand it, without, however, becoming schizophrenic.

There is, then, an almost complete correspondence between the extremes and the means in Grotjahn's account and what I take to be the Greek.

One can well believe that this "happy," or higher, narcissism represents an end worthy of striving for, especially since it has latterly seemed to an increasing number of mortals that their former value systems have left much to be desired. But what if, as Ellul and others contend, the technological society is autonomous? What if it has its own imperatives? In these circumstances, the happy narcissist would be living in a fool's paradise. Only if he can contrive not only to ignore the gadgets, but also not to be enslaved by them, can we speak with any confidence at all of the eudaimonia of the Greeks as a summum bonum in an increasingly technologized society.

Author's Response

Martin Grotjahn, M.D.

Beverly Hills, California

To answer the discussants in detail would amount to writing a new essay on the place of the psychoanalyst shaping the new great society of the future. It would amount to writing an analytic Utopia, which of course is badly needed. Since this, however, is too big an assignment, I conclude with my thanks to the contributors who discussed my essay—and to Dr. Masserman.

Professor William Langer criticizes the narrow basis of this analytic study. From Freud's time on, sweeping and valid analytic assumptions have been made on just such narrow basis, which horrifies the historian, disgusts the statistician, but stands up well against the nagging doubts of time. The analysis of one asthma case or of a few national-socialistic leaders has allowed quite accurate conclusions to the psychodynamics of asthma or Nazi-ideology.

The Forum

Title **The Need of Patients to Act Out During Analysis**

Author **Herbert A. Rosenfeld, M.D.**

Has been engaged in training analysts and lecturing at the Institute of Psychoanalysis in London since 1949. In his private practice he has treated many psychotic and borderline patients by psychoanalysis. He has written several papers on patients whose analysis presents difficult technical problems, such as narcissistic, schizophrenic and depressed patients. Some of his work has recently been published in the book, *Psychotic States*.

Discussants

Mark Kanzer, M.D.

Clinical Professor of Psychiatry at the State University of New York, Medical College (Downstate), where he is a member of the psychoanalytic faculty. He served as a participant and reporter of the panel on "Acting Out" at the Spring Meeting of the American Psychoanalytic Association in 1956 and has written two additional papers on this, as well as many other subjects.

Elliott Jaques, M.D., PH.D.

Professor and Head of the School of Social Sciences at Brunel University, London, England. He is a member of the Board of the British Psycho-Analytical Society and was formerly its Honorary Scientific Secretary. One of his activities has been that of the application of the theories of Melanie Klein to the treatment of psychosis.

James S. Grotstein, M.D.

Clinical Instructor in Psychiatry at the University of California at Los Angeles; he is on the faculty of the Los Angeles Psychoanalytic Institute and also teaches at its Extension Division. He is co-author of "Projective Identification in the Therapeutic Process," which is to appear in the spring issue of the "International Journal of Psychoanalysis."

Phyllis Greenacre, M.D.

Clinical Professor of Psychiatry at Cornell Medical School and a Training Analyst of the New York Psychoanalytic Institute of which she was President. She has written books and papers dealing with various phases of transference, acting out, creativity and psychoanalytic studies of the infancy and development of great artists.

The Need of Patients to Act Out During Analysis [1]

Herbert A. Rosenfeld, M.D.

London, England

More than 50 years ago, Sigmund Freud discussed acting out: "We may say that here [in analysis] the patient remembers nothing of what is forgotten and repressed but that he expresses it in action." Freud then relates the acting to the repetition compulsion and continues: "As long as the patient is under treatment he never escapes from this compulsion to repeat; at last one understands that it is his way of remembering. . . . We soon perceive that the transference is itself only a bit of repetition and that the repetition is the transference of the forgotten past not only to the physician, but also on to all the other aspects of the current situation. We must be prepared to find, therefore, that the patient abandons himself to the compulsion to repeat, which is now replacing the impulse to remember not only in his relation with the analyst but also in all other matters occupying and interesting him at the time." (6)

Freud emphasizes that acting out is intimately bound up with the transference which inevitably penetrates into all aspects of the patient's life. He also states clearly that we must recognize the reactivation of past experiences, which means acting out, as the method by which the patient remembers.

I fully accept Freud's views that this reactivation or acting out is a necessary part of any analysis and I propose to call this *PARTIAL ACTING OUT* to differentiate it from excessive or total acting out, which Freud discusses in the second part of the same paper. Here Freud states that acting out is related to the strength of the patient's resistances.

Melanie Klein extended Freud's work in her paper on the "Origins of the Transference": "My conception of the transference as rooted in the earliest stages of development and in deeper layers of the unconscious is much wider and entails a technique by which from the whole material presented the unconscious elements of the transference are deduced; for instance, reports of patients about their everyday lives, relations and activities, not only give insight into the function of the ego, but also reveal, if we explore their unconscious content, the defenses against the anxieties stirred up in the transference situation. For the patient is bound to deal with conflicts and anxieties re-experienced toward the analyst by the same methods as he used in the past. That is to say, he turns away from the analyst as he attempted to turn away from his primal objects; he tries to split the relation to him, keeping him either as a good or as a bad figure; he deflects some of the feelings and attitudes experienced toward the analyst on to other people in his current life, and this is part of acting out." (10)

I would develop this view still further: I believe the patient's need of excessive acting out is always related to an excessively aggressive turning away from the earliest object. If there has been little hostility, we encounter only partial acting out, even when early oral phases are re-experienced, provided the transference is fully understood and interpreted. (Excessive acting out can be produced *artificially* by faulty psychoanalytic technique or by an analyst who projects his own problems into the patient and so forces him to act out.

[1] This is a shortened version of the paper, presented at the Los Angeles Psychoanalytic Society on April 22, 1965, which will appear in Dr. Rosenfeld's book, *Psychotic States* (International Universities Press).

Fenichel and Greenacre have stated it is often the counter-transference of an ill-adjusted analyst that drives patients to excessive acting out.)

In following Melanie Klein's theories of early infantile development, I suggest that the infant always experiences love and hate toward the breast from the beginning of life. The first three months, approximately, of the infant's life are characterized by splitting[2] the relationship to the breast into a good and bad one, and also by schizoid defense mechanisms which are used by the infant to deal with his anxieties which at this earliest phase of development are of a paranoid type. The extent of the paranoid anxiety relates to the strength of the infant's hostile feelings experienced during this early phase and this hostility depends again both on external and on internal inborn factors.

If the hostility, and so the paranoid anxiety, in this early phase is not excessive, the split between the loved and the hated object is never very rigid; the infant soon begins to realize that his love and hate are directed toward one and the same object. This enables him to experience guilt and depression and the anxieties then center round the fear of losing the loved object. This increases his capacity to feel love and to introject a good object more securely, which again strengthens his ego and makes it possible for him to bear frustration without entirely losing his love. This phase of development has been called the "depressive position."

If, however, in infancy excessive hostility and consequently excessive paranoid anxiety is experienced, then fixation to the object in the paranoid-schizoid phase occurs. The stronger the fixation and the greater the split between a bad and an idealized object the greater the difficulty of later working through the depressive position, on which depends the individual's capacity to cope with frustrations without entirely losing the good object.

It is such a patient, who is fixated in the paranoid-schizoid position, who tends to act out excessively, constantly repeating his early relations to objects. He deals with frustrations by splitting the analyst into a good and a bad object, and he acts out continually, projecting the good or the bad figure of the analyst on to an external object. This cannot lead to insight, because some acknowledgment of a relationship to the analyst in which good and bad feelings can be tolerated simultaneously is necessary for any real insight to develop.

The therapist must analyze, in the transference, the patient's fixation on the paranoid level of development, which prevents him from working through his depressive feelings. Then love and hate become less split up; both can be increasingly experienced towards the analyst as one object. This brings insight to the patient about the hostility in his excessive acting out. Depression will emerge in the transference and acting out will decrease.

However, there is a danger that the analysis of an excessively acting out patient may follow another course. He may suddenly attempt to give up most of his ego activities and his external relations to objects in everyday life and show markedly regressive behaviour in the analysis, acting like a small dependent child.

The risk of such a regression is greater when the analysis has succeeded in mobilizing positive transference feelings and the patient becomes aware that all his object relations and activities, including his adult sexuality, are based on a completely hostile turning away from the primary object, which the analyst represents. He then feels intense guilt about all activities outside analysis, because they represent a hostile independence of the analyst. These guilt feelings are very difficult to bear,

[2] (Edit. Note: In M. Klein's theories, splitting is a necessary mental mechanism for normal infantile development, it is the excessive use of splitting which has pathological results.)

because they contain not only depressive but strong paranoid elements. If the depressive anxieties in the superego predominate, the need to make reparation can assert itself and the excessive acting out gives way to normal cooperation in analysis.

If, however, paranoid anxieties in the superego gain the upper hand, the attempt at reparation fails and the patient is driven back to the earliest fixation to the mother on the paranoid-schizoid level. This is the moment when we have to deal with the regression in the transference and the patient starts to act out excessively with the analyst.

The patient now anticipates that the analyst will actually retaliate for all the hostility that the patient expressed toward him in his excessive acting out, with similar hostile activities. He therefore tries with every means at his disposal to get friendly acting out from the analyst to obscure and counteract these fears.

The analyst must realize these overwhelming demands for a good relationship cover an intense persecutory fear—corresponding to the patient's hostile activities when turning away from his primary object. If analysis of the persecutory fears gradually succeeds in mobilizing his depressive anxieties and need to make reparation, the regressive acting out diminishes.

Clinical Example:

After excessive acting out, this patient was heading for total regression. There had been constant real danger of her stopping analysis, to permanently reside in a mental hospital or to commit suicide. She was suffering from severe hysterical depression and eating difficulties. She had previously acted out excessively her aggressive turning away from mother to father at weaning time by turning away from the analyst to an idealized male figure in her current life. When she later became aware that all her intellectual activities and her interest in men were related to her contempt and total hostility toward her mother, she felt that she had to return to a good relationship to me, as the mother, instead of abusing and ridiculing me constantly as she had been doing for some time. She tried to cooperate again and, after some weeks, said she had no other friends than me, demanded constant reassurance and love from me, and also demonstrated every day that she was less able to look after herself.

In one session, she behaved like a small child, who could do nothing, not even walk or think. She said now I had to do everything for her, I must take her to a nursing home because she would be unable to talk and feed herself and would die. She then ceased to respond to anything I was interpreting and lay motionless. This situation seemed quite alarming until I interpreted to her that she could not talk or move because she felt everything she was doing was wrong and so had to stop it. She replied almost immediately, that all day long, the only thing she had been thinking was: "Everything I am doing is wrong. I cannot go on. I must stop it."

I interpreted she felt her friendship with other people and all her activities, walking, talking, eating and even thinking, seemed to her a hostile act against me, which was why she had to stop them. She almost immediately became able to think and to cooperate better in the sessions. This situation had of course to be worked through many times, but the analysis was able to prevent total regression.

One of the main difficulties in this analysis was her constant pressure to drive me to acting out. She was desperate to see me behave in a friendly way, because she was afraid of my cruelty. A particular anxiety was that I wanted to make her totally dependent on me to show her that I as a mother was superior to her as the baby, then I would abandon her, as she in the earlier phase of analysis had been attempting to do to me. While she was constantly looking for a loving mother in external life, her internal mother was felt to be extremely cruel, corresponding to her own hostile turning away from mother in infancy; therefore no external figure could be trusted.

Many patients fixated on the paranoid-schizoid level present additional problems, which complicate treatment. Early excessive splitting interferes with the capacity for verbal thinking and sublimation, as well as other aspects of ego development. (3,13) This increases the patient's tendency to deal with difficulties by action rather than by thought.

Greenacre (7) points out that the patient who acts out has suffered "more or less emotional disturbances in the early months of infancy with increased orality, diminished tolerance of frustration and a heightened narcissism." Greenacre also found disturbances of verbal thinking, which, however, she connects with difficulties in the second year.

Acting Out of Chronic Schizophrenic Patients:

Let us briefly examine the acting out of chronic schizophrenic patients. We expect extreme tendencies to act out during analysis, both because of the degree of the schizophrenic's fixation in the paranoid-schizoid position and the intense hostility with which he had turned away from his primary objects. Also the acute confusional state against which the latent and chronic schizophrenic patient constantly has to defend himself greatly increases his need to act out. If the analysis is making progress and the emotions related to the confusional state appear, the patient uses excessive acting out as a defense.

In my paper, "Notes on the Psychopathology of Confusional States in Chronic Schizophrenia," (12) I suggested that when the schizophrenic patient is making progress in analysis and splitting processes lessen, a state of confusion is likely to occur. I described how when love and hate come nearer together and aggressive impulses predominate, the patient does *not* experience guilt and anxiety, and as a result better integration. Instead, his love and hate and his good and bad objects become confused. I thought the schizophrenic's state of confusion must be based on states of confusion in earliest infancy, when good and bad objects could not be kept apart. I suggested that splitting processes became reinforced or new ones developed as a defense against the confusional state.

In later papers on schizophrenia, I concentrated more on the importance of confusion of self and object caused by projective identification as one of the features of the confusional state.[3]

Melanie Klein, in her book *Envy and Gratitude*, (11) greatly clarified the problem of confusion and confusional states. She states that excessive envy, a corollary of the destructive impulses, interferes with the building up of a good object so that the normal split between the good and bad breast cannot be sufficiently achieved. The result is that later differentiation between good and bad is disturbed in various ways. For example, she suggests that excessive envy both interferes with the capacity of the infant for complete satisfaction, even if external circumstances are satisfactory, and also increases the intensity and duration of sadistic attacks on the breast. This makes it difficult for the infant to regain the lost good breast. Melanie Klein feels the basic failure to split the good from the bad object is responsible for states of confusion in early infancy and later on.

Conclusions:

The excessive acting out of the schizophrenic starts as a defense against the con-

---

[3]I am not ignoring external factors. Schizophrenics frequently have a history of traumas in early infancy, but often the external difficulties are slight and the severity of the illness is quite out of proportion to the external factors.

fusional state and is an attempt to keep love and envy separate. There is an attempt to achieve splitting between a good and bad object, but it fails. What we see expressed in the acting out is a series of abnormal splitting processes in which the love object is devalued, split up and projected into many devalued objects. The resultant confusion and uncertainty about the goodness or badness of the object is relatively unimportant, since the objects are so numerous.

To briefly compare the excessive acting out of the non-schizophrenic with that of the schizophrenic: both types are strongly fixated in the paranoid-schizoid position and have experienced intense hostility from both internal and external sources. But there are important differences:

In the first group, who may be neurotic or manic-depressive, the splitting between good and bad object *has been achieved*. This splitting is often excessive with a deep gap existing between a highly idealized and an extremely bad object. The split is exploited by the acting out when the primary object generally is completely devalued and the secondary one is idealized.

In the schizophrenic group of patients, excessive envy plays a decisive part, the split between the good and bad object has *never* been achieved. Consequently, the aggressive turning away from the primary object, which also is devalued, does not lead to an idealization of secondary ones, but to a succession of objects, which are never experienced as wholly good or bad.

Summary

Some acting out is an inevitable part of any analysis, because in the transference the patient repeats the way he has turned away from his infantile object relations, in particular from the primary relation to mother's breast. Whether the patient acts out partially or excessively depends on the degree of hostility with which he turned away from this object.

The patient who rejected his primary object with excessive hostility, and therefore acts out excessively, is also strongly fixated to his primary object at the earliest level of development, the paranoid-schizoid position—and has a predominantly persecutory superego. These factors would explain why patients who act out excessively show a strong tendency to regress to this early fixation when they begin to experience guilt about their excessive acting out in analysis, affecting all their activities in everyday life.

Patients who have turned away from their primary object with less hostility act out only partially in analysis and show themselves capable of object relations, characteristic of having reached the depressive position. The therapeutic task with excessive acting out is to analyze the fixation to the paranoid-schizoid position, the paranoid anxieties related to the hostile turning away from the primary object, and the defenses which prevent normal working through of the depressive position. If we succeed in mobilizing depressive anxiety, guilt and reparation in our patient, he becomes more cooperative and excessive acting out ceases.

In the latent or chronic schizophrenic, the acting out takes a different course, because in his excessive acting out he turns away from a state of confusion, where good and bad objects cannot be differentiated. This makes his acting out a particularly difficult task; because it is analytic progress which threatens to bring on an acute confusional state, often leading to temporary hospitalization or interruption of the analysis.

The psychopathology of the acute confusional state has been greatly clarified by the discovery of the role which excessive envy plays in preventing normal splitting. This has opened the way to better understanding and analysis of the schizophrenic's basic anxieties and his defenses against them, of which excessive acting out is an important one.

Bibliography

1. Altman, L. "On the Oral Nature of Acting Out," J. Amer. Psa. Ass'n; Vol. 5, 1957, pp. 648-662.
2. Bird, B. "A Specific Peculiarity of Acting Out," J. Amer. Psa. Ass'n, Vol. 5, 1957, pp. 630-647.
3. Bion, W. R. "Development of Schizophrenic Thought," Int. J. Psa., Vol. 37, 1956, pp. 344-346.
4. Fenichel, O. "Neurotic Acting Out," Psa. Review, Vol. 32, 1945, pp. 197-206.
5. Ferenczi, S. "Technical Difficulties in the Analysis of a Case of Hysteria." In *Further Contributions to the Theory and Technique of Psychoanalysis*. London, Hogarth Press, 1950, pp. 189-197.
6. Freud, S. (1914) "Recollection, Repetition and Working Through." In *Collected Papers*, London, Hogarth Press, Vol. 2, 1946, pp. 366-376.
7. Greenacre, P. "General Problems of Acting Out," Psa. Quart., Vol. 19, 1950, pp. 455-467.
8. Kanzer, M. "Acting Out and Its Relation to the Impulse Disorders," J. Amer. Psa. Ass'n, Vol. 5, 1957, pp. 136-145.
9. ———. "Acting Out, Sublimation and Reality Testing." J. Amer. Psa. Ass'n, Vol. 5, 1957, pp. 663-684.
10. Klein, M. "The Origins of Transference," Int. J. Psa., Vol. 33, 1952, pp. 433-438.
11. ———. *Envy and Gratitude*. London, Tavistock Publications, 1957.
12. Rosenfeld, H. "Notes on the Psychopathology of Confusional States in Chronic Schizophrenia," Int. J. Psa., Vol. 31, 1950, pp. 132-137.
13. Segal, H. "Some Aspects of the Analysis of a Schizophrenic," Int. J. Psa., Vol. 31, 1950, pp. 268-278.

36 Woronzow Road
St. Johns Wood
London N.W. 8, England

Discussant

Mark Kanzer, M.D.

New York, New York

Dr. Rosenfeld calls attention to two different types of acting out described by Freud. The differentiation is indeed important and deserves more attention than it usually receives. However, the comparison here suggested between "partial" and "total" (excessive) acting out does not seem especially felicitous in conveying the essence of the distinction—at least from Freud's point of view.

"Partial" acting out, which might perhaps better be designated as "primary acting out," occurs spontaneously not only in neurotic but in normal persons, as Freud came to recognize.[1] "Total" (or secondary) acting out, like the transference neurosis to which it belongs, is in part an artifact produced by regression, resistance and other features of the analytic situation. It is therefore not necessarily the case, as we might suppose from Dr. Rosenfeld's nomenclature, that in the one instance a memory is partly recalled in action and in the other totally recalled. One might even expect the opposite, since the original neurosis cannot always be transformed into a transference neurosis, while the latter is already in the process of being verbalized. Actually, memories, in the course of analysis, undergo a piecemeal emergence that involves alternations between acting out and verbalization as interrelated parts of the same process. These therefore bear a complementary as well as an antagonistic relationship to each other.

There are also functional differences between spontaneous (partial, primary) and

[1]Freud, S. (1920) "Beyond the Pleasure Principle." In *Standard Edition*, London, Hogarth Press, Vol. 18, 1955, pp. 7-64.

treatment-induced (total, secondary) acting out, just as there are between spontaneous and treatment-induced dreams. The development of the one is related to adaptation in everyday life and to realistic as compared to unrealistic action; the other is related to the analytic setting and conformity with the fundamental rule. The meaning of "excessive" acting out would have to vary accordingly. Spontaneous acting out may be excessive as judged by normal standards of behavior in impulse neuroses or schizophrenic confusional states. Transference acting out was considered by Freud as excessive when it resulted in actions that impeded the progress of treatment —e.g., a hasty marriage.

The true contrast to "excessive" is "insufficient" acting out; both must be measured in relation to "optimal" acting out, which aids in the reconstruction of the past and the validation of interpretations. Modern conceptions place acting out in a more complex framework than its resistant use as an alternative to verbalized memories. As a form of behavior, it should be brought into conjunction with realistic action and the phase-specific development of the motor apparatus in securing satisfactions through mastery of the external world. Acting out usually represents a fixation on an earlier and now inappropriate means of securing such motor mastery, as by regression to the stage of magic. If the analyst cannot be charmed in the session through the magic of words, then perhaps he may be influenced in some substitutive form by action between sessions, as by the hasty marriage (which is not in itself the repetition of an infantile memory!).

Such an interpretative approach is not likely to derive behavior in direct genetic continuity from the infantile responses to the breast. The complex interrelationships of memory and personality organization must be taken into account, as encountered in analytic experience. If Dora is taken as the prototype, her re-enacted behavior will be found to reflect relatively recent events rather than the infantile period. She did not limit herself to the repetition of these events but varied them by identification with the aggressor and by effective application (from her standpoint) of past learning to present needs. As Erikson[2] maintains her actions must also be seen in relation to the typical problem-solving of adolescents as well as the tenuousness of the therapeutic alliance that she established with Freud. Only the sincere commitment of the patient to verbalization makes it possible to distinguish the resistant and alternative channeling of thought into action.

If we are to follow Freud in his formulations, then the aim of the analyst is to convert such acting out into verbalized recall. This is not likely to succeed where the postulated original memory is that of the breast. Dr. Rosenfeld himself does not propose such a solution. He offers us instead a renewed example of the great difficulties in combining two very different frames of reference.

Discussant

James S. Grotstein, M.D.

Beverly Hills, California

Dr. Rosenfeld has attempted to clarify the process of "acting out" in analysis by tracing it back to its genesis in the splitting process in the paranoid-schizoid position of early infancy, and he has gone one step further in elaborating the crucial differences in the origins of schizophrenic and non-schizophrenic "acting out."

Essentially, he states that, in non-schizophrenic "acting out," *excessive splitting* between the "good" and the "bad" breast, due to

[2]Erikson, E. H. "Reality and Actuality." J. Amer. Psa. Ass'n, Vol. 10, 1962, pp. 451-474.

excessive hostility, causes a violent turning away from the primal object (breast-mother) and an equally intense need to idealize the secondary object. The "acting out" would, therefore, be a defense against intolerable guilt which would emerge if "good" things were remembered about the unequivocally "bad" objects. "Acting out" is, therefore, a manic defense against this unacceptable feeling. In the analytic transference situation, it is shown by excessive "acting out" behavior, which is resistant to insight and parallels an excessive idealization or contempt of the analyst without mitigating ambivalence.

In schizophrenics, "acting out" is a defense against a confusional state caused by *insufficient splitting*, owing to the operation of excessive envy, which does not allow for sufficient development of the good object and, thus, does not permit clear distinction between "good" and "bad"; hence, the confusional state.

I feel Dr. Rosenfeld has greatly added to our understanding of this vexing and recalcitrant problem and has given "acting out" a new dimension which has hitherto been lacking. We always understood "acting out" as a defense against memory, and we knew it was oral in origin. Beyond that, we were at sea. Now we have a guide to follow, namely, the relative degree to which the patient is fixated in the paranoid-schizoid position, with its attendant splitting between excessively "good" and "bad" objects, and the violence of the turning away from the primal object. The degree to which the patient can be brought into contact with his depressive feelings, and the inevitable ambivalence which attends this phase, is, therefore, decisive not only in our evaluating the relative fixedness of the symptom, but also points out the necessary direction of our work, namely, in helping the patient "achieve" contact with his depression.

In schizophrenic "acting out," Dr. Rosenfeld has also greatly helped us by pointing the way to the central cause of the condition and the hitherto relatively unknown confusional state, against which "acting out" acts as a defense. In his elaboration of the effects of excessive envy, he has made quite clear why even normal splitting does not sufficiently occur, and he shows how "acting out" not only defends against the confusional state and the awareness of envy, but also is a desperate means of trying to achieve object separation, but on a futile basis.

I find myself in complete agreement with Dr. Rosenfeld's thesis and wish only to make an additional comment of my own. I feel that the proclivity to "act out" in analysis can be greatly lessened and earlier understood and resolved if we begin the analysis with consistent interpretations about potential basic mistrust of the analyst. This maneuver anticipates all kinds of splitting, including "acting out," and helps to foreclose on any attempts to "act out" the analysis elsewhere. In the case of schizophrenics, it helps them to establish a firm relationship with an analyst who can anticipate and deal with their fears of their own envious and projective attacks which, in lieu of trust, eventuate a negative therapeutic reaction.

Discussant

Elliott Jaques, M.D., PH.D.

London, England

Dr. Rosenfeld has discovered a fundamental fact about acting out, in his relating of the nature of the patient's acting out with the nature of his turning away from his primal objects in the early infant situation.

The distinction made by Dr. Rosenfeld between, on the one hand, the infant, capable of strong love and hate, and on the other hand, the infant who cannot make such emotional discrimination, is of the greatest theoretical and practical importance.

The deep splitting and intense depressive anxiety which characterize the patient capable of love and hate, is consistent with organized psychic activity, even when the patient is acting out. But the underlying psychic confusion which accompanies failure to discriminate between good and bad objects leads not just to anxiety about the analysis of acting out, but its replacement by confusional states.

The importance of these confusional states can be seen especially clearly in those agitated depressions which are at the boundary between psychotic depression and schizophrenic states. Analysis of the commonly excessive acting out is inevitably followed by severe confusional states and outbursts of intense anxiety.

It may well be that these confusional states are particularly characteristic of the borderline depressive-schizophrenic states, since it is precisely at the point where the infant is learning to cope with ambivalence—that is, at the transition from the paranoid-schizoid position to the depressive position—that a failure of capacity to distinguish between good and bad objects is most likely to occur.

Discussant

Phyllis Greenacre, M.D.[1]

New York, New York

Dr. Rosenfeld's paper is one that I find very interesting. Since the Kleinian approach is one which has special concern with the early months of life and especially the preverbal period—and that is a period the effects of which on later developments have greatly preoccupied me—it is naturally a strong temptation to undertake a comparison of the different points of view. I believe also that the way in which the events of that period are reconstructed and interpreted to the patient in the transference setting may be very important in affecting the degree and nature of acting out during analysis.

I would certainly agree with Dr. Rosenfeld that some acting out is inevitable in any analysis of depth and that in that sense there is a "need" for it. However, when it is massive and/or is not brought sufficiently into the analysis by the patient it seems to me both to endanger the efficacy of the analysis itself and to run the risk of creating severe and not always reversible complications in the patient's life.

While I found Dr. Rosenfeld's paper aroused many helpful questions in my mind, I did miss in it a sufficiently detailed consideration of technical procedures and of the nature of the acting out involved, to give me a feeling of assurance that I would be understanding him accurately if I undertook critical comments.

I suppose there are so many publications all the time that it is impossible to keep up with even the major literature. I am aware that I certainly cannot do justice to all the psychoanalytic literature based on Mrs. Klein's theories, much as I might wish to. I note, too, that while Dr. Rosenfeld quotes generously from my early (1950) article on "General Problems of Acting Out," he has not utilized a later article (1963) on "Acting Out in the Transference" (J. Am. Acad. of Child Psych., Vol. II, No. 1), nor any of the other references to acting out in other articles of mine, especially one (1959) on "Technical Problems of Transference" (J. Am. Psa. Ass'n, Vol. 7, pp. 492-502).

I assume that he may share my difficulties in keeping up with everything published, even on subjects in which one is greatly interested.

[1]Dr. Greenacre was not able to write a thorough discussion of the paper, but made the following brief discussion, and permitted its publication.

Author's Response

Herbert A. Rosenfeld, M.D.

London, England

My paper was to clarify the transference problems of the acting out patient and to show that technique depends on clearly understanding the underlying causes of the acting out. Dr. Greenacre, who is herself greatly interested in the problem of acting out, feels I have not sufficiently discussed the technical procedure. I advocate bringing the problem which causes the acting out into the transference *on the right level*, for instance, a patient may act out by grossly promiscuous behaviour, which might be diagnosed as a defense against bringing his oedipal conflict into the transference. But detailed scrutiny of the patient's behaviour often reveals the acting out to be a defense against his early infantile dependency on the analyst-mother. In order to diminish the acting out, it is necessary to bring into the transference the exact details of the way the patient turns away from his dependency on the analyst as the feeding mother.

Dr. Kanzer criticizes the terms I use and among other points stresses the tendency of the acting out patient to manipulate the analyst. To invent new terms is a difficult task and in order to avoid confusion I defined as clearly as possible what I mean by partial and excessive acting out. In *Psychotic States*, I describe in much detail the manipulating and controlling behaviour of some acting out patients who exert strong pressure on the analyst, trying to draw him into acting out. Acting out behaviour is seldom an exact replica of the early infantile situation; patients often use their later experiences particularly their ego activities to act out the aggressive turning away from analyst-mother. These patients are particularly afraid of understanding their acting out in the transference, because they fear they will be faced with almost total regression during the analysis, as I described.

Dr. Grotstein stresses the tendency of manic acting out to diminish when the patient becomes able to face his guilt and depression. Dr. Grotstein emphasizes the importance of analyzing the patient's distrust of the analyst early in the analysis; I assume he refers to patients where the analyst appears as an idealized figure and the negative transference is split off on to people in the current life situation. I agree that it is important to interpret the split off negative transference and the paranoid anxieties related to it as soon as possible in the transference. However, I found in patients who have a deep split between an idealized and a bad persecutory object that interpretations of the positive and negative transference do not stop the tendency to act out until the splitting has diminished.

Dr. Jaques stresses the importance of excessive acting out as a defense against confusional states. He particularly describes the confusional anxieties which occur in psychotic states when the splitting diminishes and good and bad objects and part of the self can no longer be distinguished from one another. The analysis of confusional states which are based on a failure to acquire the capacity for normal splitting or differentiation between good and bad objects in early infancy is extremely difficult unless their basic psychopathology is clearly understood. Melanie Klein, in her book, *Envy and Gratitude*, has thrown light on the origin of the early confusional states which have become gradually more accessible to analysis.

Title **On Freud's Concept of Dream-Action**

Author **John A. Lindon, M.D.**

Editor of "The Psychoanalytic Forum" and Contributing Editor of the *Annual Survey of Psychoanalysis*. He is Assistant Clinical Professor of Psychiatry at the University of Southern California and on the faculty of the Southern California Psychoanalytic Institute. He dreams of being creative.

Discussants

J. O. Wisdom, PH.D.

Has come from the London School of Economics to be Distinguished Visiting Professor of Philosophy and Senior Foreign Scientist Fellow at the University of Southern California, where he taxes graduate students in the philosophy of science. He has published papers in "The International Journal of Psycho-Analysis," and a book, *The Unconscious Origins of Berkeley's Philosophy*. He was President of the Society for Psychosomatic Research.

Sandor Lorand, M.D.

Clinical Professor of Psychiatry at the Downstate Medical Center, University of the State of New York. He is founder and former director of the Division of Psychoanalytic Education at the State University. He is a former President of the New York Psychoanalytic Society and the Psychoanalytic Association of New York, of which he is now Honorary President. Since 1928, he has taught in both Institues on technique and on advanced studies of dream interpretation. He has authored three books, edited thirteen, and has written frequently on dream interpretation.

Daniel C. Siegel, M.D.

On the faculty of the Southern California Psychoanalytic Institute. For ten years he has been Consulting Psychiatrist to the California Institute of Technology, seeing students and faculty members in consultation and psychotherapy. He is involved in research projects concerned with the nature of scientific creativity, and in his psychoanalytic practice treats many scientists.

Bernice T. Eiduson, PH.D.

Director of Research at the Reiss-Davis Child Study Center, Los Angeles. She is co-author of *Biochemistry and Behavior* and author of *Scientists: Their Psychological World*. Data on a five-year follow-up investigation of the research scientists she studied originally is now appearing.

On Freud's Concept of Dream-Action

John A. Lindon, M.D.
Los Angeles, California

Twelve years after the publication of his *Interpretation of Dreams*, Sigmund Freud wrote about a new concept, "dream-action," (Traumhandlung), in "Dreams in Folklore" by Freud and Oppenheim. (6) The only copy of the paper, handwritten by Freud, disappeared for 45 years!

That such a paper had been written was not known until 1956, when Oppenheim's daughter, who was then living in Australia, brought it to the notice of a New York bookseller. Strachey (18) states that the disappearance of the paper—"is no doubt accounted for by the fact that soon afterwards Oppenheim became an adherent of Adler's and, along with five other members, resigned from the Vienna Psychoanalytic Society, October 11, 1911."

Strachey (18) points out that in the 1911 edition of *The Interpretation of Dreams*, Freud announced in a footnote that a paper on dreams in folklore would soon appear, but in subsequent editions the footnote was deleted. Strachey (19) believes that "the concept of dream-action, or at all events the term, vanished with the paper and does not reappear anywhere in Freud's writings."

I believe Freud's concept of dream-action to be a valuable addition to our present understanding of dream psychology, more than a half century after it disappeared.

In the paper, Freud described examples of dreams in folklore in which the dreamer awakened to find himself actually doing things similar to what he had been dreaming about, e.g. defecating on the spouse, manipulating the sexual organs of the spouse, etc. Freud states "... that the dream-action with which they end must have a meaning and must be the one intended by the latent thoughts of the dreamer. If the dreamer defecates over his wife at the end of it, then the whole dream must have this as its aim and provide the reason for this outcome." (6)

I wish to report a clinical example illustrating Freud's theory in the dream of a physician. The dream-action, a medical discovery, seemed to "be one intended by the latent thoughts of the dreamer." And the whole dream seemed to have this dream-action "as its aim and provide the reason for this outcome."

I attended a medical convention with a friend who is a cardiac surgeon. He introduced the speaker as "one of the rare breed of men who have had an original idea in medicine." He described Dr. V.'s revolutionary idea: to remove atherosclerotic plaques in coronary arteries by surgery. Dr. V. then fascinated his audience with a description of his research which led to the successful performance of such operations on otherwise hopeless patients.

When the meeting ended, I talked with Dr. V. and his wife and our mutual friend, the cardiac surgeon, who later told me much about Dr. V., which coincided with my observations. Dr. V. was a warm, friendly and charming man whose passive-dependent character was conspicuous for a practicing surgeon; he was too modest about his accomplishments. He and his wife seemed to have a good relationship. From our conversation I learned he was naive about psychoanalysis and the unconscious. I was quite surprised, therefore, that when I asked him how he had come to such original thinking, particularly since he was not a cardiac surgeon, he replied, "It all started with a dream; the dream led me to it."

The *dream*: "I was operating on my wife's

aunt. I actually had gone into the chest and was using a corkscrew device to pull out the atherosclerotic plugs in the coronary arteries."

The dream awakened him in the night and it seemed important to him, enough so that he awakened his wife and told it to her. He urged her to remember the dream and to remind him of it in the morning. (This was unusual behavior.)

He spontaneously related that the aunt of whom he dreamed had died of a coronary occlusion six weeks before the dream, and that both he and his wife had particularly loved her. Dr. V. continued, "The day following the dream I happened to go down to the pathology lab to see about a report on a surgical specimen I had sent in and I happened to get into a conversation with the pathologist. He started needling me: why don't surgeons excise the short portions of the coronary arteries that are atherosclerotic and do transplants with pieces of bronchial arteries?" Dr. V. and his pathologist friend bantered for a few minutes. Neither was serious, and the subject was forgotten. Later that day he returned to pursue the idea with the pathologist, this time seriously.

Within three weeks he had received approval for a formal research project which, three years later, led to the first surgical removal of coronary plaques being performed on a patient. He had gone back to the pathologist "because of this dream the night before. It seemed to give impetus to the whole thing." Dr. V.'s wife confirmed the content of the dream and that it came before the conversation with the pathologist.

The pathologist's facetious suggestion to transplant pieces of bronchial artery was the basis of the original research project with dogs. This method was unsuccessful because of technical factors. But the research did lead to the technique now in use, which essentially is using a corkscrew device to pull out the atherosclerotic plugs—just as Dr. V. had dreamed.

Dr. V.'s mother had died at an advanced age some three years before his dream. She had lived thirty miles away from Dr. V.'s home; he and his wife visited her several times a month. It seemed Dr. V. and his wife had a good relationship with her. During one of their visits to Dr. V.'s mother, she brought up a *dream* she had the night before: "I was getting ready to take a trip to Europe and I purchased a big steamer trunk at Wanamaker's. I was dragging the trunk after me when I ran into Selma (her deceased husband's dead sister). I was surprised to see her and asked her what she was doing. She said she was leaving on a trip to Europe. I told her I was planning to go to Europe also, and she admonished me, asking why did I bother dragging the trunk when I could have Wanamaker deliver it."

Dr. V. and his wife thought nothing of this dream at the time. They had their visit and left. While driving the thirty miles home, Dr. V. suddenly became upset, turned to his wife and said, "My mother is going to die, that's what the dream is all about." He stopped at the next service station, rushed to the telephone and called his mother to ask if anything was wrong with her health. She reassured him that she felt fine, but at his insistence she agreed to get a check-up the next day. He immediately telephoned her physician and arranged for the examination. There were no unusual findings. Two days later she had an acute coronary occlusion and was hospitalized; the next day she was dead from a second coronary.

Further information showed Dr. V.'s conflicts about aggression, expressed in difficulties in disciplining his children and in asserting himself professionally. Also, he was emotionally inhibited in performing the operation he had conceived.

Discussion of the Clinical Material:

Three aspects present themselves chronologically: his mother's telling him her dream and her death, the death of the aunt and his dream concerning her, and the pathologist's saying what he did at that particular time. Let's look at them in reverse order.

Dr. V.'s wife confirmed both the manifest content of Dr. V.'s dream and that the dream came before his conversation with the pathologist. Neither Dr. V. nor his wife felt it was retrospective falsification. Is it not likely that Dr. V. unconsciously led the conversation to the subject matter and stimulated the pathologist's kidding remarks? If so, why did Dr. V. need the external figure to tell him he should do what he'd just dreamed of doing? Whom did the pathologist represent in Dr. V.'s unconscious mind?

The death of the beloved aunt would be likely to re-awaken feelings associated with the death of his mother three years earlier. Without additional associations, the latent dream content and the dream interpretation remain obscure, but six weeks after the aunt's death, his manifest dream content was that he omnipotently was performing an unheard of operative procedure, with a unique instrument, in a field of surgery which was not his, and that the aunt was alive.

At this point, questions and speculative answers present themselves so rapidly that the psychoanalyst must stop before he performs a complete psychoanalysis without an analysand.

One could speculate that the material reported predominantly represents a man's attempt to deal with his aggressive instincts and reawakened anxiety and guilt feelings, or one could ask if his libidinal instincts were released from some inhibitions so that he was more free to explore hidden areas in the body.

Perhaps once again it was a successful fusion of conflicting emotions which allowed the discovery. The dream fulfilled an unconscious wish and helped in the process of working through and mastery of reality.

Discussion of "Dream-Action" and the Literature:

There is much to suggest that Dr. V.'s dream fits into Freud's concept of dreams which are dreamt to provide the reason for the dream-action. In Dr. V.'s case his dream-action followed within hours of having the dream.

Many questions come about the dream and the subsequent action leading to the medical discovery:

What forbidden gratification was there in the dream to cause the unconscious censor to awaken him?

Why did the dream seem important to a man who was not dream oriented or one to lend much credence to the unconscious, with the exception of his mother's dream?

Why did he awaken his wife, tell her the dream, urge her to remember the dream and remind him of it in the morning, (something he had never done before), instead of his writing the dream down so he could recall it the next day? (This was his custom with night phone calls.)

Why did he need the pathologist to tell him to do something he had just dreamed of doing? Why didn't he mention the dream to the pathologist?

Why did he have to follow the pathologist's suggestion of transplanting pieces of bronchial artery and take two years to come to the successful technique which essentially was just as he had dreamed it?

Why his need to attribute much of the responsibility for the discovery to the dream, as if to disclaim personal responsibility?

Why was he emotionally inhibited in performing the operation he had discovered even though professionally competent to do such surgery?

It was surprising that this man would be so insightful about his mother's dream, and attribute such importance to the dream that he acted upon it with urgency. What part did this experience of three years before play in his using a dream to lead him to the unconsciously forbidden new operation?

Simmel (16) points out many of the potential decompensating influences in the profession of medicine. Grotjahn (8) observes that "a surgeon, in particular, not only is allowed but is invited to cross taboos, which is the great advantage and great danger of being a physician."

Bertram Lewin (12) pointed out in discussing certain insomnias that when the "wish to sleep has come to mean to sleep forever with the deceased love object, the resistance to sleep may be set up." Perhaps Dr. V. awakened because of the danger of sleeping forever with the loved aunt-mother, symbolized in his dream, ". . . I *actually* had gone into the chest . . ." (Dr. V.'s emphasis verbally).

Dr. V.'s awakening his wife and telling the dream to her could be his urge to be able to go back to sleep, reassured against the danger of sleeping forever by having put the dream into the omnipotent pre-oedipal mother-wife, who as a good wife of a busy surgeon would soothe him back to sleep. He also put the responsibility onto her of retaining and recalling the dream in the morning, almost as if to make it her dream, perhaps thereby to have her, as a maternal superego figure, share the responsibility for whatever came of his dream.[1]

His manipulating the pathologist could be seen as his need to have superego approval of the father, a role pathologists fill in the unconscious of the surgeons I have analyzed. His emotional inhibition in performing the surgery may indicate that these attempts to obtain superego approval were only partially successful.

[1]This may also indicate that the content of the dream related to her. (2) Coodley (1) points out the dream could represent regressive phallic aborting attacks on the pregnant mother-wife, with the atherosclerotic plugs being the unborn fetus.

Probably the best known examples of dreams related to scientific discoveries are those of Einstein, Kekule and Descartes. Albert Einstein reported that his formula for the theory of relativity came to him in a dream where he saw: $E = mc^2$. Friedrich Kekule, an organic chemist, reported that his discovery of the benzene ring came to him in a dream in 1865. He was thinking of combinations of atoms, dozed off, and in the dream the atoms became snakes chasing each other, then grabbing each other's tail and forming a ring. (9)

In the cases of Einstein and Kekule, this seems to have been a working through of the day residue with a continuing of the mental activity in the dream in such a way as to preserve sleep; formulae were coming to mind with no apparent conflict. These two dreams fit well Freud's description of "dreams from above" (4) and Lewin's classification of "dreams of visual thinking." (14)

The dreams of Descartes are another matter. The then 23-year-old philosopher-mathematician attributed crucial importance in the development of his scientific thinking to his dreams of November 10, 1619, which he felt were divinely inspired. (17) In a similar way, Dr. V. attributed such importance to his dream for his discovery.

Schoenberger (15) feels that Descartes' dreams came after he had arrived at the essence of his discoveries, not before as Descartes claimed. J. O. Wisdom (20) agrees and analyzes Descartes' dreams as dealing with some of the conflicts aroused by the discovery: increased oedipal anxieties, castration anxiety, fear of the mother-church, etc. Lewin (13,14) concurs with Wisdom, adding that Descartes' dream represented a continuing struggle to preserve sleep from the disturbing bodily sensations which marked the prodromata of a migrainous or convulsive attack.

Yet Freud (5) classified Descartes' dreams as "dreams from above, that is to say, they are formulations of ideas which could have been created just as well in a waking state as during the state of sleep and which have derived their content only in certain parts from mental states at a comparatively deep level. . . ."

We can resolve this seeming disagreement with Freud by broadening Freud's concept of dream-action. Descartes' ideas—and Dr. V.'s—"could have been created just as well in a waking state" except for the inner need to deny personal responsibility for what the discoveries unconsciously symbolized.

In Descartes' case, *inverse* dream-action is seen. The anxiety aroused by the discoveries led him to attribute "crucial importance" for the discoveries to dreams which came *after* he had arrived at the essence of his discoveries.

Kris writing "On Inspiration" (11) reports "the aggressive meaning of creativity leads to the quest for an authority whose advice frequently represents the patient's own ideas." May this not explain Dr. V.'s seeking out the pathologist, and Descartes' attributing his discoveries to divine inspiration?

Schoenberger (15) believes Descartes' dreams came as an expression of the uncertainty and anxiety accompanying his having made the scientific discovery, which "enabled the philosopher to gain possession of his mother." Schoenberger analyzes the dreams as a working through, a reconstituting of the superego identified with the object which he had once wanted to destroy, ". . . the mainspring of scientific thought, as indeed of so many human activities, is the striving to regain possession of the tender mother whom everyone is destined to lose in the course of his development and whose death must have been for Descartes, then a child in his second year, the supreme tragedy of his life."

Schoenberger's interpretation of the scientific activity as well as the dreams of Descartes as unconscious restitutive acts aimed at undoing unconscious, fantasied destructive attacks on the internalized mother, seems pertinent to Dr. V.'s dream in which he omnipotently was restoring what he as a child may have fantasied destroying. One aspect of Dr. V.'s dream, and the dream-action, and the subsequent scientific work may have been the unconscious working through of the guilt and loss in an attempt to find the cure for the very illness which had killed aunt and mother.

Summary

Attention is directed to a "new" paper by Freud (the existence of this paper was unknown until 9 years ago) with a new concept: "dream-action." Freud's concept was that there are dreams which are dreamt to provide the reason for the action which occurs both in the dream and in reality.

The author extends the concept of dream-action; and re-examines Descartes' dreams, which are shown to be examples of inverse dream-action.

An example of "dream-action" is presented, utilizing a physician's dream which led to a medical discovery. Conjectures regarding the meanings of the dream, the scientific creativity and the need for the mechanism of dream-action are given.

Bibliography

1. Coodley, A. Personal communication to the author, Oct. 23, 1965.
2. Ferenczi, S. (1913) "To Whom Does One Relate One's Dreams." In *Further Contributions to the Theory and Technique of Psychoanalysis.* London, Hogarth Press, p. 349.
3. Feuer, L. S. "The Dreams of Descartes," Amer. Imago, Vol. 20, 1963, pp. 3-26.
4. Freud, S. (1922) "Remarks Upon The Theory and Practice of Dream Interpretation." In *Standard Edition*, Vol. 19, London, Hogarth Press, pp. 109-121.

5. ———. (1929) "Some Dreams of Descartes' A Letter to Maxime Leroy." In *Standard Edition*, Vol. 21, London, Hogarth Press, pp. 197-204.
6. Freud, S. & Oppenheim, D. E. *Dreams in Folklore* (written in 1911, first discovered in 1956, first published in 1958). New York, Int. Univ. Press, 1958.
7. Grotjahn, M. "Dream Observations in A Two-Year-Four-Months-Old Baby," Psa. Quart. Vol. 7, 1938, pp. 507-513.
8. ———. Personal communication.
9. Holleman, A. E. "History of Benzene," Fünfzigjähriges Benzolstudium, Vol. 20, 1915, pp. 459-488.
10. Klein, M. *Envy & Gratitude*. New York, Basic Books, 1957.
11. Kris, E. "On Inspiration," Int. J. Psa., Vol. 20, 1939, pp. 377-389.
12. Lewin, B. "Sleep, the Mouth, and the Dream Screen," Psa. Quart., Vol. 15, 1946, pp. 419-434.
13. ———. *Dreams and the Uses of Regression*. Freud Anniversary Lecture Series, New York, Int. Univ. Press, 1958.
14. ———. "Knowledge and Dreams," Bull. of Philadelphia Ass'n for Psa., Vol. 12, 1962, pp. 97-111.
15. Schoenberger, S. "A Dream of Descartes: Reflections on the Unconscious Determinants of the Sciences," Int. J. Psa., Vol. 20, 1939, pp. 43-57.
16. Simmel, E. "The 'Doctor Game,' Illness and the Profession of Medicine," Int. J. Psa., Vol. 7, 1926, pp. 470-473.
17. Smith, N. K. *New Studies in the Philosophy of Descartes*. London, Macmillan, 1952.
18. Strachey, J. Editor of *Dreams in Folklore* by Freud & Oppenheim, New York, Int. Univ. Press, 1958.
19. ———. Personal communication to the author, Aug. 9, 1965.
20. Wisdom, J. O. "Three Dreams of Descartes," Int. J. Psa., Vol. 28, 1947, pp. 11-18.

10921 Wilshire Boulevard
Los Angeles, California 90024

Discussant

J. O. Wisdom, PH.D.

London, England

I would first make a comment on the role of the pathologist for Dr. V. and on his invoking the aid of his wife. Though a technical expert, the pathologist is a servant: his position is that of a key subordinate whose duty it is to guard his master from making mistakes; and, like many such subordinates, he is a confidant. One central reason for needing a confidant in the situation could be this. The innovator is necessarily, in the sphere of his innovations, cut off from all his fellows. However quickly he may share his discoveries, he is for a time completely alone. He even knows he may, like Semmelweis urging hygiene at childbirth or Simpson urging the use of chloroform, become ostracized.

Even the success of his innovation may not help him; but it is his one chance, and if he is wrong he is held beneath contempt. So he needs a confidant to mitigate his loneliness, and perhaps to foreshadow a future good reception, forgive him if he is successful (or if he fails), and to save him from error (one thinks of Freud and Fliess). But, in preparing to be alone at all, he is willing to invent a sphere with no other human beings in it—which is not far off a sphere in which he has destroyed all others. And an innovation destroys what has gone before by rendering it obsolete. I would say that a necessary condition for being able to face this would be that the innovation would be felt to be equivalent to the damage, a psychical restoration.

Applying this, I would suppose that Dr. V.'s innovation restored to life his aunt-in-law and his mother, which required the sanction of his unconsciously damaged and jealous wife (eminently compatible with Coodley's conjecture of phallic abortive attacks); and restored them by a means that rendered their doctors obsolete, which required the sanction of the pathologist, in his capacity as confidant. (Further, the reason of waking would then be anxiety concerning the jealous wife and superseded colleagues.)

Another question that arises concerns wish-fulfillment. Since a dream of the kind Freud described is realized while it is being dreamt, the dreamer experiences fulfillment; hence there would seem to be no motive for the dream in the sense of no unfulfilled wish awaiting fulfillment. This may have disturbed Freud. In this connection we may note that the physical realization is not seen until the dreamer wakes, but it is experienced in a tactile and kinaesthetic way, so that there is a split between the two modalities. If, therefore, we seek an unfulfilled wish, this could lie in *the need to visualize* the tactile and kinaesthetic experience.

Such a conjecture would be in line with the fact that Dr. V. would not himself perform the operation he invented. Thus the reassuring illusion can be preserved that what is dreamt need not to be taken much to heart because of being *only* a dream.

In another connection,[1] I have suggested that certain dreams with such a function are a defense against psychosomatic disorder. One could perhaps regard these as attempts to avoid involvement with the body, and regard dreams of scientific discovery as attempts to reach the body. The simultaneously realized dreams described by Freud might prove to be a combination of the need to avoid the realization and the equal need to attain it. Enough has been said to show that considerable differences might show up from the empirical study of this family of dreams. Thus Dr. Lindon is surely right that there is more to be learned about dreams by exploring Freud's idea.

[1]Wisdom, J. "A General Hypothesis of Psychosomatic Disorder," Brit. J. Med. Psychol., Vol. 26, 1953, pp. 15-29.

Discussant

Sandor Lorand, M.D.

New York, New York

The essay by Dr. Lindon brought to mind the famous chemist Kekule who declared that his discovery of the Benzol Theory (Benzol ring) started with a dream of his. Kekule, in his dream, saw various shapes and forms (atoms) moving in front of his eyes, moving in a long row, first the larger shapes followed by smaller ones, twisting and turning like snakes. Then one of the snakes caught its own tail in its mouth. Kekule suddenly awoke. The rest of the night he spent working out his hypothesis. He interpreted his dream in a way which showed that he understood his dream wish—and the relationship between the dream and his scientific discovery.

Dr. Alfred Robitsek published Kekule's interpretation adding his own thoughts and elaboration concerning the latent content of Kekule's dream and his observation about "not dream oriented" peoples' capacity to understand their dreams.[1]

I agree that Dr. V.'s dream fits into Freud's concept about "dream-action" as well as in the category that Freud called "dreams from above" in his remarks about the interpretation of a dream of Descartes.[2]

These dreams, Freud explained, are a "formulation of ideas that could have been

[1]Robitsek, A. "Symbolishes Denken in der Chemishen Forschung," Imago, Vol. 1, 1912, pp. 83-90.

[2]Freud, S. "Brief an Maxim Leroy uber einen Traum des Cartesius." In *Gesammelte Werke*, London, Imago Publishing Co., Vol. 14.

created just as well in the waking state as in a state of sleep." Freud described his position in the analysis of this type of dream, "We cannot understand the dream. The dreamer, or the patient, can translate it immediately and without difficulty. The dreamer in such dreams as 'dreams from above' interprets without difficulty because the dream's content is close to his conscious thoughts."

S. Schoenberger cites Freud's further remark in connection with the dream of Descartes, "Even when the material available is unsatisfactory and incomplete, it sometimes enables us to make constructions with useful results."[3] In *Papers on Technique* (Std. Ed. Vol. 12), Freud remarks, "An unusually skillful dream interpreter may sometimes find himself in the position of being able to see through every one of the patient's dreams without requiring him to go through the tedious and time-absorbing process of working over them." Freud showed us that he was dependent on hypotheses. We can assess the possibility of interpreting a dream using intuition and knowledge of symbols which may elucidate the interpretation.

The hypotheses upon which rests our understanding of the latent content of Dr. V.'s dream seem entirely feasible. Freud stated, "Dreaming is a piece of infantile mental life." If we consider Dr. V.'s information about his mother's dream—three years earlier—as associations to his present dream—the latent wish of his discovery dream can be reconstructed.

Dr. V. understood and interpreted his mother's dream correctly. In her dream she is intending to leave for Europe (abandoning him), meeting in the dream her dead sister-in-law (Dr. V.'s aunt—who can also be represented as mother). The deceased husband (Dr. V.'s father, who also abandoned him in death) is thus also in the dream. His mother's dream disturbed and upset Dr. V. because his interpretation was that it foretold her death. This dream of his mother's mobilized feelings from infantile years. Death wishes against father and mother, pre-oedipal, oedipal, and post-oedipal conflicts, dependence, frustrations, aggression—all are mobilized and cause panic in Dr. V.

After mother's death, the conflicts were repressed. The beloved aunt (mother image) dies of coronary occlusion (the illness his mother died of). Undoubtedly the aunt's death revived once more acutely all the libidinal drives, ambivalent oedipal feelings about his parents, his distress connected with his mother's death (also father's) with all the concomitant guilt. In his dream he is trying to make restitution for his early hidden sexual aggressive drives, which occurred in spite of the superego threat—and in competition with his father.

There is no dreaming without censorship. When the dreamer attempts to fulfill an infantile wish, the superego re-establishes its authority against it. The dreamer complies with the censor, modifying the wish. Not being able to perform the operation by his new method would be one of the superego's punishments. (Operation equals forbidden competition with father on all levels in relationship with mother, etc.) The pathologist who needles him stands for the original superego. His facetious remarks, in fact, did provide a hint for the new surgical procedure.

I see as the main motive in the dream, the restitutive elimination of the guilt for the oedipal wishes, libidinal and destructive, as Dr. Lindon suggested.

---

[3]Schoenberger, S. "A Dream of Descartes: Reflections on the Unconscious Determinants of the Sciences," Int. J. Psa., Vol. 20, 1939, pp. 43-57.

Discussant

Daniel C. Siegel, M.D.

Pasadena, California

Dr. V.'s dream which led to an important medical discovery is an example of true scientific creativity. This subject interests me greatly because of my association with the California Institute of Technology, where as a psychotherapist, administrative consultant and research worker I have seen hundreds of scientists and would-be scientists of all levels of training and scientific sophistication. After reading Dr. Lindon's paper, I recalled a case where a dream led to a scientific discovery which seems to fit Freud's concept of dream-action. A young astro-physicist, who suffered from severe work inhibition had been in analysis with me for two years. He had done original and outstanding work early in his career but had been unable to produce anything of significance since receiving his doctorate degree five years previously.

It became clear that oedipal and castration anxieties were important determinants in his choice of profession. His mother had died suddenly when he was five years old. The analysis revealed that he sought his mother as he scanned the heavens with a telescope, first as a hobby and later as a profession.

Despite much evidence in the two years of analysis, he still denied his sexual desires for his mother, his wish to be with her even in death and his aggressive drives toward father.

He had been working for a year on a mathematical problem which was the keystone to validating his earlier discovery, which, if confirmed, would be extremely important. He felt he wasn't getting anywhere (which was true) and would berate himself as "impotent"; he felt he was "a boy trying to do a man's job."

One day he came to his analytic hour in a highly elated state and began talking as soon as I greeted him. He began by saying that he had "the strangest dream last night and that everything is beginning to clear up."

The *dream* was a long one. In essence it had to do with his looking through the telescope at the Palomar Observatory, which is located on top of a high mountain. He is observing the moon, which is heavily veiled by many layers of gauze-like material. Then he is at the side of the moon laboriously pulling each layer of material away one at a time. Finally he can see the moon clearly and studies it carefully. Suddenly, he is surprised to see "the man in the moon" and he awakens instantly.

Although certain that there was more to the dream he immediately wrote down those portions he could recall, something he had never done before, and returned to sleep. He slept soundly and awoke feeling elated. When he looked at his notes he was amazed to see in addition to some key words about the dream that he had also written a mathematical formula. He had no memory of writing this formula nor of a dream containing it or related to it. There was no doubt that he had written the formula upon awakening from the dream.

The formula gave the clue for solving the problem which had eluded him for a year. He worked hard all day following the dream and for the next six weeks at which time he successfully solved the problem.

Many associations to the dream came into the analytic hours for several weeks. The various reconstructions they led to need not concern us in discussing this paper. However, the patient himself as well as his father was "the man in the moon." Primal scene material, sexual wishes for mother, as well as the wish to be with mother forever no longer could be denied.

The portion of the dream, if there had been any, relating to the mathematical formula was never recovered. His discovery which was validated had to do with some of the properties of the moon's atmosphere. The dream itself served the analysis well; at the same time what can now be called the dream-action led directly to a scientific discovery.

My studies of scientists have consistently impressed me that scientific creativity is not the result of an accident, but rather the end product of hard work in an individual who is "more open-minded, obviously because he has a greater capacity to free himself from his subjective immediate needs for satisfaction." (Franz Alexander in "Neurosis and Creativity.")

My last comment is to recall what Freud implied and Ernest Jones made explicit: "In the formation of a dream no intellectual operation of any sort is carried out; the dream work is concerned solely with translating into another form various underlying dream thoughts that were previously in existence. No creative work whatever is carried out by the process of dream making; it performs no acts of decision, calculation, judgment, comparison, conclusion, or any kind of thought," and further, "any part of a dream that appears to indicate an intellectual operation has been taken bodily from the underlying latent content, either directly or in a distorted form." (E. Jones, "Freud's Theory of Dreams" in *Papers on Psychoanalysis.)*

Discussant

Bernice T. Eiduson, PH.D.

Los Angeles, California

This essay adds another fascinating page to the abundant lore on the creative process. In the retrospective account of this interesting discovery, Dr. Lindon has skillfully retained some of the "surprise element" that Dr. V. must have experienced first-hand, and that we have come to recognize as a useful clue in identifying a product as truly creative. (Novelty, a recombination of previously unrelated matrices of thought, improbability, and significance rather than triviality, are some of the other indices.)[1]

In the creative literature the dream has, of course, been cited very frequently as the context in which the solution to a problem becomes apparent. Compilations of self-revelatory accounts of the creative processes show that many dreams have led to outstanding and revolutionary developments in science.[2]

At present, there is no evidence to indicate whether the dream state itself is as important a precipitant for the creative contribution as it would seem on the surface. There are no figures on the frequency with which dreams lead to creative products, especially as compared with other states of consciousness, or as compared with the incidence expected on the basis of chance. Nor do we know much about the mental environment that the dream state provides, particularly in regard to conditions which might be conducive to creative activity. We do, however, have some hunches about the need for abandoning usual cognitive habits in order to produce a creative product, and can speculate that customary styles of thinking are likely to be restructured when the usual figure-background relationships become reversed or changed in certain ways, as they are in dream states. But what becomes dislodged and at what time and under what conditions remains unknown.

Although we have long had access to accounts of discoveries that share the temporal gaps that Dr. V. described between experiences

[1]Bruner, J. S. "Conditions of Creativity," in Gruber, H. E., Terrell, G. and Wertheimer, M. (Eds.), *Contemporary Approaches to Creative Thinking.* Ch. 1, 1-30. New York: Atherton Press, 1962.

[2]Eiduson, Bernice T. *Scientists: Their Psychological World.* New York: Basic Books, 1962.

and ideas that become related ultimately, and that display the same circuity in associative patterns, we have made little headway in understanding the course of their vicissitudes. And we have not gone much beyond some very detailed and precise descriptions in formulating the stages of the creative process. Our informational hiatuses about both the dream state and about creative activity make it difficult to evaluate critically the creative-activity-during-dream data.

One of the crucial problems which is relevant here is the questionable reliability of retrospective reporting. Sophisticated studies of living creative persons show that it is extremely difficult to establish the points at which old ideas become interlocked or recombined with each other in novel ways.[1]

Dr. Lindon has turned to certain apparent features of Dr. V.'s character structure and some of the libidinally-charged content which had become restimulated under the press of reality events. As Dr. V.'s dream illustrates, the ways in which libidinal drives and conflicts over-determine dream content are very compelling.

When artists or scientists tell us of the cognitive aspects of creative activity, the role of the irrational is regularly emphasized. Poincaré called the first stage of creative endeavor the "useless" labor which incites the unconscious mind to further work; Henry James described the probing of the "depths of unconscious cerebration." The forty scientists I studied told of the deliberate ways in which they try to "woo their unconscious."[3,4] As scientists have become more psychologically sophisticated, they even tell us how irrational factors compete with rational considerations for many scientific areas in which there is a choice.[3,5]

In a somewhat analogous situation to that described by Dr. Lindon, Barber and Fox sought understanding by relying more heavily on ego considerations.[6] Through direct interviews with two researchers, Barber and Fox were able to reconstruct a very plausible set of socio-psychological conditions, professional interests, and scientific roles of each man to explain his particular response to a serendipitous experience.

When any attempt is made to understand a dream, or a single experience, or a group or series of historical or current events in the life of a creative person, the same dimensions and conceptual framework that we use in regard to the non-creative individual, must be applied. Thus, only a multi-levelled, multi-dimensional view which takes into account the circumstances or conditions of the discovery, the lines of the creator's ego development, as well as his instinctually-bound motivations, and their relationships and interaction to each other, is in order. Anything less, it seems to me, is bound to be too narrow to provide meaningful psychological data. It may also have the unfortunate side effect of reinforcing the outdated stereotypes about creative persons which then mitigate against finding answers to the pointed questions that John Lindon has raised.

---

[3]Eiduson, Bernice T. "Artists and Non-Artists: a Comparative Study." *Journal of Personality*, 1958, 26, 13-28.

[4]Ghiselin, B. (Ed.) *The Creative Process.* New York: Mentor, 1955.

[5]Ghiselin, B. "The Creative Process and Its Relation to the Identification of Creative Talent," in C. W. Taylor and F. Barron (Eds.), *Scientific Creativity: Its Recognition and Development*, Ch. 29, 355-364. New York: John Wiley & Sons, 1963.

[6]Barber and Fox, R.S. "The Case of the Floppy-Eared Rabbits: an Instance of Serendipity Gained and Serendipity Lost." *American Journal of Sociology*, 1958, *64*, 128-136.

Author's Response

John A. Lindon, M.D.

Los Angeles, California

The dream of Dr. Siegel's patient may seem like a "dream from above" or an indication of analytic progress that he could face both discoveries: his own about the moon and his analyst's about his unconscious. But it is an example of "dream-action": while dreaming of pulling away the moon's veils, he awakened and wrote the mathematical formula which was to pull away some veils of the moon in reality. The dream bore the responsibility for the formula becoming manifest.

Dr. Lorand rightfully points out that Dr. V.'s father is also represented in his mother's dream and how this mobilized guilt feelings over infantile death wishes toward both mother and father.

It is striking how much Dr. Eiduson's remarks—and Dr. Lorand's and Dr. Wisdom's—could apply to the example given by Dr. Siegel. Perhaps for creative people, dreams serve as a "regression in the service of the ego" to perform a creative act which might not come to consciousness in other ways. One wonders what device will be used as psychoanalytic sophistication spreads and people no longer can disclaim responsibility for their dreams. Perhaps dream-action like grand-hysteria will disappear.

Professor Wisdom interprets the role of the pathologist as that of a key subordinate and confidant. The creative scientist must be able to destroy what had gone before by rendering it obsolete, must have "a good conscience"—which Dr. Wisdom's interpretation of the pathologist's role fits well. The need for an *externalized* good conscience was apparent; perhaps every innovator needs it. Although it is his striving for a good conscience which stimulates his creativity as reparation for fantasied destructiveness, the innovator probably must have external reassurance also to overcome his inner doubts. Without both he may be impotent.

I see creative scientists as unconsciously destroying what had gone before by rendering it obsolete—but then rebuilding and extending it, making a bridge to the new knowledge. This does more than to undo damage; it is experienced unconsciously as an acknowledgment of one's indebtedness, and as an expression of gratitude toward one's teachers in life—(which includes peers, students, spouse, children, friends, etc., as well as one's literal scientific teachers)—all the way back to father and to mother, the first teacher. It becomes more than an atonement, it is a tribute.

Dr. V.'s inhibition in performing the operation probably is more than fear of the forbidding father of the oedipal period. It is also a hidden attack on father making him so bad a father that he does not allow even this sublimation. Such a fantasied bad, persecutory father could fit in with Dr. Wisdom's comments about defending against the psychosomatic disorder.

Title **From Gradiva to the Death Instinct**

Author **Lawrence J. Friedman, M.D.**

Training Analyst in the Los Angeles Institute for Psychoanalysis. He was Dean of the Institute's Training School, President of the Los Angeles Psychoanalytic Society. Dr. Friedman has written psychoanalytic papers and a book, *Light Up the World . . . Letters from a Psychoanalyst.* Two of his major fields of interest are concerned with Shakespeare and with psychiatry and the law.

Discussants

Mortimer Ostow, M.D.

Associate Attending Psychiatrist at Montefiore Hospital in New York City, and Visiting Professor of Psychiatry at the Jewish Theological Seminary. He has followed the controversy on the death instinct for a number of years and has made some contributions to this and other aspects of instinct theory, relating them to concepts which have been developed in ethologic theory.

Max Schur, M.D.

Clinical Professor of Psychiatry, Downstate Medical Center, State University of New York, Training and Supervising Analyst, Division of Psychoanalytic Education, Downstate Medical Center, State University of New York. Author of the following books which pertain to Dr. Friedman's paper: *The Problem of Death in Freud's Writing and Life,* and *A Reconsideration of the Concepts Id and the Regulatory Principles of Mental Functioning.*

Hanna Segal, M.B.CH.B.

Training Analyst in the London Institute of Psychoanalysis, and is a well known exponent of Melanie Klein's work. She has published many papers, two most relevant to this subject are "The Fear of Death" and "A Psychoanalytic Approach to Aesthetics." She wrote *Introduction to the Work of Melanie Klein.*

Martin Grotjahn, M.D.

Has long been interested in problems of death and dying, and has reported about them in several essays.

Jacques Choron, PH.D., D.S.SC.

Has been a member of the Faculty of the New School for Social Research in New York, since 1957. During the current academic year he is a Fellow at the Center for the Scientific Study of Suicide in Los Angeles, and Visiting Professor of Psychiatry (Philosophy) at the University of Southern California. He is the author of the following books, among others: *Death and Western Thought,* and *Modern Man and Mortality.*

Victor Calef, M.D.

Associate Chief of the Mount Zion Psychiatric Clinic and a Training Analyst in the San Francisco Psychoanalytic Institute.

From Gradiva to the Death Instinct

Lawrence J. Friedman, M.D.
Beverly Hills, California

Sigmund Freud's "Beyond the Pleasure Principle" (6) introduced the death instinct. It led to controversy and confusion among analysts. His theory remained a side-issue in the last 45 years and did not affect basic concepts since the majority of analysts do not accept it and hardly discuss it. There are some who do and who have revised their theoretical thinking accordingly. (30) There are others who feel that the theory helped to clarify the concept of aggression by recognizing the existence of an independent destructive drive. The clearest formulations were developed by H. Hartmann, E. Kris and R. Loewenstein. (27)

Fenichel's "Critique of the Death Instinct" (3) summarizes well the objections. According to Fenichel it is neither necessary nor useful to accept the theory of the death instinct despite the existence of ambivalence toward love objects. He does not believe that we are dealing with two different instinctual qualities, but with a contrast between two forces which originally had a common root.

It is not the purpose of this paper to discuss the validity of the death instinct theory. Rather, an attempt will be made to explain the development of the death instinct in Freud's life and theoretical thinking. In recent years publication of material from three different sources makes such a study feasible: Freud's letters to W. Fliess; (16) S. Bernfeld's extensive research; and the biography of Freud by Ernest Jones. (29)

Freud's book *Delusion and Dream in Jensen's "Gradiva"* (7) appeared in 1907. Jones comments that Freud greatly enjoyed writing this book: "The Gradiva book is one of three of Freud's writings to which the word 'charming' can most fittingly be applied, the other two being, in my opinion at least, the book on Leonardo (12) and the essay on the 'Three Caskets.' (19) It is written with such delicacy and beauty of language as to rank high and compel admiration for its literary qualities alone." (29) Freud gave the impression that W. Jensen's novel was beautiful and great literature. Actually critics view the story as almost devoid of beauty and literary qualities.

What is the reason for the discrepancy between the general literary criticism and Freud's enthusiasm for the novel—and what aroused Freud's great interest in it? According to Jones it was Jung who called Freud's attention to the book and that Freud wrote the study to give Jung pleasure. Freud was always impressed with the psychological understanding of writers and artists and he contrasted their intuition with the lack of insight shown by psychologists.

Jensen's *Gradiva* tells the story of a young archeologist, Dr. Norbert Hanold, who was devoted to scientific work to the exclusion of all other interests including the opposite sex. One day his attention was caught by an ancient bas-relief, the figure of a graceful woman walking. He fell in love with this ancient portrait and could not think of anything else. He ascertained this to be a work of the early Pompeii period and called the woman Gradiva. While preoccupied with his fantasies about her, he had a *nightmare*:

"He was in the city of Pompeii and Vesuvius was erupting. In the distance he noticed Gradiva. In his awareness of impending catastrophe, he cried out; she turned her face to him, then walked on unconcernedly toward the temple of Jupiter. At the entrance she sat down, her head sinking slowly onto one of the steps. Her face turned pale. He ran to her, and found her sleeping peacefully while she was slowly buried by a rain of ashes."

Awakening from the dream, he looked out the window and to his amazement noticed a girl on the street, who looked and walked exactly like the Gradiva of his dream. He rushed after her, but she disappeared.

Following the dream, he resolved to search for traces of the model used by the artist. His travels took him to Pompeii. One day, walking among the ruins, he noticed a girl, the image of Gradiva. In his fantasy or delusion he was convinced that she was Gradiva who, from time to time, emerged from her grave and then returned to it. In the next few days they had several conversations. Gradiva turned out to be his childhood sweetheart, Zoë (meaning: life) Bertgang. (The name Gradiva derives from the word walking which is included in Zoë's last name— "gang" meaning walking.) Their talks cured him of his delusions. The story ended with the recovery of his early memories, the reawakening of his repressed love for Zoë, and their plans to get married.

Freud interpreted the Gradiva story as a re-emergence of a repressed, unconscious memory of Hanold's love for a childhood sweetheart and the fulfillment of unconscious oedipal wishes. Zoë's situation in the novel was that of a substitute wife to her widowed father. Professor Bertgang, her father, is pictured as a somewhat ridiculous old man. Gradiva thus represented a substitute for the desired mother. There is a parallel to this relationship in Freud's life. His mother was a charming, clever, witty woman, feminine in appearance even in her old age. Freud's father was considerably older than his mother. In early childhood fantasies Freud might have utilized this age difference to eliminate his father as the sexual partner of his mother, substituting instead his half-brother Phillip.

Freud had described a screen memory of his in a paper entitled "On Screen Memories." It dealt with the analysis of the following childhood memory: "I see a thickly covered green meadow, rectangular and gently sloping. In the green are many yellow flowers, evidently the common dandelion. Above the meadow stands a farmhouse. Two women are busily talking before the door. One is a peasant with a kerchief on her head, the other a nurse. Three children play on the meadow. I am one of the three, between two and three years old. The others are my cousin, a year older than I, and his sister who is almost exactly my age. We are picking the yellow flowers and each of us already holds a bouquet of them. The little girl has the prettiest bouquet, but suddenly as if by agreement we boys fall upon her and tear the flowers out of her hand. She runs up the meadow crying, and to comfort her, the peasant woman gives her a large piece of dark bread. As soon as we see that we throw the flowers away, hurry to the house and demand bread. We get it, too. The peasant woman cuts the loaf with a long knife. I remember how delicious the flavor of this bread was. And that is the end of the scene." (Bernfeld's translation.)

In the screen memory the picture is not as clear as in the Gradiva story, but the same motive of repressed sexual desire develops as the analysis progresses. The little girl possibly represents Freud's two and a half years younger sister, perhaps also his half-brother's daughter; the peasant woman and the nursemaid are oedipal mother figures. Freud's interpretation leads to forbidden sexual desires toward early love objects.

Present day knowledge of Freud's early childhood coupled with Bernfeld's convincing conclusion that the "patient" in the screen memories is Freud himself seems to justify the assumption that Freud identified himself with young Dr. Norbert Hanold, Dozent of Archeology, in the Gradiva novel.

The similarities are striking. The young archeologist exploring antiquity, the past, the hidden, the covered-up, would be a fitting description of a psychoanalyst, especially of Freud himself. As far back as the "Studies in Hysteria" (18) and "The Aetiology of Hysteria," (5) Freud compares the process of psychoanalysis with that of excavating a buried city. Furthermore, young Hanold's preoccupation with his scientific interest to the almost complete exclusion of everything else, is comparable to Freud's adolescence and young manhood. There are other similarities, such as Freud's interest in archeology and his life-long love for Italy as the burial ground of antiquity.

One might almost deal with the story of Gradiva as if it were one of Freud's dreams with remarkably few distortions. Freud's analysis emphasizes repressed infantile sexual desires. He did not interpret the ambivalence toward love objects with expressions of hostile, destructive wishes and their defenses.

Several symbols in *Gradiva* and in "Screen Memories" center around idealization. This was true of Gradiva's character and her appearance, her feet and her walking. Freud also idealized the novel itself and the author's psychological understanding. The literary beauty of Freud's review and analysis of the novel is yet another form of this idealization.

Idealization is expressed in a variety of ways in the screen memory: the general pleasant atmosphere, the love of the yellow flowers, the enjoyment when eating the bread, the idyllic countryside. What is the explanation for this idealization and over-valuation? Does it serve a defensive function?

First of all, why is Gradiva dead? Are we to understand it in terms of the repression of infantile sexual desires only or are we justified in assuming destructive wishes toward this early love object who, in his jealous fantasy, is buried alive in the arms of her lover by the rain of ashes? What is the meaning of the severe anxiety in the nightmare? The impending catastrophe and destruction of the beloved Gradiva symbolized the threatening breakthrough of repressed death wishes. Zoë reproached Hanold that for many years he behaved toward her as if she were non-existent —meaning, dead. In Pompeii, Hanold gave Gradiva a white flower, the flower of death. In his guilt he later gave her roses, the flowers of spring, of love and new life. When he yielded for the first time to his uncontrollable desire to touch her, he pretended to aim at a pestering fly, but hit Gradiva who responded as if attacked. Hanold ran away, filled with resentment and tortured with guilt.

Expressions of ambivalence are manifold throughout the story. There is a constant shift between love and hostility, between life and death accompanied by anxiety and guilt. There is a continuous struggle with feelings of ambivalence toward an early love object. The happy ending is a triumph of love over destruction.

The little girl in the screen memory could represent Freud's sister, approximately two and a half years younger than Freud himself. This would place Freud's recognition of his mother's pregnancy at about the age of two. It is conceivable that a little boy of this age would have feelings of hostility toward mother, her pregnancy and the newborn sister. Furthermore, when Freud was nineteen months old, his baby brother, then eight months old, died. This event seems to have left a lasting impression on him, and have formed the basis for severe conflicts about death wishes. In a letter to Fliess he recollects "evil" wishes toward his rival and added that their fulfillment in his death had aroused self-reproaches. (*The Origins of Psychoanalysis*, a letter dated 1897.) Then, within a period of approximately eight years, his mother was pregnant six times. In other words, during the first ten years of Freud's life his mother was almost constantly a "Gradiva" (sic). With a tempting slip of the pen the nursemaid and the peasant woman of the screen memory would represent the life-giving, nursing mother. In the screen memory hostility toward the mother figure was not expressed, possibly because it was less acceptable than jealousy toward the little girl, who at the same time could be used to displace the hostility from the mother figure.

Freud's biography reveals periods of strong ambivalent struggles. Among them are his discovery of cocaine, followed by alternating feelings of idealization and anger toward his later wife, feelings of elation and despair, feelings of intense love for her and the equally strong feelings of hostility toward other members of her family, especially her mother; his ambivalent relationship to his superiors and co-workers.

Ambivalent conflict was also expressed in his idealization of his birthplace, his love of ancient civilizations, particularly Rome, and his long drawn out struggle to fulfill his desire to visit there. On the other side is his often expressed dislike of Vienna, his lifelong desire to leave that city, and his inability to do so until it was forced on him.

Another ambivalent struggle has been described by Erikson in his interpretation of the Irma dream "The Dream Specimen of Psychoanalysis." (2) Other examples may be found in Freud's "The Moses of Michelangelo" (13) and "The Theme of the Three Caskets." (19)

It seems that hostility toward father figures aroused in Freud less anxiety and guilt than hostility toward early mother figures. The ambivalence may be split into hostility toward the father and idealization of the mother. Such idealization was as strong in the chivalrous attitude toward women in the Victorian era of Freud's youth, as it is in the artificial "mother culture" of our time.

At the time Freud wrote about the screen memory, he was involved in the great emotional struggles of his life: his self-analysis. Fliess was the central figure during this period and Freud's reaction to him was similar to the transference reaction of a patient to his analyst. This transference was a highly ambivalent one, and for a while dominated by unrealistic idealization of Fliess.

The concept of ambivalence was already anticipated by Freud in the "Studies in Hysteria" (18) and was expressed clearly in the "Interpretation of Dreams." (11) Freud traced his ambivalence to his relationship with his childhood playmate, his one year older nephew, which determined the pattern of many of his later relationships: "An intimate friend and a hated enemy have always been indispensable to my emotional life; I have always been able to create them anew and not infrequently my childish ideal has been so closely approached that friend and enemy have coincided in the same person; but not simultaneously, of course, as was the case in my early childhood." (29)

The knowledge of Freud's ambivalence conflicts is important for the understanding of his death instinct theory. Freud's theory is only partially based on clinical experience, like repetition compulsion, the drive to mastery of reality and ambivalence. Fenichel, for instance, states that the death instinct finds its explanation in two roots, namely, speculatively in the conservative character of the instincts and clinically in the existence of aggression. I would like to propose two more contributing influences. The first one seems to be a literal transposition into psychological formulations of the antithetical forces of synthesis and disintegration existing within all biological units. The second, and possibly the more important one, the severe traumatic experience in Freud's own life, namely, facing the actuality of death by a painful, destructive cancer.

Freud learned early from his admired teacher, Bruecke, that all forces within the organism are reducible to the forces of attraction and repulsion. Antithesis is the essence of life for all biological units, and is expressed in every cell in the continuous process of synthesis and disintegration. It is natural that psychoanalytic psychology should express the ever-present antithetical forces observed in biology in a variety of ways, such as the concepts of bi-sexuality, a conscious-unconscious, id-ego, ego-superego, pleasure-pain, love and hate.

The assumption of a pre-ambivalent, conflict-free stage in the psychic development was given up by Freud and replaced by the dual instinct theory. (8) Ambivalence was recognized in the earliest relationship of the child to the mother and as part of all object relations. The ego's incessant struggle for integration, independence or identity on the one hand, and on the other, the organism's, the individual's dependence on external objects for libidinal gratifications assures the maintenance of ambivalence toward love objects throughout life. The economic distribution of the antithetical forces of love and hate is one factor determining the outcome for successful or disturbed object relations.

Through Freud's self-analysis the pathological aspects of the ambivalent forces seem to have been resolved sufficiently so that they did not interfere seriously with his personal and scientific achievement. At the time of the cocaine episode the balance in the antithetical struggle shifted from near success to failure. This is quite a contrast to the happy ending of the Gradiva story, or the decision in the "Moses of Michelangelo," where Freud shows that in the conflict between constructive and destructive desires Moses chooses the constructive one. So did Freud.

Freud developed the death instinct theory at the time when he knew or anticipated that he was suffering with cancer of the jaw. Thus he was forced to face the reality of death from a painful, destructive illness. This must have initiated and reactivated anxiety and guilt connected with destructive drives especially regressive death wishes toward early love objects. Identification with these early love objects changes the direction of the destructive drives toward the internalized objects within the ego and reinforces the anxiety created by the reality of death. Pathological manifestations of this process might find expression in depression, in neurotic fear of injury, partial or total destruction, or the neurotic fear of death. Jones states: "Freud at the age of sixty superstitiously believed that he had only a couple of years to live." This was in 1916, and "Beyond the Pleasure Principle" was published four years later; the cancer was even later than that.[1]

At the age of two Freud suffered an injury to his jaw, which left a lasting, visible scar. The cancer of the jaw may have activated infantile ambivalent conflicts. The formulation of the "far-reaching speculative concept of the death instinct" may have served a defensive function against destructive wishes. Thus the instinctual quality of the death instinct can be understood as being borrowed from aggressive drives. These drives are now turned toward the internalized objects, and so toward the ego itself. Such development was described in "Mourning and Melancholia." (14) The concept of the death instinct seemed to represent a protection for the ego against destructive forces.

It is possible to deal with the concept of the death instinct as if it represented a fusion of two antithetical forces, similar to the antithesis love and hate. The love aspect of this antithesis finds its expression in increased narcissism, fitting into Freud's formulation: "Narcissism is the libidinal component of the ego." (15)

---

[1]For details about Freud's thoughts on illness and death, see Max Schur, *The Problem of Death in Freud's Writings and Life* (1966 International Universities Press, to be published).

This increase in narcissistic self-love counteracts the destructive aspects of the antithesis, namely, destruction directed toward the self, in this way maintaining the integrity of the ego and controlling or lessening anxiety.

Thus in the concept of the death instinct Freud re-established an apparently harmonious balance of the antithesis of love and hate, severing the connection from the original love objects and dealing with it in terms of the ego. A fusion, a synthesis of the energies of love and hate is the sine qua non of healthy ego functioning. When ego energies are combined with the rare and unknown determinants of the creative abilities of a genius, they may result in such great discoveries as are exemplified in Freud's scientific achievements.

What Freud expressed in "Beyond the Pleasure Principle" in terms of the ego, is expressed in the "Three Caskets" in terms of the libidinal aspects of the ambivalent relationship toward the love object (the mother). In this paper, (19) Freud analyzes the scene of the suitor's choice between the three caskets in *The Merchant of Venice* and the conflict of King Lear in relationship to his daughters; man's imagination rebels against the recognition which warns him that he, too, is a part of nature and therefore subject to the immutable law of death. So man in his imagination replaced the Goddess of Death with the Goddess of Life and therefore "the third of the sisters is no longer death, she is the fairest, best, most desirable and most lovable among women. Nor was this substitution in any way difficult: it was prepared for by an ancient ambivalence. . . . The Goddess of Love herself who now took the place of the Goddess of Death had once been identical with her. . . . Thus man overcomes death, which in thought he has acknowledged. No greater triumph of wish fulfillment is conceivable." Talking of Lear, he says: "Lear is not only an old man; he is a dying man. . . . Eternal wisdom, in the garb of the primitive myth, bids the old man renounce love, choose death and make friends with the necessity of dying." In his closing remarks, Freud states that "one might say that the three inevitable relations man has with women are here represented: that with the mother who bears him, with the companion of his bed and board, and with the destroyer. Or it is the three forms taken on by the figure of the mother as life proceeds: the mother herself, the beloved who is chosen after her pattern, and finally the Mother Earth who receives him again." In death, through reunion with Mother Earth, the ambivalent conflict is eliminated and a non-ambivalent oneness is established. It seems that this concept expresses denial of death, both in terms of destructive wishes toward the love object and the destruction of the self.

Freud does not emphasize the importance of aggression, guilt and anxiety in his analysis of *Gradiva*, but he does describe one of his own personal experiences which illuminates precisely this conflict. On one occasion a young girl walked into his office. Against his better judgment he couldn't help seeing in her one of his former patients who had died years before of Basedow's disease (hyperthyroidism). For a long time he was unable to overcome the uncomfortable feeling and nagging guilt that he might have contributed to her death through careless medication. Looking at this girl, he could not free himself of the thought: so it is true that the dead may return. His discomfort changed to shame when the girl, also suffering from Basedow's disease, introduced herself as the sister of the deceased patient. This experience speaks for itself and supports the interpretation of the *Gradiva* story as given here.

Although there must be many factors contributing to Freud's concept of the death instinct, his severe illness and the reactivation of his ambivalent conflicts and his life-long preoccupation with death may have been of importance. For Freud this concept served as an attempt to clarify aggression, and at the same time as a defense against guilt and anxiety.

The defensive character of the death instinct theory is expressed in Freud's own words in "Beyond the Pleasure Principle," "... That everything living must die out of inner causes. ... We are accustomed to think that such is the fact, and we are strengthened in our thought by the writings of our poets. Perhaps we have decided to do so because there seems comfort in this faith. If one has to die oneself and if one has to lose at first one's beloved ones through death, then one would rather want to submit to an inexorable law of nature than chance.... But perhaps the faith in the inner lawfulness of death is just one of the illusions which we have created in order to stand the difficulty of existence, of living."

Bibliography

1. Bernfeld, S. "An Unknown Autobiographical Fragment by Freud," Amer. Imago, Vol. 4, 1946, pp. 3-19.
2. Erikson, E. H. "The Dream Specimen of Psychoanalysis," J. Amer. Psa. Assoc., Vol. 2, 1954, pp. 5-55.
3. Fenichel, O. "Critique of the Death Instinct." In *The Collected Papers of Otto Fenichel, First Series.* New York, W. W. Norton and Co. 1953, pp. 363-372.
4. ———. *The Psychoanalytic Theory of Neurosis.* New York, W. W. Norton & Co. 1945.
5. Freud, S. (1896) "The Aetiology of Hysteria." In *Collected Papers*, London, Hogarth Press, Vol. 1, 1948, pp. 183-219.
6. ———. (1920) "Beyond the Pleasure Principle." In *Standard Edition*, Vol. 18, London, Hogarth Press, 1955, pp. 3-64.
7. ———. (1907) *Der Wahn und die Traume in W. Jensen's Gradiva.* Vienna, Heller, 1907.
8. ———.(1915) "Female Sexuality." In *Collected Papers.* London, Hogarth Press, Vol. 5, 1950, pp. 198-204.
9. ———. (1900) "Fetishism." In *Collected Papers.* London, Hogarth Press, Vol. 5, 1950, pp. 198-204.
10. ———. (1915) "Instincts and Their Vicissitudes." In *Collected Papers.* London, Hogarth Press, Vol. 4, 1948, pp. 60-83.
11. ———. (1900) *Interpretation of Dreams.* New York, Basic Books, 1955.
12. ———. (1910) "Leonardo da Vinci and A Memory of His Childhood." *Standard Edition*, Vol. 11, London, Hogarth Press, 1957, pp. 59-137.
13. ———. (1914) "The Moses of Michelangelo." In *Collected Papers.* London, Hogarth Press, Vol. 4, 1948, pp. 257-287.
14. ———. (1917) "Mourning and Melancholia." In *Collected Papers.* London, Hogarth Press, Vol. 4, 1948, pp. 152-170.
15. ———. (1914) "On Narcissism: An Introduction." In *Collected Papers*, London, Hogarth Press, Vol. 4, 1948, pp. 30-59.
16. ———. *The Origins of Psychoanalysis: Letters to Wilhelm Fliess.* New York, Basic Books, 1954.
17. ———. (1899) "Screen Memories." In *Collected Papers*, London, Hogarth Press, Vol. 5, 1950, pp. 47-69.
18. ———. (1895) "Studies in Hysteria." In *Standard Edition.* London, Hogarth Press, Vol. 2, 1955, pp. 1-305.
19. ———. (1913) "The Theme of the Three Caskets." In *Collected Papers*, Vol. 4, 1948, pp. 244-256.
20. Grotjahn, M. "About the Representation of Death in the Art of Antiquity and in the Unconscious of Modern Men." In Wilbur, G., *Psychoanalysis and Culture.* New York, Int. Univ. Press, 1951, pp. 410-424.
21. ———. "The Defenses Against Creative Anxiety in the Life and Work of James Barrie," Amer. Imago, Vol. 14, 1957, pp. 143-148.
22. ———. "Ego Identity and the Fear of Death and Dying," J. Hillside Hospital, Vol. 9, 1960, pp. 147-154.
23. Hartmann, H. "Comments on the Psychoanalytic Theory of the Ego." In *The Psychoanalytic Study of the Child.* New York, Int. Univ. Press, Vol. 5, 1950, pp. 74-95.
24. ———. "The Mutual Influences in Development of Ego and Id." In *The Psychoanalytic Study of the Child.* New York, Int. Univ. Press, Vol. 7, 1952, pp. 9-30.
25. ———. "Notes on the Theory of Sublimation." In *The Psychoanalytic Study of the Child.* New York, Int. Univ. Press, Vol. 10, 1955, pp. 9-46.
26. Hartmann, H., Kris, E. & Loewenstein, R. M. "Comments on the Formation of the Psychic Structure." In *The Psychoanalytic Study of the Child.* New York, Int. Univ. Press, Vol. 2, 1946, pp. 11-37.
27. ———. "Notes on the Theory of Aggression." In *The Psychoanalytic Study of the Child.* New York, Int. Univ. Press, Vol. 3 & 4, 1949, pp. 9-36.
28. Jensen, W. *Gradiva.* 1903.

29. Jones, E. *The Life and Works of Sigmund Freud.* New York, Basic Books, 1953.
30. Nunberg, H. *Principles of Psychoanalysis.* New York, Int. Univ. Press, 1955. [Edit. Note: See also Melanie Klein's and Karl Menninger's writings.]
31. Schur, M. "The Problem of Death in Freud's Writings and Life (Fourteenth Freud Anniversary Lecture)." Psa. Quart. Vol. 34, 1965, pp. 144-147.

436 N. Roxbury Drive
Beverly Hills, California 90210

Discussant

Mortimer Ostow, M.D.

New York, New York

I have some question of the propriety of using Freud's biographical data for psychoanalytic speculation about his motives and about the sources of his ideas. Biography warrants scholarly attention in order to study the characteristics of unusual personalities, the sources of their contributions, and just how they managed to influence the culture in which they lived. Nevertheless, it seems to me perhaps tasteless to make such an intimate study of one dead so recently. This applies especially if one uses biographical material and inferences from it, in order to evaluate the man's contribution.

I do not believe that Dr. Friedman is implying that if we can reconstruct Freud's motives for working out the theory of the death instinct, then we are justified in considering the theory discredited. Demonstrating Freud was concerned with oedipal conflicts at the time that he described the theory of the Oedipus complex, does not discredit it. Freud has tempted us, almost invited us, to subject him to psychoanalytic scrutiny, by contributing autobiographical material in his writings. Moreover his biography furnished the entire psychoanalytic profession with a well-documented, extensive case history which one can adduce to demonstrate one point or another.

Freud disguised much of his autobiographical material, and we may infer he wished to retain his privacy. It is presumptuous to imagine that we, at such a distance, and from such fragmentary material could draw inferences about Freud which he himself could not. We could certainly hesitate to discuss analytically in a public forum, material derived from any of our patients, living or dead, even if that patient had let it be known he had been in analysis.

We know that the work people select to do and the contents of their thoughts often represent an attempt to deal with unsolved problems. Therefore it should be no surprise that a man approaching the age at which his father died, an age which brings limitations of energies and capacities, should turn his thoughts to death. When a painful and threatening illness supervenes, these adversions to death will necessarily be reinforced. Ancient Jewish folklore attributes the erotic poetry of the Song of Songs to Solomon's youth, the practical wisdom for the management of everyday affairs of the Book of Proverbs to Solomon's maturity, and the cynicism of the Book of Ecclesiastes to his old age. It was only to be expected that when Freud's interest turned to the phenomenon of death he should be concerned with its biologic nature, human psychologic responses to anticipating death, and how men conceive of it.

Dr. Friedman suggests that by declaring aggressive wishes to be representatives of an agency external to the ego, an agency which intrudes upon and presses the ego, an individual may relieve himself of the guilt which these impulses incur when they appear within the ego. It is evident that a man will contrive and cling to opinions in scientific matters which his own dynamic needs require, so as to hold anxiety or guilt at a minimum. It does indeed seem reasonable to suppose, as Dr. Friedman does, that an analyst may select that variant of analytic theory which most complies with his own dynamic needs which he has not mastered in his own analysis.

Secondly, Dr. Friedman has suggested that the concept of a death instinct provides a kind of comfort, a method of becoming reconciled to death. He calls attention to a statement that Freud made to the same effect. Can the acceptance of an intellectual principle provide comfort in the presence of anxiety, especially since the idea in question not only fails to alleviate helplessness, but actually asserts the helplessness? To follow Freud's argument, summarized by Friedman, the idea represents an unconscious conviction that one is submitting to a Liebestod, to the ministering attentions of a benign parent, especially the mother. One gains courage from trust in this mother's concern and love and possibly by identifying with her.

What we are dealing with here seems to me essentially a religious position. That is, one acquires strength from seeing oneself as a component of an invulnerable, immortal and omnipotent superentity, and also from permitting oneself to be absorbed and incorporated by it. This dynamic attitude is an affective commitment which differs from conventional religion only that in the case of the latter, the conscious fantasies accompanying the affective commitment are based on supernatural concepts. But it is the attitude of willingly giving oneself to incorporation which is the basic element of religion, rather than the mythology which constitutes the conscious representation of that attitude.

To summarize, whether or not what Dr. Friedman has proposed is true of Freud, one can concur with the principles he proposes for relating the subject of a man's scientific interest to his dynamic concerns. He has also performed a service in demonstrating that what purports to be a scientific judgment may actually be an affective commitment which is identical with, or at least strongly resembles a religious commitment.

Discussant

Max Schur, M.D.

New York, New York

I read with pleasure Dr. Friedman's interesting paper. I was especially impressed by his subtle discussion of the themes of the *Gradiva* and of the "Three Caskets" in Freud's work. I will give this part of his paper credit in my forthcoming book on *The Problem of Death in Freud's Writing and Life* (International Universities Press, to be published in 1966). Also, I dealt extensively with the theoretical aspect of Freud's death-instinct concept in a chapter of a monograph on *The Concept Id and the Regulating Principles of Mental Functioning*.

Unfortunately, Dr. Friedman's main point concerning the reasons in Freud's personal life which led him to the death-instinct theory in 1919 is based on incorrect information. That the death of Freud's daughter did not precede Freud's formulation of his death-instinct theory had already been stated by Jones (Vol. III, pp. 40-41). I will publish additional proof to that effect in my book.

Dr. Friedman's assumption that Freud's cancer had already started years before 1923 is also based on errors which can be traced to various publications (Hitschmann, Wittels, Eckstein). It was, for instance, assumed that a so-called "epulis" was the beginning of Freud's cancer. An "epulis" is an "inflammatory granuloma," which in old pathology textbooks was also called "giant-cell sarcoma." It gets this name only because one finds in it certain giant cells, but it is never malignant. Freud's cancer was also linked to an injury of his jaw at the age of two. However, he had a scar over his *left* lower jawline—while his cancer was on the right side (see Jones, Vol. I, p. 7, footnote i). Freud did not have a "cancer of the jaw" but a malignant epithelioma, based on a leukoplakia.

In spite of these incorrect sources of information, Dr. Friedman will find some formulations about the adaptive value of Freud's death-instinct theory in my books which are not too dissimilar from the views expressed in the last paragraph of his paper, in which he calls—as I also do—upon Freud himself to support his ideas.

Discussant

Hanna Segal, M.B.CH.B.

London, England

Dr. Friedman's interesting article traces the genesis of the concept of the death instinct in Freud's own psychological preoccupation. His thesis is: (a) that Freud arrived at the concept of the death instinct as a way of mastering his own anxiety about death, stimulated by his cancer—"Thus man overcomes death, which in thought he has acknowledged. No greater triumph of wish fulfillment is conceivable," (b) that the concept of the death instinct is a defense against guilt about aggression, the denial of destructive impulses in relation to his mother being characteristic of Freud and often reflected in his psychological formulations, (c) that the anxiety about his own death may have led to a regression with a reactivation of his original ambivalence towards his mother, thus necessitating the formation of the concept of the death instinct as a defense.

I should like to examine these contentions separately. It seems to me quite likely that Freud's anxiety about his own death, as well as his preoccupation with death in the broader context of the 1914-1918 war, was a contributory factor in his wish to tackle the problem of life and death and the psychological meaning of death. Such a preoccupation, however, is not itself pathological; indeed, coming to terms with the finiteness of life in general and the idea of one's own personal death in particular seems to be a fundamental psychological task in middle age. Elliott Jaques, in a paper entitled "The Mid-Life Crisis,"[1] on the basis of his analysis of middle-aged patients and his study of the mid-life crisis in the life of artists, arrived at the conclusion that the basic problem of middle age is the acceptance of the idea of one's personal death. He also suggests that this task is particularly in the foreground in the creative artist, whose capacity to work breaks down if he cannot deal with this problem. When he can deal with it and come to terms with death, his work achieves a new richness and maturity. In my paper "The Psycho-Analytic Approach to Aesthetics,"[2] I also came to the conclusion that the artist must come to terms with death as a precondition for truly creative activity.

Thus, to my mind, not only is Freud's anxiety about his own death part of a normal process of maturing, but his dealing with it by expanding his work and introducing a new concept is a further proof of his creative genius. "Thus man overcomes death, which in thought he has acknowledged" may be not the great achievement of wish fulfillment, but just a great achievement.

Anxiety about death is neither the prerogative of middle age nor that of an artist. It is the successful overcoming of this anxiety that characterizes the latter. Fear of death, and the struggle with it, seems to be an inseparable companion of life. It is a curious inconsistency of Freud that he never altered his original view that in the unconscious and in the mind of the child there is no concept of death, except by extension of castration anxiety. This seems a direct contradiction of his concept of the death instinct and his hypothesis that, under the stimulation of the anxiety provoked by the death instinct, the organism deflects it outwards. Surely this anxiety would not be an extension of the castration fear, but a more primitive anxiety of being annihilated by the death instinct; and, indeed, observation of small children shows that death, their own as well as their object's, is often on their minds and is frequently both acted out and verbalized. The analysis of small children reveals fears more primitive than castration anxiety and pertaining to fantasies of death, such as fears of disappearance, dissolution, fragmentation, disintegration, etc.

What is the instinctual source of this anxiety? In her analysis of children, Melanie Klein discovered an inner world in the child's mind containing fantastical, threatening and death-bringing figures, early aspects of a superego, terrifying in their lethal power. The analysis of the child's fantasy life soon revealed that the primitive, terrifying aspects of these internal figures sprang from the child's projected destructiveness. When the projections were analyzed, the internal figures lost their terrifying power. She was confirmed in her belief in the importance of the child's destructiveness. Melanie Klein has given as much weight to the destructive impulses as to the libido and worked out the vicissitudes of the destructive drives parallel to and in conflict with the libidinal ones.

However, could not all these phenomena be accounted for by primary destructive drives? Is it necessary to postulate that the destructive drives themselves are due to the deflection of the death instinct? This leads to Dr. Friedman's second point, that the concept of the

---

[1]Jaques, E. "The Mid-Life Crisis." Presented to the British Psa. Society. To be published shortly in Int. J. Psa.

[2]Segal, H. "A Psycho-Analytic Approach to Aesthetics." In Klein, Heimann, and Money-Kyrle, *New Directions in Psychoanalysis*, New York, Basic Books, pp. 384-405.

death instinct may be a defense against the admission of aggression. If he were right about this, it would, to my mind, invalidate the concept as being a defense against a true realization. It is indeed true that aggression is a concept which does not get easy acceptance. The concept of the libido may be resisted in the world at large, but it is fully accepted by the psychoanalysts. As has been noted many times, aggression is a poor relative, often ignored or explained away even by psychoanalysts. If the concept of the death instinct were such a good defense against the acceptance of aggression, why has it not been more universally accepted? On the contrary, the concept of the libido has the widest acceptance, that of aggression comes second and the death instinct is the most strongly resisted of all. Furthermore, it is precisely those analysts, e.g., followers of Melanie Klein, who attach the most importance to the conflict between libido and aggression, who are more inclined to accept the concept of the death instinct.

A concept, such as the one of life and death instincts, cannot be viewed as true or false. It can only be validated as useful or useless. If all clinical phenomena could be explained by the conflict between libidinal and destructive drives, the concept of the death instinct would not be useful and could be misused for defensive purposes, so the validation of this concept must lie in the clinical field. There are phenomena, not fully covered by using the concept of aggression toward an object, which are more adequately covered by using the concept of the death instinct. Freud himself thought that this was the case with masochism. It is, however, in work with schizoid and schizophrenic patients that Kleinian analysts find the clearest clinical evidence of the operation of the death instinct. Severe anorexias also often reveal anxieties related to a direct operation of the death instinct.

In contrast to Freud's statement that the death instinct is mute and can be observed only in its derivatives, in the schizophrenic it can often be observed operating directly and violently. One example of such an operation of the death instinct is "pathological projective identification."[3] In this form of projective identification, the primary attack is on the self. Whenever the ego experiences anxiety or pain, the part of the ego which experiences it is destructively splintered and projected into the object. The aim of this splintering and projection is to get rid of awareness. Here the aggression is directed primarily against the self; the aim is not to experience, that is, not to live. In a paper entitled "Some Schizoid Mechanisms Underlying Phobia Formation," I described a patient who wakes from a dream saying "I scatter, I splatter and I sink." In the session it became clear that her reaction to any stimulus of pain was a wish to disintegrate and abolish awareness.

The concept of the death instinct is an inevitable corollary of the pleasure-pain principle. Freud's idea of the motor discharge in order to "disemburden the psyche from stimuli" could be seen as the operation of the death instinct. In terms of the pleasure-pain functioning, whenever life does not offer pleasure and pain arises, the quickest way of getting rid of the pain is death. The point was very succinctly made by a schizoid patient, who was a corset fetishist. His fetishistic ritual represented a return to the womb and union with mother as a painless state. This patient was extremely intolerant of frustration. He once propounded quite seriously that, if he ever had sciatica, he would painlessly commit suicide. He saw no reason why he should suffer pain. Probably at the primitive level there is a part of everyone which feels the same way, and only when the wish to live is strong enough, and objects are invested with libido,

---

[3]Bion, W. R. "Development of Schizophrenic Thought," Int. J. Psa., Vol. 37, 1956, pp. 344-346.

can the wish to die rather than experience pain be overcome.

In the last few pages of *Martin Eden*, Jack London describes the hero committing suicide by drowning. The passage conveys something of the basic struggle between the life and death instinct. Martin Eden finds himself trying to swim: "It was the automatic instinct to live. He ceased swimming, but the moment he felt the water rising above his mouth, his hands struck out sharply with a lifting movement. 'The will to live,' he thought, and the thought was accompanied by a sneer." The contempt for the part wishing to live, similar to the contempt I described in the patient above, is strongly brought out. "'The will to live,' he thought disdainfully." All the pain in drowning he attributes to this will to live. "'This hurt was not death' was the thought that oscillated through his reeling consciousness. It was life, the pangs of life, this awful suffocating feeling. It was the last blow life could deal him."

Melanie Klein accepts the concept of the life and death instincts as a basic meta-psychological concept and she bases her ideas of the early object relations and ego structure on the polarity of instincts. In her view, there is sufficient ego at birth to experience anxiety and to use primitive mechanisms of defense. It is the ego, therefore, which responds to the anxiety stirred by the death instinct by deflecting it. Freud saw this deflection as a conversion into aggression. In Melanie Klein's view, this deflection consists partly of a projection into an object and partly of a conversion into the aggression against the now threatening object. In deflecting the death instinct, the ego produces the first splitting within itself between the life and death instinct, and in the object, between the ideal object to which the infant's libido is directed and the persecutory object toward which hate is directed. The introjection of these early objects forms the basis of ego and superego structure.

It has been argued that this emphasis on the polarity of the instincts does not allow for the importance of environment. This does not at all follow. Mother's handling of the baby is vital for the outcome of the instinctual conflict. She must not only provide sufficient love and care to help the infant's libido to develop and grow, she must also be able to contain and deal with the infant's projection of the death instinct.

Discussant

Martin Grotjahn, M.D.

Beverly Hills, California

Freud was preoccupied with thoughts of death and dying from early childhood to old age. As in the life of many great men, mortality and immortality were driving motives in his work and achievement. It is possible that his theory of the death instinct grew out of this conflict about the acceptance of human fate and acceptance of death as a part of reality. It is also possible, or at least within the field of imagination, that it is this type of personality who always lives in or near the awareness of death (which includes a constant guilt about murderous hostility) who may finally develop cancer.

Freud's cancer is more a symbol, a sign, a mark of death, than that it prompted him to write about death instincts. The development may have proceeded from preoccupation with death to scientific elaboration and perhaps to psychosomatization in the form of a cancerous growth.

Freud faced death directly and courageously. He expressed that once when he said: "I think of death every day. This is a good training."

One more remark about the "charm" of the story of the "Three Caskets," of the Gradiva story: This is for me another indication of the symbolic presence of death in Freud's life. The symbols of death in dreams are often beauty. The whole problem, the sadness of true beauty lies here.

There are at least three groups of clinical phenomena which can be used to justify the assumption of the death instinct: the repetitious nature of childhood play, the repetitive nature of the transference neurosis, and the repetition compulsion, as for instance, in the dreams of the traumatic neurosis. In my mind all of these three phenomena do not justify the death instinct theory, but relate to the drive for mastery which is inborn in all humans as it is significant to all life as we know it.

It is possible that this type of mastery includes the final mastery of death. After all death is a part of reality and has to be mastered. This final victory over narcissism marks the step between maturity of a man to the wisdom of old age. We finally come to deal with death and dying (I have expressed these lines of thought carefully, avoiding any hints to Freud's personality in my paper: "The Fear of Death and Dying," Journal of the Hillside Hospital, Vol. IX, July 1960).

Discussant

Jacques Choron, PH.D., D.S.SC.

New York, New York

I did not find this paper sufficiently stimulating. There is little new in it and I feel that as long as the author deals with the "development of the death instinct in Freud's theoretical thinking" he should have at least mentioned Freud's precursors and their possible influence. For instance, he does not consider Schopenhauer (whom Freud himself cites), or the famous passage in Leonardo da Vinci's *Notebooks*, or Metchnikoff's "instinct de la mort." For details I must refer to my book *Modern Man and Mortality*, New York, Macmillan, 1964.

Discussant

Victor Calef, M.D.

San Francisco, California

"And here I may be allowed to break off these autobiographical notes. The public has no claim to learn any more of my personal affairs —of my struggles, my disappointments, and my successes. I have in any case been more open and frank in some of my writings . . . than people usually are who describe their lives for their contemporaries or for posterity. . . ." (Postscript to An Autobiographical Study, Freud, page 73, Vol. XX, St. Ed.)

Freud did not exaggerate. Few scientific writers have revealed as much of themselves. Certainly, no one has permitted the products of his creativity to be so closely juxtaposed to portrayals of his own unconscious mental processes and the most intimate personal details. It is easy to get glimpses of his mental life, both the superficial, manifest contents as well as the unconscious ones. It hardly requires conjecture, and certainly not the psychoanalytic methodology to know that Freud was preoccupied with death before, during, and after the time that he had his cancer (and certainly at the time that he pronounced his theory of the "Death Instinct").

Insofar as Dr. Friedman takes internal and external events and suggests a relationship between them he is using a part of the psychoanalytic method. And insofar as he finds that certain persons in the external world (even fictitious ones) can be the objects of identifications and projections, he is still using another part of the same method. There is a great deal more, however, to the analysis and genetic reconstruction of instinct, defense, and compromise formation. I doubt whether the use of a novel which Freud over-idealized and liked (Jensen's *Gradiva*) is a substitute for free association and can be treated like a dream or a symptom. *Gradiva* was for Freud a proof of his method and thoughts; the book recapitulates the essence of analytic theory and thought; a magnificent confirmation of his life-work. No greater narcissistic joy can be imagined! It resembles his dreams not at all while it does reflect much that is real in his life.

Freud's preoccupation with death was undoubtedly as intense as his preoccupation with life (for which there also is abundant evidence). He was aware of the quality of his involvement with death long before his cancer was incipient. There is little doubt that during his illness it takes on special intensity. He writes to Abraham: "... Though I am supposed to be on the way to recovery there is deep inside a pessimistic conviction that the end of my life is near. That feeds on the torments from my scar which never cease. There is a sort of senile depression which centers in a conflict between an irrational love of life and more sensible resignation.... If I am deceived and this proves to be only a passing phase I shall be the first to note it and then once more put my shoulder to the plough." (Page 68, Vol. III, Jones, *The Life and Works of Sigmund Freud*.)

Only very few would believe that in 1915 Freud had any premonition of his subsequent illness. His interest in death, however, is clearly demonstrated by 1915 when he took a walk, so he wrote, with a "taciturn friend" and a "famous young poet" who argued that there was no joy in nature's beauty because it was transient. (Freud on Transcience, *Collected Papers*, Vol. IV, page 79.) His recognition of the pain and difficulty of renunciation of an object of love as the essence of mourning, his rejection of the pessimism in the poet's feelings about transcience, his rejection of immortality as requisite for the appreciation of art and nature, these are not the pronouncements of a man who has refused to face his thoughts on death. Could he have allowed them to be taken over by the repressing forces? The pain and the consequences of the thoughts about death must have played some part in the production of papers like "Mourning and Melancholia," on "Transcience," "Beyond the Pleasure Principle," etc.

Certainly, Freud was aware of the clinical implications of aggression when he spoke of the partial instincts of sadism and masochism, or when he described Little Hans' difficulty (reported in 1909) as an ambivalence conflict or as the expression of a death-wish. It is true that Freud sometimes denied aggression, ambition, or hostility but recognized the unconscious elements within himself of those very traits by the reaction formation against them. It is only in "Beyond the Pleasure Principle" that he finally finds a primary position to give "aggression" in his theoretical system. It becomes elevated to an instinctual force, instead of an uncertain and derivative position.

There can be no doubt then about the presence in Freud of elements of aggression and the fears of death. However, an attempt to relate his interests and his theory hardly permits the conjecture that a theoretical construction (a principle of mental functioning) is identical to a defense. To discover the existence of conflictual material is not identical to a discovery of how conflict was resolved; nor is it identical to the discovery of a symptom.

Dr. Friedman does seem to believe that the "death instinct" idea was a defense directed against aggression and death wishes; and that it allayed the fear of death (punishment) by ascribing "death" and "death wishes" to an inexorable fate, thus to avoid guilt. It is not clear whether Dr. Friedman uses the concept "defense" to mean a mechanism, or a compromise formation, or whether he wishes to include sublimation as one of the defenses. To conceive of the death instinct theory as a compromise formation, as formed in the same way as a symptom, is to say that it is a piece of the return of the repressed.

If we compare the hypothesis of the death instinct to something like Little Hans' phobia, the two do not have the same characteristics. The little boy's instinct became distorted and unrecognizable both as to its aim and its object, by displacements and other defensive maneuvers. How can the death instinct theory be conceived as the defensive products, the vicissitudes of an instinct? The "death instinct" might represent a turning-upon-the-self of the aggressive instinctual wishes. But we cannot find how the aims of the objects of the instinct are distorted by the defensive process. For the death wishes to return as a death instinct hardly seems a repression. If the death wish is distorted only into a death instinct as a punishment by a turning-against-the-self, it would not constitute a symptom (to paraphrase Freud). The burden of proof remains with those who insist that such a theory is a defense to show just what are the vicissitudes of the instinct by a better demonstration of the distortions. It would be necessary to demonstrate how the secondary defensive operations achieve changes in the aim and object of the instinctual forces. A conversion from death wish to death instinct does not disguise or change the wish.

If the theory were now compared to a compulsive symptom, the typical reaction formations present in the compulsive symptom created by the isolations and the undoings will be found absent. Once again it becomes impossible to conceive of Freud's theoretical construction as having a defensive function comparable to symptom formation.

In lieu of considering the death instinct as a piece of the return of the repressed, one might consider that Freud's awareness of his own instinctual life permitted him to give up (and to thus control) much that was aggressive in his nature. Such renunciations permitted a narcissistic retreat, (i.e. permitted his self-analysis) and also freed the instinctual investments. This permitted them access to the associative channels for working-over and other channels of discharge upon new objects. This process sounds more like sublimation than defense.

Whether a product of neurotic defense or sublimation, the theory of instincts (and certainly the death instinct) is neither validated nor invalidated by these considerations. It was not the intent of this discussion to explore the death instinct as a theory. Most of those who feel that the death instinct has to be invalidated do so on the grounds that it is a speculative theory, philosophical in nature, grounded in a somewhat spurious biology, and based on little or no clinical evidence of a psychological character. The death instinct theory will be proven as invalid only when the economic and clinical issues involved are taken into consideration by a show of the inapplicability of any analogies between mental functioning and the laws of inertia.

Dr. Friedman is not concerned with invalidating the death instinct and does not join those who condemn the theory in the usual ways. His conjecture is somewhat unique in suggesting that the theory of the death instinct is a product of defense.

There is at least one author, Maryse Choisy, (*Sigmund Freud: A New Appraisal*, 1963, The Citadel Press), whose views are remarkably like those of Dr. Friedman in some respects. Choisy finds Freud's death instinct theory not only defensive but arising out of the mystical and religious. She renders Freud into a believer. I believe that the analysis of Freud by Choisy is not only fallacious in several respects, but is also a rather uncomfortable fulfillment of Freud's prediction that his biographers would go astray.

Obviously Freud did struggle with tremendous energies including powerful unconscious aggressive drives associated with much guilt. Some of those struggles were rendered into symptoms, like the travel phobia. However, the development of the theory of instinct as a product of defense will probably have to be rejected in favor of ascribing it to mental processes related to mastery, integration, and sublimation.

Author's Response

Lawrence J. Friedman, M.D.

Beverly Hills, California

It is impossible to give full credit to the discussion here. That it ranges from limited acceptance to total rejection, even scorn, proves the importance of the matter.

The need to understand man's violence is more urgent than ever. If we find the answer it will be through psychoanalysis. If the concept of the death instinct is valid, it does not explain aggression. It does not exclude an independent aggressive drive, a drive for hatred and destruction—as Freud described it. In his letter to Einstein in September, 1932, twelve years after the publication of *Beyond the Pleasure Principle*, he wrote: "We believe in the existence of an instinct of that kind and have in fact been occupied during the last few years in studying its manifestations." ("Why War?" *Coll. Papers*, Vol. 5, 1932.)

Perhaps the problem is that we do not differentiate between the death instinct and the aggressive drive; equating them does not explain hatred and destruction, within the framework of Kleinian thinking or outside of it. To call it a religious experience is begging the question, it negates the life work of Freud and all psychoanalytic knowledge.

"Defense" does not mean only pathology. Adaptation, mastery and the various defense mechanisms can be successful, promoting healthy functioning—or unsuccessful, leading to pathology. We also know that defenses can break down.

It is conceivable, even probable, that there is unconscious awareness of a destructive illness long before the conscious recognition. I am convinced also that it makes no difference whether we call Freud's illness cancer, malignant epithelioma, epulis or leukoplakia. Any of them can mobilize anxiety. Whether the scar is on the right or left it can be the connecting link, reactivating guilt over infantile and unconscious hostility.

I believe the death instinct concept postponed and complicated understanding man's violence, hatred, and destructiveness; I tried to understand the reasons for its creation. This was my conscious motivation, not a desire to analyze Freud, as some believe. Of course, I cannot vouch for my unconscious any more than the discussants can for theirs; for "... if we are to be judged by the wishes in our unconscious, we are like primitive man, simply a gang of murderers. It is well that all these wishes do not possess the potency which was attributed to them by primitive men; in the crossfire of mutual maledictions mankind would long since have perished, the best and wisest of men and the loveliest and fairest of women with the rest." (Sigmund Freud, "Thoughts on War and Death," *Coll. Papers*, Vol. 4, 1915.)

The Forum

Title Character and Life Circumstance in Fatal Accident

Authors

Robert E. Litman, M.D.

Associate Clinical Professor of Psychiatry at the University of Southern California and on the faculty of the Southern California Psychoanalytic Institute. Since 1958 he has been Chief Psychiatrist of the Suicide Prevention Center and has published more than twenty papers on aspects of self-destructiveness, including suicide, accidents and sexual deviations.

Norman Tabachnick, M.D.

Associate Clinical Professor of Psychiatry at the University of Southern California. He is Associate Chief Psychiatrist at the Los Angeles Suicide Prevention Center and on the faculty of the Southern California Psychoanalytic Institute. His major research interests in the past ten years have been in various clinical and theoretical aspects of self-destruction and related issues. He has had fifteen papers published on these and other topics.

Discussants

Milton L. Miller, M.D.

Professor of Psychiatry at the University of North Carolina at Chapel Hill. He is Chairman of the University of North Carolina-Duke Psychoanalytic Institute. Dr. Miller is the author of twenty-seven articles on psychoanalytic topics, psychosomatic disorders, and a book, *A Psychoanalytic Study of Marcel Proust*. He was the first President of the Southern California Psychoanalytic Institute.

Catherine L. Bacon, M.D.

Clinical Professor of Psychiatry at Temple University, Philadelphia, Pennsylvania. She was a Training Analyst at the Chicago Institute for Psychoanalysis from 1940-1952 and at the Philadelphia Psychoanalytic Institute from 1952 to the present. Her special interests have been in schizophrenia, the perversions, psychosomatic medicine and she has published in these fields.

E. Stengel, M.D.

Professor and Head of the Department of Psychiatry at the University of Sheffield, England, and a member of the British Psychoanalytic Society. He has studied suicide for many years and is the author of *Suicide and Attempted Suicide*.

Harold Marcus, M.D.

Instructor in Psychiatry at Columbia University, where he is on the Faculty of the Psychoanalytic Clinic for Training and Research. He is an Associate Attending Psychiatrist at Mount Sinai Hospital in New York. His two year controlled study of accident-repeaters among employees of a large department store in New York City is about to be published.

Character and Life Circumstance in Fatal Accident[1]

Norman Tabachnick, M.D.

and Robert E. Litman, M.D.

Los Angeles, California

Fatal accident is for the psychoanalyst a neglected issue and a fascinating enigma. Apart from the provocative contributions of Sigmund Freud and Karl Menninger, in one direction, and Franz Alexander and Flanders Dunbar, in another, there is little analytic thinking or research in this area. Yet the important challenges and opportunities in this field become quickly apparent. Not only would the study of fatal accidents itself have valuable theoretical and practical import, but light also might be cast on a number of additional issues. These include (a) data relative to the "death instinct" controversy, (b) the relationship between accidental and suicidal death, and (c) the role of unintended action and activity in human life (and death).

For the past two years, a group of Southern California psychoanalysts have been studying fatal and near-fatal accidental death.[2] It is the intent of this article to summarize some of this group's theoretical constructs, focusing on those common character traits and life circumstances which are frequently found in situations of accidental death.

[1]The research upon which this article is based was supported in part by a grant from the Foundations Fund for research in psychiatry.

[2]The members of this group have included Drs. Marvin Osman, Warren L. Jones, Jay Cohn, August Kasper, John Moffat, Lionel Margolin and Glen Flagg.

Review of Literature:

Psychoanalytic thinking on accident probably begins with *The Psychopathology of Everyday Life.* (1) In this book Freud listed some of the causes of ordinary bungled actions. They included (a) self-punishment related to guilt (b) self-injury as a sacrifice to ward off a greater disaster (c) accident as a manifestation of an unconscious desire to dispose of a depreciated object (d) accident as a desire to make contact with an erotic object, and (e) accident as a means of avoiding unpleasant situations.

These methods had in common that the accidental occurrence was a vehicle for the expression of some unconscious impulse; unconscious because the impulse itself or the complex of which it was a part was foreign to the usual consciously accepted attitudes of the individual.

Something more was required to explain serious and fatal accidents. Here Freud's thought turned to the death-instinct and its manifestations. "Anyone who believes in the occurrence of half-intentional self-*injury*—if I may use a clumsy expression, will be prepared also to assume that in addition to consciously intentional suicide there is such a thing as half-intentional self-*destruction* (self-destruction with an unconscious intention) capable of making skillful use of a threat to life and disguising it as a chance mishap."

These conceptions were later reaffirmed and elaborated by Karl Menninger. (2) The crucial explanatory concepts in this view are that accidents arise from the tendency of certain unconscious forces to move toward active expression and that among these forces is a self-destructive trend.

A different approach to accident was provided by Dunbar, (3) Alexander, (4) and others, who in more recent years popularized the concept of the "accident-prone" individual. They studied the victims of a wide range (in terms of severity) of accidents. The victims were described as quick, decisive, active, impulsive, independent and adventurous. They made up their minds quickly and moved toward immediate goals. They reacted to illness with bravado, fatalism or a play for secondary gain. Immediately prior to the accident, there had been some change in the life situation which had threatened their autonomy.

These investigators agreed with Freud and Menninger that accidents were expressions of unconscious tendencies, but the direction of their thinking was different in two respects. First, they did not see the value or necessity of postulating an unconscious suicidal trend. Secondly, they emphasized that *character structure* was an important issue in understanding who will have an accident and why he will have it.

Present Research:

The following observations and theoretical formulations are based on the study of the lives of about 35 accident victims. The majority of these people had serious or fatal accidents.[3]

Most of them were the drivers in one-car accidents (the car smashed into a stationary object, went over a cliff, etc.). In many cases, additional information was gathered from interviews with relatives, friends and other knowledgeable contacts of the victims. (In the cases of those who died as a result of the accident, such interviews were of necessity the only source of information.) The period of time spent on each case varied from a few hours (in which both an objective and associative interview was conducted) to 30 or 40 interviews over a period of many months.

The focus of the rest of this article will be on the two aspects of accidental phenomena named in the title—the character traits of the accident victims and their life situations at the time of the tragedies. We do not intend to suggest that consideration of these aspects will provide a complete, or even the most pertinent view, of accidental phenomena. They rather reflect the beginnings of the theoretical efforts of our group.

In passing it is interesting to note the emphasis of each of the psychoanalytic investigators of accident. Freud's studies were mainly aimed at the demonstration of unconscious forces within man. He also tried specifically to demonstrate the manifestations of an unconscious self-destructive tendency. Dunbar and Alexander focused on character traits which were pertinent in the accident-prone indivival. Our work continues the exploration of character traits, but is also importantly concerned with the life situation in which the accident takes place.

The Significant Character Trait—Impulsive Activity:

A prominent character trait of the accidental victims was impulsive activity. They tended —at certain times—to react to frustrating, disappointing or humiliating stresses with immediate outbursts of affect-laden action that was not clearly related to the execution of their consciously designated goals. Here are some examples: a young man calls a girl friend for a date, but is turned down. He slams the receiver onto the hook and rushes to his car, which he drives aimlessly and speedily for about twenty miles.

A skilled artisan is criticized by a foreman to whom he considers himself superior. He utters a curse and "walks off the job."

Such examples were found many times in the lives of our subjects. A study in which accident victims were compared with those who died in other ways tended to emphasize the

[3]We gratefully acknowledge the cooperation of Los Angeles County Chief Coroner, Dr. Theodore J. Curphey, whose office gave invaluable assistance in the study of the deceased victims.

greater presence of impulsive activity in the lives of the former. (5)

What can be the meaning of such a mode of functioning? We believe that from one standpoint it is regressive and has in common with other regressive modes an attempt to symbolically move into a previous developmental epoch. The latter is one which was felt to be more gratifying and freer of problems than the present one.

However, regression may take many forms. Why do accident victims move into impulsive activity? It is our belief that this occurs so that they may recapture the feeling of adventurous daring which was present during an earlier period of impulsive activity. During this early period (let us say around the time when the infant begins to walk) there is a great deal of risk-taking associated with impulsive activity. For example, picture an infant learning to walk. Both because of internal developmental pushes and external expectations (or demands, or whatever) psychological energies are focused on *trying* to walk, but there is also an accompanying fear (of falling and being hurt). This is based partially on the reality experiences of the child and also, to some extent, mirrors the fearfulness of the surrounding adults. Thus to actually *make* the attempt to walk involves taking a risk and being daring.

Normally one expects that being daring carries with it a certain amount of pleasure. There are many possible sources of such pleasure—to name but two, the internal pleasure (of mastery) and the external approval (for mastering). Both of these tend to place a premium on the infant's willingness *to dare*, which preceded the accomplishment of the motor task.

At any rate, the feeling of pleasure and daring seems to be the sought-for feeling which constitutes the attraction to regressive, impulsive activity. This pleasure in daring, and especially in daring action, was noted in many other areas of accident victims' lives besides those associated with their accidents. One could go so far as to call the subjects addicts—addicts who turn to the comforting use of action when they encounter certain stressful situations.

But of course there is danger in the inappropriate use of impulsive action. As in other regressions, there is a tendency to miss noting that some of the situation is changed from the period of infancy or childhood. In infancy there were guarding adults nearby to protect against too radical consequences of the youngster's actions, but in adult life these safeguarding others may not be present. Of course it is precisely under these circumstances (when one is neither vigilant oneself, nor has others around who will be vigilant for him) that many serious or fatal accidents occur.

To summarize: Impulsive action is a particularly favored regressive movement for many accident victims. Its value lies in the associated feeling of being daring and brave. However, since it does not take into consideration the total responsibility which the individual is facing, it carries with it serious and sometimes fatal consequences.

The Life Circumstance—New Responsibility:

Having identified impulsive activity as a *crucial mode* of *reacting* in severe accident victims, what can be discerned about the *crucial precipitating stress* which may give rise to this mode?

Our initial bias was to search out some disturbing situation which had occurred just prior to the mishap. Conceptualizing accident as an analogue of suicide, we thought we might find real or fantasied loss of an important object. Also when we became aware of the sensitive pride of accident victims, we thought that humiliations or indications that the victim was not making a good appearance or performance might precede the accident. However, neither of these conjectures was borne out by our studies. As a matter of fact, most of the subjects we studied seemed to be living in anticipation of changes, probably for the better. Some of the young people were about to enter college, a number of the men were conducting successful courtships or planning marriage, some people had recently received promotions at work.

These observations suggested that in (some at any rate) accident victims the assumption of new responsibility provides a situation of general tension which may lead to an accident.

How can new responsibilities—transitions to importantly different living situations—act as stresses to the human being? Such situations can and have been discussed from a number of viewpoints. We believe that an important overview might start with the conception that such transitions disturb an individual's sense of personal identity.

Human beings need for a strong sense of identity has become increasingly important in the understanding of human behavior. A sense of identity may be defined as a feeling that one's life goals and the means which are utilized to achieve them have a certain pattern of consistency which has significance both for the individual and the society in which he lives. From this definition, it is apparent that an individual's sense of identity can be described from two usually interrelated points of view. One deals with the various expectations and demands which society makes upon an individual. The other root of identity has references to the feeling of self-sameness and continuity, which emerges from a person's sense that he is following goals and using methods which are importantly his own.

It is then apparent that as new responsibilities, which may be assigned by society or the individual or by both, are undertaken, various types and degrees of identity crises might occur.

Although limitations of space do not allow detailed exposition of case material, we would state that the concept of identity crisis as a reaction to assuming new responsibility can usefully be applied to our studies. Many of our subjects were young adults, in many ways "older" adolescents, facing a number of situations characteristic of that time of life. Such situations simultaneously present possibilities of intriguing gratification and threatening challenge. As so well described by Erikson, (6) these are situations of "identity" crisis. However, identity difficulties are not limited to the period of adolescence. For example, a married man whose wife of twenty years suddenly dies, a person moving to a foreign country—these individuals also face crises in their feelings of self-sameness and continuity.

In fact, at any point in the span of life the urge that comes from within or the demand that is made from without can thrust one into a desired but frightening situation which challenges one's sense of identity. At such a time, individuals may lose the qualities of soberness and deliberateness that have attended the previous conduct of their affairs and fall back on more immediate and primitive methods of reacting. These methods are chosen because they had once been effective in dealing with problems and for some reason are particularly significant to the specific individual. What is here emphasized is that inept (in one sense) though these methods turn out to be, they have the purpose of coping with new situations and restoring a feeling of steady identity.

For the accident victims, these methods included the movement into direct, impulsive and relatively unconsidered action. Earlier, some of the specific developmental, psychological qualities of impulsive action, which makes it comforting, were described and we can understand that some people may be drawn to utilize it.

One last point: An unresolved problem resulting from the "accident-prone" work of

Dunbar and Alexander, was the question as to why accident-proneness was not a continuous and persistent finding. Most people were accident-prone for only short periods of time. Our work suggests that this phenomenon might be explained, at least to some degree, by the following hypothesis: Accident-proneness is dependent on the tendency of a given individual to move regressively into psychological states of impulsive activity. Such states are often transient because they are attempts to deal with identity crises, which in most people's lives come infrequently and last for relatively short periods.

Summary

Previous work in the psychology of accident has provided intriguing leads to the understanding of this phenomenon, but has left important unresolved issues. Our interest in this field has led to the formulation that fatal accident is often significantly linked to two factors: (a) A tendency to move into a psychological state, characterized by impulsive activity. (b) A life situation in which the transition to new responsibilities produces a situation of crisis.

Bibliography

1. Alexander, F. "The Accident-Prone Individual." Public Health Reports, Vol. 64, 1949, pp. 357-362.
2. Dunbar, H. F. *Psychosomatic Diagnosis.* New York, Hoeber, 1943.
3. Erikson, E. H. "The Problem of Ego Identity." In Identity and the Life Cycle. *Psychological Issues.* Vol. 1, No. 1. New York, Int. Univ. Press, 1959, pp. 101-164.
4. Freud, S. (1901) "The Psychopathology of Everyday Life." In *Standard Edition*, London, Hogarth Press, Vol. 6, 1950, pp. 1-279.
5. Menninger, K. A. "Purposive Accidents As an Expression of Self-Destructive Tendencies." Int. J. Psa. Vol. 17, 1935, pp. 6-15.
6. Tabachnick, N. et al. "A Comparative Psychiatric Study of Accidental and Suicidal Death." (To be published in Arch. Gen. Psych.).

2521 West Pico Boulevard
Los Angeles, California 90006

Discussant

Milton L. Miller, M.D.

Chapel Hill, North Carolina

The authors' suggestions that fatal accidents are linked to: (a) a psychological state characterized by impulsive activities; (b) transition to new responsibilities producing a crisis situation, stimulate ideas for further discussion.

In psychoanalytic work we see impulsive urges such as fight or flight occurring when repressed anger appears. The strength of the impulse in its relation to the ego and superego functions are important factors in the outcome.

What causes the faulty reality testing that contributes to many fatal accidents? Insofar as these accidents are connected with personal negligence, risk, or misperception, rather than unforeseeable mechanical failure or pure chance, is there a lack of that armor that helps caution to function almost automatically? Where there is intense unconscious involvement, we may be dealing with a lack of ability to test reality. In some individuals this may stem from an unconscious sense of omnipotence related to the elated phase of a manic-depressive cycle. The defense of denial is part of a distorted sense of danger versus security. This may be responsible for failure to control a swift vehicle or perceive brake failure beforehand. Fear of passivity may enhance substitution of an elated, active mood for repose. Danger is denied, or projected, condensed, isolated—e.g., the driver's fantasies may be hostile, self-destructive, or associated with power.

Elation or defiance may mask depression or diffuse anger; the flight fantasies may take the place of alertness about the current scene. Erroneous appraisal of power in others or in other vehicles is apt to be part of the general imbalance of a manic state. A feeling of enhanced potency versus denial of dependence or need for help from others is an important factor. The driver's vehicle or his strong body symbolize a fountain of strength, potency and security, to himself. His prime urge is to manipulate others, to be omnipotent: thus there is a certain superficiality in his estimate of how the manipulation is to take place. Perception of current reality is forfeited to some degree in favor of unconsciously idealized eternity. There may even be a lack of clear distinction between realities of what life and death are. This is characteristic of certain very youthful attitudes, particularly among disturbed adolescents, and among those under the influence of stimulants. The omnipotent fantasies of manic-depressive persons fit this picture.

Mild mood swings are fairly common among so-called normal people, but in the latter are usually kept under control. The point of turning from a depressive to a manic phase may be connected, particularly, with suicidal accidents. This is less obvious because the manic mood is a mask of enthusiasm about life, hiding the same dynamic constellation of frustrations as the depressed phase, but emphasizing speed and noise rather than slowness and self-effacement.

Discussant

Catherine L. Bacon, M.D.

Philadelphia, Pennsylvania

I should like to suggest that the authors' description of the accident victim reminds one of the hypomanic character. The defense in the hypomanic is denial and what is denied is most importantly a fear of death: a fear of being killed by a jealous parent.

In this regard a story of Kafka's comes to mind. A young industrialist has just had two happy experiences. He has doubled the business of his old and paralyzed father's firm and has become engaged to a beautiful young aristocrat, a woman of a class to which his father could never have aspired. He goes in joyfully to break the news to his father, also saying that he and his bride-to-be would be most happy to have his father live with them. Instead of pleasure, the father hurls the most awful curses at the young man, who then flees from his father's house and drowns himself. We see here the hypomanic mood with the total denial of his father's probable jealousy, followed by a swift, unexpected, jealous and brutal attack by the father, followed by suicide.

In most patients I have seen, the "attack" comes from the superego, following the hypomanic mood, and is seen as an expression of jealousy in the outside world.

The problem of character, identity and identity crisis follows from this. For instance, in business, if one has the reality of being a good subordinate and hence being loved by the chief, a promotion which this type of character reacts to with joy, nevertheless, puts him into a position of competing with the chief in reality or fantasy. His identity therefore becomes that of a competitor instead of a subordinate. In the hypomanic character the conflict is not conscious nor is it worked through by the ego, but instead it may be worked through regressively in taking unwarranted risks, as though both to do something dangerous and to deny the danger.

The differential diagnosis between patients who react to the hypomanic mood with subsequent depression, schizophrenia or perverse activity, and those who seek out dangerous situations is by no means clear to me, but I think the authors have made a promising start.

Discussant

E. Stengel, M.D.

Sheffield, England

The paper has the merit of clarity and conciseness. It is easy to follow the authors' thesis. However, one would like to know more about their concepts and their clinical observations before accepting their conclusions. The specificity of the traits and the life situations singled out by the authors has not been convincingly established. The authors' concluding formulation presents an hypothesis which is still in need of validation.

The observation that accident-prone persons are impulsive is not more than a clinical impression which would have to be confirmed by systematic studies. What does "impulsiveness" mean in this context and why does it take that particular form? Impulsive action could take other directions, such as eating, drinking, playing an instrument, taking sexual action, etc. Accident- and suicide-prone persons take *aggressive* impulsive action. The authors do not refer to aggressive impulses. This seems a deficiency in their theory. It is irrelevant for their thesis whether one adheres to the theory that aggression is due to frustration or whether one assumes a primary aggressive drive.

The authors identify the risk-taking aspect of accident- and suicide-prone behaviour with the daring exploratory activities of the child. Is this justified? The latter is ego-syntonic, i.e., approved by the ego and usually by the superego, i.e., by the parents and society. The accident- and suicide-prone person in endangering himself defies his superego and society. He unconsciously wants to hurt others.

The authors regard assumption of new responsibility leading to identity crises as a specific source of stress. This will be difficult to prove. Nowadays most people, especially the young and middle-aged, have recently taken on, or are going to take on, or hope to take on new responsibilities.

The factors singled out by the authors may play a part in accident proneness, but only in the context of a multiplicity of factors among which aggressive tendencies and lack of adequate emotional relationships are likely to be important.

Discussant

Harold Marcus, M.D.

New York, New York

Received as *The Forum* went to press.

I think the authors oversimplify when they select a single character trait and label it "the significant character trait." To determine what produces the accident syndrome, one must study the total person, which is done best by psychiatric or psychoanalytic study of the subject himself. Information from friends and relatives is superficial, subjective, biased, and may even be imaginary; it is not reliable as a scientific tool.

The authors say that the purpose of the impulsive activity is pleasure and approval and they relate it to the infant's attempting to walk. No evidence is given for these explanations. I do not believe the purpose is pleasure or approval, or that it is a regression. I think the "impulsive act" probably is to discharge extreme *anger* which the accident victim is unable or afraid to express in an open, direct and adaptive way. The impulsive act is akin to a childhood temper tantrum.

The authors' second point is that the assumption of new responsibility is the stress that precipitates the accident. No evidence is presented for this conclusion either. What was the time relationship between new responsibility and accident? Was anything else going on in the victim's life at the time of the accident? What happened the day of the accident? What feelings did he have? These important questions are not answered. To find these answers, the investigator must interview the accident victim himself very soon after the accident, before amnesia sets in.

In my study of a group of accident repeaters and a control group of people on the same job who had no accidents, I found that the typical accident repeater had great anger which he suppressed and was disorganized, disorderly, careless. He was a passive, dependent character. The accident serves as, (a) a substitute outlet for suppressed anger, (b) self-punishment for sexual guilt, and (c) a way of getting care, attention and dependency gratification (listed in order of frequency).

The person who has a fatal accident, especially in an automobile, may be different than the on-the-job accident repeater, but I question whether the difference is qualitative or quantitative.

Authors' Response

Norman Tabachnick, M.D.

and Robert E. Litman, M.D.

Los Angeles, California

All the discussants note that denial, counter-depression and hypomanic elements predominate in this group of accident victims. By contrast, suicide victims tend to have been masochistic, immobilized and depressed. Dr. Bacon's interpretation of the identity crisis fits a number of our cases, although not all of them.

Dr. Stengel is correct in pointing out that our formulations are only hypotheses which point toward further research efforts. It is true that we have sidestepped the issue of "aggression" deliberately. We are trying to feel our way toward a psychoanalytic view of *action*, one of the weakest areas of psychoanalytic theory. So far the aggression concept has not been extremely helpful. To illustrate: Suicide by shooting oneself in the head is "aggressive"; accidentally driving one's car into a tree at high speed is also "aggressive." Our pilot studies indicate that the character and life situation for these two types of deaths are quite different—and in some ways opposite.

Professor Stengel reminds us of the multiplicity of factors involved in "cause," and the lack of adequate emotional relationships in some self-destructive persons. He points in directions which we intend to follow. This paper is only a first step toward a comprehensive description of the psychology of accidents.

Dr. Miller's comments on faulty reality testing are especially pertinent to the problem of fatal accidents. Fantasies of power and omnipotence are regular features of patients who have survived near-fatal accidents. These individuals seem to have peculiarly intimate body-ego relationships with their automobiles. Dr. Miller's insight concerning "the point of turning from a depressive to a manic phase" is most perceptive, and strengthens one of our formulations: that the crucial factor which suicide-prone and accident-prone individuals have in common is a weakness of the integrating and synthesizing functions of the ego which allows two distinct patterns of activity and passivity to co-exist without resolution into either a manic or depressive phase.

In this sense, suicide-prone and accident-prone states are reciprocals. In suicide-prone states, masochistic, passive and immobilization defenses predominate. A suicidal act occurs when there is a breakthrough of (self-destructive) action. In the accident-prone individual, denial, counter-depressive and action defenses predominate. He places himself in dangerous and risky situations to strengthen his feelings of invulnerability and omnipotence. At this point an accident may be caused by a breakthrough of passivity which precipitates withdrawal of attention or loss of control; or the driver may simply exceed the capacities of the self-preservative functions of the ego.

The Forum

Title **The Psychodynamics of Concentration Camp Victims**

Author **Klaus D. Hoppe, M.D.**

Psychoanalyst and Director of Research at the Hacker Clinic in Beverly Hills, California. For several years he has evaluated concentration camp victims, and has written over one hundred twenty detailed psychiatric opinions in response to German Indemnification offices and courts, and has treated several survivors in extensive psychotherapy. He has published many papers in this field in English and German.

Discussants

William G. Niederland, M.D.

Clinical Associate Professor of Psychiatry, State University of New York, Training and Supervisory Analyst, Psychoanalytic Division of the State University of New York, Chief Consulting Psychiatrist to the Altro Health and Rehabilitation Services, New York City, and author of several papers dealing with concentration camp survivors.

Paul Chodoff, M.D.

Associate Clinical Professor of Psychiatry at George Washington University in Washington, D.C., and on the faculty of the Washington Psychoanalytic Institute. In the past five years, he has examined more than eighty applicants for damages to their health under the Restitution Laws. He has published on this subject and is the author of a chapter dealing with it which will appear in a forthcoming supplementary volume of the *American Handbook of Psychiatry*.

Paul Friedman, M.D., PH.D.

Psychoanalyst, a former lecturer of the New York Psychoanalytic Institute, and an Attending Psychiatrist at Mt. Sinai and Beth Israel Hospitals in New York City. In 1946 and 1947, Dr. Friedman made surveys of the psychological conditions of the survivors of Nazi concentration camps in Europe and Cyprus. He was a member of a mission in 1949 at the invitation of the Israeli Government to organize a mental hygiene program in Israel. He has since published several articles on these subjects.

Edith Jacobson, M.D.

Visiting Professor of Psychiatry at the Albert Einstein College of Medicine, a former President of New York Psychoanalytic Society. She has been training analysts and lecturing at New York Psychoanalytic Institute for twenty-five years. She has published many psychoanalytic papers, and a book, *The Self and the Object World*.

The Psychodynamics of Concentration Camp Victims

Klaus D. Hoppe, M.D.
Beverly Hills, California

Although twenty years have passed since the end of the Third Reich, interest focused on the victims of German concentration camps has been increasing rather than decreasing. The reasons for this development are not only the dramatic trials of war criminals and the growing number of scientific and fictional publications concerned with the conditions inside the camps, but equally so the emotional and physical condition of the former camp inmates. It has been a surprising and alarming fact that many victims of concentration camps suffer more from the after-effects at the present time than they did five, ten or fifteen years ago. Our endeavor to understand the psychodynamics of concentration camp victims seems, therefore, particularly urgent and warranted.

E. A. Cohen, (6) an inmate of concentration camps himself, examines the psychology of the inmates during their incarceration from a psychoanalytical point of view. He describes states of depersonalization, stupor and fright as initial reactions followed by mourning, guilt feelings and apathy in the stage of adaptation. He emphasizes the importance of the life instinct for survival and points out that the enforced regression results in partial identification of the victims with the SS as punitive parental images. In the final stage of resignation, the camp inmate directed his hatred against himself (see also Bettelheim [3]) and experienced the primal father as the group ideal.

The fact that the victims still show many of the foregoing features provides the basis of our present understanding.

Since the greater number of victims remained depressed, and since being uprooted from their closely-knit families served to deepen their depression (32) let us first discuss the psychodynamics in the case of chronic reactive depression.

We find that the degree of loss of self-esteem is proportionate to the degree of chronic reactive depression. (20) The depth of depression depends on the extent of the narcissistic regression and of the defusion of libidinal and aggressive instinctual drives. Federn (10) has described the final phase of overwhelming pain as apathy. This concept fits into Greenson's (16) statements, Bibring's (4) emphasis on the loss of self-esteem, and Jacobson's (24) formulation on the "return to a position of participation, but in the worthlessness instead of the value of the love object."

Erikson (7) believes that the regression to, and fixation on, the earliest infantile stages is based on a lack of basic trust as well as the state of helplessness and hopelessness. Moreover, there is a marked disturbance in the victim's relationship to the past and future as constitutive elements of temporal conception. They often perceive time as standing still and remaining motionless within their life cycle. This diffusion and loss of time perspective may cause a continuous identity diffusion, (8) particularly in adolescent inmates of the concentration camp.

These victims show a submissive, compliant and always fearful attitude, since they are still afraid of punishment and retaliation from authority figures. Hartmann, et al (19) see such victims as continuing to direct their deneutralized aggressive drives against themselves. As a result, there occurs a deepening of depression or, if the ego-boundaries are cathected, a resomatization (31) which is manifested in their psychosomatic complaints.

Few of the inmates, however, have been able to react to their highly traumatic experiences with aggression. To begin with, their hatred was provoked by—and turned against—the external enemy, on whom it remained fixed. In the course of time, the hate spread to include all Germans, and, finally, the whole world that had permitted such cruelty. These fixations and generalizations provide a ready avenue for projecting internal conflicts and for full-fledged rationalizations. The inmates who developed a chronic reactive aggression (20, 21) were never in danger of unconsciously relating to their torturers as to parental figures. They were protected from such a regression by a firm ego ideal, by shame, pride, and the idea of having a mission. (22) In them, there occurred a permanent transforming of inner superego forces to the outside, i.e., an externalization of the negative conscience. (9)

However, not all of the deneutralized aggression is externalized and projected upon persons and institutions outside. The hate creates new guilt feelings which are turned against the self in a punitive way. These guilt feelings are especially aggravated when the patient's hate-addiction (20,22) turns also against the members of his own family. The victim experiences his relatives, who seem to force him to continue a tortured life, as representatives of his externalized negative conscience.

Another important effect of such deep regression seems to exist when a victim states, time and again, that he died at least twice every day in Auschwitz—first, when passing the SS guards at the gate at dawn, and then again in the evening. It is easy to understand why today he feels dead. Many of the victims express doubt and uncertainty as to whether they really exist here and now. They experience the repetitive recollections and dreams of their suffering of more than twenty years ago as reality, whereas the present life has the quality of a dream. Such depersonalization and derealization, such splitting of the ego and estrangement from the world around, seem to be connected with a preoccupation with the victims' own bodies. Niederland (29) has emphasized how the enforced shift of the body cathexis in relation to various body parts results in a changed self-image.

These observations and psychodynamic inferences are guideposts for helping the victims in psychotherapy find their way back to themselves and to society. Based upon my own experiences with several victims in psychoanalytically-oriented psychotherapy, I would like to outline and summarize the most significant psychodynamic factors concerning the patient, and certain requirements on the part of the analyst.

A. *Concerning the Patient:*

1. The above-mentioned regression to, and fixation on, pre-oedipal stages, enforced by the gruesome experiences in the concentration camps, makes the therapeutic regression more difficult. (2)

2. Childhood experiences and conflicts are suppressed, repressed and denied by clinging to the "negative myth" of the concentration camp, or idealizing the patient's own childhood. (5) Childhood conflicts are sometimes covered up by aggressive and revengeful fantasies toward the torturers. I found support for the hypothesis that a certain amount of neurotic predisposition proved helpful, in many cases, in surviving concentration camp because of stronger defense mechanisms and childhood fixations. (20)

3. The severe guilt of the survivor (28, 34) can, at times, be traced back to infantile guilt feelings caused by death wishes toward parents and siblings. A further determining factor for the guilt feelings seems to lie in the severe conflict between self-preservation and family ties.

4. The body image is disturbed due to the shift of the body cathexis and the enforced ex-

tinction of any sense of shame in the camps.

5. Superego development very frequently is impaired through destruction of the ego ideal and through the fixation on a masochistic, submissive attitude towards authority figures. De-neutralized aggression is either turned against the patient's own self (thus increasing the depression), or is focused as hate-addiction upon an externalized negative conscience.

6. The socio-cultural background of the victim has to be taken into consideration. It has been shown, for example, that examination of Jewish family life in a small village in Eastern Europe furnishes valuable clues, especially for the development of a strict superego. (35)

7. The adaptation to and re-routing of victims in the adopted country has frequently failed. The neurosis of uprooting, (30) and revival of oral wishes, (25) already noted in refugees and immigrants, may have intensified the disturbances caused by the concentration camp experiences.

B. *On the Part of the Therapist:*

1. He is required to show attentive consistency, empathy and compassion without being overwhelmed by his own feelings of sympathy.

2. His permanent interest in the patient's motivation, (17) the transference neurosis and the working alliance, (17) is essential.

3. He must firmly work through the patient's resistance, (11,12) which is particularly expressed against the association of concentration camp sufferings and childhood experiences.

4. He has constantly to seek a fruitful and balanced relationship between abstinence and gratification of the patient's needs.

5. It is necessary for him to listen patiently to repetitive recollections of cruelties, dreams of persecution, and encounters with death.

6. He should openly admit his mistakes in the treatment (13,14) and constantly control the counter transference.

These principles, basic for every psychoanalytic treatment, are of particular significance in psychotherapy with concentration camp victims. Their observance is instrumental in overcoming the initial doubt that human beings exposed to such extremes of cruelty can be helped.

It seems especially important that the therapist work through his own guilt feelings, which may be the result of the therapist's life in Nazi Germany or his lack of open resistance. His guilt feelings become evident, for example, if we find him reporting his own sufferings under the Nazi regime, (27) or by evading the patient's recollections of cruelties. The therapist should constantly be prepared to be identified with the aggressor, and to scrutinize his own tendencies to give in to the patient's demands.

The realization of these psychodynamics and the consideration of specific phenomena of transference and counter-transference may establish the basis for improving the victim's condition with the help of psychotherapy. Our own rather encouraging results (23) correspond with the experience of Niederland, (29) Trautman, (34) and Edith Ludowick-Gyomroi. (26) Tas, (33) arrived at the same conclusion, giving psychotherapy in the concentration camp; Friedman, (15) and Bastiaans, (1) reported improvement and changes through psychotherapy a few years after liberation.

While the inconceivable suffering deliberately imposed on human beings by others cannot be comprehended—indeed, shock and shame is inherent in every encounter with victims of concentration camps—it is the therapist's role to steer a course between the Scylla of over-identification and the Charybdis of so-called scientific detachment. The empathic understanding of psychodynamics may enable the therapist to endure the recollections of gruesome experiences by reflection, and help alleviate the plight of the victims.

Summary

The psychodynamics of former inmates of German concentration camps, suffering from chronic reactive depression, are described and compared with the psychodynamics of those survivors who reacted to the same horror with chronic aggression. Emphasis is laid on the difference in depth and degree of regression to and the fixation on infantile stages, enforced by the experiences in the camps. The symptomatology consists of disturbances of ego- and drive-development, such as apathy, loss of self-esteem, distrust, defusion of instinctual drives, resomatization, depersonalization and hate-addiction or intersystemic conflicts and defense mechanisms such as guilt of the survivor, identity diffusion, repression, denial and externalization of a negative conscience.

Based upon these concepts, the most significant factors concerning psychotherapy of concentration camp victims are outlined. In addition, certain requirements on the attitude of the analyst are stressed.

Bibliography

1. Bastiaans, J. *Psychosomatische Gevolgen von Onderdrukking en Verzet.* Amsterdam, Noort-Holl. V.M., 1957.
2. Benedetti, G. *Klinische Psychotherapie.* Bern, Huber, 1964.
3. Bettelheim, B. *The Informed Heart.* Glencoe, Illinois, Free Press, 1960.
4. Bibring, E. "The Mechanism of Depression." In Greenacre, P., *Affective Disorders.* New York, Int. Univ. Press, 1953, pp. 13-48.
5. Chodoff, P. "Late Effects of the Concentration Camp Syndrome." Arch. Gen. Psychiat., Vol. 8, 1963, pp. 323-333.
6. Cohen, E. A. *Human Behavior in the Concentration Camp.* New York, Universal Library, 1953.
7. Erikson, E. H. *Childhood and Society.* New York, Norton Co., 1950.
8. ———. *Identity and the Life Cycle.* New York, Int. Univ. Press, 1959.
9. ———. *Young Man Luther.* New York, Norton & Co., 1958.
10. Federn, P. *Ego Psychology and the Psychoses.* New York, Basic Books, 1952.
11. Freud, S. "On Beginning the Treatment." *Standard Edition,* Vol. 12, London, Hogarth Press, 1958, pp. 123-144.
12. ———. "Remembering, Repeating and Working Through." *Standard Edition,* Vol. 12, London, Hogarth Press, 1958, pp. 145-156.
13. ———. "Constructions in Analysis," Int. J. Psa., Vol. 19, 1938, pp. 377-387.
14. ———. "Analysis Terminable and Interminable." *Standard Edition,* Vol. 23, London, Hogarth Press, 1964, p. 216.
15. Friedman, P. "Some Aspects of Concentration Camp Psychology." Amer. J. Psychiat., Vol. 105, 1949, pp. 601-605.
16. Greenson, R. "The Psychology of Apathy." Psa. Quart., Vol. 18, 1949, pp. 290-302.
17. ———. "The Working Alliance and the Transference Neurosis." Psa. Quart., Vol. 34, 1965, pp. 155-181.
18. Hacker, F. J. "Treatment Motivation," Bulletin of the Menninger Clinic, Vol. 26, 1962, pp. 288-298.
19. Hartmann, H., Kris, E., and Loewenstein, R. M. "Notes on the Theory of Aggression." In *The Psychoanalytic Study of the Child.* New York, Int. Univ. Press, Vol. 3-4, 1949, pp. 9-36.
20. Hoppe, K. "Verfolgung, Aggression und Depression," Psyche, Vol. 16, 1962, pp. 521-537.
21. ———. "Persecution, Depression and Aggression." Bulletin of the Menninger Clinic, Vol. 26, 1962, pp. 195-203.
22. ———. "Persecution and Conscience." Psa. Review, Vol. 52, 1965, pp. 106-116.
23. ———. "Psychotherapie bei Konzentrationslageropfern." Psyche, Vol. 19, 1965-66, pp. 290-319.
24. Jacobson, E. "Contribution to the Metapsychology of Cyclothymic Depression." In Greenacre, P., *Affective Disorders.* New York, Int. Univ. Press, 1953.
25. Krystal, H. and Petty, T., "The Dynamics of the Adjustment to Migration." The Psychiat. Quart., Supplement, Vol. 37, 1963, pp. 119-133.
26. Ludowyk-Gyomroi, E. "The Analysis of a Young Concentration Camp Victim." In *The Psychoanalytic Study of the Child.* New York, Int. Univ. Press, Vol. 18, 1963, pp. 484-510.
27. Meerloo, J. "Neorologism and Denial of Psychic Trauma in Extermination Camp Survivors." Amer. J. Psy., Vol. 120, 1963, pp. 65-66.
28. Niederland, W. "The Problem of the Survivor." J. Hillside Hospital, Vol. 10, 1961, pp. 233-247.

29. ———. "Psychiatric Disorders Among Persecution Victims." J. Nervous and Mental Disease, Vol. 139, 1964, pp. 458-474.
30. Pfister-Ammende, M. "Psychologie und Psychiatrie der Internierung und des Fluechtlingsdaseins." In *Psychiatrie der Gegenwart*. Berlin-Göttingen-Heidelberg, Springer, 1961, pp. 760-791.
31. Schur, M. "Comments on the Metapsychology of Somatization." In *The Psychoanalytic Study of the Child*. New York, Int. Univ. Press, Vol. 10, 1955, pp. 119-164.
32. Strauss, H. "Besonderheiten der Nichtpsychotischen Seelischen Stoerungen bei Opfern der Nationalsozialistischen Verfolgung und ihre Bedeutung bei der Begutachtung." Nervenarzt, Vol. 28, 1957, pp. 344-350.
33. Tas, J. "Psychical Disorders Among Inmates of Concentration Camps and Repatriates." Psychiat. Quart., Vol. 5, 1951, pp. 679-690.
34. Trautman, E. "Psychiatrische Untersuchungen an Ueberlebenden der Nationalsozialistischen Vernichtungslater 15, Jahre nach der Befreiung." Nervenarzt, Vol. 32, 1961, pp. 545-551.
35. Zborowski, M. and Herzog, E. *Life Is With People*. New York, Univ. Press, 1952.

160 Lasky Drive
Beverly Hills, California

Discussant

William G. Niederland, M.D.

New York, New York

I should like to comment briefly on two aspects of Dr. Hoppe's presentation:

1. The factor of *guilt*, usually is an ungoing and unsettling process—often of an insidious character—in the whole survivor pathology. The apparently paradoxical problem of guilt in survivor populations has been described in the literature, (Rosenman, 1956; Niederland, 1961; Lifton, 1963), but has perhaps not been sufficiently considered in the dynamics of these patients, much less in the forensic-psychiatric evaluation of their conditions for the German compensation courts. It is indeed one of the most bitter ironies in this situation, so replete with tragedy and bitterness, that feelings of guilt accompanied by shame, self-condemnatory tendencies and self-accusation's should be experienced by the *victims* of the persecution, and apparently much less (if at all) by the perpetrators of it.

I have never had an opportunity to examine the latter; however, from my work with hundreds of persecution survivors, I know their feelings of guilt and shame are of the most profound order and stand at the bottom of many of their clinical manifestations: withdrawal from social activity, seclusiveness, brooding preoccupation with the past, depression as well as fear of renewed persecution, anxiety attacks, inability to enjoy even the most innocent pleasures or distractions (a movie, a book, a carefree evening, etc.,). I became especially aware of the severe burden of guilt these people carry when I explored what I have called the *symptom-free interval*, i.e., the period of relative freedom from symptoms some of these patients experienced between the time of liberation and their emigration to the United States.

The survivors indicated that during the years following their liberation they remained relatively free from disabling symptoms and self-punishing tendencies so long as they could fantasy their dead family members might miraculously reappear, and during their exposure to the considerable adjustment difficulties and hardships of settling in a new country. When, in the end, they had to recognize that there was no hope, however *magically* resorted to in their thinking, of a return of the lost relative—many of them developed the typical *survivor syndrome,* which I have described in my previous papers, (1961, 1963, 1964) and whose clinical and dynamic features coincide in large measure with the findings by Hoppe and other authors, (Bastiaans, Eissler, Chodoff, Venzlaff, V., Baeyer, R., Trautman).

2. Another factor in the understanding of the survivor syndrome is the *far-reaching somatization* of the complaints. I have hardly seen any concentration camp survivor who does not suffer from headaches, chronic sleep disturbances, muscular aches and pains, gastrointestinal or cardiovascular manifestations, etc. In the absence of specific organic findings these complaints are often dismissed as hypochondriacal or labeled—again for the German compensation courts—with outright derogatory and self-righteous labels by certain court or consular psychiatrists.

It seems to me that in patients whose survival depended for years *on the appearance and functioning of their bodies* mainly, in whom even a minor reduction of musculoskeletal strength or function, or any alteration of their physical appearance or bodily efficiency would have been followed by their incineration in the gas chambers, the cathexis of the body image has changed *in toto*—just as their conscious outlook on life, people, etc., has changed as a result of their disastrous experiences.

Discussant

Paul Chodoff, M.D.

Washington, D.C.

Dr. Hoppe lays great stress on the psychodynamic importance of the narcissistic regression which took place in concentration camp victims, and which, he feels, prepared the ground for later-developing psychopathological states of chronic reactive depression and chronic reactive aggression. I agree that regressive behavior, to some extent, was almost universal in the camps, being induced in the prisoners by the overwhelming infantilizing pressures to which they were subjected.

However, it is worth pointing out that such behavior may have actually served an adaptive function, thus constituting a kind of regression in the service of the ego, since regressive prisoners, immersed in fantasies, were likely to be docile and submissive toward the SS, and thus have a better chance of escaping retaliatory measures.

Unlike Dr. Hoppe, I do not find evidence, as a result of my admittedly relatively superficial examinations of concentration camp victims, for the hypothesis that a neurotic predisposition had survival value because of, "stronger defense mechanisms and childhood fixations." It was my impression, rather, that many of these individuals had been active, enterprising persons who had not been "Musselmen" in the camps, but who had tried hard, sometimes with much ingenuity, to save their lives, an observation which would suggest a certain degree of emotional health.

The somewhat related question of whether psychological and physical trauma can alone produce the symptoms of a traumatic neurosis without participation of the deeper layers of the personality laid down as a result of earlier traumatic experiences is one of great theoretical interest for psychoanalysis. It seems to me that the evidence from studies of sufferers from the Concentration Camp Syndrome, the combination of anxiety and psychosomatic symptoms, obsessive rumination and depression which is the most common form of later psychopathology, although inconclusive because of the paucity of reliable accounts of the pre-morbid personalities and developmental experiences of the survivors, tends to support that theory of traumatic neurosis which emphasizes the role of the traumatic events themselves over that of predisposing personality factors.

The ubiquity and uniformity of the symptomatic picture displayed by most concentration camp survivors seems to be better explained as a consequence of overwhelmingly intense traumata producing similar effects in many individuals of different personality structure, rather than as stemming from presumed specific fragilities in pre-morbid personalities. At any rate, intensive study of concentration camp victims, such as Dr. Hoppe is doing, should shed light on this controversial issue.

Dr. Hoppe mentions those guilt feelings which the therapist himself may experience as a result of his life in Nazi Germany or his lack of open resistance there. However, even if the therapist or examiner has never been in Germany, he may have to deal with countertransference feelings of guilt, as a result of the mute reproach offered by these people who have been in such a holocaust which he himself has been spared. Such countertransference guilt may take the form of an over-identification with the victims, or a reaction formation in the form of a turning away from them, along with skepticism about their claims of suffering, both of which attitudes, as Dr. Hoppe mentions, can seriously interfere with therapeutic efforts.

I want to conclude my discussion with some remarks about the very interesting phenomeon of "survival guilt," which has been noted by almost all who have had professional contact with concentration camp survivors. In one case which I have been treating intensively, I found the kind of guilt feelings caused by infantile death wishes toward parents and siblings, which Dr. Hoppe believes to be an important factor in the later development of guilt and depression in these cases. In my patient, such early death wishes toward a mother and brother were in the course of succumbing to normal processes of repression and sublimation in early adolescence. The war led to her being incarcerated with her mother in Auschwitz, where her mother's helpless behavior required my patient to care for the latter at the risk of her own life. This experience had the effect of reviving the earlier death wishes toward her mother, which became fixated, and have now become a very troublesome part of her post-war personality structure.

However, this is not, by any means, the only factor which is responsible for the presence of disabling feelings of guilt among survivors. In some cases, such feelings have been attributed to specific episodes, such as when a prisoner had taken an action which led to the saving of his own life at increased risk to another. One must remember that to survive in a Nazi concentration camp took both luck and a determined drive toward self-preservation, requiring the kind of behavior from which the patient would recoil in other circumstances. The fact that the selection of someone else for extermination or for a particularly life-threatening assignment enhanced one's own chances of staying alive may have had the effect of promoting unconscious death wishes toward others. Whether or not such death wishes had infantile antecedents, they could later on generate feelings of guilt, just as in the cases of certain emotional disturbances occurring among combat veterans.

That facet of survival guilt, which refers to the guilty feelings of many survivors over the very fact that they have remained alive when so many others have died, regardless of their own individual behavior, may be a factor of psychodynamic importance in the perpetuation of neurotic symptoms. Some survivors are unable to give up their memories and their symptoms, and live more satisfactorily in the present, because unconsciously this would amount to forgetting their murdered parents and siblings.

It may also be that, in certain characterologically pre-disposed persons, for whom their persecutors have become internal objects, to get well would amount to forgiving these persecutors. These survivors must go on suffering in order to continue to bear witness to the cruelty with which they were treated. They suffer so that the world will not forget.

Discussant

Paul Friedman, M.D., PH.D.

New York, New York

Dr. Hoppe has given a succinct summary of the more salient problems concerning the victims of the Nazi concentration camps.

Despite the many studies conducted in the past twenty years, we still have a great deal to learn about the psychopathology of the people who lived under the Nazi death threat for years on end. More than two decades have passed since the collapse of the Third Reich and the liberation of the concentration camp survivors, and yet the ineffaceable characteristics of their deep traumatizations can be detected almost as easily today as when we first encountered them. They still continue to display the typical apathy, the so-called "affective anesthesia," the same detachment and distrust toward the world as I was able to observe when I met with them on my surveys of D. P. camps in Europe in 1946, and in Cyprus in 1947.

Dr. Hoppe correctly refers to the fact that the processes of repression were so powerful and all-embracing that they entirely distorted the structure of the ego and its synthetic function, but in many instances, this repression also made survival possible.

In a paper written in 1948,[1] I attempted to show how the reality had to be denied, not partially but totally in order to survive, and also how profound a distortion of the social sense this denial inevitably entailed. This was particularly typified in a case history of a young girl whom I interviewed in Cyprus in 1947. The sole survivor of her family, she had been assigned to the crematorium staff at Auschwitz. She accepted the Nazi version that the women to whom she handed towels were "'going for a bath." The cries and screams of the children who had been herded past her came back to her later in a psychotic episode that she developed during the Cyprus detention. When she told me her story after she had recovered from her acute hallucinatory episode, she could not understand how she could have been so "stupid" as not to grasp the reality and the true situation when it was taking place.

This girl's experience can stand as a kind of prototype for all. To one degree or another, they all stifled their true feelings, they all denied the dictates of conscience and social feeling in the hope of survival, and they were all warped and distorted as a result.

I wish to make only one comment in regard to the problem of aggression which Dr. Hoppe treats quite extensively in his paper. It constituted one of the most challenging and paradoxical phenomena of concentration camp life.

---

[1]"The Road Back for the DP's." *Healing the Psychological Scars of Nazism.* COMMENTARY, December 1948, Vol. 6, No. 6.

Further studies are necessary to penetrate the psychogenesis of such paradoxes as the extremely low incidence of suicide among Nazi concentration camp inmates. Incidentally, even the collective hatred against the enemy was later displaced and diverted from its original goal. The identification with the aggressor, a phenomenon so frequently encountered among the survivors of the Nazi concentration camps, perhaps typifies this most eloquently.

Another problem worthy of a special study is the notion of the so-called passive masochistic surrender of the Jews to the Nazis. This notion which has recently been the subject of much controversy and which has caught the fancy of some serious psychoanalytic thinkers is in my mind a "psychologistic sophistication" which defies all objective historical facts.

Discussant

Edith Jacobson, M.D.[1]

New York, New York

My own observations on the "Psychological Effect of Imprisonment," referred to inmates of the state prison—i.e., to a situation quite different from that in the Nazi concentration camps. However, this paper and another one on "Depersonalization," confirmed the frequency of initial "states of depersonalization, stupor and fright," the "enforced regression," and also, in some persons, the partial identification with the Nazi authorities. This last point was probably much more significant in concentration camp victims than in the political prisoners whom I observed.

[1]Dr. Jacobson was not able to write a thorough discussion of the paper, but made the following brief discussion, and permitted its publication.

I also pointed to the disturbance in the sense of time of prisoners, which has been so beautifully described by Thomas Mann in *The Magic Mountain*.

What I should like to emphasize as a helpful protection from regression and depression is the aggressive "spite" reaction which in some persons, (prisoners and concentration camp victims) successfully supported their wish and efforts for survival.

I have not had any therapeutic experiences with survivors who had lost their families in concentration camps. But I want to emphasize the excessive greed reactions commonly shown by survivors—who did *not* lose members of their family—after their liberation.

Author's Response

Klaus D. Hoppe, M.D.

Beverly Hills, California

In appreciation of the discussion remarks I should try to respond as succinctly and thoroughly as possible.

Partial identification with Nazi-authorities is outstanding in depressed survivors; agressive victims were protected from such a regression mainly due to a firm ego-ideal. They are consequently comparable to the political prisoners whom Dr. Edith Jacobson studied. Aggressive "spite" reactions in camp or jail represent a starting point for hate-addiction.

Dr. Friedman's case history of the young victim illuminates connections between concentration camp existence and schizophrenic and psychosomatic disorders. Regarding the, "astonishingly low incidence of suicide," survivors frequently reported that co-inmates killed themselves running into the electric barbed wire. Besides, we might consider the undramatic form of chronic suicide consisting of loss of self-preservation and indifference toward death. Only constant care and comfort from a relative or close friend prevented several inmates from falling into such a state. As Luchterhand said, "the pair was the basic unit of survival."

I agree with Dr. Niederland regarding the importance of survivor guilt but I cannot consider it the most pathogenic single factor. From a genetic viewpoint, guilt feelings are characteristic of the phallic level; a regression to pre-oedipal stages is, however, distinctively noticeable in most victims. Despair, anxiety, lack of self-esteem and apathy are also found in former inmates without survivor guilt as well as in Jewish people who lived in illegality or under discrimination. The symptom-free interval was often not only relative but rather a phase of psychic suffering in secrecy due to a deep distrust of the world around.

Finally, I should like to respond to Dr. Chodoff. The differentiation between chronic reactive depression and chronic reactive aggression is mainly based on the observation that aggressive survivors are not suffering from a narcissistic regression. Unlike Dr. Chodoff, I would not regard adaptive functions in camp as regression in the service of the ego. According to Kris, regression in the service of the ego applies to the field of art and symbol formation. Maybe some extraordinary human being could remain creative even in camps as Frankl noted. I referred to "gallows humor," and to breaking through of mimetic impulses in some inmates. During psychotherapy several former inmates stressed they would have never survived without their extreme pride, doubt and distrust of others. In comparison with total apathy this certain amount of neurotic predisposition proved helpful.

A more or less marked symptom-free interval after liberation as well as the different degree of psychopathology contradict an equation of effects after persecution with a traumatic neurosis. I agree that a non-German examiner, too, may have to deal with countertransference feelings of guilt. The supposed disagreement derived from Dr. Chodoff's adding "there" to my sentence, ". . . or his lack of open resistance." Dr. Chodoff's psychodynamics considerations of survivor guilt appear most provoking and should be studied further.

I would like to thank all four discussants for their profound remarks.

Title **Sudden Death at Impasse**

Author **Leon J. Saul, M.D.**

Professor of Psychiatry at the Medical School Hospital of the University of Pennsylvania, Psychiatric Consultant to Swarthmore College, and a Training Analyst of the Philadelphia Psychoanalytic Society. He was one of the original group which established the American Psychosomatic Society and its journal. He has published four books and about one hundred twenty-five papers, many of them dealing with emotions and their effect on the body.

Discussants

Paul Dudley White, M.D.

Clinical Professor of Medicine at Harvard University and Consultant to Massachusetts General Hospital. He has studied and taught cardiology for more than fifty years. He was President of the American Heart Association, and the International Society of Cardiologists and serves as a Consultant to more than a dozen foreign countries.

Philip Solomon, M.D.

Associate Clinical Professor of Psychiatry at Harvard Medical School and Physician-in-Chief, Psychiatry Service, Boston City Hospital. He has published some one hundred articles in the fields of neurology and psychiatry. Dr. Solomon wishes it known that he is not now but once was a resident of Beverly Hills!

M. Ralph Kaufman, M.D.

Director of the Institute for Psychiatry of Mt. Sinai Hospital, Clinical Professor of Psychiatry at Columbia University, and a member of the New York Psychoanalytic Society. He has long studied the impact of emotions on the body and has written extensively on psychosomatic medicine.

C. W. Wahl, M.D.

Associate Professor and Chief of the Division of Psychosomatic Medicine in the Department of Psychiatry at the University of California at Los Angeles, Consultant to several hospitals and a member of the Southern California Psychoanalytic Institute. He is the editor of *New Dimensions in Psychosomatic Medicine*, and of *Sexual Problems in Medical Practice* (in press). He has contributed to eight other books and has published twenty-six papers.

Phillip H. Wells, M.D.

Director of the Wells Medical Group and President of the Wells Foundation for study in the field of emotional illness. He has been a family physician for thirty-three years. Dr. Wells combines psychiatry with general medicine and has had unusual opportunity to use the insight of dynamic psychiatry in observing and treating the dying patient.

Sudden Death at Impasse

Leon J. Saul, M.D.

Media, Pennsylvania

The possibility of sudden death from psychogenic causes has long been known. Walter Cannon, for example, has a paper on Voodoo Death. (1) Curt Richter has discussed sudden unexplained death in men and in animals. In speaking of cases in humans, and in asthmatics in particular, he concludes that some instances occur in situations of hopelessness—"literally a giving up when all avenues of escape appeared to be closed and the future holds no hope." (3)

It was most interesting to read this sentence after already having written the following: Three cases in my experience, although a very small series, suggest by their similarity a certain mechanism in what might possibly be one form of psychosomatic death. This may be that certain persons with their particular physiological and psychological make-ups, when in unbearable situations of impasse, of "no exit," in which they cannot fight and from which they cannot escape, suddenly die. George Engel, with Arthur Schmale and others of his associates have been studying relationships of separation and depression to disease. (4)

The following vignettes demonstrate what is probably a special case of this over-all subject although in these depression and separation were not central features but a certain kind of hopelessness was present. The point is related to the physiological and psychological disturbances seen in separations when the last libidinal tie to another person is severed; when the last human bond is broken.

A professional man of about 45 reached such an impasse. He found himself in a totally unbearable situation, and felt forced to leave for another town. Just when he was ready to make this move, there developed in the town to which he was going difficulties which made this move impossible. Although in an anguished quandary, he boarded the train for the new locale. He had burned his bridges and now the bridge he planned to cross was demolished. He could see no third alternative. About halfway in the trip, at a ten-minute station stop, he got out to pace the platform. He saw clearly that he could not go on and neither could he return. The conductor called, "All aboard!" He could neither reboard the train and go on, nor return home. No exit. He dropped dead on the platform of what autopsy showed to be a cardiac infarct. There had been no previous medical history of significance. He had been traveling with a friend, a professional person, who witnessed this.

A young woman of 33, with a history of occasional mild asthma, married and had four children. Her husband had a violent temper. When angry he sometimes smashed furniture and had struck her. She feared him and complained of his behavior. Her complaints, however, began to go far beyond the reality. He improved in attitudes and behavior appreciably, but she increasingly accused him of all sorts of plots against herself and the children. These became paranoid delusions. She was not amenable to treatment. She broke with her parents. Despite every effort by her husband, she could not live with him or near him for fear of his plots. But she could not leave either. Every solution seemed impossible. She saw no exit. At this point she developed status asthmaticus and died, despite the best medical care in a fine hospital.

A man of 40 had every asset except the capacity for independence and responsibility. His parents were wealthy and arranged important positions for him, thinking that responsibility would mature him. It did not. He enjoyed the income and prestige but ignored the jobs. His wife left. He could not get another position. He craved the money and prestige to maintain his self-esteem. But his family had financial reverses. He contracted gambling debts. If he did not pay them he would be beaten up, at the least. His parents, however, finally gave an adamant, "No." He sat at his desk, having just phoned his mother to no avail. He saw no way out. He keeled over with a fatal cardiac infarct, confirmed at autopsy.

These notes are extremely brief for reasons of discretion, as the people were all prominent in the community, but further details do not add significantly so far as I can see. These cases fully support Richter's conclusion as to death on the psychological level in a situation of hopelessness, and are in direct line with the findings of Engel, Schmale and others. The physiological mechanism is not known, but Richter suggests that overstimulation of the vagal system and perhaps of the adrenal sympathetic also may play a part. It is a question whether, among the many more usual outcomes for persons in impasse, such as depression, suicide, psychosis, or alcohol, psychosomatic death is one.

Death occuring at situations of impasse may only mean that the stress mechanism, in man or any animal, has been overstrained. "Emotional death" in animals is recognized by ethologists as ensuing when the conditions of living become too difficult. (2)

Summary

Two men and a woman, their personalities and life situations known in considerable detail, when in situations which for them represented complete impasse, with no exit, with no flight or fight possible, died suddenly, one in status asthmaticus, the other two of cardiac infarcts.

Bibliography

1. Cannon, Walter. "Voodoo Death", Am. Anthropologist, Vol. 44, 1942, p. 169.
2. Carrighar, Sally. *Wild Heritage.* Boston, Houghton Mifflin Co. 1965.
3. Richter, Curt. "The Phenomenon of Unexplained Sudden Death." In Feifel, H. *The Meaning of Death.* New York, McGraw Hill, 1959, pp. 302-317.
4. Schmale, Arthur, Jr. "Relationship of Separation and Depression to Disease," Psychosomatic Medicine, Vol. 20, 1958, pp. 259-277.

Supported by Public Health Research Grant (MH-07615-01)

275 Highland Avenue
Media, Pennsylvania 19063

Discussant

Paul Dudley White, M.D.

Boston, Massachusetts

"Sudden Death at Impasse" is a fascinating subject, and, as in the two patients noted by Dr. Saul, both male aged 40 and 45 years respectively, coronary insufficiency is probably the most common explanation. In both of those cases autopsy is said to have shown myocardial infarction but this can happen without any actual infarction and simply from the coronary insufficiency itself. I myself have never seen a patient who died suddenly without adequate pathological explanation, and I know of only one case in a series of two thousand reported by Dr. H. Martland,[1] a coroner, some years ago which was not explained by obvious pathological findings at autopsy.

That one case was a young colored man who came to a clinic to have treatment for a skin blemish on his face. He had hoped that this might be removed by some local application, but he was told that it had to be treated by cautery or excision and for this purpose it was necessary to use local anesthesia. He protested but was finally persuaded to allow the doctors to go ahead, but he was obviously terrified by the idea. He dropped dead at the moment that the needle was approaching his skin, and at post mortem examination no abnormalities were found. This is quite probably one of the rare cases of cardiac standstill or ventricular fibrillation induced reflexly by fright or some nervous mechanism such as Dr. Saul has described.

I suppose that the young woman with her status asthmaticus reacted to her impossible situation in life in a similar manner, but by a different mechanism.

We do know that vagal and other influences superimposed on a sensitive S-A nodal pacemaker can cause cardiac standstill both in animals and in man, but death therefrom is of course extraordinarily rare, unless there is already serious disease, most commonly of the coronary arteries.

[1]Martland, H. "Sudden Deaths With Reference to Their Prevention." In *Proceedings New England Heart Association*, 1940, p. 42.

Discussant

Philip Solomon, M.D.

Boston, Massachusetts

One of the rules in statistics and in the laws of probability is that the likelihood of two events coinciding may be found by multiplying together the likelihood of each event. If, for example, the likelihood of a man dying in his 45th year of a sudden heart attack is one in a hundred thousand and the likelihood of his being previously in utter despair is one in a thousand (both generous figures), then the two events will coincide with a frequency of one in a hundred million. But there are several million men in this country every year who are age 45, so that every few years, entirely through the operation of chance and with no cause and effect relationship, we should expect a man of 45 to reach a hopeless impasse and suddenly drop dead of a heart attack. The same holds true for a man of 40, and in status asthmaticus for a woman of 33. In fact, since we are equally impressed when a man or woman of any age becomes acutely depressed and drops dead of any "psychosomatic" cause, we should keep in mind that adding up the probabilities would quite likely lead us to expect events of this nature to occur by happenstance alone every few days somewhere in the country. We would expect, further, that now and then a physician would come to know not only the facts about the death but also something of the emotional antecedents and wonder about the relationship. Rarely, it would seem, a psychoanalyst would find himself in the picture, or would be brought in, and he would not wonder, he would seem to know.

In courses in formal logic, one learns of "the error of the positive instance." The Negro who commits rape is seen as "typical"; Negroes who do not commit rape and white men who do are ignored—these are negative instances. There are surely a great many men and women who reach impasse and do not die of heart attacks and status asthmaticus, and huge numbers who do die of these disorders while in a joyful state or peacefully asleep in bed. These considerations and the statistical ones above do not, of course, disprove the contention that impasse played a part in bringing about the demise of the author's three individuals. They do offer another, and I think, more likely explanation for the facts. To reach the reliable truth, one would have to undertake an enormously involved, extensive, and difficult controlled study.

Discussant

M. Ralph Kaufman, M.D.

New York, New York

Dr. Saul presents an interesting thesis in his paper. I have had experience with patients who have reached an impasse and who have made suicidal attempts or have successfully committed suicide. This constellation as a setting in which a solution by suicide occurs fits in with my own clinical experience.

The patients presented by Dr. Saul, however, do not appear to be in the category of Cannon's Voodoo Death. Two of his patients died from demonstrated cardiac infarction and one during status asthmaticus. In the cardiac death, it might be quite possible that the coronary arteries were already implicated and that the contribution of the impasse represented an increased stress situation in a pre-prepared "somatic" situation.

Unfortunately, we do not know as to whether the patient with status asthmaticus had a previous history of asthma and if so, what had been the manifestations. There is no question that any individual episode of asthma may be triggered off by the stimulus of a conflict situation, which in this instance perhaps led to the status.

These patients may perhaps represent the utilization of somatic systems in the service of an unconscious suicidal wish. However, they do not fall into the "unexplained" deaths.

Discussant

C. W. Wahl, M.D.

Los Angeles, California

It is encouraging to see, in Dr. Saul's paper, a recrudescence of interest in the long neglected topic of psychogenically induced death, but it it well to remember that sudden death for psychic reasons is much more complex than it appears and it apparently can be caused by more than one mechanism. Intense fright by producing vagal inhibition can produce what the idiom, "a heart-stopping fear" would lead us to expect, namely, instantaneous death. However, this mechanism cannot account for the slow death by convulsions of a Samoan native who, with horror, realized that he had touched the tabooed chief's tinder box, nor can it account for the famous subject who was led to believe falsely that he was being exsanguinated but who died a hypotensive death, just as if his veins had been opened. And how are we to account for the surgical patient who is certain that he is to die, sustains a trivial operation, but does not recover; or the patient with mild pneumonia who loses his will to live and dies to the dismay and confoundment of his physicians? We do not understand the physiology or biochemistry of these states, much less the psychology.

I do not share Dr. Saul's view with Richter that sudden death occurs only when one is in a stage of inassuageable hopelessness. It also may occur when one *expects* death.

I hope that this brief, fascinating, clinical note will prompt more of us to be alert for the possibility of psychically induced or facilitated demise. It is an area rich with promise concerning essential life processes. The understanding of it can be of enormous help in elucidating that dim penumbra where psyche and soma meet, here with such devastating consequence.

Discussant

Phillip H. Wells, M.D.

Arcadia, California

Received as *The Forum* went to press.

The response of the unconscious to impasse is dramatic. Besides being an escape it is also a call for help. Depression, attempt at suicide, psychosis, alcoholism, and somatic illness such as coronary occlusion, status asthmaticus, etc., all represent a regression or retreat or a cry for help. Somatic illness like a suicide attempt or any other of the mechanisms of the unconscious may be overplayed and result in death.

In my thirty-three years of practice I have witnessed a number of deaths at impasse. Usually my view in retrospect as a psychopathologist like that of any pathologist is better than my early appreciation of a man's need and of how I might fill it. When we recognize the urgency of the cry for help early enough we can sometimes satisfy the need and perhaps prevent death.

This past year a dependent artist of 44 was sent to me because of narcotic addiction. He had had a coronary infarction two years before and had taken morphine and Demerol in large doses ever since. His activities were grossly restricted. He complained of abdominal distress and occasionally of chest pain if he did not have adequate narcotics. I placed him in a locked ward where his choices and activities were restricted and controlled and I confronted him with his anger and greed. He promptly gave up his needs for drugs and became interested in reactivating himself. He returned home after a month of increasing activity during his confinement.

In the home situation with its increased pleasures and demands he did well until he wanted his therapist and could not get him quickly enough and became angry. He had chest pain and wanted to go back to the locked ward. I gave him extra attention and his pain abated when I was with him, only to return when I left. I placed him in an open hospital instead of the locked ward that he pleaded for and there his pain was only relieved by my presence. Heroic doses of morphine did not control it. His greedy demand for me and his anger were evident. He died within a few hours of the time I left him after not acquiescing in his plea to be put in the locked ward. I had felt he needed more medical care than the locked ward afforded.

This man had coronary disease, but he also had a remarkable ability to constrict his arteries and produce ischemia and infarction when overcome by his demanding, infantile rage.

Author's Response

Leon J. Saul, M.D.

Media, Pennsylvania

I greatly appreciate the interesting, stimulating remarks of the discussants. Dr. White's point regarding coronary insufficiency is most relevant. In reply to Dr. Kaufman's question: the young woman did have a history of previous attacks of asthma, a few times a year and quite mild. In response to Dr. Wahl's comment: there is no disagreement, as I did not mean to imply that sudden death can have only a single cause, or can occur only at impasse. My note reports on one, single setting which seemed connected with its occurrence. It may occur in other settings as well. The whole story would lead, as Dr. Solomon suggests, to an enormous study; but I think he will agree that the history of medicine shows that suggestive clinical observations have stimulated our observation and increased our knowledge, and may still do so. Dynamic psychiatry today, while drawing on every relevant field, is still rooted in the daily clinical observations of the physician.

The Forum

Title **Reflections on Training**

Author **Lawrence S. Kubie, M.D.**

Clinical Professor of Psychiatry at the University of Maryland, Lecturer in Psychiatry at Johns Hopkins, Visiting Professor of Psychiatry at Jefferson Medical College and Consultant on Training and Research at Sheppard and Enoch Pratt Hospital. He is Editor-in-Chief of "Journal of Nervous and Mental Diseases." In his 45 years in psychiatry and psychoanalysis he also has taught at Yale and Columbia Universities and the New York Psychoanalytic Institute. He has authored more than 270 works.

Discussants

Carl Binger, M.D.

Honorary Physician at the Massachusetts General Hospital and Honorary Consultant at Harvard University Health Services. He is a psychoanalyst, psychiatric educator and prominent leader in the psychosomatic field.

John A. P. Millet, M.D.

Professor of Psychiatry at the New York School of Psychiatry and Honorary Consultant to the Columbia Psychoanalytic Clinic. He was President of the Academy of Psychoanalysis. For more than 30 years, he has taught psychiatry and psychoanalysis and has published many works, among them "The History of Psychoanalysis in America."

C. H. Hardin Branch, M.D.

Professor and Chairman of the Department of Psychiatry, University of Utah College of Medicine. For eight years he was on the American Board of Psychiatry and Neurology, and served as President of the Board for one year. He was President of the American Psychiatric Association.

Ives Hendrick, M.D.

Clinical Professor of Psychiatry Emeritus, at Harvard Medical School. He was President of the American Psychoanalytic Association. He has been active in the development of the teaching program of the Boston Psychoanalytic Institute since 1930 and was Chairman of the Board of Professional Standards of the American Psychoanalytic Association. Among his best known publications are *Facts and Theories of Psychoanalysis*, *The Birth of an Institute*, an account of the development of the Boston Institute, and during 1965 he published *Psychiatry Education Today*, on teaching methods in psychiatry.

Harvey D. Strassman, M.D.

Career Teacher Trainee at the National Institute of Mental Health and a Lecturer in Psychiatry at the University of California, California College of Medicine, Los Angeles, California. He has been on the Clinical Faculty of two other medical schools and a Consultant at Metropolitan State Hospital and Veterans' Administration Hospital, Sepulveda, California, teaching and supervising psychiatric residents. More recently he completed the Medical Teachers Course at the University of Illinois, under the auspices of the Office of Research in Medical Education.

Sigmund Gabe, M.D.

Training Analyst and Director of the Training School, Southern California Psychoanalytic Institute, and Associate Clinical Professor of Psychiatry at the University of Southern California. He is a Coordinating Editor of the *Annual Survey of Psychoanalysis*, and co-author of "Psychotherapy—Its History and Present Situation" in *Modern Abnormal Psychology*.

Charles W. Tidd, M.D.

Professor of Psychiatry at University of California at Los Angeles, and a psychoanalyst. He is actively interested and engaged in teaching psychiatry to medical students and to residents in psychiatry. He has written several papers dealing with the subject of psychiatric education including "The Use of Psychoanalytic Concepts in Medical Education" and "The Humanities and the Study of Medicine."

Edward D. Hoedemaker, M.D.

Associate Clinical Professor of Psychiatry at the University of Washington and is in private psychoanalytic practice in Seattle. His particular interests are the intensive therapy of severe character disorders, and psychoses, about which he has published several papers.

(EDITORS' NOTE: We present this paper because it is a discussion of an important controversial issue. Perhaps this issue is *the* crucial problem for the future of psychoanalytic and psychiatric education.

Dr. Kubie's reflections as presented here are based on quotations from an interview given to Katherine B. Hartman published as "Rebel in Retirement"(1) and now revised by Dr. Kubie. Certain passages not pertinent to our selected topic were eliminated.

By way of introduction, Dr. Kubie said, "Elmer Davis wrote that the chief consolation of growing old is that you don't have to worry about the effect of things on your own future when your future is behind you. You're free at last to say what you believe without fear of what you may lose. All the more obligation, Davis said, to speak out.")

Reflections on Training

Lawrence S. Kubie, M.D.

Baltimore, Maryland

My return to the study of the psychoses after 30-odd years which had been devoted chiefly to studying the neurotic process was the beginning of an exciting re-education. It shook me out of many preconceptions, changing my ideas about almost everything. (15)

One of the lessons I learned was that the sequence of steps in training for psychiatry should be reversed and much of the content changed. For this there are many reasons.

In the first place one of the facts which I learned after returning to the psychiatric hospital was that episodes of psychotic disorganization always precipitate out of the neurotic process under certain quite specific types of impasse. Furthermore, no patients are psychotic all the time. Even within a brief interview, interludes of neurotic reorganization occur. The road to health leads back to and finally through the prepsychotic neurosis. Consequently the student and therapist of the psychosis must be prepared by previous experience and training to utilize these moments of neurotic reorganization. Clearly the inexperienced resident, who knows nothing about the neurotic process or how to deal with it, is unprepared for this. The young student of psychiatry must first understand how to relate to the neurotic process in himself and in others. He can start this best by studying the complex processes of growth, observing the subtle early neurotic deviations from normal psychological development. He must learn that once such deviations arise they are maintained primarily by unconscious conflicts which give rise to neurotic symptoms, which in turn feed back new distortions of life, which then give rise to new conflicts and new secondary symptoms to produce further distortions, out of which a third order of symptoms evolve, etc. It is this chain of reverberating reactions which constitutes the neurotic process; and it is out of this that psychotic disorganization may precipitate, but only under certain specific circumstances. (16)

Moreover, to confront an inexperienced resident abruptly with a psychotic patient hinders his development of empathy with psychotic illness and the understanding of it. To the extent to which psychotic behavior is alien and strange, it will be upsetting to him; and his own anxieties will warp his reactions. One will react to his own anxieties by saying or doing too much, another too little. Whole schools and theoretical rationalizations are built on this. Either way golden opportunities for therapy may be lost. Usually they return; but all too often this return does not happen for months. (11)

Letting a young physician, just out of his medical internship, examine and treat psychotic patients, as almost all psychiatric hospitals do today, is roughly equivalent to putting a scalpel in the hands of a young resident in surgery and asking him to take out a brain tumor.

Therefore, I repeat my conviction that the young psychiatrist should begin his training where he can observe and learn how to deal with those early deviations from normal development which set the neurotic process in motion; e.g., in the pediatric ward and the nursery. He must study both normal and sick children at play, at home and at school. Later he must work with the neuroses of puberty and adolescence, and then of young adults. In this way he will become familiar with the neurotic process as it evolves, as a basis for his work with the psychosis.

If I had the power, I would not allow a young resident to examine or treat a psychotic patient until he had spent several years dealing with the neurotic process in a variety of settings, under intensive supervision.

Pilot tests of such a reversal of training should receive watchful and critical but explicit support from the American Psychiatric Association, the American Psychoanalytic Association, and the American Board of Neurology and Psychiatry; because no hospital can afford to take steps which would alienate these bodies or which might endanger the standing of its residents; since in various ways training must be approved by those bodies if residents are to be admitted later to examinations before the specialty boards.

In theory many people agree to this plan; but feel that the practical obstacles are too great. Certainly if the change-over were to occur everywhere at once, which is hardly probable, the shortage of psychiatrists in hospitals would increase for several years. On the other hand, an initial series of modest pilot tests, followed by a gradual change-over, if there seemed to be improvement in the quality of patient care and resident training would not be disrupting.

Related to the above suggestion but not

identical with it is the argument for a School of Psychological Medicine for the training of *non-medical behavioral scientists*, to be carried out under the joint auspices of a Medical School and the Departments of Behavioral Science of the University. (10)

As I have repeatedly emphasized, the most significant objection raised against this proposal arises out of a fear that it would widen the gap between somatic and psychological medicine. Actually it is quite possible that its effect would be just the reverse, and that the implementation of this proposal might in fact close that gap, for reasons which have been discussed elsewhere. (3,6,14) About this one thing is certain, namely that if medical psychiatry refuses to make even pilot tests of such a plan, the psychologists will go it alone. This would indeed be unfortunate; because then the gap would become unbridgeable.

It is my conviction that every Department of Clinical Psychiatry should be the point on which all behavioral sciences converge. A department of psychiatry without a school of psychological medicine behind it would be as anomalous as a department of clinical medicine would be without the converging disciplines of the preclinical years of the medical curriculum. Yet in psychiatry as in somatic medicine it is the clinical challenge which puts our effective knowledge to its ultimate tests: i.e., to recognize normal development, to identify distortions from normal development and their origins, to predict their courses, to alter their course, to reverse them, and ultimately to prevent them. This should be the model for a School of Psychological Medicine.

A Doctorate in Psychological Medicine would not be a "quickee." It would take six to eight years after college; but this is only one-half to two-thirds of the time it takes to train a Board-approved psychiatrist fully. Yet this would mean that in addition to the present quota of medically trained psychiatrists our existing facilities could produce about twice as many fully qualified psycho-diagnosticians and psycho-therapists, each of whom would finish his training at an earlier age than the medically trained psychiatrist and would therefore have more years of useful professional life ahead of him. This of course raises the problem of maturity; (9) but the answer to this does not depend on the additional years of the full medical curriculum but on the ultimate solution of some of the underlying problems of education in general. (2,4,5) Such additions to the ranks would also reduce the cost of psycho-therapy. (6,12)

To staff such a plan we will need a preliminary 10 to 15 year period for the special training of a cadre of new teachers. Initially it may be necessary to endow their training and also their initial training of others as well. Yet without some such honest, all-out program, all the current bally-hoo about mental health centers is not realistic, honest, or humane.

The curriculum would include basic human biology, physiological and psychological growth process, the comparison of psychological development in different cultures, both human and subhuman (i.e., ethology), practical psychiatric social work, sociology, experimental psychology (again both human and subhuman), genetics, clinical psychology (including the design and validation of test instruments), education and learning theory, linguistics and communication theory, psychopharmacology, dynamic psychopathology, psychodiagnosis and all forms of psychotherapy including psychoanalysis. (3,6,10)

The place of personal psychotherapy and of psychoanalysis in such a training program will have to be re-examined. That a therapeutic change and growth is indispensable for every young psychiatrist I have no doubt. On the question of how best to achieve this, no one has the right to be dogmatic or to lay down universal rules. I have observed that by working intensively for a long time under analytically trained supervisors, by studying themselves through tapes and films of their own behavior with their patients and in group therapy sessions, and by comparing themselves with their fellows, *some* trainees are able to achieve an unexpected degree of freedom from the unresolved residues of unconscious childhood conflicts, which can otherwise dominate our thoughts, feelings, purposes, and behavior throughout life. For these men a personal analysis can safely be postponed. In others this "spontaneous" emancipation does not occur, and a personal analysis is indispensable early. About this I have slowly reached the unanticipated conclusion that the "training" analysis often has a better chance of being therapeutically effective either some years before formal training is begun, or alternatively very late in training. Introducing it with the onset of training may be a traditionally entrenched error. All of these questions should be reconsidered and retested without dogmatism.

I am sure that psychiatry will ultimately work out an integration of various psychotherapeutic and physiological methods. Among these the enduring values of some aspects of psychoanalysis are clearly established. As an exploratory device and as an instrument for research, it has played a unique role. As a therapeutic device it needs many technical changes. In both technique and theory there is much that needs to be reevaluated and retested by the application of methods which have only recently become available to us. The use of tapes and films of residents in action will make enormous differences both in the training of residents and in research. To me it is a constant source of amazement that the study of the human mind made any progress at all as long as it had to depend on man's fallible memory of his fallible perceptions of fleeting experiences which were charged with feeling. (7,8) Further progress must be based on the study and restudy of tapes and films. (13) Yet many of my colleagues are still afraid to introduce such techniques because of the artifacts that instruments inevitably introduce. To them I answer that every instrument for observing or recording which science has ever introduced has changed somewhat that which was being studied. Science advances not by abandoning these devices, but by learning how to keep such changes relatively constant and how to evaluate them and their influence.

From time to time, there have been signs that these suggestions are gaining a thoughtful hearing. It is significant that the *Journal of Medical Education* published my article on this subject so promptly last year. (10) Furthermore, I remember the first time that I presented the idea of a medical subdiscipline before a body of my colleagues. It was in 1956 at a meeting in Philadelphia of the Edward Strecker Society. Dr. Strecker himself was the first discussant. My heart sank as he started out by saying slowly, "I have been opposed to this all my life." Then after a long silent pause, he continued, "And I think I've been wrong. I do not think there is any other solution." (6)

We face a paradox: progress requires change, but this in turn triggers every neurotic defense that opposes change. The nervous system itself, human nature and human institutions have a built-in tendency to remain unaltered, to continue doing as they have been doing. It is hard to free ourselves from the obligatory stereotypes of our own psychological processes sufficiently to enable us to reach out into the future with greater flexibility.

Bibliography

1. Hartman, Katherine B. "Rebel In Retirement," Smith Kline and French's *Psychiatric Reporter*, Vol. 22, September-October 1965.
2. Kubie, L. S. "The Forgotten Man of Education," *Harvard Alumni Bull.*, Feb. 1954, Vol. 56 (No. 8), pp. 349-353.

3. ———. "The Pros and Cons of a New Profession." A Doctorate in Medical Psychology, *Texas Reports on Biology & Medicine*, Fall 1954, Vol. 12 (No. 3), pp. 692-737.
4. ———. "The Search for Maturity in Pre-Professional Education," *Clinical Research*, April 1959, Vol. 7, No. 2, pp. 177-183.
5. ———. "Education and the Process of Maturation," pp. 7-18, from *Today's Children Are Tomorrow's World*, Associates of Bank Street Coll. of Education, Fifth Annual Conf., Feb. 1957, New York, p. 68.
6. ———. "The Need for a New Subdiscipline in the Medical Profession," read before the Strecker Soc., Philadelphia, Dec. 10, 1956; *Arch. of Neurol. and Psychiat.*, Sept. 1957, Vol. 78 (No. 3), pp. 283-293.
7. ———. "Research into the Process of Supervision in Psychoanalysis," *Psychoanal. Quart.*, April 1958, Vol. 27 (No. 2), pp. 226-236.
8. ———. "The Neurotic Process as the Focus of Physiological and Psychoanalytic Research," read in part before the Royal Soc. of Med., London, Sept. 1957; *J. of Ment. Science*, London, Apr. 1958, Vol. 104 (No. 435), pp. 518 536.
9. ———. (Editorial) "The Maturation of Psychiatrists or The Time That Changes Take," *Jour. of Nervous and Mental Disease*, Vol. 135 (No. 4), Oct. 1962, pp. 286-288.
10. ———. "A School of Psychological Medicine Within the Framework of a Medical School and University," from the *Journal of Med. Education*, Vol. 39 (No. 5), May 1964.
11. ———. "Traditionalism in Psychiatry," *Jour. of Nervous and Mental Disease*, July 1964, Vol. 139 (No. 1), pp. 6-19.
12. ———. (Editorial) "The Changing Economics of Psychotherapeutic Practice," the *Jour. of Nervous and Mental Disease*, Vol. 139 (No. 4), Oct. 1964, pp. 311-312.
13. ———. "The Scientific Problems of Psychoanalysis." Ch. 17, pp. 316-340, from *Scientific Psychology*, ed. Wolman, Benj. B. and Nagel E., Basic Books, Inc., New York, 1965, p. 620.
14. ———. (A Doctorate in Psychotherapy) "The Reasons for a New Profession," read at the Gould House Conference, Ardley, New York, Apr. 1963. (IN WORK)
15. ———. "The Psychoanalyst Returns to the Hospital," read at the International Congress on Psychiatry, Montreal, Canada, June 1961. (IN WORK)
16. ———. "The Relation of Psychotic Disorganization to the Neurotic Process," read at the midwinter meeting Amer. Psychoanalytic Ass'n, December 1965, New York. (IN PRESS)

3900 N. Charles Street
Baltimore, Maryland 2128

Discussant

Carl Binger, M.D.

Cambridge, Massachusetts

Dr. Kubie's "Reflections on Training" are written in his usual clear and incisive style. This has its risks for the reader, because the author is so logical and persuasive that one finds oneself agreeing with him too readily.

Kubie says, "The sequence of steps in training for psychiatry should be completely reversed and the content changed. The young doctor should first learn about neurotic illness before he deals with the psychoses." I am in complete agreement. My own training is testimony to my views. I came at psychiatry from internal medicine by way of analysis and dealing with neurotic patients and believe it helped me understand psychotic patients more readily than I would have had I followed the more conventional route.

I am not wholly persuaded that the psychosis precipitates out of the neurotic process under stress, but this point need not be argued here. I concur with Kubie's belief that a young psychiatrist should begin his training where he can observe some of those early deviations from normal which can lead to neurotic illness. This subsumes the presence on pediatric wards, nurseries and adult medical wards of people capable of instructing young psychiatrists. Of course, there should be such. In my own clinical teaching I constantly find that a medical or surgical ward of a general hospital offers superb material for demonstrating neurotic disturbances.

The suggestion that such a complete reversal of training must come from the top—from the American Psychiatric Association, the American Medical Association, the American Psychoanalytic Association and so forth—seems to me a trifle unrealistic. Revolutions don't start at the top. They arise out of gradual and cumulative feelings of discontent plus intelligent leadership.

Such a revolution as Kubie pictures, and which I agree is most desirable, should be planted in one or two congenial medical schools after sufficient preparation with ample Foundation support. A graduate from such a revised curriculum might well afford to forego the sanctity of Board approval or at least wait for it.

Kubie's proposal for a School of Psychological Medicine seems to me part of this same reform movement. Psychiatry is in great need of a sound base in the psychological and social sciences. Where would medicine be if it had gone it alone without the foundation of pathology, physiology and immunology on which it was built? Dr. Kubie should be congratulated and thanked and, above all, helped to put some of his good ideas to work.

Discussant

John A. P. Millet, M.D.

New York, New York

Dr. Kubie has attempted in a short summary to give us the benefit of his thinking on the important subject of the future education and training of the psychiatrist of tomorrow. There is a good deal of evidence that changes are already in the wind, and that some of the reforms which Dr. Kubie thinks should be introduced have been given a try-out. There is a growing momentum in the effort to cut down the hospital population and to develop all-inclusive centers for preventive services, emergency care, and rehabilitation of ex-hospital patients. For the future it is the hope that the hospital will come to be an emergency resource rather than a facility for residential confinement, and so will come to be thought of as an essential part or the center of a total community program, rather than an isolated institution.

The vast programs of community psychiatry now in the planning stages will necessitate the recruiting of numbers of mental health personnel to man the new facilities. This challenge must somehow be met by our specialty if we are not to lose the leadership position in the planning and implementing of these community programs, to which tradition and special competence entitle us. Programs of psychiatric education in future must take into account this need above all else. The day of the psychoanalyst and his couch as the image of the only reputable psychiatrist is due for a fade-out. There are fewer and fewer young psychiatrists who consider complete psychoanalytic training a necessity, although a large majority are either deciding on a personal analysis or join some group therapy sessions in their own hospitals in the hope of acquiring greater sensitization to the subtleties of emotional exchange and of stress reactions in themselves.

Dr. Kubie is right in emphasizing the resistance to change in long-established systems, but the image which he presents as the ideal image for a modern psychiatrist seems to come close to the traditional image of renaissance man. I doubt whether we could expect many men and women today to consider such a total enlightenment as either possible or necessary to the practice of a profession.

This doubt by no means implies that some exposure to the fields of knowledge listed in his proposed curriculum for the degree of Doctor of Psychological Medicine could not be made possible in the course of residency training. Given the relative shortage of psychiatrists to the hospitalized patient community there is clearly little that can be done in the way of individual or even group psychotherapy. The best that can be expected is some exposure under supervision to the principles governing the choice of therapies in different nosological categories.

Since the decision to become a psychiatrist is often arrived at after exposure to clinical practice has begun, it is hard to see what educational changes can be specially chosen to prepare the medical student for the specialty of psychiatry other than those which should form the basic requirement for all physicians, those which equip him to keep abreast of the advances in all significant areas of medical science and to broaden his horizon of human sympathy and understanding. Of such component parts is the true physician put together, and the psychiatrist of tomorrow should be prepared to honor this ancient tradition.

Discussant

C. H. Hardin Branch, M.D.

Salt Lake City, Utah

This discussion by a very thoughtful and progressive person in the training field comes from a great length and breadth of experience. Dr. Kubie's well known suggestion of the development of a doctorate in psychological medicine has stimulated much discussion in the training area.

His complaint that the young psychiatrist is exposed first to the psychotic patient will fall on many receptive ears and I, too, feel that this is reversing the process which should be followed. His suggestion that the young psychiatrist should first be exposed to early human psychological development by the observation of children, especially in the pediatric wards and in the nurseries, is a good one. This process has, I believe, been fairly thoroughly investigated by such schools as Western Reserve and actually is the kind of experience which many medical students have even before they graduate from medical school.

In the specialized psychiatric training area we have found that it is useful to start some of our first-year residents on child psychiatry, at least to the extent that they have a chance to observe behavior of children and participate in the family inter-reactions which characterize therapy with this age group.

My support for Dr. Kubie's views is based on a somewhat different concern: starting the young psychiatrist in the hospital with psychotic patients and leaving the outpatient work to the latter part of the residency sets up a sort of hierarchy. By implication, the least trained person is qualified to handle the sickest patient, whereas outpatient psychotherapy, presumably largely with neurotics, is a kind of exclusive activity which can be handled only by the most experienced resident. This attitude is further underlined by some practicing psychiatrists who tend to transfer their patients if intercurrent developments require hospitalization.

The situation would be adequately handled if residents in psychiatry started with outpatients or inpatients, depending on the scheduling situation, without particular reference to whether the patients were psychotic or neurotic. Toward the end of their training, the residents should be required to handle a microcosm of the practice situation. This would encompass both inpatients and outpatients, with a clear implication that the skill required for the care of psychotics and neurotics is about equal.

Dr. Kubie assumes incorrectly that a reversal of this process might alienate the Board. On the contrary, the American Board of Psychiatry and Neurology in no way spells out the sequence of events in the training programs. The Board merely insists that the training be adequate to prepare the resident for the practice of general psychiatry.

The Board has always made every possible attempt to encourage innovations as long as they are consistent with this over-all philosophy; no hospital need fear a lack of approval of its residency program simply because it places inpatient experience later in the training program than ordinarily.

I can see absolutely no technical obstacle in the way of implementing a broadening of the training base along the lines Dr. Kubie suggests.

Discussant

Ives Hendrick, M.D.
Boston, Massachusetts

Dr. Kubie states a training problem of first importance when he reminds us that the psychiatry resident is exposed immediately to clinical responsibilities for which he has little preparation. With this, your discussant is fully in agreement.[1,2,3] For the obvious fact is usually overlooked, that five or six years of medical school and internship provide intensive training in clinical and preclinical medicine, but little training and experience in those psychological observations which are basic in psychiatry. This should be recognized as fundamental in planning a residency program. It never is.

Yet I am not in agreement with some of the proposals which Dr. Kubie derives from this major premise. Thus, Dr. Kubie thinks of a series of conflicts while the individual is developing that lead to more and more complex neurotic symptomatology whose breakdown produces psychosis. But I conceive of healthy, neurotic, and psychotic modes of thought and adaptation as active in the personalities of all individuals at all stages of development;[4] breakdown of neurotic adjustment is indeed important in the outbreak of some psychoses, but I do not consider it primary in all.

Secondly, Dr. Kubie thinks that because the newness and incomprehensibility of psychotic thought for the beginner in psychiatry is so difficult, his training program should be reformed by providing several years of experience with psychoneurotic patients before he begins to tackle psychotic cases. My own experience is that while some students do much better at first with neurotic patients, there is also a goodly percentage of beginners who feel more at home, more "objective" and more interested at first with psychotics. Indeed the lives of senior American analysts of our generation show their interest in psychiatry had first been awakened by learning to understand a delusion or hallucination by the study of the patient's mental content. My own opinion as to whether it is better to begin with neurotic or in-patient cases, is that it depends partly on the type of training institution, but, in any case, work with both psychotics and neurotics during some period of a resident's first year is highly desirable.

[1]Group for the Advancement of Psychiatry (1947), First Report of the Committee on Medical Education. Report No. 3

[2]Hendrick, Ives (1951), "A Fundamental Reform in Psychiatric Education." Unpublished manuscript read at Veterans' Administration Hospital, Downey, Ill., Feb. 19, 1951. Abstract prepared for Committee on Dynamic Psychiatry, Second Conference on Psychiatric Education, American Psychiatric Association, 1953.

[3]Hendrick, Ives. *Psychiatry Education Today*. New York: International Universities Press (1965).

[4]Hendrick, Ives. "Psychoanalytic Contributions to the Study of Psychosis." J.A.M.A., vol. 113: 918 (1939).

Dr. Kubie further proposes that psychiatry could best be taught by patterning a training program on the sequence of the phases of pre-adult development—that cases should first be studied in the pediatric ward and nursery, then the child, the adolescent, and finally young adult patients. Aside from the question at what age will the resident see his first geriatric patient, this might well be a logical plan for an academic lecture course, but our experience shows that this is not the way we learn from clinical material. It is for good pragmatic reasons that psychiatry with adults is generally considered a prerequisite for child psychiatry, and the psychoanalysis of adults is regarded as a necessary foundation for the analysis of children. One reason is found in the differences in communication by children, and especially the increasing limit of verbal communication as one's inquiries go back to infancy.

Dr. Kubie and I are, however, in agreement about the need for a new medical school program for education in psychiatry which will solve important difficulties resulting from the traditional situation of six years of medical training before the future psychiatrist even begins to concentrate on intensive work with psychiatric material. A proposal to abbreviate a few courses in medical school so that a quarter of the time of the future psychiatrist could be spent on psychiatric studies has been discussed here and there since the first meeting of the Committee on Medical Education of G.A.P. (1948).[1] The inclusion of more social science and behavioral theory in some medical schools today has not solved it, as this is no beginning at all in the development of experience with the techniques and facts of clinical psychiatry; and a School of Psychology independent of good medical training encounters the same objection.

Discussant

Harvey D. Strassman, M.D.

Los Angeles, California

Many training problems have been incorporated by Dr. Kubie under this one title. All are worthy of consideration as they are the psychiatric training problems of the future, but space limits discussion to only two.

The traditional assignment of residents to psychiatric hospitals was not changed when psychoanalysis began to influence psychiatric training because it was at the hospital that the resident could study the unconscious in its most florid form. Before the advent of the somatic therapies and psycho-tropic medication, patients expressed unconscious impulses verbally and/or behaviorally, and the resident had an opportunity to relate primary process to symptoms. This opportunity is still present, but with present therapeutic measures, one must be where the acute patient is admitted.

The resident can observe the original instinctual drive and its restitution by the ego in the psychotic leading to an understanding of dynamic ego psychology and the roles of the super-ego and ego-ideal. This learning experience permits the resident to study the psychodynamics of the individual as he appears at a particular cross-section of his life and to relate psychoanalytic theory to the patient. The hospital experience also demonstrates to the resident another use of psychodynamic understanding of the patient besides that of "the talking therapies." He can apply his psychodynamic knowledge in the development of a milieu which will assist the patient in the return to his pre-morbid state.

Psychotherapy of the psychotic patient or any patient, is inappropriate at an early level of training. Learning how to be sensitive to one's own emotions, how to listen, to understand the unconscious in its expression through derivatives, and the contribution of emotional development to emotional problems is the beginning resident's task. The observation of children, adolescents, and adults of all ages would assist the resident in learning.

With the increasing sophistication in psychiatry through undergraduate medical education, entering residents will already have knowledge and understanding of dynamic principles. Psychiatric residency training should provide the opportunities to apply those principles in the development of skills.

When Dr. Kubie presented his creative plan of the Doctorate of Psychological Medicine, it was considered a radical departure from tradition: he was prophesying the medical problems of the future. The necessity for the highly trained physician to be the leader of a team who directs the health needs of a community through paramedically specialty-trained individuals is the subject of conferences now taking place.

A number of institutions have curricula designed to produce experts in "Human Development." These curricula combine psychology, sociology, education and some anthropology, with just enough biology to produce a base for the understanding of the other courses. None is complete enough in itself to provide the basic biological and psychological understanding of man provided for in medical or psychological education. None includes neurophysiology of emotions, or an acquaintance with disease process. A deficiency in these programs is that the student has no opportunity to experience treating people with disease and accepting the responsibility for their life and death.

At a medical school, a student in psychological medicine would be able to have sufficient experiences without entering into depth medical education. The psychoanalytically trained psychiatrist would still be the person most able to diagnose and treat the more difficult psychiatric problems.

Radical revision of graduate psychiatric and psychoanalytic training is necessary now so that our specialty is not left behind when the revisions being made in medical education become a fact in the education of physicians.

Discussant

Sigmund Gabe, M.D.

Beverly Hills, California

To meet the problems presented by the ever-widening demand for psychiatric services, Kubie has proposed the creation of a new subdiscipline of medical psychology.

I have serious reservations about this proposal. By asking the medical profession to endorse and help implement such a system of training of non-medical personnel, Kubie is requesting the relinquishment of the principle that the treatment of illness, whether bodily or mental, is the sole responsibility of the physician. Lay therapy would thus be sanctioned as a permanent institution.

It is highly questionable that the average graduate of a school of medical psychology would be as well trained to handle all psychiatric problems as the average psychiatrist. The fact that he will be practicing under certain indispensable safeguards will make the medical psychologist dependent on the psychiatrist and the problem of first and second class citizenship in the psychiatric field will continue to exist.

There is no denying the desirability of upgrading the training of the clinical psychologist by incorporating into it some exposure to clinical medicine and medical ethics so long as the clinical psychologist is going to attempt to treat patients. However, I have not been aware of any ground swell of support for the plan on the part of the psychologists. Perhaps they see no pressing need to graft the medical disciplines to their training.

Kubie's proposal is predicated on the assumption that the existing system of medical education is unequal to the task of training a sufficient body of psychiatrists in the foreseeable future to meet the community's needs. I do not share this pessimism. What is needed is the creation of a greater awareness on the part of medical educators, and of the educated public generally, of the overriding importance of greatly expanding the training of psychiatrists. Once this problem is fully recognized, the means for meeting this challenge will be generated. If the energy and money required to set up the School of Medical Psychology would be used to establish new medical schools and to attract young people in larger numbers to the study of medicine, a substantial increase in trained psychiatrists and analysts could result.

Kubie has argued persuasively for the need to draw into psychoanalysis practitioners from the behavioral sciences and the humanities in order to give impetus to a mutually fructifying interchange of influences. With this idea there can be no disagreement. However, is it necessary to create a new and numerous body of professionals to reach this desirable goal? Could not this same purpose be achieved by accepting for full psychoanalytic training a select cadre of well-qualified workers from the allied disciplines who have already demonstrated a creative potential in their own fields? This idea has indeed already been accepted by the American Psychoanalytic Association. However, it is being implemented far too cautiously and hesitantly. Perhaps we should not be so concerned lest some of these workers forsake their primary purpose of research and turn into practicing clinicians, thus prying open a little wider the door to lay analysis. In view of the impressive contributions that lay analysts have already made to the scientific edifice of psychoanalysis, we are justified in going ahead more boldly with the policy of training in psychoanalysis a cadre of scientists from the allied disciplines.

While seeking to strengthen the training of psychotherapists by advocating a greater exposure to medical knowledge, Kubie would weaken it by adopting the position that a personal psychoanalysis is not an essential ingredient in the training program. It is true that many practicing psychotherapists have not had the benefit of a personal analysis and that some of them by virtue of innate intuitive gifts may even do good work. However, reliance on intuition alone has its dangers. It will not protect the therapist from the existence of emotional blind spots in himself or from the tendency to project the derivatives of his own unconscious conflicts onto his patients. Nor can we really expect, except in rare instances, that working with patients under supervision, self-scrutiny with the aid of tapes and films and some exposure to group therapy will free the trainee of unresolved childhood conflicts.

Even though, at present, it is not feasible to offer psychoanalysis to all who may wish it, we should nevertheless hold to the principle that anyone who intends to practice psychoanalytic psychotherapy should himself undergo a meaningful psychoanalytic experience. In our eagerness to respond to the crying social needs, we must be on guard not to try to gain quantity of needed personnel at the expense of quality of standards.

Discussant

Charles W. Tidd, M.D.

Los Angeles, California

In his paper on "training," Dr. Kubie presents his ideas with freshness and vigor, which should not surprise anyone who knows him. It is evident his ideas have come out of long experience and formulated after much thought and consideration.

The first proposal, that "... the sequence of steps in training for psychiatry should be reversed and much of the content changed" has much merit. To add to Dr. Kubie's arguments for his proposal, I would emphasize the element of anxiety which affects most first-year residents when they are faced with the task of attempting to look at the psychopathology in floridly psychotic patients; in my opinion this often results in the erection of defensive barriers which may, in some, never be overcome. It is easy for administrators and other staff members to forget how frightening it can be for someone who has had little or no experience with psychotic patients, to be confronted with the massive irrationality found in such patients. This is particularly important in programs where the staff is permanently established; it is necessary and important to remind ourselves that we start each year with untrained residents and, in many instances, with the fiction that the first-year resident is "responsible" for a group of patients and is expected to "treat" them—an obvious impossibility.

Dr. Kubie believes it would be better to introduce the students to, "... the complex processes of growth, observing the subtle early neurotic deviations from normal psychological development."

Again, I agree, because I have seen such a program work, not for residents but for medical students. In this program which extends over four years, the student, in the first and second years sees some psychotic patients in a carefully protected setting. In the third year he begins work with the less ill individual patient in the out-patient department. In the fourth year the students see the more severely disturbed psychotic patients in the hospital. There is considerable evidence to indicate that such a program is effective.

It may well be that the most important factor in the process has to do with the people involved—the students and teachers. Given bright, well-motivated residents and competent teachers who want to teach, I believe the format of the program is relatively unimportant. In addition, I should like to make a plea that the word "education" be added to the word "training" in this program.

Dr. Kubie's proposal for the establishment of a School of Psychological Medicine also deserves careful consideration. Due to limitation of space I will make only one comment: if it is possible to set up such a curriculum that in it we preserve the most important single element in the medical tradition—the welfare of the patient comes first—I for one would like to see it tried.

Discussant

Edward D. Hoedemaker, M.D.

Seattle, Washington

Dr. Kubie is to be commended for directing his talents and interest to matters concerning the proper training of the psychiatrist; important changes are undoubtedly indicated. For instance, it has long been remarked that the psychiatric resident finds himself treating psychotic patients before he has had an opportunity to know what he is doing or what he is trying to do. One finds oneself saying that he should start with neurotic patients and "work up" to treating psychotics almost as though it were a question of starting with easy problems and progressing to those which are more difficult.

I will comment on two of Dr. Kubie's themes, themes which are among those from which he appears to derive his sweeping recommendations in regard to the training of the young psychiatrist or psychotherapist. It should be pointed out in the connection that my comments are actually directed toward only a part of his argument and are not to be construed as opposition to his main thesis— the need for radical reexamination and change of our present methods of training psychotherapists. I do not feel sufficiently informed to discuss this main theme here.

First, a word about Dr. Kubie's statements, some of which are made almost as pronouncements, and some of which, if taken literally, do not meet the facts as I see them. Surely Dr. Kubie's return to the study of psychoses has not shaken him out of his ideas "about almost everything." Surely his comments have to be understood to some degree as reflections of his mood of enthusiasm as arising from his examination of the psychopathology of the psychoses (and it is an exciting experience) and from his natural desire to improve the training of young psychiatrists. For instance, his statement that "Letting a young physician, just out of his medical internship, examine and treat psychotic patients . . . is roughly equivalent to putting a scalpel in the hands of a young resident in surgery and asking him to take out a brain tumor," is somewhat inaccurate. The back ward schizophrenic, treated by a series of neophyte and ambitious therapists is still undeprived of his chance for full recovery (assuming, of course, that psychosurgery and unrelated organic illnesses have not taken their toll). The neurosurgical patient under the uncertain scalpel of the beginner will never be the same, even if he lives.

Many have successfully treated schizophrenic patients who have been in the hands of several therapists of various degrees of training and experience; indeed, this is the usual experience of the mature therapist. While the experiences of these patients have not been such as to allow recovery and some have even made progress impossible, and still others have brought about further psychotic manifestations, the psychotic has faced early in his life external objects who have been many times more dangerous to him than any young resident could be, provided that the treatment attempt is limited to psychotherapy. When regular supervision is added to this (and it always should be), I think the danger to the patient is far less than Dr. Kubie appears to believe.

An analogy of avowedly questionable value has come to mind on reading Dr. Kubie's thoughts about the too early encounters between the psychotic and the neophyte therapist. Dr. Kubie fears that the young resident's theraputic ego is not sufficiently trained and lacks necessary control and, therefore, for the welfare of both, they should be kept apart. It is not the resident who is required to encounter people who are too sick for him, it is rather the very immature ego of the schizophrenic-to-be which has had to encounter objects of great danger to itself, before which it has reeled in disorganized flight with the development of homicidal and other impulses toward the parental objects and consequent and necessary dedifferentiation in defense. (A schizophrenic patient of mine tried to kill her mother at the age of eleven.)

I am suggesting here that the ego of the young resident is perhaps tougher than Dr. Kubie implies and that the resident can (with control) face psychotic pathology rather early in his training without great danger. Also, from the viewpoint of the schizophrenic patient, it is not so much the immature resident from whom the patient should be protected. The protection he needed was protection from parents who were psychologically in fact not qualified to raise that particular child. What I mean to say is that Dr. Kubie appears to have overemphasized the dangers of these early therapeutic encounters and in so doing to have lost sight of some of the values to be derived from early therapeutic encounters with the psychotic patient.

This leads to my next comment which has to do with Dr. Kubie's theme that the study of neurotic pathology should precede the study of the pathology of psychoses. I think that both learning processes should proceed concurrently because both rest (but in different degrees) upon the same foundations. Whereas, the successful development of a healthy internalized object is a sine qua non for the recovery of the psychotic, the reenforcement and enrichment of the neurotic's internalized object spells the difference between changes in the neurotic's psychological appearance on the one hand, and changes which represent basic and lasting improvement on the other. Because of this, the training of a therapist should be directed toward the development of empathy and insight regarding the early object-subject relationships including loss of object. I think that these phenomena are especially well seen in the adult schizophrenic and are demonstrable, and therefore attempts to treat the schizophrenic patient should be in the resident's training picture early.

In this connection, while I agree in general with Dr. Kubie's theme that it would be better for all concerned for the beginning resident to spend the majority of his time in studying neurotic pathology, when he says, "To confront an inexperienced resident abruptly with a psychotic patient hinders his development of empathy . . ."; and, "To the extent to which psychotic behavior is alien and strange, it will be upsetting to him; and his own anxieties will warp his reactions"; and later, ". . . golden opportunities for therapy may be lost," I feel that Dr. Kubie's statements lend a dramatic and somewhat emergent quality to the treatment of the psychotic that somewhat overshadows the benefits to be derived from early contact with psychotic pathology. In this connection I do not mean to deny that treatment of the psychotic has dramatic elements. Other experienced therapists of schizophrenics report missing again and again the meaning of certain communications only to have the significance finally dawn upon them including the underlying neurotic dynamics.

I object to Dr. Kubie's implication that the chances for meaningful treatment will be lost for long periods due to the inexperience of the therapist and therefore he should not be in contact therapeutically with the psychotic until he understands neurotic pathology and its treatment. That the therapist will need understanding of neurotic pathology to successfully deal with psychotic pathology goes without question, but a good argument can be made that the therapist, in order to obtain the most lasting and beneficial results in the treatment of a neurotic person, will need some capacity for empathy with the disorganized ego of the psychotic. The training experience of study of neurotic and psychotic people should proceed concurrently and the values of each experience should contribute to the values of the other.

Dr. Kubie, I know, agrees that other factors not related to the ordering of therapeutic experiences also determine the final skills of the therapist of the psychotic. In this regard one is tempted to say that, unless transitory loss of object and threatened loss of object have been part of the therapist's personal experience, together, of course, with their subsequent thorough analysis with insight, that therapist may not be able to develop adequate understanding of the plight of the psychotic ego to allow more than very moderate success in treatment. His chances of developing such understanding are greater if such object losses have continued after his development of speech and therefore can be more effectively formulated, made conscious, and turned to the aid of his ego in his therapeutic efforts. It is concentration upon elements such as these in training programs rather than upon the order in which the resident encounters kinds of psychopathology that are perhaps more important. It is understandable then that the writer experiences twinges of psychic pain when Dr. Kubie lists, "... practical psychiatric social work ..."; "... experimental psychology (again, both human and subhuman) ..."; and "... psychopharmacology ..." in his proposed curriculum. Shades of Meyerian psychobiology?

Author's Response

Lawrence S. Kubie, M.D.

Baltimore, Maryland

It is not possible to summarize and answer these discussions fully. To do this would take more time and space than is available. Therefore I will touch on only those points which are of special interest to me.

I feel encouraged by the fact that of the eight discussants, four tend on the whole to support changes such as those which I suggest, in each case with some helpful and thoughtful reservations. Three are strongly opposed to these recommendations, although even these find many issues on which they agree with me. One discussant is so balanced that I cannot in fairness say that he is pro or con. This is a higher level of agreement than would have existed even a few years ago. Some disagreements seem to be natural reactions to my over-emphatic mode of expression. Some disagreements are based on a misunderstanding either of the reason why I recommend a change, or of its precise nature. To unravel this would require my restating their position, restating my own, indicating the discrepancy and then correcting it. I fear that four sentences of correction for each misunderstanding are too many. Let me therefore be more general.

My suggestions are in two parts: one has to do with the sequence of training and the other with the question whether the time has come for the medical profession to take over responsibility for training a new subdiscipline, i.e., for training non-medical behavioral scientists for psychodiagnosis and psychotherapy, with a special form of licensure for practice. I have argued in favor of this development for a long time, although I had started from the opposite conviction. I wonder if it is significant that this whole issue receives far less attention from the discussants than does my more recent suggestion that the sequence of training should be reversed. Many ancient arguments are not even mentioned; such as the fear that the non-medical psychodiagnostician and psychotherapist might overlook an organic process. Can it be that the temper of the times have changed and that most colleagues now agree that adequate organization and a proper licensure can take care of this? Nor does any discussant ask whether men so trained will give up experimental work for practice. Here too they may agree that we will have the same spread between investigators and practitioners in such a subdiscipline, as we find among medical psychiatrists.

I find it interesting that none of the discussants mentions the two most important objections, which I have discussed at length in various papers. First is the question of human maturity. Men trained in this program will be six to ten years younger than the psychiatrist who has completed his training and starts in practice in his late thirties (as Lewin and Ross have shown). The fact that they will begin practice younger makes more men available to meet community needs and for more years; but will they be mature enough? I have discussed this at length so many times that I will not go into it here except to say that this cannot be solved apart from the more basic problem of how to make the long educational process into a maturing experience instead of a prolongation of adolescence. The second serious problem is the question of whether or not this will introduce a wedge between somatic and psychological medicine. I have often pointed out the importance of this issue; but I have also presented arguments for believing that the effect will be quite opposite, i.e., that it will draw somatic and psychological medicine closer together. Strangely enough this is not considered by any of the eight discussants.

Before leaving this whole problem, let me add that although the need for more men is one of the important reasons for training non-medical behavioral scientists, there are other deeper, pervasive cultural reasons as well. These, too, are not taken up by my discussants, although I have discussed them at length in previous writings.

Let me now consider the arguments over the reversal of the sequence of events in training. Here I find much misunderstanding, but also many interesting issues. Two advance the argument that in the psychosis unconscious processes are acted out. This of course is true in some measure; but as Freud pointed out they are acted out disguised, just as they are in dreams; and if we want the resident to study the interplay of conscious, preconscious, and unconscious processes where they are transparently displayed, we will turn his attention to infancy and childhood, to watch and listen to the child. Here the process occurs without the same degrees of distortion which occur in the neurosis, the dream or the psychosis. This is one reason why working with infants and small children is such a superb preparation for work with the neurosis and ultimately with the psychosis.

One discussant implies that the psychiatric hospital and the couch have outlived their usefulness. I have long since given up any notion that either carries any magic, but I am also far from accepting the current fashion that they are useless. But whether they are or not is irrelevant to the suggestions which I am presenting.

One colleague wholly misunderstands my picture of the neurotic process and of the relation of psychotic disorganization to it. About this I can only refer him to recent papers on this which are in press, but not yet in print. Nor does the fact that some residents feel more comfortable with the psychotic impress me as it impresses this same critic. In my experience this occurs where the young man's own neurosis is deeply and painfully challenged by the neuroses of his patients. To me this only means that he will have to work this out before he will be able to become a participant-observer in the study of either. (v.i.)

In their discussions two emphasized certain psychoanalytic formulations about the psychoses. Without discussing whether these formulae have universal validity, I would point out that a strong argument can be made that no resident should attempt such formulations of the psychosis until he has worked over this carefully on the neuroses of his patients and perhaps indeed on himself.

These last paragraphs lead to the question of the importance of a personal psychoanalysis for training. I do not doubt its importance, but I would emphasize the possibility that there may be other ways to achieve the same goal with our residents, and that one of these is the closely supervised work with children and neuroses.

In general my major plea is that we must be more willing to make experiments in new directions, and I close with a word of thanks to my colleagues for their thoughtful and helpful discussions.

Title The Cannibalistic Impulses of Parents

Author George Devereux, PH.D.

Psychoanalyst and ethnologist, is Professor of Research in Ethnopsychiatry, Temple University School of Medicine (currently on leave). His special fields of interest are psychiatric illnesses of non-Occidental and ancient peoples, theoretical foundations of psychoanalysis and of the social sciences and theory of psychoanalytic technique. He is the author of six books and some one hundred fifty articles.

Discussants

Alfred Coodley, M.D.

Associate Clinical Professor of Psychiatry at University of California at Los Angeles, a member of the Southern California Psychoanalytic Society, and a Contributing Editor of *Annual Survey of Psychoanalysis*. For fifteen years as Consultant to the County Juvenile Hall, he has studied aggressive and destructive children and their parents. He has been a parent twice but denies ever having been a cannibal!

Irene M. Josselyn, M.D.

Training Analyst and Chairman of the Child Analytic Committee of the Southern California Psychoanalytic Institute; Clinical Professor of Child Psychiatry, University of Southern California, and faculty member of the School of Social Work, Arizona State University. She has written three books and many articles dealing with the psychological development and problems of children and adolescents.

Rudolf Ekstein, PH.D.

Training Analyst at the Los Angeles Psychoanalytic Institute and Director of the Project on Childhood Psychosis at the Reiss-Davis Child Study Center. He is the co-author of *The Learning and Teaching of Psychotherapy*, has published more than a hundred papers concerning psychoanalytic technique and theory, and concerning his research work with psychotic and borderline children.

Konrad Lorenz, M.D., PH.D.

Has taught anatomy, zoology, psychology and comparative ethology at universities throughout the world. He is the author of *King Solomon's Ring*, *Man Meets Dog*, *Animal Stories* and many other books and scientific papers. He is Director of the Max Planck Institute in Germany.

The Cannibalistic Impulses of Parents

George Devereux, PH.D.

Paris, France

> *If one has humbled oneself all one's life long in order to avoid painful conflict with facts, one tends to keep one's back bowed in one's old age before any new fact which may appear.*
>
> S. FREUD

Purpose:
The present study has two purposes:

1. It seeks to present data pertaining to the cannibalistic impulses of parents and to demonstrate that these impulses underlie a psychic structure which—*qua structure*—originates in adulthood, and therefore cannot be considered either as a simple elaboration of infantile cannibalistic impulses, nor as a reaction to the cannibalistic impulses of children, i.e., it is not "counter"-cannibalistic. On the contrary, it is proposed to show that an objective scrutiny of enormous masses of psychological, historical, ethnological and zoological data make it imperative to assume that the *specifically cannibalistic*—as *distinct* from simply oral-aggressive—impulses of children are reactive and "counter"-cannibalistic, being elicited by the cannibalistic impulses of the parents. The term "children"—as distinct from "infants"—is used advisedly in this context, since the infant is, because of its inability to think conceptually, as incapable of having *specifically* cannibalistic fantasies as an animal is incapable of committing "incest" in the *human* sense of that term. (22)

2. An attempt will be made to examine the problem of the singular lack of psychoanalytic interest in the problem of adult—and, a fortiori of parental—cannibalistic impulses, as shown by the topical index of Grinstein's work, (17) and to suggest that this systematic neglect is not fortuitous, but represents a both psychologically and culturally determined scotomization of this important problem.

Parental vs. Filial Cannibalistic Impulses and Acts:

In a previous paper (7) it was shown that the so-called counter-oedipal attitudes of parents are actually *prior* to the oedipal attitudes of children, and serve as triggering mechanisms for the latter.

The present study proposes to demonstrate the priority of the allegedly "counter"-cannibalistic impulses of parents, as against the posteriority of the reactive, i.e., genuinely counter-cannibalistic, impulses of the child. Proof of this will be adduced primarily by means of an analysis of the unconscious *reciprocal* relationship between the characteristic oral cravings of pregnant women and the oral cravings *imputed* to the infant, and especially to the unborn, aborted or murdered neonate. The word "imputed" is of crucial importance, since these cravings are, of necessity, gratuitous imputations to foeti or to dead infants.

Such a method is bound to be fruitful, since the analysis of impulses gratuitously and arbitrarily imputed to unborn or dead babies, which cannot possibly have a realistic basis, tends to bring out the unconscious attitudes of the adult both toward the living child's *real* oral cravings and aggressivity, and toward the adult's own oral needs, which he projects upon the infant. In fact, after being suitably distorted and reinterpreted, the infant's real and intense oral cravings may even be *exploited* by the adult for the purpose of masking his own neurotic attitudes toward such infantile cravings. This is very similar to the manner in which certain neurotics in analysis appeal to (their conception of) reality, in order to justify and to rationalize their neurotic attitudes.

Such maneuvers are quite common: Thus, an American Indian woman analysand sought to avoid insight into her provocatively hostile behavior, by blaming all her setbacks on discrimination against Indians. (8)

The oral cravings of pregnant women, which are quite real, are part and parcel of the Euro-American folklore of pregnancy. Similar cravings occur also in other areas, and are part of the folklore of pregnancy in those areas. Two examples, chosen almost at random, will illustrate this:

The parents of an unmarried Swahili girl become suspicious if she suddenly develops unusual cravings for certain foods, and subject her to a physical examination to ascertain whether or not she is pregnant. Pregnant Swahili girls tend, moreover, to take an intense dislike to some young man or woman living in the same house; a fact which presumably underscores the aggressive components of the pregnant woman's food cravings. (34)

Hawaiians believe that after the first few months of pregnancy the woman usually experiences a strong craving—called *hookaukau*—for some special food, such as certain kinds of seafood or fruit. Thus, Kekuipoiwa, while pregnant with the future King Kamehameha the Great, craved to eat the man-eating nihui shark's eyes, which were eventually obtained for her at great risk. The kahuna (medicine-man, diviner), therefore predicted that Kekuipoiwa would give birth to a chief whose eyes would flash anger like those of the tiger shark, and whose power would be like that of the nihui shark. This prophecy frightened the chiefs so much, that they conspired to kill this dangerous child.[1] In commenting upon this incident, our ethnological authority specifies that it is not the food eaten by the mother which affects the character of the unborn child, rather it is the inborn nature of the foetus which induces special food cravings in the mother. (18) In other words, the *responsibility* for the mother's violent oral cravings is *attributed* to the unborn child. Moreover, these Hawaiian data resemble the Swahili data in stressing the hostile and even "man-eating" oral cravings of at least one mother.

Oral Cravings Imputed to Dead Infants:

Two examples, chosen among many, suffice to illustrate this fantasy.

A Hawaiian woman—apparently in a state of advanced pregnancy—walked to a distant village in order to visit a relative. While en route, she miscarried a foetus sufficiently developed to enable her to determine that it was a male. She wrapped the foetus in her undergarment and placed it under some convolvulus vines, intending to pick it up after the visit, and to take it home to her husband. She then calmly went on and visited her relative, as planned. When she was walking back to her own village, accompanied by her brother, she discovered that the foetus, which she had hidden under the vines, had disappeared. A few weeks later, while she was fishing, her nipple was seized by a small shark, who began to nurse at her breast. The fact that the markings of this shark resembled those of the undergarment in which she had wrapped the foetus, made her realize that the sea gods had taken the foetus and had transformed it into this shark, which many Hawaiians subsequently saw at a certain spot, near the shore. Similar stories are told by other Hawaiians. (25)

This narrative stands in need of comment. The fact that a woman in an advanced state of pregnancy—as one may judge from the state of development of the foetus—took such a long walk for a very trivial reason and reacted so casually—not to say callously—to her miscarriage, suggests that we are dealing here with a pseudo-miscarriage. Otherwise stated, this woman's long walk suggests a—perhaps only preconscious—intention to induce an abortion

[1]Compare the conspiracy to kill the infant Kypselos, of whom it was prophesied that he would displace the Bakchiads and become tyrant of Korinthos. (Herodotus V, 92.)

by means of overexertion. It is true, of course, that the Hawaiian data surveyed in connection with my study of abortion among primitives, (9) did not include overexertion as a means of inducing abortion. This, however, is almost certainly a fortuitous omission, partly because the technique of overexertion is extremely widespread,[2] and partly because data on abortion for most primitive tribes—Hawaii included—are so sketchy and fragmentary that the failure of our Hawaiian sources to mention this particular technique is almost certainly accidental, especially since abortion was quite common in Hawaii. In brief, the tenuous motivation of a strenuous walk in a state of advanced pregnancy, taken in conjunction with the mother's casual attitude, inevitably suggests either an intentional abortion, or one induced, "accidentally on purpose." What is certain is that this miscarriage, whether actively intended or passively endured, was for this woman the organizing focus of an abortion fantasy.

If an illegitimately impregnated Aleut girl kills her baby, its ghost will haunt the village every night in the shape of a k'dah bird, which can be heard crying. Since this haunting can produce major disasters, it is necessary to put an end to it. The murderess therefore exposes her breasts, so as to lure the bird to it. The bird is then captured and ripped apart; this ends the haunting. (35)

The data just presented indicate that intense oral cravings are imputed even to dead infants and that these cravings are believed to be actualized by non-human reincarnations of the infant. These reincarnations appear to be dangerous creatures: the man-eating shark in Hawaii and the k'dah bird which causes disasters among the Aleut.

Discussion:

It seems hardly necessary to stress that the beliefs just described have no bearing upon the actual oral cravings of real infants. They simply reflect the nightmarish and revengeful *quality* which adults arbitrarily *impute* to the *genuine* oral cravings of children. Otherwise expressed, they once more demonstrate how neurotically unrealistic many of the ideas of adults about children really are. (10) They show only what adults apparently *need* to believe about children since many of these beliefs are little more than the projection of adult needs on the child. It is therefore desirable to scrutinize next some aspects of the oral cravings of pregnant and parturient females, both animal and human.

It is a well known fact, which does not stand in need of elaborate documentation, that cravings for certain specific foods may be mobilized by what Cannon called, "the wisdom of the body." Thus, when rats who have been experimentally deprived of some important nutritional element, are presented with a variety of foods, only one of which contains the needed substance, they will select that particular food. Zoologists feel, moreover, that the female animal, which just gave birth to her young, devours the placenta and the cord, because they contain certain active substances which help her body achieve the hormonal shift from the pregnant to the lactating state. Sometimes the craving to devour the placenta and the cord can even lead to the devouring of the young. Lorenz, (21) describes in great detail the sucking jaw-and-lip movements of the bitch while cleaning up her puppies' navels. Sometimes this sucking becomes so intense that it culminates in the devouring of the puppy, the first bite being taken from the puppy's navel. The eating of the afterbirth, as a therapeutic meas-

---

[2] A cursory glance at the tabulations of data in my book gave a list of twelve tribes using unspecified "overexertion" and twenty more using a specified form of overexertion, such as jumping off high places. It was a standard technique in Europe, and Hippocrates himself, taking pity on a pregnant flute-girl, advised her to dance and to leap strenuously. (24)

ure, is also reported from some of the most backward tribes of Eastern Siberia. (9,24)

There are cogent reasons for assuming that the impulse to eat the afterbirth—and possibly even the baby—is quite strong also in the human female, though this impulse is culturally implemented only in the form of a projection and/or reaction formation. Thus, in very many primitive groups elaborate precautions are taken to hide and otherwise to safeguard the afterbirth and the cord from scavenger animals. A perhaps more explicit and culturally implemented defense against maternal cannibalistic impulses is the rule that during the postpartum period the Mohave mother must not eat any meat whatsoever. (5) In some cases maternal or parental cannibalistic impulses are only vicariously implemented. The most striking example of this was reported from New Guinea, where every woman of a certain tribe must take her first-born baby to the ravine, where the farrowing sows are kept, and must toss it to the sows, who promptly devour it. The woman then takes one of the farrows belonging to the sow who first attacked her baby's corpse and nurses it at her own breast. (12) A less obvious example is the sacrificing of children to Moloch: the infants were thrust into the maw of this bronze deity.

On a broader, and even more relevant level, the eating, and occasionally even the marketing, of the flesh of one's children was a common occurrence both during medieval famines and during the great post-revolutionary famine in Russia. According to Multatuli, (23) it formerly occurred also in Java, where the compulsory cultivation of cash-crops repeatedly caused disastrous famines. In at least two Australian tribes—the Ngali and the Yumu, (27)—in times of famine the women even abort (or are made to abort), in order to feed the rest of the family. In another Australian tribe, (20) if the family starved, the small baby was killed by knocking its head against the shoulder of its older sibling; its flesh was used to feed the older siblings, and also the rest of the family. In brief, in times of famine, child cannibalism was quite common among primitive Australians, many of whom preferred to kill a useless baby, rather than a useful dingo hunting dog. It seems reasonable to assume that the peculiar technique of killing the baby by knocking its head against its sibling's shoulder simply seeks to "exonerate" its parents. It is, moreover, quite erroneous to suppose that the Australians do not love their children. So great an expert on Australia as the late Gèza Róheim once cited to the present writer a case—whether from a published source, or from personal observation can no longer be recalled—in which a small child, with whom his parents had been playing quite affectionately during the day, was killed and cooked for dinner. It is not a tasteless witticism to recall in connection with this incident the familiar parental endearment: "I love you so much, that I could eat you." We shall return to this matter shortly.

Thus, the eating of children in times of shortage is far from rare. By contrast—and this is most significant—one hardly ever hears of hungry children killing their parents in order to eat them. In fact, the present writer has yet to come across such a case, either in primitive or in modern society.

So far we have dealt chiefly with child cannibalism which is due to famine. As regards *ritual* cannibalism, the situation is somewhat different. Although the ritual cannibalization of children by their parents and by the ritual associates of the parents is quite common—for example in connection with the poro and/or leopard men rites of West Africa, (1)—in some instances the eating of parents who died of a natural cause is deemed to be an act of piety—a fact already reported by Herodotus, (III,38).

A partly economically and partly psychiatrically motivated form of cannibalism, called "windigo" is fairly common among many Algonquian tribes of Canada. Teicher's outstanding monograph, (33) which summarizes everything known on the subject, lists seventy *known* cases, presented and analyzed in more than sixty quarto pages. The "windigo" experiences intense cannibalistic cravings, often directed at his own children. In order to make this urge more ego-syntonic, he sometimes hallucinates them as beavers, which are considered a delicacy.[3] In some cases, when the cannibalistic urge becomes uncontrollable, without ceasing to be highly ego-dystonic, the "windigo" either begs to be killed, or else flees into the forest, so as to have no opportunity to eat a human being, and especially not his own children or kin.

The point I seek to make is an extremely simple one, which legislators quite as much as psychoanalysts have chosen to ignore: although law and public opinion penalize parricide infinitely more severely than infanticide —as though the impulse to commit parricide were much stronger and therefore needed to be curbed by more violent means, statistics tell a very different story. Throughout the course of history, infinitely more children were killed (and/or aborted) by their parents than parents killed by their children. Likewise child sacrifices are more common than parent sacrifices. Books on history, ethnology, criminology, comparative religions . . . and even the daily press . . . all tell the same story. These are hard facts, which simply cannot be reconciled with the arbitrary thesis that the cannibalistic impulses of children are more intense than and also dynamically and genetically prior to the cannibalistic impulses of adults, and that children groundlessly fantasy their parents as potential cannibals. These hard facts cannot be disposed of by the often repeated and completely untenable thesis that "reality cannot be analyzed,"—*especially* when the reality to be analyzed concerns human beliefs and practices. Nor can these inescapable conclusions be circumvented by insisting that, since everything originates in childhood, adult cannibalistic impulses must also originate in childhood. The fallaciousness and speciousness of this particular argument, when used in this context,—*and it has been so used!*—can be readily grasped once one understands that even though *ultimately* everything goes back to childhood, it need not necessarily go back to a *genetic* or *biological* substratum, but may result from a childhood *experience* . . . i.e., from the *impact* of the adults' cannibalistic impulses upon the infant's psyche. In fact, it would represent both a methodologically undesirable multiplication of entities—already objected to by Newton—and be contrary to ordinary biological knowledge to postulate a specific, innate, "cannibalistic impulse." All this, "Which came first: the hen or the egg?" type of reasoning disturbingly resembles the kind of *pseüdobiologia phantastica* of which too many examples still survive in certain dark corners of psychoanalytic theory. We shall return to this point later. For the moment it suffices to state a very simple fact: it is never the child, it is always the parent who says: "I love you so much, that I could eat you." It is not the Duauan child, it is the Duauan father who takes his little son's penis in his mouth and "tenderly" pretends that he will swallow it. (26) This too, is a fact hard to dispose of by appeals to traditional "theory." Lagrange's famous statement, "Nature is not concerned over the analytical[4] difficulties wherewith it confronts the scientist," might profitably be taken to heart also by psychoanalysts. Freud teaches the same lesson when he insists—albeit in a most unfortunate context[5]—that he

[3]When, in the famous film "Gold Rush," Charlie Chaplin and a big bully starve in an Alaskan cabin, the bully first hallucinates Chaplin as a rooster and then tries to kill and to eat him.

[4]In scientific French "l'analyse" means differential and integral calculus.

[5]In a discussion of the "reality" of telepathy. (14)

at least would always bend his back before a fact, and had done so all his life.

The real problem confronting us is therefore not so much the objective understanding of the child's *genuine* (though reactive) cannibalistic impulses, which no one would deny, as the exploration of the conscious and unconscious *need* of layman and expert alike, to derive the parents' child-directed cannibalistic impulses from the (imputed and unprovable) *innate* cannibalistic urges of the child.

The nightmarish quality of the child's oral cravings is the first problem to be considered, since it is obviously possible to postulate the existence of cannibalistic impulses in the child, without being necessarily obliged to view—as Melanie Klein and some of her followers do—the child's entire psyche as a self-perpetuating chamber of horrors. In fact, the very extremeness of these imputed characteristics makes one suspicious of their validity; here, if anywhere, Shakespeare's dictum about protesting too much is applicable. Moreover, such a conception of the infantile psyche is altogether incompatible with the Hartmann-Kris-Loewenstein theory of the infantile ego. In legal parlance one might, therefore, speak of a "self-serving" adult conception of the child's psyche, which justifies much parental sadism, just as an Eighteenth Century theory which made animals into mere machines, "only behaving as though they felt pain, but actually feeling none," justified a great deal of callousness toward animals.

The failure to recognize specifically adult forms of cannibalism is a second obstacle to insight into the real (derivative) nature of infantile cannibalistic—as distinct from oral-biting—impulses. If one *compulsively* starts from the theory that, "everything begins in childhood, since man was a child before he became an adult," one disregards such obvious and strictly adult forms of "cannibalism" as that of the bitch or sow who eats her young. Quite apart from the fact that such complex and highly structured behavior *could* not originate in early infancy, the most obvious point to be made is that small puppies or piglets do not have young which they *could* eat; moreover, they do not, in fact, eat their mother, nor do they apparently *try* to do so.

The avoidance of any discussion of parental cannibalism—which, as we saw, is extremely widespread—when contrasted with the many studies devoted to infantile "cannibalistic" impulses clearly suggests that we are confronted here with a scotoma. This finding parallels the fact that—even though there is hardly a case on record of a child castrating its father—much is written about the child's wish to kill or castrate his father, but very little about the parent's wish to castrate his son, except for passing references to threats of castrating masturbating children. Yet, in a great many cases, the castration of the child by the father, or at the instigation of the father, is a fact. Both in China and in the Near East parents did sell their children to be made into eunuchs. In Byzantium, eminent families sometimes had their sons castrated, in order to insure that they would become high court officials. In still other cases they castrated them because they feared that the Emperor—always afraid of being dethroned by the scion of a highranking family—might otherwise execute their sons. This list could be considerably extended and would get unmanageably long if one included in its scope the castration of children by parent-substitutes: States, Kings and even the commonwealth of Kansas, where, as late as the late 1940's the *castration* (not sterilization) of feebleminded children was routinely performed in some state institutions, and was vehemently defended in the official organ of the Kansas Medical Society. By contrast, the *only* instance known to me in which a father was castrated by his son was reported by Herodotus (VIII, 105-6): Hermotimos, as a boy, was captured and sold to a maker of eunuchs, named Panionios, who castrated him.

Later on Hermotimos, having became Xerxes' favorite eunuch, pretended to be grateful to Panionios and invited him to visit him with his family. He then forced Panionios to castrate his own sons, and the sons to castrate their father. The near-total absence of any systematic discussion of *parental* castrative impulses is, thus, strictly comparable to the lack of interest displayed by psychoanalysts concerning parental cannibalistic impulses.

The Child as a Parasite:

The conception of the child, as one who eats up his parents, can be readily documented. The Papuans of Geelvink Bay perform many abortions, because, in their opinion, children "destroy" their parents. (29) The Mohave Indians hold that after a certain degree of intrauterine development is reached, the foetus feeds on the semen which the mother's sex partner injects into her genitalia. (4) The concept of the child as a "malignancy" exists even in medical science. Thus, in commenting upon a vulgar ditty, in which the foetus was referred to as a "tumor," a physician, in a *serious* discussion, assured the writer that the similarity between an embryo and a tumor was a rather close one. Perhaps the most "sublimated" fantasy of infantile cannibalism is the tenacious myth of the pelican father, who supposedly feeds his brood by tearing open his own breast—though in reality he feeds his young with partly ingested food *stored* in a sac under its beak. It is presumably not a coincidence that the favorite poem of a young psychiatrist—who had *recently* become a father—was precisely a famous French poem about this bit of "unnatural history." In fact, though he spoke French rather poorly, this young colleague actually learned the poem by heart and recited it in and out of season.

What actually takes place in the case of most animals feeding their young is a *temporary inhibition of the swallowing reflex*, while they bring food to the young in their mouth or beak. This inhibition may, conceivably, represent a greater "strain" for the adult animal or bird than does the inhibition of the hand-to-mouth reflex in man, or the inhibition of the claw-to-beak reflex in predatory birds, who carry the prey to their young in their claws.

It certainly cannot be denied that parents do sometimes deprive themselves orally for the sake of their children. Among the poor, this deprivation is largely quantitative, except that, in times of real scarcity, it is the breadwinner who gets the lion's share, in order to be able to keep on working. Among the richer classes the deprivation is usually a qualitative one. Titbits (from "*teat*") tend to be reserved for the children.

Case 1: An analysand reported that his well-to-do parents always reserved the titbits for the children. However, when one day the analysand protested against some parental exaction and contrasted the freedom of his friend X with the oppressive control which his mother exercised, the mother replied: "In this house you get the titbits. The same is not true of your friend's home. I know it for a fact that one day your friend X was eating a raisin pudding and set the raisins aside, saving them all for the last mouthful. His mother let him do it, but when he was ready at last to eat his hoard of raisins, she simply reached over and took them for herself. We do not behave that way toward you. *Therefore* we are entitled to absolute obedience." This remark casts a flood of light upon one of the reasons why parents find it advantageous to *exaggerate* the oral needs of children . . . even of those in the latency period. It is hardly necessary to add that this man's analysis disclosed, beyond a shadow of doubt, that the obedience demanded by his parents practically required flexibilitas cerea and amounted to a total "devouring" of the child's distinctive identity.

In brief, the oral self-denial of the parents —in order to gratify the oral needs of the child

—is a mechanism whose animal prototype is the inhibition of the swallowing reflex. It is, at the same time, interpreted by the parent (and by the adult in general) as evidence of a kind of infantile oral aggression, amounting (as in the pelican myth) to cannibalism, and is felt to be characteristic of the child.

Speaking both tentatively and in an admittedly speculative way, what appears to be at the root of this tendency to equate—or at least to correlate—the feeding of children with cannibalistic impulses on the part of the child, is the fairly complicated mechanism which we observe in the parturient bitch: after the placenta and a sufficient (but not excessive) length of the cord is eaten, and the puppy is licked clean, there occurs an inhibition of the swallowing reflex. Without the inhibition of this reflex the puppy itself would also be eaten. However, the reflex is not inhibited *until after* the placenta and the cord have been swallowed. Indeed, when Lorenz gave a bitch, who had just finished cleaning up her litter a newborn puppy whose navel cord had already been removed, the bitch, in trying to bite off and to eat the (non-existent) cord, actually devoured the puppy, starting with the navel-area. (21) One also wonders whether the inhibition of the swallowing reflex, while bringing food to the young, may possibly be an extension of the inhibition of that reflex after the cleansing of the newborn puppy is completed.

Degrees of "Cannibalism" in Babies:

A curious cultural variation on the theme of cannibal babies is the belief that some babies are more cannibalistically inclined than others. According to an extremely ancient Hungarian folk belief—which demonstrably goes back to the time when the Hungarians still lived in Asia—the shamans are born with teeth and bite the mother's nipples. (28) Exactly the same belief is found among the Mohave Indians, (3) who also believe that if a pregnant woman's husband kills a snake, the child's head will resemble that of a snake, and its bite will be poisonous. They therefore do not nurse such babies, but—sometimes successfully—try to keep them alive by feeding them mush. (11) In certain other tribes the baby's cannibalistic impulses are believed to be directed chiefly at other babies (sibling rivalry).

Case 2: An American Indian woman, possessing the equivalent of a college degree, made the following statement in the course of her analysis: "When I was a child, my favorite story was the old Indian tale about a cannibal baby. This baby would sneak away from its cradle-board at night and devour other babies, returning to its cradle at dawn with its mouth smeared with blood, and with bits of baby-flesh caught between its teeth. I used to feel so sorry for this cannibal baby; it must have felt very uncomfortable with bits of flesh caught between its teeth! . . . I wished I could make it more comfortable, by picking its teeth clean."[6] The tribe to which this woman belonged was characterized by an especially high degree of both sibling rivalry and adult aggressive competitiveness.

The identification of this adult woman with the mythical cannibal baby was even more far-reaching than the above data indicate. Angry because she had been weaned quite early, not only by her own tribe's standards, but even by modern occidental standards, she developed early in life a marked aversion to milk, and boasted of drinking coffee already at the age of six months. She ferociously envied men because, as she saw it, they could gain access to a woman's breast under the ***pretense*** of cohabiting with her. Above all, while loathing milk, she would become almost lyrical about the "wonderful, smooth, bland taste of (blood red!) Delaware Punch" (a not very popular soft drink).

---

[6]This fantasy is a striking parallel of the zoological fact that the crocodile keeps its maw open, while a smallish bird picks its teeth and mouth clean of food debris.

This case clearly suggests that childhood cannibalistic impulses are:

1. Elicited by severe oral frustration at an early age;[7]

2. Reinforced by elements of sibling rivalry, especially if the formerly frustrated child is obliged to watch the nursing of younger siblings, and

3. Are *structured into* a cannibalistic fantasy by means of stories told *by* adults *to* children,—for example by means of the Cannibal Baby story. The same can, of course, also be accomplished by the type of cannibalistically worded tenderness, ("I could eat you") found in Europe and in America, or by the Duau-type paternal "caress" mentioned above, or, simply, by behaving in an oral-cannibalistic manner toward the child.

In this context special mention should be made of the fact that overt or implicit castration threats are often *cannibalistically worded.* ("The cat will take your penis." "A bird will peck at your penis," etc.) It is certainly not without significance that among certain North Siberian tribes both reindeer and dogs are castrated by *biting off* their testicles. (2)

Counter-Cannibalistic Impulses:

The few passing allusions to the cannibalistic impulses of adults found in the psychoanalytic literature[8] state, in so many words, that parental cannibalistic impulses are *reactive* or "*counter*"-cannibalistic. Such, however, is the meaning which at least the present writer seems to discover between the lines of these studies. Be that as it may, what is quite certain and what actually matters, is that, to the best of my knowledge, no one has so far stated that parental cannibalistic impulses toward the children were *primary*, and the corresponding impulses and fantasies of children *reactive*, i.e., "counter"-cannibalistic. Yet, this conclusion seems inevitable in the light of the aforementioned data, which could easily have been multiplied almost *ad infinitum.*[9]

It is hard to escape these simple facts, though some have tried to do so. The theory based on *pseudobiologia phantastica*, which argues that since everything starts in childhood, cannibalistic impulses must *also* start there, does not, as we saw, face two crucial problems:

1. Even *reactive* fantasies can start in childhood, so that the demonstration of the existence of infantile cannibalistic fantasies simply does not suffice to prove that they are "innate"; they can just as well be—and, in fact, *are*—reactive and "learned."

2. The cannibalistic pattern is simply too complex and requires too much conceptual thinking to come into being in early childhood, i.e., before the child even knows the difference between animate and inanimate, let alone between human beings and animals.[10]

---

[7]In this patient's tribe the normal weaning age is between 2½ and 3 years. She was weaned prematurely, due to her mother's illness.

[8]Adult cannibalism and cannibalistic fantasies have been so systematically ignored, that Grinstein's *Index*, (17) lists, under the two headings "Anthropophagy" and "Cannibalism," exactly four papers. It does not give cross-references to "Oral Sadism" and the like, but most of the papers listed under the latter headings pertain chiefly to infantile cannibalistic fantasies, or to the infantile sources of such impulses.

[9]Even Greek mythology is replete with such data: The devouring of the *infant* Dionysos by the Titans; Dionysos himself as a cannibal in his adult "omophagous" role, (clearly a *reactive* fantasy!); the cooking of Pelops by his father and the consuming of his shoulder-blade by Demeter who, being at that time in a severe state of depression due to the loss of her daughter Persephone, is inevitably cannibalistically disposed; the cooking of Thyestes' children and their "unwitting" eating by their father, the murder and cooking of Itys by his vindictive mother Prokne, who then fed his flesh to his father Tereus, etc.

[10]Similarly, as Lowie so rightly stressed, (22) an animal cannot commit "incest" because he does not understand the *meaning* of "parent." Yet, human beings—including so great a thinker and so excellent an observer of animal reproduction as Aristotle—do *impute* even to animals a "horror of incest." The same objection can be raised against Melanie Klein's conception of "oedipal" impulses during the first year of life. In order for a child to have "oedipal" (i.e., not simply "sexual" or "aggressive") impulses, it must first *understand* the

A few words should now be said about the place of biological facts in psychoanalytic reasoning. It would be insensate to deny the psychological importance of man's biological substratum. It is equally senseless, however, to forget that psychoanalysis is *quite specifically* a *human* psychology; in fact, it is the *only* psychology that applies to man as a *human being*. This definitely implies that, in *psychoanalytic* discourse, physiological and zoological data can only be used for the purpose of characterizing the *terrain* on which, and the *raw material* by means of which, dynamic processes characteristic of the *human* psyche *only*, unfold themselves. This, too, was clearly stated by Freud in the memorable passage of "Totem and Taboo," (15) where he correlates the genesis of the Oedipus complex with the coming-into-being, or at least with the differentiation of man, as a culture-creating being, distinct from animals. The fact that he then proceeded, as an afterthought, to provide a "biological" and "paleopsychological" explanation for all this—although the facts, illuminated by his flash of genius spoke so clearly that no further explanation was needed—is best forgotten and is certainly not to be imitated. Least of all is it to be imitated in the form of certain common or garden varieties of paleo-bio-psychological speculations, which have no standing whatsoever in the realm of a *scientific* psychoanalysis.

Summary

1. There exists a reciprocal relationship between the cannibalistic impulses of parents and those of children.

2. The available facts lend no support to the (implicit) official assumption that the cannibalistic impulses of children are primary, and those of parents secondary or reactive.

3. Massive data prove that the child's specifically cannibalistic impulses are induced by, and therefore epiphenomenal to, parental cannibalistic impulses. Once established, the cannibalistic impulses of the child can, however, enter into a relationship with the (pre-existing) cannibalistic impulses of the parents. This relationship is then one of mutual induction.

4. The near-complete bypassing of parental cannibalistic impulses in psychoanalytic literature suggests the presence of massive resistances against this insight; more massive perhaps than those which account for the fact that the child's Oedipus complex was discovered long before the so-called counter-oedipal complexes of the parents . . . and this *despite* the fact that one of Freud's first discoveries was the role of (real or imaginary) parental seduction. Hence, any attempt to clarify the real sources of cannibalistic fantasies and impulses must inevitably include an analysis of the resistances and scotomata hindering insight into parental cannibalistic impulses.

5. One final result of the immense discrepancy between the large amount that is known of the neurotic attitudes of children toward adults and the little that is known of the neurotic attitudes of adults towards children—which includes outright, self-exonerating, (6,16) fantasies about the nature of children, disguised as scientific discourse, (10)—is that the bilaterality and reciprocity of adult-child relationships and attitudes has been quite systematically and also quite grossly underestimated and soft-pedalled. Noted exceptions are Ferenczi's memorable paper on the confusion of tongues between children and adults, (13)—and also certain of Spitz's papers on hospitalism and other subjects. (30,31,32)

meaning of kinship . . . which is one reason why, with an unerring sureness of touch and acuity of observation, Freud ascribed the genesis of the "oedipal" impulse to the third or fourth year of life, when "father" and "mother" do begin to have a meaning for the child.

These papers blazed a new trail, in that, unlike many others, their authors did not assume *a priori* that in the interaction between child and adult it is the child *only* who speaks the "jabberwocky" of the primary process and of the unconscious.

Bibliography

1. Beatty, K. *Human Leopards.* London, H. Rees, 1915.
2. Bogoras, W. *The Chukchee.* New York, G. E. Stechert, 1904-1909.
3. Devereux, G. "Mohave Orality," Psa. Quart., Vol. 17, 1947, pp. 519-546.
4. ———. "Mohave Pregnancy," Acta Americana, Vol. 6, 1948, pp. 89-116.
5. ———. "Post Partum Parental Observances of the Mohave Indians." Transactions of the Kansas Academy of Sciences, Vol. 52, 1949, pp. 458-465.
6. ———. *Reality and Dream: Psychotherapy of a Plains Indian.* New York, Int. Univ. Press, 1951.
7. ———. "Why Oedipus Killed Laius," Int. J. Psa., Vol. 34, 1953, pp. 132-141.
8. ———. "Cultural Factors in Psychoanalytic Therapy." J. Amer. Psa. Ass'n, Vol. 1, 1953, pp. 629-655.
9. ———. *A Study of Abortion in Primitive Societies.* New York, Julian Pr., 1955.
10. ———. *Therapeutic Education: Its Theoretical Bases and Practice.* New York, Harper, 1956.
11. ———. *Mohave Ethnopsychiatry and Suicide.* Bureau of American Ethnology, Bulletin 175, Washington, D.C., 1961.
12. Dupeyrat, A. *Savage Papua.* New York, Dutton, 1954.
13. Ferenczi, S. "Confusion of Tongues Between Adults and Children." In Balint, M., *Final Contributions to the Problems and Methods of Psychoanalysis.* New York, Basic Books, 1955.
14. Freud, S. *New Introductory Lectures on Psychoanalysis.* London, Hogarth Press and the Institute for Psychoanalysis, 1933.
15. ———. "Totem and Taboo." In *Standard Edition,* Vol. 13, London, Hogarth Press, 1955, pp. 1-161.
16. ———. "Moral Responsibility for the Content of Dreams." In *Standard Edition,* Vol. 19, London, Hogarth Press, 1961, pp. 131-134.
17. Grinstein, A. *The Index of Psychoanalytic Writings.* Vol. 5, New York, Int. Univ. Press, 1960.
18. Handy, E. S. C., Pukui, M.K., and Livermore, K. "Outline of Hawaiian Physical Therapeutics," B. P. Bishop Museum Bull. 26, 1934.
19. Herodotus, *The Persian Wars.* New York, Random House, 1947.
20. Howitt, A. *The Native Tribes of South-East Australia.* London, Macmillan and Co., Ltd. 1904.
21. Lorenz, K. *Man Meets Dog.* London, Methuen, 1954.
22. Lowie, R. "The Family as a Social Unit." Papers of the Michigan Academy of Science, Arts and Letters, Vol. 18, 1933, pp. 53-69.
23. "Multatuli." (Edward Douwes Dekker) *Max Havelaar.* Edinburgh, Edmonston and Douglas, 1868.
24. Ploss, H., Bartels, M., and Bartels, P. *Das Weib in der Natur- und Volkerkunde.* Berlin, Neufeld and Henius, 1927.
25. Pukui, M. "Hawaiian Beliefs and Customs During Birth, Infancy and Childhood." B. P. Bishop Museum Occasional Papers, Vol. 16, 1942.
26. Róheim, G. "Psychoanalysis of Primitive Cultural Types." Int. J. Psa., Vol. 13, 1932, pp. 1-224.
27. ———. *Psychoanalysis and Anthropology; Culture, Personality and the Unconscious.* New York, Int. Univ. Press, 1950.
28. ———. "Hungarian Shamanism." In Róheim, G., *Psychoanalysis and the Social Sciences.* Vol. 3, New York, Int. Univ. Press, 1951, pp. 131-169.
29. Rosenberg, S. *Reistochten naar de Geelvinkbaai op Nieuw Guinea 1869-1870.* The Hague, 1875.
30. Spitz, R. "Fruhkindliches Erleben und Erwachsenenkultur bei den Primitiven." Imago, Vol. 21, 1935, pp. 367-387.
31. ———. "Hospitalism: An Inquiry into the Genesis of Psychiatric Condition in Early Childhood." In *Psychoanalytic Study of the Child,* New York, Int. Univ. Press, Vol. 1, 1945, pp. 53-74.
32. ———. "Anaclitic Depression." In *Psychoanalytic Study of the Child.* New York, Int. Univ. Press, Vol. 2, 1945, pp. 313-342.
33. Teicher, M. I. "Windigo Psychosis," Proceedings of the 1960 Annual Spring Meeting of the American Ethnological Society. Seattle, Washington, 1960.
34. Velton, C. *Sitten und Gebrauche der Suaheli, nebst Einem Anhang uber Rechtsgewohnheiten der Suaheli.* Gottingen, Vandenhoeck, 1903.
35. Veniaminov, I. "Kapinski ob ostrovakh Unalashkinskago otedela." (Notes on the Islands of the Unalaska District). St. Petersburg, 1840.

Poste Restante
Bureau 115
Paris, France

Discussant

Alfred Coodley, M.D.

Los Angeles, California

Dr. Devereux seeks to demonstrate that primary parental cannibalistic impulses arise de nouveau in adult life and that psychoanalysts by and large have a major resistance to accepting this concept.

He pursues his thesis with intensity and has corralled evidence from anthropology, animal psychology, and even from Charlie Chaplin movies to establish his premise. In doing so he cuts a wide swath through the psychoanalytic community, leaving Melanie Klein among others, lying in its wake while he assures us that analysts have been guilty of protesting too much in denying what is so obvious to Dr. Devereux.

One is tempted to feel Dr. Devereux is guilty of post hoc, ergo propter hoc reasoning in his conclusion from such salient facts as the greater incidence of parent-child cannibalism as compared to child-parent cannibalism. This seemingly becomes one of the critical proofs for his formulation.

Expressions such as, "I could eat you up," are focused upon as revealing the true core of primary adult aggressive cannibalistic impulses. Devereux resorts to calling upon the final authority of Sigmund Freud to substantiate the, "avoidance of painful conflict with facts." He points out, for example, that, "piglets moreover do not in fact eat their mother nor do they apparently try to do so." One could counter with the observation by Boehm that animal crackers, loved by children, are significant remnants of early cannibalistic fantasies.

Devereux seems to attribute primarily malignant motives to adults as he describes the, "nightmarish and revengeful quality they impute to the genuine oral cravings of children." The latter are apparently viewed as benign innocent angels devoid of any cannibalistic urges though possessing oral sadistic impulses.

Analysis of patients with depression and addiction have shown that the sadistic incorporative fantasies of eating persons or parts of persons were not of a later development but were operative during the oral phase.

In essence, Dr. Devereux struggles mightily to make his point (and most certainly it is an absorbing idea worth examining), but one central core question remains unanswered or even unasked. Where does one find any explanation—psychological, physiological, or epistemological—in his paper to account for the presence of cannibalistic impulses *arising in adulthood*? Rather, he devotes most of the paper to proving that infantile cannibalism is a reaction to adult cannibalism. In fact, at no time is there any mention of the possibility that long-repressed instinctual impulses may reappear in adult life.

Devereux's iconoclastic approach to current psychoanalytic thought in this specific area or any other for that matter is perfectly justified if he provides us with a reasonable, logical, and theoretically sound substitute. Such a substitute is missing.

Discussant

Irene M. Josselyn, M.D.

Phoenix, Arizona

Dr. Devereux raises the interesting question of why we do not recognize the cannibalism of adults as such as a separate psychological entity. I suggest that the "cannibalism" of adults of our culture is unique only in the sense that it is a normal maturation of an infantile state. There is a tendency to respond to behavior in an adult as if that which is mature is the result of abandonment of the infantile core of the personality, rather than the manifestation of maturation of that core.

Maturity is then seen in the limited way the peak of a mountain is seen when its base is obscured by clouds. The concept of sublimation has fostered this approach. In spite of the fog, however, the base of the mountain remains the base for its peak.

As we examine the peak, we may falsely identify the base of it unless we trace carefully the contour of its structure. As Dr. Devereux has stressed, the visible psychological peak of adult "cannibalism" may not have as its primary base the oral aggressive impulses of infancy.

Our understanding of the first year of life remains speculative. The concept of the symbiotic relationship between infant and mother would, within our present knowledge, seem to describe most clearly the early state of the infant-mother relationship. The mother is aware of her separateness from the infant but feels herself emotionally to be, and responds as if she were, one with him.

From the standpoint of the mother the symbiotic relationship between the infant and the mother brings out clearly that the mother has never destroyed the bridge, but is able, under stimulus of motherhood, to dispel the fog that has hidden it. She holds her infant in her psychological uterus, until the infant is ready for psychological birth as a self. This early oneness with the infant has been described by others as regression on the part of the mother; is it not rather a reactivation of a capacity that has remained dormant until needed? If the mother is able to allow psychological birth and still retain her arc of the bridge between herself and the child, she remains empathetic to the child, and what was an infant-mother symbiotic relationship becomes a child-mother, more mature symbiosis.

If there is any validity to the concept of maturation of the infantile pre-psyche and psyche, a capacity for a mature symbiotic relationship would be not only the basis of deeply meaningful relationships between mother and child, between marital partners, and friends but also the basis for empathy with others. Maturation of the infantile symbiosis is manifested by a capacity to feel as one with another and yet retain an awareness of separateness.

Paralleling the early maturational phase of the symbiotic relationship is the change in the nature of the oral drive, with oral aggressiveness becoming manifest. As biting, instead of sucking becomes the mode of intake of food, the infant becomes aware that biting may be destructive. The implication that biting may have for the relief of the sore gums over the erupting teeth cannot be ignored either; biting becomes a means of relieving tension. Loud voices "taken in" by the ears become associated with punishment or an alarm signal. Objects "taken in" by the eyes become pleasant or fear-arousing. Thus in many ways stimuli that previously brought a reflex response now have vague, affective meanings of pleasure or displeasure. The bridge between the own self and the object becomes not only a way to maintain a oneness, but also a pathway for threats of danger and means of being dangerous.

Destructive responses that are fused with the maturing symbiotic state remain, to greater or lesser degree, an integral part of the maturation of the latter. Thus, perhaps the mother who says to her small child, "I could eat you up" is expressing a deeply repressed wish to destroy. Is not possibly the more overwhelming impulse in many such remarks to eat the child up so that the child will again become a physical part of her as he was earlier?

In my experience it is not unusual for a

child to indicate the anxiety he experiences from this parental expression. In some cases exploration has revealed that the child did not fear physical damage, but rather the loss of the sense of self, a return, forced by the mother, to the immature, undifferentiated state of infantile symbiosis. The "smothering" mother, seen frequently in the relationship of a mother to an asthmatic child often seems to be striving in her smothering to make the child one with her as he was as an infant.

Thus, I would raise the question whether the uniqueness of adult "cannibalism" is indicative basically not of reactivation in the adult of infantile oral aggressive impulses, but rather the maturation of the symbiotic relationship, contaminated to a greater or lesser degree by the developmental vicissitudes of other psychological components, particularly those of destructive nature.

When, under conditions of starvation the infant is killed to feed the other members of the family, the mother *may* symbolically be giving a part of herself that, under those circumstances, since it is an unproductive part of herself, is wisest to give. Is it also possible that among primitive tribes the sacrifice of an infant to a god is a recognition of the supreme parent's reluctance to give up a part of himself —one of his young children? He is appeased if the infant is returned to him to be consumed, and thus become again a part of him. In other words, primary "cannibalism" is not destructively motivated; it becomes destructively motivated when contaminated by other factors. The dog eats its puppy if a distortion has occurred as a result of the cord being cut by others; the mother becomes destructively cannibalistic if one need becomes too contaminated by other needs.

Discussant

Rudolf Ekstein, PH.D.

Los Angeles, California

Upon my first reading of Devereux's stimulating paper, I was tempted to agree with his forceful points regarding parental cannibalism. I did not need the distance device of anthropological evidence but simply reminded myself of all the "devouring" parents I had come to see in work with children, particularly psychotic children and those suffering from borderline conditions. I enjoyed vicariously and temporarily the frequent regression (in the service of the professional ego) of child analysts who blame parents for the difficulties of their child patients. But after I felt almost completely devoured by Devereux's insistence, I started to reflect like Jonah in the stomach of the whale; I began to think as to how I could get out of the whale and do a bit of counter-cannibalistic discussing.

I recalled with pleasure another paper of Devereux's in which he explained the Oedipus complex as a counter-homicidal act in defense against the wish of Laius to murder helpless baby Oedipus. I imagined King Laius consulting a Freudian analyst. He would have gotten him then to discover the Laius complex instead of the Oedipus complex whereas Devereux would have blamed the father of Laius as the one who instilled in Laius murderous wishes. Devereux struggles with the issue as to which came first, the chicken or the egg, when he thinks that he can "present data demonstrating that the cannibalistic impulses of parents underlie a psychic structure which *originates* in adulthood," (italics mine). He might as well say that *The Three Contributions to a Theory of Sex* are but a projection of adult love life into the innocent mind of the child. He would not be the first one to claim that nor would he be the last one if he cares to think that way. I know he does not. To suggest that an adult state of mind originates in adulthood is to maintain an arbitrary dividing line in development and to suggest that everything that went on before is irrelevant. All oral aggressive impulses of children or babies can be characterized as incorporating, destructive, expulsive, etc., and thus can be seen as the precursors of later developments such as adult cannibalism, frequently reawakened and reinforced (and there indeed Devereux is correct) at the time of childbirth and by the challenge of a new and anxiety-arousing parental function.

I believe that Devereux searches for blame rather than for cause, over-stresses adult behavior, and under-stresses the primitive, incorporative thinking of children as well as the functions of early mechanisms of introjection and incorporation, etc. He makes the same mistakes as the Kleinians, except his is the counter-mistake: they believe the content of early and primary process-oriented thinking to be explanatory, while he believes that the fantasy or the thought of the adult, frequently on a quasi-secondary process level, is explanatory. Cui bono? His is a technical "scotoma" in as much as his stress—while irrelevant for etiology, (what one assumes to be the cause is arbitrary)—would change analytic technique. I suspect he wants to be culture-bound rather than stressing analytic work in terms of the revival of the infantile neurosis through the transference neurosis.

I think of the case of a vegetarian father who, when in anger, bit his own children. Were he to be analyzed successfully and cured of his paternal cannibalism, he would trace it back to early oral strivings he never mastered; he would blame his parents for not having given him enough help, for having identified himself with their wish of swallowing him up; then he would accuse his analyst, and he would make biting, chewing remarks; he would swallow and bite interpretations like he bit the milk-giving or milk-withholding breast. Finally, he would discover that he became what he was now through struggling against that which he was as a child and as an infant. At first he was oral aggressive, incorporating and suffering as a baby from *undifferentiated cannibalism*—eating himself and mother simultaneously without capacity for discrimination. Later he developed an unsuccessful vegetarian character and after analysis "cured" him, he may well have become a steak eater and may have restricted himself to biting remarks about scotomatas of others. But then, neither Dr. Devereux nor I are vegetarians although we like biting discussions as well as stretching points.

Discussant

Konrad Lorenz, M.D., PH.D.

Frankfurt, Germany

Received as *The Forum* went to press

I am afraid Dr. Devereux misquoted me: that bitch did not devour her foster child but finally reared it successfully. (The female that did devour her baby was a leopard.) I do not believe that the specifically human tendencies to cannibalism, for which there seems to be ample psychoanalytical evidence, have anything to do with the occasional eating of young mammals by their parents.

An omnivorous animal will eat practically any creature that is palatable and small enough to be killed. It is not the eating of the baby but the inhibition to do so which needs an explanation. Indeed this inhibition is very easily destroyed by abnormal circumstances or by damage to the parent animal's health. So I think that it is rather misleading to apply the term of cannibalism to the eating of conspecifics in animals at all.

On the whole, "cannibalism" is quite rare among higher vertebrates. Fish, which do not perform any sort of parental care and which always produce large numbers of progeny, are about the only vertebrates I know that will eat babies of their own kind uninhibitedly. As practically all fish will eat small fishes, it does not matter if their own species is among those trying to devour the young, therefore no selection pressure is brought to bear on the development of mechanisms inhibiting "cannibalism."

Author's Response

George Devereux, PH.D.

Paris, France

Dr. Josselyn, in a few extremely condensed and intricately wrought paragraphs, presents the substance of what I hope will eventually be published as a major original paper. She starts from a different set of facts, reasons along different lines and reaches conclusions which, in my estimate, are fully compatible with mine and complement them in important ways. Such convergent discussions are a basic procedure in all sciences and especially necessary in psychoanalysis which deals with overdetermined phenomena. I am grateful to her for having given me a fair hearing and for having used my paper in the manner in which I hoped it would be used.

Drs. Coodley and Ekstein adopt in their discussion a tone whose appropriateness for a scientific debate the reader may judge for himself. I do not propose to follow their example.

Underlying my argumentation is Freud's explicit statement that the instincts become monstrous only as a result of repression. This permits us to visualize the infant as a hungry wolf; we may *not* visualize him as a psychotic, ghoulish werewolf. He enjoys biting the nipple but does not know and does not care about its being *human* flesh. His actions do not imply that he dreams in the cradle of feasting on corpses at Dracula's wedding with a vampire. Drs. Coodley and Ekstein argue about as follows: Crawling is instinctual and matures into walking, running and (sometimes) into winning an Olympic race; this "proves" that the infant, in crawling, dreams of Olympic victories. Because I disagree with this—strictly culturalist!—conclusion, I am *said* to disagree also with the premise, which I would not dream of doing.

Both allege that, because I refuse to view the infant as a rabid werewolf, I therefore necessarily view him as a cherub. I have shown in my book, *Therapeutic Education*, that both these conceptions of the infant are self-serving adult fantasies.

Both agree that I am a heretic: Dr. Coodley, *because* I disagree with Melanie Klein, Dr. Ekstein *even though* I disagree with Melanie Klein. The discussants' notions of what constitutes "orthodoxy" do not seem to overlap. Dr. Coodley blames me for demolishing a theory without offering a substitute. That substitute was provided long ago by Freud. Dr. Coodley's statement that the analysis of depressives and alcoholics *proves* that cannibalistic fantasies go back to the oral period, fails to differentiate between facts on the one hand and certain analysts' inherently unprovable reconstructions and certain patients' retroactive fantasies on the other hand. As Dr. Josselyn rightly observes: "Our understanding of the first year of life remains speculative." I simply object to *inherently unprovable* extreme speculations.

The Boehm argument, viewed realistically, only proves my point: Children are *taught* that crackers represent animals; they are *taught* that it is *therefore* "fun" to eat them. That is precisely my point, and the failure to grasp this makes Drs. Coodley's and Ekstein's allegation that I grapple with hen-and-egg problems otiose.

I cannot begin to refute all the factual misstatements and views erroneously imputed to me by Dr. Ekstein: His misstatement of what my Laius paper is about; what I would say to Laius in analysis; the inference that I consider the "Three Contributions" an adult projection, etc. He states that an adoption of my views would modify psychoanalytic technique; he does not say why; moreover, he is wrong. He implies that I am a culturalist; he should know that I have always opposed the culturalist fallacy.

The fact seems to be that Drs. Coodley and Ekstein do not condemn what I *did* in fact say, but only what they would *wish* I had said in order to justify their tone and their cries of "heresy."

I believe my basic arguments to be simple and precise enough to require no further clarification. I will add one brief example to my central argument that, in order to be a cannibal, one must be able to differentiate between human and non-human flesh, just as, in order to be a vegetarian, one must be able to differentiate between meat and vegetables. Thyestes, deceived by Atreus into eating the flesh of his children, can be called a "cannibal" only in the crudest descriptive sense. Seen psychoanalytically, he simply ate "meat" for dinner. And if it be speciously argued that he knew unconsciously that it was human flesh, this means that his unconscious awareness presupposed a conscious awareness of the difference between meat and human flesh.

These are the key points of my argumentation and these points Drs. Coodley and Ekstein signally failed to grapple with and to refute. Their supercilious sarcasms, their shouts of "heresy" and their insistence on imputing to me views I do not hold, leave my arguments intact and that is all that matters in a scientific context.

Freud as a Psychoanalytic Consultant: From Some Unknown Letters to Edoardo Weiss[1]

Edited by
Martin Grotjahn, M.D.
Beverly Hills, California

Introduction: Edoardo Weiss, Freud's Pioneer in Italy

Edoardo Weiss was born in Trieste on September 21, 1889. Weiss showed early an interest in the natural sciences and in his high school days already decided to study medicine, with a view to specializing in psychiatry. His first reading, in 1905, of Freud's "Die Traumdeutung," and "Der Wahn und die Träume in W. Jensen's Gradiva," made a deep and lasting impression on him.

In 1908 he enrolled at the medical school of the University of Vienna. In spite of his awareness of the hostility among the leading professors toward Sigmund Freud's teachings, Weiss in early October 1908, visited Freud, who was then 52 years old, in order to ask his advice on how he could be trained in psychoanalysis. In his interview Freud inquired about Weiss' background and personal life. At this time, Freud was advising everyone intending to become a psychoanalyst to undergo a personal analysis, although until then not all of his few early followers had been analyzed. Therefore, he suggested Paul Federn, who had joined Freud's group in 1902, as the most appropriate analyst for Weiss. The association with Federn proved to be of decisive influence and significance for Weiss. The analysis itself lasted about eighteen months, and developed into a life-long friendship.

His training in general medicine lasted six years, and he specialized in neurology and psychiatry, which were then closely intertwined. Concurrently Weiss attended Freud's lectures, in addition to his regular course of medical studies. His teachers included such eminent figures as Frankl-Hochwart, Obersteiner, Marburg and Wagner-Jauregg. In 1913 Weiss became a member of the Vienna Psychoanalytic Society, presided over by Freud and attended all the Wednesday evening meetings.

At one of these meetings Freud presented for the first time his anthropological interpretation of totem and taboo, which later formed the basis of his classical work.

After the meetings Weiss would join a group of analysts—Paul Federn, Otto Rank, Hanns Sachs, T. K. Friedjung, Victor Tausk and others—at the Café Bauer. Freud was always present at these gatherings, and it was here that he spoke of matters rarely touched upon at the Society meetings. For instance, once he expressed his conviction of the existence of telepathic phenomena, adding, however, that he could not make this public, since psychoanalysis was already under fire on so many other counts. At this point Tausk remarked that believers in telepathy might accuse him of telepathically communicating to his patients the complexes he ascribed to them. This appealed to Freud's sense of humor, and he laughed heartily. Not long afterwards he published a short paper on telepathy, which was characterized by great caution and tentative formulations; years later he discussed the subject more extensively in his, "Neue Folge der Vorlesungen zur Einführung in die Psychoanalyse."

When the first World War broke out Weiss was called into the Austrian army, where he served as a medical officer. After the war he settled once more in Trieste and became asso-

[1]Published with the agreement of Edoardo Weiss, M.D., Chicago, Ill., and the Sigmund Freud Copyright, Ltd., London, Managing Director, Ernest Freud.

ciated with the psychiatric hospital there, besides starting his private practice. At this time he would travel to Vienna about once a year to consult about his patients with Freud. Between visits the two men corresponded about case material.

These "Letters of Consultation" are perhaps the only ones of their kind. Only occasional remarks in the published works of Theodor Reik hint at similar consultations. In these letters, Freud gives advice in matters of diagnosis, analytic technique, prognosis and other details. Freud gives advice, discusses questions, talks about his experience; he encourages, warns, interprets and frankly evaluates. He speaks about therapeutic ambition; recommends the use of predictions; he advises interruptions of analysis, and when to talk with parents; he mentions indications and counter-indications of what analysis can do and be expected to do. He discusses some worthwhile —and not so worthwhile—patients. He agrees to see Dr. Weiss and his patients in consultations, lets both come to Vienna for a personal interview, but warns this must not only be the wish of the Doctor, but also of the patient. It shows us Freud in the light of a senior friend and consultant.

Edoardo Weiss continued his pioneer work for psychoanalysis in Italy, by translating some of Freud's works. These included "Vorlesungen zur Einführung in die Psychoanalyse," "Totem und Tabu," and later, the "Neue Folge der Vorlesungen zur Einführung in die Psychoanalyse." A series of lectures which Weiss gave at the invitation of the Trieste Medical Association was published by Hoepli, Milan, in 1931 *(Elementi di Psicoanalisi)*. Freud himself wrote the introduction to this book.

In many of his letters Freud speaks with affection and recognition to his colleague, thirty-three years his junior. Weiss is Freud's representative in Italy, his most active and loyal worker, the tough and most enduring pioneer, who needs and receives encouragement, direcrection, advice, praise and recognition over the many years of letter writing. Technical, theoretical, organizational questions are asked and answered, warnings are given about moving medical practice, possible immigration, world politics, and repeatedly the question of psychology and occultism is taken up and extreme discretion advised by anyone leading in the psychoanalytic movement—an advice which Weiss followed through all his life.

In 1931 Weiss moved to Rome, where, within the next year, he founded the Italian Psychoanalytic Society and its journal, the "Rivista Italiana di Psicoanalisi." During the following years his publications included the article on psychoanalysis in the *Enciclopedia Italiana* and *Agorafobia e Isterismo d'angoscia* (Rome: Paolo Cremonese, 1936).

Weiss' last visit to Freud took place in 1937. It was on this occasion that Freud expressed his horror at the political prospects for the near future. He was glad to be old. When Weiss mentioned the young and their fears for the future, Freud replied: "You are right: only the young, and not the old, have cause to fear what is coming."

Weiss had always been an opponent of fascism, and from 1930 he experienced increasing difficulties from an ecclesiastic psychiatrist. In 1933 the "Rivista Italiana di Psicoanalisi" was ordered to suspend publication. When the fascist government, under the pressure of the Nazis, introduced racist measures, Weiss emigrated to the United States (January 1939). He first went to Topeka, Kansas, where he worked at the Menninger Clinic. From there he moved to Chicago (in 1940), where he was associated with the group of Franz Alexander. He has lectured at psychiatric hospitals and at universities, and from 1959 to 1961 he was visiting professor in the Department of Psychiatry at Marquette University, Milwaukee. He lives and has his private practice in Chicago.

Weiss has introduced many new concepts in psychoanalysis. In 1922 he published his studies on the psychogenic nature of bronchial asthma. Methods, interpretations and results of these studies were used as models for the psychosomatic studies at the Chicago Institute for Psychoanalysis many years later.

Another clinical report influenced the course of psychoanalytic research greatly. Weiss studied development and maturation of normal heterosexual love. He found that men regularly and normally project their own feminine components and unconscious trends upon the woman and love it there. Women in turn project their masculine trends upon their husbands and love it in their men. In later years, Melanie Klein independently developed this concept into her term of: "projective identification."

His most important concepts may be summarized as follows:

1. On paranoia.—Paranoic patients sense as real the contents of their delusions and hallucinations. Weiss found that the "feeling tone" with which they perceive such contents is different from that with which they perceive the real, external world. This knowledge can be utilized for therapeutic purposes.

2. "Psychic presence"—is a concept introduced by Weiss. It refers to the powerful mental images of other persons that determine some features of our conscience.

3. The notion of the "ego passage" of persons with whom one identifies one's self.—This explains different features of psychotic states.

4. When dealing with Freud's related theories about the death instinct Weiss differentiated between death instinct and aggression.

Elaborating on Federn's phenomenological approach to the study of the ego and the psychoses, which diverged from Freud's teaching, Weiss has contributed to the understanding of the process of identification, particularly of the vicissitudes of internalized representations of other persons as they are manifested in various psychotic disorders. Weiss has also described the phenomena of the postclimactic libidinal efflux and the postclimactic depression. He remained in close contact with Federn until the latter's death in 1951. In accordance with a request in Federn's will, Weiss edited a collection of his writings under the title *Ego Psychology and the Psychoses*. (New York; Basic Books, 1952).

In 1966 Edoardo Weiss published once more in detail, a personal and scientific description of Paul Federn as a man and as a scientist. This profile of his great teacher was published as a chapter in *Psychoanalytic Pioneers*, (editors: Franz Alexander, Samuel Eisenstein and Martin Grotjahn. New York, Basic Books, 1966).

Weiss' other publications include *Principles of Psychoanalysis* (New York: Grune and Stratton, 1950), *The Structure and Dynamics of the Human Mind* (New York: Grune and Stratton, 1954), *Agoraphobia in the Light of Ego Psychology* (New York: Grune and Stratton, 1964), as well as some one hundred papers on psychoanalysis in various scientific journals.

Weiss' wife, Vanda, obtained her M.D. in Vienna and now practices psychotherapy. He has two sons and adopted a daughter, the only survivor of his wife's brother's family.

Prof. Dr. Freud

28. May 22
Wien IX., Berggasse 19

Lieber Herr Doktor

Busy with many things I can send you only now, on this Sunday, the requested opinion about your two impotent ones. Not an easy task! Because you know so much yourself I cannot easily find out where you might have overlooked something.

The first [patient] . . . is obviously a worthwhile human being, he deserves to be treated more and might have a good chance. It seems that he has not opened up to you completely and as long as this is not the case one does not get the material for a reliable judgment. However, six months are not a long time and there is still hope. Perhaps you show him too much impatience and therapeutic ambition, instead of concentrating only on his personal conquest.

Therefore, I believe: no setting of a termination date. The difficulty lies obviously in his relationship to men (the father, with whom he cannot identify you easily). In regard to masturbation only hold it up to him that he would block definitely his normal way to woman, and that abstinence in spite of occasional breakthroughs would be worth his while analytically. It is not easy to guess about the other motives which sustain his impotency. Perhaps even the woman was a father substitute for him, and satisfied his feminine [trends][2] with her masculinity.

Regret and atonement and that means guilt feelings as motive for a fixed frustration by the woman can hardly be doubted. I do not favor substitution through prostitution. It is better to let him practice total abstinence until he interrupts it temporarily by masturbation. He will cause by it no permanent damage to his potency. This is proven by his behavior in his marriage. No attempt to burden him with our emancipated opinions about sexual intercourse. I am not sure that I could offer anything to you with these remarks. The problem is essentially a technical one.

The second case . . . is obviously a scoundrel who is not worth your trouble. Our analytic art fails with such people. Also our insight cannot yet look through their dominant dynamic relations. I do not answer him directly [since I] assume that you will send him away.

Many thanks for the second volume of the translation. I hope it will soon be worthwhile for you as the interest now has strengthened so much in France and Spain.

Would you have each of the two patients send 100 lire to. . . .

With cordial greeting,

Yours, Freud

Prof. Dr. Freud

11 June 1922
Wien IX, Berggasse 19

Lieber Herr Doktor

Nothing to take so seriously! An analyst must be prepared for such small accidents, especially in a hostile environment. Consider furthermore that, regretfully, only a few patients are worth the trouble we spend on them, so that we are not allowed to have a therapeutic attitude but we must be glad to have learned something in every case. A patient, who tells about his analysis everywhere, by the way, aims from the beginning to expose analysis.

Of course I agree that you complete the interrupted translation of T. u T.[3] and certainly time will be found in Berlin or Vienna for a talk with you. Furthermore the failure of my referrals until now will not keep me from sending to you everything which belongs in your district.

With cordial greeting,

Yours, Freud

Prof. Dr. Freud

4 March 23
Wien IX, Berggasse 19

Lieber Herr Doktor

I believe that your patient shall not give in to the repetition-compulsion and [should] continue the treatment. His dream shows that in his case it is jealousy which he has shoved from the mother onto you; he wants to be the

---

[2] [Words enclosed in brackets are the translator's addition.]

[3] *Totem and Taboo.*

only one. Since he cannot be that with you either, he wants to extort your love by leaving you according to [his] old pattern. Naturally he lives through his unconscious complexes by projecting them into the transference; [he] uses his feminine attitude toward his father as resistance. I imagine that he, neglected by the mother, looked for a while for closeness with the father, this too without success.

He probably married out of unconscious guilt feeling, and also in order to have some reason to reproach you, and with that he can prove that you do not like him.

This chapter of the treatment, guilt feeling and struggle against the feminine attitude toward the father, is naturally the most difficult and most important one. A lasting success is possible only after the accomplishment of this work. Don't leave him to the demon!

With cordial greeting,

Yours, Freud

Prof. Dr. Freud

2 April 23
Wien IX, Berggasse 19

Lieber Herr Doktor

I regret that answering your inquiry has been postponed due to the Easter holidays. Fortunately I see that you are completely equal to the situation.

Your opinion is certainly right. In the explanation you only omit the search for vengeance as the driving motive. How the situation will work out cannot be predicted safely. It is to be hoped that you will keep the upper hand. Frequently one finds himself too weak when things have developed that far. The only protection in such cases is the well-timed prediction and the announcement of a turn to a disappointment, so that one may later quietly remind [the patient] that one had known it all along. Then one can wait unfalteringly until the patient has stormed enough ["sich ausgetobt hat"]. If one has missed the prediction then one has to toil really hard later and one gets into a disadvantageous position because the confession of one's own interest rekindles the need for revenge in the patient.

Beside the need for revenge one may assume an intense guilt feeling in the patient who acts out and one can talk about that too. Altogether it is not an easy experience. It is a therapeutic *bis aller* that the patient gets himself well by cussing [schimpfen] physician and analysis and this too one must mention to him.

With cordial wishes also for the outcome of this case,

Yours, Freud

Prof. Dr. Freud

12 February 24
Wien IX, Berggasse 19

Lieber Herr Doktor

On the 4th of February I received a long registered letter from . . . , which leaves no doubt about the diagnosis "querulierende Paranoia." I quote only the one remark, that the book "The Ego and The Id" is based on observations of his case. Otherwise the letter is quite impertinent, aggressive and without practical point. I believe it is necessary to inform you about this step of your former patient, but I hope that you will not allow the whole thing to affect you. Perhaps one should be warned from this experience never to publish a patient['s case] and never to request his cooperation before the treatment is terminated.

By the way, there remains the question whether this attitude of the patient is a passing one and is his way of separating himself from his physician, in which case the whole thing did not mean much. Many a patient has cursed his way to health ["es haben sich schon manche Patienten gesundgeschimpft"]. Or, you have had the bad luck to run into a latent paranoia and through the cure of his neurosis you may have freed the way for a more serious sickness. That happens to each one of us occasionally and there is no protection against it.

With cordial greeting,

Yours, Freud

Prof. Dr. Freud

9 February 1934
Wien IX, Berggasse 19

Lieber Herr Doktor

It is very difficult to assume the responsibility in such a case. Therefore, I must refuse emphatically to advise you and will tell you only how the case appears to me and what I would do according to my experience. Without obliging you to anything.

These patients are very dangerous, in proportion to their intelligence, since they do not use their intelligence to control their passions, but in order to indulge them. In the case of Miss . . . [there] are furthermore two other signs of danger. To begin with, she knows exactly what special importance her recovery has for you and then she once obtained a great concession from you. I mean, you should not have allowed her to exchange the prescribed position for one more pleasant to her.

The cure of such a severe hysteria has been rarely accomplished successfully by me without loss and retreat ["ohne Einbusse und Abzug"]. As a rule the treatment had to be abandoned, [the patient] often apparently in bad condition and after the patient of this kind had satisfied her resistance and her hostile transference she permitted herself to draw some possible advantage from the treatment and accomplished—belatedly and spontaneously—a far reaching improvement. Naturally no complete solution. A part was retained and in any case the physician was cheated of his triumph. With very understanding parents one can prepare for such outcome but one does not meet them frequently. One could point to similar delayed reaction, for instance after taking the health-resort treatment in Bad Gastein.

From the dreams of your patient is to be concluded that she will run away from you and I believe that she will do that. Anticipating that, I would propose in advance an interruption of perhaps six months with the readiness to see her then again in case she wants it and still needs it. Do not promise her recovery during this interruption. However, hint at this possibility to the parents who should not say anything to her about it.

One cannot speak of mistakes in your case, only of variations of requirements ["nur um Abänderung der Anforderungen"].

With cordial greeting,

Yours, Freud

P.S. The patient, with whom you were here to see me will probably not give in as long as she can guess how much her recovery means to you.

PROF. Dr FREUD

WIEN IX., BERGGASSE 19

28. 1. 22

Lieber Herr Doktor

Durch vielerlei in Anspruch genommen, gehe ich erst an diesem Sonntag daran, Ihnen die gewünschten Aufklärungen über Ihre beiden Jugendlichen zu schreiben. Keine leichte Aufgabe! Da Sie selbst soviel wissen, kann ich nicht leicht herausfinden, wo Sie etwas übersehen haben könnten.

Der erste, Johann L., ist offenbar ein wertvoller Mensch, verdient noch weiter behandelt zu werden u hat wohl auf gute Chancen. Er scheint sich Ihnen noch nicht völlig erschlossen zu haben, u so lange dies nicht geschehen, bekommt man nur ungenügendes Material. [illegible] Monate noch keine [illegible] erzielt [illegible] u es kann noch [illegible] lange dauern [illegible] für ihn [illegible] anstatt sich nur auf [illegible] [illegible] Erinnerungen [illegible] Persönlichkeit [illegible] Also ich meine [illegible] offenbar in seinem Verhältnis zum [illegible] Vater, [illegible] kann [illegible] [illegible] identifizieren [illegible] [illegible] ihm immer vor, dass der [illegible] stellen [illegible] durch [illegible] sich [illegible] verlangen würde, und dass [illegible] trotz ihrer [illegible] [illegible] durch [illegible] analytisch der [illegible] [illegible] [illegible] [illegible] Motiven [illegible] [illegible] ist nicht leicht, [illegible]

ergaben. Vielleicht war auch ihr [illegible] Charakter-
satz für ihn, der mit ihren maskulinen Eigen-
schaften seine femininen gestützt. Man
könnte also Schuldgefühl als Motiv der
[illegible]* Verdrängung der Weibes-
[illegible] kaum zu bezweifeln. Den Ersatz durch
Alkoholismus halte ich nicht für günstiger, [illegible]
ihr volle [illegible] leben zu lassen, die
er ja zeitweise durch [illegible] unterdrückt.
[illegible] wird, wäre kein besonderer
Schaden geschehen, das zeigt ja sein Ver-
halten in der Ehe. Keine Absicht ihm
[illegible] fremden Einsichten über den Homo-
erotismus aufzudrängen. Ich bin auch sicher
dass ich [illegible] in dieser Bemerkung etwas
bieten konnte. Das [illegible]
lich ein Wechselspiel. [redacted] ist ein offenbar zweiter Fall [illegible] nicht [illegible]
[illegible] der [illegible]
unserer Analyse. Kunst versagt bei solchen
Leuten auch unsere Einsicht vermag in die
ihnen [illegible] dynamischen Verhält-
nisse noch nicht zu durchschauen. [illegible]
ihm nicht direkt anzunehmen, dass [illegible] weg-
schicken werden. [illegible] Band der
[illegible] für den zweiten [illegible]
[illegible] Ich hoffe, Sie wird [illegible] Frank-
[illegible] Interesse im [illegible]
[illegible] ganzen [illegible]
[illegible] von jedem der beiden [illegible]
wollen Sie [redacted]
[redacted]

Mit herzlichem Gruss
Ihr Freud

PROF. Dr. FREUD

WIEN IX., BERGGASSE 19

11 Juni 1922

Lieber Herr Doktor

Nichts schwer nehmen! Auf solche kleinen
Unfälle muss der Analytiker gefasst
sein, besonders in einer feindlichen
Umgebung. Bedenken Sie auch dass
[illegible] die wenigen Patienten die
[illegible] noch sind die wir auf Sie ver-
Mühe [illegible] so [illegible] gar nicht
[illegible] [illegible] sondern
Charakteristik [illegible] an jedem Fall
froh sein müssen etwas gelernt zu haben
irgend der Abfall von seiner Analyse
[illegible] liegt es übrigens von vornher-
ein [illegible] die Analyse abbrechen
[illegible] darauf an, [illegible]
Natürlich bin ich [illegible] Überzeugung
dass Sie Ihr [illegible] vollenden u. gewiss
von T. u. Berlin oder Wien [illegible] Zeit
[illegible] Aussprache mit Ihnen freuen,
[illegible] in Wiederholung meiner
[illegible] werden [illegible] davon
[illegible] allein [illegible] zu schützen.
[illegible] Ihnen zu
gehört, ja [illegible] Mit herzlichem Gruß

Ihr Freud

PROF. Dr. FREUD

WIEN IX., BERGGASSE 19

4 März 23

Lieber Herr Doktor

Ich glaube, Ihr Patient soll dem Wieder-
holungszwang nicht nachgeben und die [illegible]
fortsetzen. Sein Traum zeigt dass es sich
bei ihm um Ersatzlust handelt, die er
von der Mutter auf die [illegible]
will der [illegible] sein. Da er es auch bei
[illegible] nicht sein kann will er [illegible]
Mutter durch [illegible] [illegible] liebe
[illegible] natürlich [illegible]
erzwingen [illegible] in der [illegible]
[illegible] durch [illegible] also seine
Übertragung [illegible] zum Vater als Wieder-
feminine [illegible] dass er von
stand. [illegible] Mutter [illegible]
der [illegible] Vater [illegible]
lang [illegible] Erfolg
[illegible] auch [illegible] über Schuldge-
die [illegible] [illegible]
fühl [illegible] können [illegible] be-
[illegible] zu [illegible] dass Sie ihn nicht mögen
[illegible] Abschnitt der [illegible] Schuldgefühl
dieser [illegible] gegen die feminine Ein-
[illegible] gegen [illegible] Vater ist natürlich der
[illegible] zum wichtigsten Fundament [illegible]
[illegible] nach der [illegible] dieser [illegible]
[illegible] ihn dem Dämon über-
möglich [illegible]
lassen! Mit herzlichem Gruss

Ihr Freud

3. 4. 23

PROF. DR. FREUD

WIEN IX., BERGGASSE 19

Lieber Herr Doktor

Ich bedauere dass die Veranstalt-
ung [illegible] Antrage durch die
[illegible] verschoben worden
ist. [illegible] Stück habe ich dass
für [illegible] Situation vollkom-
men [illegible] sind.

Die Auffassung ist gewiss die
richtige. [illegible] Erklärung lassen
[illegible] das treibende Motiv
[illegible] die [illegible]
[illegible] ist nicht [illegible] zu sagen
[illegible]
[illegible]
[illegible] so weit
man [illegible]
[illegible]
[illegible] einzige [illegible] in solchen
[illegible]
[illegible]
[illegible] so dass man
[illegible]
[illegible]
und [illegible]
[illegible]
[illegible] hat man [illegible]

-erlage verlässt, so darf man
sich noch [illegible] ordentlich regen,
und damit in eine nachteilige
Position, weil das Eingeständ-
nis des eigenen Interesses
die Wahrscheinlichkeit des [illegible]
entwertet. [illegible] [illegible]
[illegible] der [illegible] [illegible]
man ein solches [illegible]
beim [illegible] der [illegible]
voraussetzen [illegible] kann auf
davon reden im Ganzen
ist es kein leichtes Verhältnis.
in [illegible] für alle
ist es daß die Sache sich doch
[illegible] auf [illegible] zu [illegible]
[illegible] zu [illegible]
muß man ihn erwarten.
Mit herzlichen Wünschen
auch für den Ausgang
dieses Falles

Ihr
Freud

PROF. DR. FREUD WIEN IX., BERGGASSE 19

13. II. 24.

Lieber Herr Doktor,

Am 4. Februar erhielt ich einen langen eingeschriebenen Brief [redacted], der keinen Zweifel über die Diagnose "querulierende Paranoia" lässt. Ich zitiere nur die eine Bemerkung, dass das Buch "Das Ich und das Es" auf Grund der Beobachtung seines Falles entstanden ist. Der Brief ist sonst ziemlich frech, aggressiv und ohne praktische Pointe. Ich halte es für notwendig, Sie von diesem Schritte Ihres früheren Patienten zu verständigen, hoffe aber, Sie werden sich die ganze Angelegenheit nicht sehr nahe gehen lassen. Vielleicht sollte man aus dieser Erfahrung die Warnung ziehen, einen Patienten nicht zu publizieren und ihn zu keiner Mithilfe heranzuziehen, ehe die Kur beendigt ist.

Es fragt sich übrigens noch, ob diese

Einstellung des Patienten eine vorübergehende ist, also seiner Art entspricht, sich vom Arzte zu lösen, in welchem Falle das Ganze nicht viel zu bedeuten hätte. Es haben sich schon manche Patienten gesundgeschimpft. Oder aber Sie haben das Pech gehabt, auf einen latenten Paranoiker zu stossen und durch die Heilung seiner Neurose der schwereren Affektion den Weg frei zu machen. Das passiert jedem von uns gelegentlich und dagegen gibt es keinen Schutz.

Mit herzlichen Grüssen

Ihr Freud

---

der entschwinden kann es sich ja bei Ihnen nicht handeln, nur um Veränderung der Anordnung.

Mit herzlichem Gruß

Ihr Freud

P.S. Die Pat. mit der Sie bei mir waren wird wol nicht nachgeben, solange sie erwarten kann, wieviel Ihnen an ihrer Herstellung gelegen sein muß.

PROF. Dr. FREUD

Lieber Herr Doktor

WIEN, IX. BERGGASSE 19.

9. 2. 1934

Es ist sehr schwer in einem solchen Falle die Verantwortung auf sich zu nehmen. Ich will darum ausdrücklich ablehnen Ihnen zu raten u. will Ihnen nur sagen wie mir der Fall erscheint und was ich an [illegible] Entscheidung thun würde, ohne Sie zu etwas zu verpflichten.

Diese Kranken sind sehr gefährlich, unheimlicher je intelligenter sie sind, da sie ihre Intelligenz nicht dazu gebrauchen ihre Leidenschaften zu beherrschen, sondern sie in deren Dienst stellen. Bei Frl. [redacted] sind noch zwei weitere Erschwerungsmomente, dass sie genau weiss welche besondere Bedeutung ihre Entscheidung für Ihre Person hat und dass sie einmal eine grosse Konzession von Ihnen erreicht hat. Ich meine Sie sollten ihr nicht gestatten [illegible], die vorgeschriebene Position gegen eine ihr angenehmere zu vertauschen. Die Heilung einer so schweren Hysterie ist mir selten ohne [illegible] und Zwang geglückt. Wieder Regelmäßig[illegible]

zu Beobachtung aufgegeben worden, oft in
erschreckend schlimmem Zustand, und
wenn sie die Tat selbst trotz ihrem Wider-
stand [illegible] Übertragung
befriedigt hatte, erlaubten sie sich, der-
selben zugänglichen Vorteil aus der bei-
zu ziehen und brachten nachträglich
und [illegible] eine sehr [illegible]
Beziehung zustande. Natürlich [illegible]
volle [illegible] Kritik [illegible]
behalten und der Arzt jedenfalls
[illegible]
Die sehr verständigen [illegible]
auf dessen Ausgang vorbereiten [illegible]
Die [illegible] nicht [illegible]
dann auf die ähnliche Nachträglich-
keit [illegible] bei [illegible]
zweifel. [illegible]
[illegible]
[illegible]
gehen wird und ich glaube, daß sie
es auch tun wird. Ich würde ihr
zuvor können [illegible] eine Unter-
brechung von etwa 6 Monaten
vorschlagen mit der Bereitwilligkeit
sie dann wieder aufzunehmen, wenn
sie es will und noch braucht. Sie
[illegible]
[illegible] aber den letzten
[illegible] Möglichkeit andeuten, die
ich ihr nicht sagen sollen.

Summaries of Scientific Meetings

Seattle Psychoanalytic Society

Contributing Editor:

Eugene Goforth, M.D.

"Masturbation and Self Esteem"

Annie Reich, M.D.

New York, New York

July 20, 1965 Meeting

On the basis of two clinical examples it was shown that the effects of childhood masturbation may sometimes not only lead to lasting anxiety, guilt feelings and feelings of inferiority but also to those feelings of grandiosity and increased self esteem.

It is the motive of the fantasy and the amount of aggression connected with it that is decisive.

In one case it was shown that the ready gratification of the fantasy led to a later difficulty of the patient in reality adaptation. In fact, this gratification became impossible because the childhood grandiosity was taken over by the superego. The other case demonstrated how the orgastic nature of childhood masturbation developed into lasting feelings of inner magic, license and grandeur which remained untouched by later experiences.

The Motivational Relevance of Hypnosis

Ernest R. Hilgard, PH.D.

Professor of Psychology,

Stanford University

October 12, 1965 Meeting

The study of hypnosis is relevant to the concerns of psychodynamics and of human motivation generally. For one thing, the continuity between what happens within hypnosis and within ordinary life means that what is learned within the special hypnotic situation is also applicable to ordinary experience. A special importance for motivational theory, especially in its ego aspects, is contributed by the way in which hypnosis goes at the heart of the problem of self-control and loss of control to another. Through manipulation of amnesia, dreams, and post-hypnotic behavior many aspects of unconscious motivation are open to direct study in a manner much less cumbersome than that of the standard psychoanalysis.

By careful consideration of the childhood origins of hypnotic susceptibility, contributions can be made by way of hypnosis to a study of parent-child relations and personality development generally. These uses are all independent of the service of hypnosis to psychotherapy. Within psychotherapy hypnosis can be used in relieving pain and anxiety, in reducing phobias, and in altering the self-image.

It is very difficult, within hypnotic therapy, to know what belongs to the hypnosis and what belongs to the therapy, for almost any therapeutic paradigm (including psychoanalysis) can make use of hypnosis as an adjuvant. Illustrations of these points were made from experiments under way in the Laboratory of Hypnosis Research, Department of Psychology, Stanford University, many of which are reported in a recent book.[1]

[1] Hilgard, E. R. *Hypnotic Susceptibility*. New York: Harcourt, Brace and World, Inc., 1965.

The Southern California Psychoanalytic Society

Contributing Editor:
Jerome L. Saperstein, M.D.

"Sigmund Freud on Suicide"

Robert E. Litman, M.D.

November 15, 1965 Meeting

The author aims to abstract from Freud's writings his observations on suicide, and to evaluate their contribution to today's understanding of suicide and suicide prevention.

Freud had considerable clinical experience with suicide patients; there are references to suicidal symptoms in all of his published case histories except that of Little Hans. By 1910 he had described: (1) guilt over death wishes, (2) identification with a suicidal parent, (3) refusal to accept loss of libidinal gratification, (4) an act of revenge, (5) an escape from humiliation, (6) a cry for help, (7) the intimate links between death and sexuality. Sadism and masochism were the deepest roots but had no satisfactory place in the instinctual theory of the time. In "Mourning and Melancholia," Freud states that the ego can kill itself only if it treats itself as an object identified with an originally external hated object.

Dr. Litman believes the associated phenomena of regression, disorganization and ego-splitting deserve even more emphasis than the hostility. Freud made no claim to the final answer to the enigma of suicide. In "The Psychogenesis of a Case of Homosexuality in a Woman," Freud wrote that suicide was multiply determined, including erotic and masochistic factors. Freud came to his death instinct theory to explain masochism (and suicide). Dr. Litman states that Freud believed suicide represented a product of man and his civilization, a consequence of mental trends found in every human being.

Dr. Litman thinks the general features of the human condition described by Freud (death instinct, ego-splitting, civilization) just begin to account for individual suicides. Specific mechanisms involve breaking down of ego defenses and the release of increased destructive instinctual energy. Predisposing factors toward suicide include, (1) disharmonious ego structure, (2) pre-oedipal libidinal fixations, (3) disease of the superego due to cruel or dead parents or inherited traits of destructiveness, (4) libidinal attachment to death, or dead loved ones, (5) vivid erotic fantasies symbolizing death wishes, and (6) self-destructive living patterns.

From his experience as Clinical Director of the Suicide Prevention Center, Dr. Litman believes that the suicidal trend in all of us is tamed and controlled by healthy identifications, defenses, and constructive ways of living. When they break down, we feel helpless and abandoned. Therapy at the Center consists of reinforcement of defenses and renewing hope and love. We have nothing better than psychoanalysis and psychoanalytic psychotherapy to treat the chronic neurotic patterns which may lead to suicide. Brief psychotherapy, group and environmental therapy increase the therapeutic range. Freud's observation on the suicidal potentialities in a symbiotic love relationship has been verified. Dr. Litman is more impressed by the helplessness, dependency and erotic themes than by the relative overemphasis on aggression and guilt. The Center stresses the mother-child pre-oedipal attachment as a reference point in contrast to Freud's usual reference to the Oedipus complex. In the Center the spirit of the group helps supply the constructive energy required to reduce the patient's withdrawal and establish communication.

Discussion:

The formal discussants were Dr. John Lindon and Dr. Norman Tabachnick. Dr. Lindon stated that Dr. Litman had evaluated Freud's contribution to our understanding of suicide in a mature and analytic way. Melanie Klein accepted Freud's death instinct theory and made valuable advances in the study of internal objects, even though the death instinct hypothesis may be questioned. One such advance is the importance of envy which Dr. Lindon found important in some patients with suicidal symptomatology. Another determinant in suicide, Klein believed, is the concern of the patient that his bad feelings may hurt the person he *now* is experiencing as good.

Dr. Tabachnick stated that instinct theory can be overemphasized to the detriment of a more complete understanding of human affairs. Freud thought of suicide in terms of a self-destroying instinct, yet research at the Suicide Prevention Center has indicated multiple motivations and factors in suicide including other than instinctual forces. This line of thinking tends to diminish the significance of the death instinct theory.

Professor J. O. Wisdom considers the main problem yet to be answered: (a) Why does a person commit suicide instead of suffering from self-reproach or masochistic fantasies, and, (b) why does a person commit suicide rather than murder? About the first he suggested that the dynamics of the difference might depend on re-introjecting a projected conflict.

The Continuing Forum

The Continuing Forum is open to all readers so that they may send their reactions, suggestions, criticism and contributions to the topics which are presented in The Psychoanalytic Forum.

To the Editors: Dr. Kubie is most persuasive and from an educationist's point of view there is much to be said for arranging a series of experiences for a learner in such a way that he deals with the least complex problem first and works towards the most complex. However, such a sequence must be tempered by a careful consideration of the motivation and preparedness of the individual learner. So I would question one thesis. The "confrontation" of the "inexperienced resident" with the "psychotic patient" need not of itself be a hindrance to the learning. And an important factor is the extent to which the young resident must assume responsibility for patient care. If there is then a keen interest in psychosis and its treatment, he may be highly motivated, thus greatly facilitating learning—as long as he is not overwhelmed with a service load and responsibility for administering patient care, for which task he is at that point ill-prepared.

Also, his proposal for a "School of Psychological Medicine" is a provocative challenge to all those concerned with psychiatric education. The unfortunate concomitant to this must also be considered: is the college graduate ready to make such a decision concerning his career without continued opportunity for exploration? Perhaps it is indeed time for all of medical education to review its position concerning early choice of and training in specialization areas.

Stephen Abrahamson, PH.D.

(Dr. Abrahamson is Professor of Education and Director of the Division of Research in Medical Education at the University of Southern California School of Medicine.)

To the Editors: I read Dr. Lindon's paper with great interest and have two main reactions: I see the paper as an interesting and stimulating contribution to the psychology of dreams, creativity and psychopathology; also, I am trying to fit this paper in with the physiological research of Kleitman, Dement, and coworkers on sleep and dreaming.

How do we correlate the report from these investigators that on the average we all dream roughly two hours a night with rapid eye movements testifying to the vivid visual imagery of our dreams, and yet most of us remember only fragments or nothing, then occasionally one dream stands out so vividly that it dominates a period of life?

One of Dement's current hypotheses about dream-sleep is that it may be a vestigial remnant of a once vital function. He suggests that "rapid eye movement" (REM) sleep is a way for the fetus and infant to exercise its brain and basic drives, but that REM sleep in adults is an atavistic function, like goose pimples. The specific physiological quality so far discovered to be associated with dreaming (in addition to the rapid eye movements) is a pervasive deep relaxation of the muscles. This is mediated through a special mid-brain mechanism. In light of the recent physiology, Freud's specific illustrations of action dreams ending in muscular action has a special meaning. It means that the REM sleep ends abruptly and is replaced by waking action, that is, the off switch in the mid-brain suddenly switches on. In narcolepsy, by contrast, there is a sudden switch from waking action to the REM sleep state.

Is the most important aspect of this paper the focus on the connection between the dream and the secondary process? I am inclined to accept Lindon's theory that the surgeon had a fairly complete fantasy about pulling out the atheromata but was afraid to take responsibility for the idea, but how does an ambivalently felt idea of this sort descend into the primary process area without being split up and displaced or reversed or disguised in some way? Is there a mid-brain switching point for secondary to primary process that becomes by-passed?

Lastly, the dream example of Dr. V., seems to belong in the category of premonitory dreams rather than literally dream-action. With all of these challenging new problems, no wonder there is a re-awakening of psychoanalytic interest in dream research.

Robert E. Litman, M.D.

Response

Should Dement's hypothesis prove correct, it is beside the point. The unconscious uses dreams for symbolic expression of conflicts in an attempt to solve them. Psychoanalysis of patients with vestigial remnants (such as supernumary nipples, cloaca, etc.) has shown how these remnants are seized upon by the unconscious and used for projection and introjection.

The idea (of the operation) did not undergo the disguises typical of dream work because it was used as day-residue. We do not have the dream's latent meanings and in the dream-action example, one unconscious wish was to have something come to consciousness by-passing responsibility. Dr. Siegel's patient having learned from two years of analysis that he was responsible for his dreams, could not dream of the formula, but instead, "found it."

About the last point, many dreams which have been categorized as premonitory may be seen as examples of dream-action. Perhaps, the anxiety which people feel about premonitory dreams is due to their inner awareness *and experience* with dream-action. I have collected several clinical illustrations for a subsequent paper on dream-action and premonitory dreams and would appreciate examples readers might send.

John A. Lindon, M.D.

The Psychoanalytic

FORUM

Table of Contents Vol. 1, No. 2, 1966

continued

The Forum

Title Psychoanalysts View Conjoint Therapy

Discussants

Moderator Alexander S. Rogawski, M.D.
Clinical Professor and Director, Division of Social and Community Psychiatry, Department of Psychiatry, University of Southern California and a Training Analyst of the Southern California Psychoanalytic Institute. He believes that thorough grounding in psychoanalysis deepens and in turn is deepened by experience and knowledge of various psychiatric settings.

Panelist Saul Brown, M.D.
Associate Clinical Professor of Psychiatry at University of Southern California and on the faculty of the Southern California Psychoanalytic Institute. He is Chief of the Department of Child Psychiatry at Cedars-Sinai Medical Center in Los Angeles. He has done extensive work in family therapy and has published several papers on family structure, dynamics and therapy.

Panelist Martin Grotjahn, M.D.
Clinical Professor of Psychiatry at University of Southern California and a Training Analyst of the Southern California Psychoanalytic Institute. He is the author of *Beyond Laughter*, *Psychoanalysis and the Family Neurosis* and Editor of *Psychoanalytic Pioneers* (together with Franz Alexander and Samuel Eisenstein).

Carl A. Whitaker, M.D.
Professor of Psychiatry, University of Wisconsin and formerly Professor of Psychiatry at Emory University, Atlanta, Georgia. His writings have been in the areas of schizophrenia and multiple therapy; he is currently working in the field of family psychotherapy.

Don D. Jackson, M.D.
Associate Clinical Professor of Psychiatry at Stanford University and Director of the Mental Research Institute, Palo Alto, California. His main interest is in human communication and problems of therapy or research within the broad spectrum of intra-psychic to interpersonal to family and community. With this sort of approach, he feels "life is sort of difficult and seven years of training analysis were insufficient."

Albert J. Solnit, M.D.
Professor of Pediatrics and Psychiatry at the Child Study Center of Yale University, a Training and Supervising Analyst, President of the Western New England Institute for Psychoanalysis, and Chairman of the Child Analysis Committee of the American Psychoanalytic Association. Dr Solnit has had numerous papers published on psychiatric and psychoanalytic problems.

Terry C. Rodgers, M.D.
Associate in Psychiatry, College of Physicians and Surgeons at Columbia University, and a Preceptor in Psychiatry (Adolescent Service) at Mount Sinai Hospital, New York City. His experience has included "conjoint therapy" of families and married couples. A recent paper entitled "A Specific Parameter: Concurrent Psychotherapy of the Spouse of an Analysand by the Same Analyst," appeared in *The International Journal of Psycho-Analysis*.

Psychoanalysts View Conjoint Therapy [1]

Panel:

Alexander S. Rogawski, M.D., *Moderator*

Saul Brown, M.D.

Martin Grotjahn, M.D.

Dr. Alexander S. Rogawski: Every thoughtful psychoanalyst experiments in his practice to improve his therapeutic results. Much of this experimentation remains unreported in the literature.

This meeting is dedicated to the exploration of the relations of conjoint therapy to psychoanalysis. I hope it will be an occasion to report freely on our experiences and actual practices.

Our panel is qualified to lead such an exchange. Dr. Martin Grotjahn has been a pioneer in this area. Since he published his book *Psychoanalysis and Family Neurosis* in 1960, a growing number of analysts have introduced conjoint and family interviewing into their therapeutic repertory. To a collection of clinical reports by psychotherapists and analysts on various approaches to marital problems, edited by Bernard L. Greene and published in book form under the title *The Psychotherapy of Marital Disharmony*, Dr. Grotjahn contributed a most interesting description of his ways of dealing with various conjoint and family situations.

For several years Dr. Saul Brown has demonstrated family interviewing at the Mt. Sinai Hospital, permitting colleagues to observe him through a one-way mirror screen. The interviews are followed by discussion of the dynamics of the family presented and of the transactions during the interview. They have aroused much interest in our professional community.

I am here as moderator. In agreement with Dr. Brown and Dr. Grotjahn, I have prepared a brief paper: "The Use of Conjoint Sessions in the Finishing Phase of Psychoanalysis or Prolonged Psychotherapy."

In general, analysts have viewed with alarm any change of the one-to-one relationship in psychoanalytic therapy. Some colleagues, with Sigmund Freud an exception, used to discourage all contacts with anyone but the patient, and this injunction extended to the patient's spouse as well. I recall some purists would even refuse to communicate with the therapist of other members of the same family. A kind of iron curtain was drawn about the analyst and his patient separating them from the rest of the world. This was considered necessary for the establishment and maintenance of an uncontaminated transference.

Such practices often resulted in considerable disturbance in the family. In retrospect, this outcome was predictable. If members of the same family become members of competing systems of trust, they are pulled in centrifugal directions. Disturbances of communication are further aggravated.

Dr. Grotjahn in one of his papers calls Freud "a negative family therapist." I suspect that Freud's writings do not always depict his actual practice. He may have in his writings expressed himself as against work with relatives, but from several personal communications with Dr. Smiley Blanton, for instance, I understand Freud had no objection to meeting with a wife or husband before, during, or after analysis. I doubt many analysts today refuse to meet with a spouse at some time, although little is written about it. I have always met with the spouse of my patients once or several times during the course of their analysis.

[1] This panel discussion was held May 29, 1965, at a meeting of the Southern California Psychoanalytic Society.

There are several reasons for this:

In the beginning of my analytic practice I was unquestionably guided by the experience I had had during my own analysis. My analyst saw my wife early in my treatment and on several subsequent occasions.

I was also curious to meet the person in reality whom I had met in a distorted form through the fantasies of my patient. The discrepancy between the portrayal by my patient and my own impression provided me with valuable clues for the understanding of my patient. The experience also forced me to recognize some of my own countertransference. On direct encounter, I was often forced to acknowledge what I had failed or refused to hear in the patient's description of his or her spouse. Thus, I often learned more about myself than about my patient in these meetings; yet, it was the patient who ultimately benefited from this clearing of my third ear.

I soon recognized that meetings with the spouse often enhanced therapeutic progress. Husbands and wives often react to the analyst as an intruder into the privacy of their marriage. The helper is perceived as a threat, as a magical destroyer, as a potential critic of their own conduct in exceedingly private situations. As a result, much conscious and unconscious resistance to the treatment is aroused in the marital partner even where he or she has initiated the therapeutic effort. I was able to observe that a face to face meeting with the spouse reduced my image from a parasitic, threatening monster to a more realistic perception. After the meeting I often felt the spouse had turned from a foe into an ally of the therapeutic process.

As a rule I scheduled such meetings two or three months after the beginning of therapy, after I had formed my first dynamic working hypothesis about the patient and had tested it in the fire of his first dreams and reactions to early interpretations. Without making this an inflexible rule, I would see husband or wife about once a year during the course of the analysis or, at times of crisis, at the request of the patient or the patient's spouse. Of course the patient always had the right to decide in advance whether such a meeting should take place. His request or his refusal, and his reactions to the visit of the spouse were all useful material for the analysis. Even the possibility of a meeting with the spouse reduced much acting out in the family which might have externally reinforced the patient's intrapsychic resistances and thus delayed the therapeutic progress.

For years I would see the marital partner alone. There were some disadvantages to this procedure. Even though I told them in advance that my obligation of full confidentiality extended mainly to the patient and that whatever they might tell me would in one form or another be brought back into the therapy, they would occasionally embarrass me by unexpected confessions. I was now faced with the difficult decision of what to do with such information. Furthermore, patients would obtain conflicting impressions from what the spouse reported on their meetings with me and what they sensed I had observed. Again, this aftermath could be usefully exploited in the analysis. But too many factors were involved to determine accurately the contributions of all individuals involved in the event.

I then began to see patient and spouse simultaneously. This was not a routine. These conjoint interviews turned out to be fruitful beyond expectation. I now had an opportunity to observe marital transactions in actuality. The intrapsychic conflicts of both partners were projected and acted out on the interpersonal stage. With my third ear sensitized by my previous experience, I could discern the many threads in the complex texture of multilevel transactions between my patient and his spouse. In addition I became aware of new aspects which had not been evident to me in the analytic one-to-one relationship.

I wish to focus on the description of a procedure which I have added to my psychoanalytic technical repertory: the use of conjoint sessions in the finishing phase of analysis. (I prefer the term "finishing phase" to the term "terminal phase" which has a macabre connotation.)

The chief task during this phase is referred to in technical language as "the resolution of the transference." The patient is to relinquish responses and attachments to the therapist which are transferred from experiences with earlier objects. Theoretically, the patient who gives up his infantile and irrational transference attitudes is able to relate himself to the therapist as an adult and perceives the doctor realistically. He is thus no longer in need of further help and is able to give up his treatment relationship.

In clinical experience, and even with patients who have achieved a good therapeutic result, this outcome is difficult to attain, the efforts are time consuming, and the final result is often far from satisfactory.

According to analytic theory the transference should dissolve through correct, well-timed, and well-formulated interpretations followed by "working through." If this were true, we would not have to resort so often to the setting of a termination date far in advance of the actual event. This technique was first introduced by Freud as an emergency measure in a case in which a patient refused to let his treatment end. It has now become an established routine procedure.

I have endlessly interpreted and "worked through" transference manifestations without being able to reduce the strength of the transference tie, and in a more comprehensive sense, without reducing the patient's attachment to me and to the treatment process.

Elsewhere I have expressed the opinion that insight helps only those who can make use of it. In other words, I do question the currently prevalent assumption that therapeutic change follows dynamic understanding. On the contrary, I have found that the patient who has improved in treatment and shows this improvement in his conduct becomes able to gain and utilize insight. The improvement is probably due to the interaction of several factors, foremost among them being the interpersonal processes in treatment akin to Franz Alexander's "corrective emotional experience." It is only after the patient has gained a wider range of freedom of decision that he can make use of his newly gained insights.

I have observed that patients are willing and able to give up the therapist as a transference object only after they have improved in their feelings about themselves and after this change has diminished their need for an anxiety reducing transference relationship.

The patient-doctor relationship is much broader than the transference which is merely one, albeit an important, aspect of it. The therapeutic situation is also a reality. For long periods of time the doctor listens to the patient with a dedication and an interest unequaled in other human situations. This is a gratifying condition. We usually hear about the pains and anguish suffered by our patients; these discomforts are unquestionably true, but so are the gratifications contained in this unique situation. The gratification aspects of therapy are usually underplayed because patients and doctors alike feel guilty over their indulging in such expensive soul-searching. Their consciences may be somewhat relieved when they stress the hardship of the procedure.

The gratification of being listened to, of having a place to pour one's heart out, of devoting time to the delving into the mysterious workings of one's mind can be habit forming. This is not merely a gratification of infantile needs. This may well be an answer to adult needs in a world in which friendship has become a rare commodity. To give up such an opportunity may become a difficult task.

Wishes and fantasies directed toward the

therapist may represent attempts to compensate for frustrations and disappointments in the patient's current life. In general, it will be easier for a patient to give up his treatment relationship if his character and circumstances have not isolated him from other social relations.

Fantasies concerning a person in common human relations are subjected to the test of actual living. In the therapeutic setting these fantasies remain unchecked. The doctor can always withdraw into his professional role, and he may never betray his shortcomings and limitations. Thus the patient has little opportunity to reduce the idealized conception of his doctor to realistic proportions. The therapist may easily remain an embodiment of all answers to the patient's unstilled needs.

During therapy the doctor-patient relationship becomes an exclusive system from which even the marital partner is kept out. The material brought up in therapy cannot be shared with anyone but the therapist. We promote this exclusiveness of our patient's relationship to us. When a patient discusses therapeutic material outside his sessions we suspect that such indiscretion operates in the service of resistance. We indicate to the patient that he had better desist from such behavior. We establish a unique form of relationship, and as the patient enters the finishing phase of his treatment, he suffers the loss of an irreplaceable confidant.

After the end of a formal and successful therapy, self-analysis takes the place of the treatment. As a matter of fact, many patients identify with various aspects of the therapeutic process such as the self-questioning, the self-observation, the creative regression that permits revelatory experience of history and meaning, and with the use of previously gained insights, to structure current experience. But in most instances such efforts will be sporadic, and the absence of a listener reduces the initiative to overcome resistance to a systematic self-search.

I have focused on factors posing problems in the resolution of a prolonged therapeutic relationship which are contributed by the patient. Obstacles of equal importance may be present in the counter-responses of the analysts.

"Counter-responses" implies more than countertransference and narcissistic investment in the patient, with infantile regressive or unconscious mechanisms. After caring for a person for some time, it seems to be impossible to avoid adult responses of interest. It becomes difficult for the therapist to give up what has become a mutual adult relationship of trust and to embark once again on a laborious process with a stranger. These factors may contribute more or less subtly to the doctor's holding on to a patient.

Recognizing such tendencies I have on frequent occasions reexamined the indications why a treatment should be continued. Franz Alexander pointed out that surgeons do not keep their patients on the operating table until all tissues are completely healed. He warned analysts not to keep their patients on the couch until some imaginary state of ideal mental health is achieved. Analysts should learn from surgeons that they are only the initiators of the therapeutic process and that the healing proceeds best under the stimulations, frustrations, and the challenges of daily living.

When I began to introduce conjoint sessions into the finishing phase, I was surprised to discover in myself tendencies to delay the discontinuation of therapy. I became aware of a reluctance to invite the spouse into the analytic session, and I realized that I was loath to surrender the intimacy which had developed between the patient and myself in the course of our therapeutic collaboration. I realized that bringing the marriage partner into the analytic situation was tantamount to bringing the patient's reality to the treatment. Our eyes had become used to the dimness in the analytic room so that we were able to see the shady and elusive but so important world of the unconscious. Now we were about to raise the shades and permit the bright sunlight to enter from the outer world. This would hurt our eyes. With the change in lighting I lost the exalted role which the patient had assigned to me. The therapeutic alliance with the patient had now to yield to an equidistant position of the therapist to both partners in the conjoint session to make it truly effective. Not only did I have to give up my special significance to the patient, but the patient had to give up his illusion that he monopolized my services. This was the very purpose of the technical innovation. What was aimed at, and what as a rule was accomplished in these conjoint sessions, was the introduction of actuality into the patient-doctor relationship, an event which resulted in the "breaking of the magic spell."

Another advantage of the conjoint sessions is the opportunity to alert the patient's partner to the changes that have taken place in the patient during his therapy, and especially to his or her changed needs. Martin Grotjahn, in his book about the family neurosis, speaks about the compensatory neurotic needs in the partners of a marriage which act as a resistance to therapeutic progress. The patient's neurosis is constantly reinforced by the neurotic counterpart in the spouse. Even after the patient's needs and patterns of behavior have changed in treatment, these changes are often not perceived by the partner who continues to operate on the basis of expectations formed in the early stages of the marriage. The presence of the analyst acts as a catalyst to reopen communications which have become blocked by the distorted perception of the other.

I have come to compare certain events in conjoint therapy as the "Telstar model." The Telstar is an orbiting satellite which establishes indirect communications between locations on the earth which for various reasons cannot communicate directly with each other. The message is beamed at Telstar from one location and received by the other as it bounces off the satellite. In conjoint sessions the therapist plays the role of the orbiting object. The messages are apparently directed to him, but they bounce off on to the other participant who is "eavesdropping" on the exchange. The "eavesdropper," out of the line of fire as it exists in a two-person exchange, and therefore with his resistance relaxed, is able to hear messages which, if addressed to him during a heated marital discussion, would never pass through the defensive sound barrier of his ears. The eavesdropper becomes aware of attitudes, needs, and aspects hitherto unsuspected in the person with whom he has been living but whose true image was distorted by stereotyped assumptions originating in his own history or in the history of the relationship.

"Eavesdropping" seems to be an infantile pleasure that stays with us most of our life. This is why the conjoint setting represents such an excellent opportunity to establish or reestablish communication. While the therapist is listening to one partner, the other partner listens in. This by itself would be useful, but, in addition, the therapist may translate or reformulate some of the statements in language acceptable to the other person. The communication begins in the office and is continued at home. The pleasure of feeling understood can be habit-forming, and it should be transferred from the therapeutic setting into the actual life of our patients.

Since I am often the eavesdropper on exchanges between the marital partners, I, too, have an opportunity to become aware of features of my patient which I had either not noticed during the individual phase of therapy or, although I had noticed them, had not been adequately worked through.

Sometimes I interlace conjoint and individual sessions with my patient, to deal with material that conjoint interviews have brought into the open.

Clinical Illustrations: Case 1. Dependency on a possessive and infantilizing mother threatened the two-year marriage of a woman in her mid-twenties. This woman would call her mother dozens of times each day to tell her about or to consult with her on every detail of her life. Progress in the analysis was slow since every move towards emancipation was perceived as a cruel abandonment of her mother and followed by severe guilt feelings. Analysis of the intense transference revealed that the patient tried unconsciously to replace her passive and ineffectual father. This man had been a great disappointment to the mother. The patient wanted to be a "better husband." The patient had married a man several years her junior, very aggressive and successful in business but passive in his sex relations. He demanded the patient take the initiative in their love making. After five years of analysis the patient came to accept herself as a woman. Gradually she excluded her mother from her marriage, which improved considerably as a result of this change. Although the patient's husband was also in treatment he seemed unwilling or unable to respond with more masculine behavior to the patient's newly awakened needs. Several consultations between the two analysts were without success. The maritally frustrated patient fantasied her therapist to be the virile man she longed for and she was reluctant to finish her treatment. Only after a series of conjoint sessions in which the marital partners worked through their changed relationship did there ensue a striking improvement in their sexual life and the treatment was brought to a satisfactory ending.

Case 2. A thirty-three-year-old social work student came to treatment after a disastrous divorce which was followed by his dropping out of school. He realized that he invariably managed to spoil his chances just as he was about to reach success. His treatment lasted twenty-six months. It revealed he was terribly afraid to reexperience the overwhelming rejection he had suffered at the age of two when his mother suddenly abandoned him. This had left him with a deep-seated feeling of unworthiness and the anticipation of new rejections. Rather than be the passive victim, he actively withdrew from projects as they neared success. During his therapy he married a woman more suitable than his first wife. He achieved an advanced level in his professional career and he established a sound basis for his new marriage. He began to speak spontaneously about the end of his treatment which seemed quite timely. But once again he was flooded by anxiety. When his therapy ended, he would feel abandoned by his doctor and also by his wife. I suggested a series of conjoint sessions but at first he objected most strenuously. Finally he agreed to a conjoint meeting but on the very evening of the appointment he created a stormy marital argument, ran away from the house and for the first time failed to come to his session. A dream revealed that he unconsciously anticipated that his wife would compare him with the therapist, become cognizant of his unworthiness and leave him. In several conjoint sessions this irrational pattern was brought out and worked through. He emerged from the experience with new self-confidence and was able to end the treatment without anxiety and in a spirit of optimism.

Case 3. A woman artist in her mid-forties had been in intensive treatment for many years, first with an Adlerian, then with a Freudian analyst, both outstanding members of their profession. She had successfully raised three children, achieved recognition in her field, yet felt dissatisfied—with herself, with her way of life—and was unable to engage in any sustained effort. Analysis revealed a deep-seated ambivalence over her role as a woman, which she feared could be fulfilled only by masochistic surrender. In her marriage to a devoted, successful but mainly business-oriented man, she felt herself not understood and mistreated. She attempted to structure the analytic situation as a source of suffering so that it would conform to her infantile fantasies about her father. Even after the analytic work was completed successfully the patient clung to her therapy, claiming that this was an opportunity for companionship which she could not experience in her marriage.

Communication between the patient and her husband which had been quite disturbed for years was rekindled when the husband joined his wife in conjoint sessions. Both partners discovered new potentials in each other, potentials unsuspected in more than twenty years of living together. The husband realized he had felt insecure in the artistic world of his wife and had therefore withheld himself from her. This otherwise self-confident man actually felt threatened by the "unpredictable" artistic temperament of his wife. The patient began to see the esthetic structure in her husband's severe burden of responsibilities. Together, they engaged in a combined artistic and commercial venture which brought them closer than they had ever been. Although the patient had been in treatment more than seven years with three therapists she was able to separate herself spontaneously from such support without anxiety.

Dr. Saul Brown: If we narrow today's issue to "conjoint therapy," and by this refer to psychotherapeutic interviewing with married couples, we present ourselves with two somewhat alternative aims.

One aim would be addressed specifically to the resolution of recurring and painful discord between marital partners. The alternative aim, which is the one Alexander Rogawski has been emphasizing, would be to facilitate therapeutic progress in that one of the two marital partners happens to be in psychoanalytic treatment. In the first instance, where one addresses himself to the therapy of the marriage, the therapy is oriented directly toward the marital discord. The therapist is making an appeal to the members to step back and try to perceive the needs of the other one, and then to live together with a greater degree of tolerance.

In the second instance, the conjoint sessions represent an effort to reduce what I would like to call the "field resistance" to therapeutic progress. The conjoint session then would reflect the recognition that the patient's inability to change constructively is a function of the psychological field of the patient and his spouse. The emotional needs of the spouse reopen anxiety or hostility in the patient. The results of the patient's maturation are not sufficient to overcome the stimulus to regression or to the repetition compulsion that comes from the actions of the spouse.

As analysts we work within a field of interaction. We take one figure out of that field—we designate that member "the analytic patient"—we make progress and then we see that the progress levels off, something happens—there isn't sufficient movement forward. We may conclude some resistance is operating in that field, not only resistance in that field, but between the patient and the spouse. Something occurs between our analytic patient and the spouse which keeps reopening regressive tendencies of anxiety or hostility. This is both a field theory statement and an intrapsychic statement about repetition compulsion. This brings us back to psychoanalytic formulations and ego theory. Resistance to change in an interactive field implies repetition compulsion within each individual in the field.

This is field theory plus ego and object-relations theory. Certain objects evoke in each other a repetition of the previously unresolved and continuingly unresolved tendencies, and a tendency either to regress in behavior or to return to the object fixations of the past.

All of this is a little different from what

Alexander Rogawski has said. There are inevitable and persistent transference distortions which no one of us is omnipotent nor brilliant enough, sometimes, to discern or to correct; and the bringing into the consultation room of the spouse is a way to modify the transference, or correct certain transference distortions, or to reduce their intensity, let's say, in the finishing phase. And it is an economical way to reduce them in terms of the countertransference. All of this allows something productive to occur for the patient.

Now, there are other ways to do this. Certain analysts, Max Sherman for example, have sometimes introduced the use of group therapy in the termination phase and used this for the analytic patient over an extended period of time. Gordon Saver does this as an economical way of rectifying, clarifying, diluting and doing away with certain transference distortion.

For all of us here there is an effective way for reducing our own transference distortions in the late phases of analysis, in that as the years go on, we come to meetings like this and see our current or former analyst in action. We sit in seminars with the analyst and little by little we dilute and correct the transference distortion. We should give our patients that opportunity in group therapy. Bringing in the spouse may do something similar, and it seems to me that is essentially what Alexander Rogawski has said.

The most persistent and repetitive pattern is some form of sadomasochism. For the sadistic partner, recurring aggression—that is, belittling, or attacking or depreciating the spouse—is ego-syntonic. For the spouse, a recurring state of low self-esteem, guilt and despair is ego-syntonic. These are ego-syntonic cycles for the two participants. It is as if the sameness of each one's self system or ego identity is insured through the continuation of this sadomasochistic pattern of object-relations. Conversely, the absence of an available external object with whom this sequence can be played out creates discomfort, turmoil, and even a compulsive search for a new person with whom all this can be acted out.

This leads into the issue of separation anxiety, which must be endured by each participant of a sadomasochistic involvement before the cyclic pattern of object-relations can be fully extinguished. When the sadistic individual discontinues his provocations of guilt, the masochistic partner also experiences this cessation of behavior as a loss, which is equivalent to an early object loss. It activates separation anxiety in the reciprocal person, with a new effort to provoke the old patterns. The availability of a steadfast third person, the conjoint therapist, the analyst who is willing to see both together, at the correct time, and to address himself to the separation anxiety—either by direct interpretation or by merely being available—this auxiliary ego for both partners increases the toleration for the separation anxiety. The analyst alone with a single patient helps the patient sustain the pain that comes with the giving up of internalized objects. This is worked through, as we all know, via the transference regression.

There may be a crossover between the two people in a marriage. It may be a crossover of unresolved developmental levels operating between the two partners. This crystallizes the sadomasochistic pattern, in spite of the individual analytic effort with one. An obvious example would be the dependency expectations of one partner who has strong oral fixations and who is sensitive to the issue of dominance and submission. Such a person experiences the oral dependent regressions and expectations of the partner as an effort to dominate. Thus the "crossover" of developmental fixations of each confuses the other and perpetuates the sadomasochistic pattern. Oral dependence of the one partner arouses a defensive-sadistic attack because it is felt by an anal partner as an effort to dominate, rather than as an expression of dependent need. The oral partner experiences the sadistic attacks as deprivation and slips into seeking dependent gratification. The anal member fights savagely to avoid the fantasied domination. Unless each individual gains more or less simultaneous awareness of the nature of his own internal need and the need of the other, he is the victim of the other's malevolence. This leads then into what I referred to earlier and what seems to have entered our analytic parlance more or less simultaneously with our interest in object representations and object-relations —the "paranoid orientation." This is a Kleinian formulation and close to Edith Jacobson's ideas. Martin Grotjahn has referred at various times in his writings to the family neurosis.

In summary, we are talking about object-relations, repetition-compulsion, and the interplay of developmental fixations between intimate partners. We are also talking about field theory and object-relations in the context of such a theory. Furthermore, we are talking about resistance to changes in the field other than the purely intrapsychic resistance.

Dr. Martin Grotjahn: Alexander Rogawski gave us a developmental picture of his experience with analytic family therapy; how he started, how he was thinking about it, how he experimented. All therapists must develop this inner freedom in order to create their own style of technique. We need freedom of work in our field. Our own analysis should safeguard us to remain within the field of psychoanalysis.

Dr. Rogawski mentioned that I once called Freud a "negative family therapist"—but quoting Freud is like quoting from the Bible! If you read Freud's case histories from the early case of Anna O. to Dora, to Little Hans, and finally to some patients who have reported on their analytic experience with Freud, you will realize that Freud knew the families of his patients and knew them well.

August Aichhorn was another early psychoanalyst who saw no conflict between individual psychoanalysis and the analytic study of the family.

Today we plan to limit our discussion to the conjoint therapy in the finishing phase of psychoanalytic therapy. I like such limitations of our discussion because it deepens our training in psychodynamic reasoning as Franz Alexander used to call it.

It is my guess that Dr. Rogawski in his further development will also see couples in the middle and in the initial phase of their psychoanalytic treatment. He will want to see with what he has to deal in therapy and how much the partner supplements the free associative anamnesis with which we start an analysis.

I want to discuss the special aspects of working through in families. During the final phase of analysis the emphasis shifts from discovery and interpretation to repetition and working through. The resistance against the application of insight and integration is difficult to overcome. At no other time of analysis do we see so clearly multichanneled and multileveled communication. If you witness a marital fight in the analytic situation, you will see how the partners battle and how they never will get to a working through because they do not realize that although they try to communicate, they actually bypass each other because they move on different levels of communication.

There is another aspect of communication which you see clearly in a long analysis: you and your patient develop a relationship and certain defenses of which you are no longer fully aware. The patient learns how to deal with the analytic situation and even how to deal with his analyst. The triangular relationship in conjoint therapy changes this for everybody's benefit.

There is one special aspect of working through in conjoint therapy which is obvious to me but which is not described in the literature. If you work with one patient in psychoanalysis you have a one-to-one relationship. The working through takes place in the analytic situation and is continued in the patient when he has left the couch. In a group the process is approximately the same. After the work in the group session, the group disperses, and it is hoped everybody will continue to work through his insight and interpretation. In contrast to this, a family is a group which does not dissolve. This is true in a couple, as it is true in a family. Conjoint psychotherapy does not end with the session: it continues. It is almost as if the marriage continues where the psychoanalysis leaves off—as originally the analysis started where the neurotic marriage failed. The circle must be closed. You could say I am idealistic and that I hope or possibly expect too much from my patients. Perhaps I do.

The modest analyst will realize that his duty is done when he activates the need to work through and the ability to communicate again. Conjoint family therapy is an excellent device to stimulate this.

I have relatively little to say to the somewhat more theoretical approach of Dr. Brown: sadomasochistic relationships are of great importance. I found it most important to see that a sadist who marries a masochist changes roles suddenly or slowly; totally, or partially or temporarily.

I would like sometime to talk about the marriage of physicians which is something very special. The physician has a great maternal feminine identification which should not be destroyed in training, because that is what makes him happy in his work, that is what he lives for, that is what helps him to deal with his sick children whom he calls his "patients." If such a man with a strong feminine trend goes home, he projects his femininity upon his wife. But the good doctor then does not let go this identification—he doesn't leave his own projected femininity in his wife, but he watches her jealously and always proves that she is not as good a mother as he is and that he must play the good mother himself even at home. This leads to desperate, painful disaster. A special aspect of this development is represented by those doctors whom every patient loves dearly with the exception of his wife, who knows that the beloved physician is a monster at home when he interferes with a woman by not allowing her to really grow up to become a mature woman.

Dr. Rogawski: When Dr. Grotjahn spoke about the family taking over the therapeutic work after hours and continuing the working-through process, I am reminded of an experience which fits very much into this—my mental health consultations with the Bureau of Public Assistance, where I, finding the best approach, selected what I call the "Work Family." These are the people who spend eight hours together in the same office—which is sometimes more than they spend with their actual family. The mental health consultation may become a catalytic experience which is then worked through over the next few weeks, so that the effect of the mental health consultation activates working out and working through.

Dr. Walter Briehl: Family therapy is an outgrowth of group therapy, and both represent major psychotherapeutic contributions in the last thirty years.

The therapy presented here should not be called "conjoint family therapy." All three speakers use the spouse as adjunct transference figure. The only "conjoint therapy" in the strictest sense of the term would be where the two partners come in on equal basis for help.

Dr. David Morgan: I like to leave the couples in groups and the individual patient on the couch. The only thing I have to give up in the finishing phase is my own neurotic transference and countertransference toward my patient. If he and I give it up we may become good friends. I find it much easier to terminate the intensive, individual phase of analysis if the couple is in a group for couples.

I want to pose a serious problem which I can't handle. I have had a group of psychiatrists for about five years. They came to me because they were sadomasochistic characters, so it has become a group where we compete for the position of Mother Superior. My wife now comes to my couples group and it seems to work out well, but I can't get psychiatrists to bring their wives. Every time I suggest it the group practically falls apart. Some of their wives are quite sick and some of the men have had a lot of analysis. Perhaps it is better for psychiatrists to stage their feminine competition without women present. I really want them to bring their wives.

I would also like to do family therapy, but I find it almost impossible to get the American family together, and I am not going to work Saturdays, Sundays and nights. So, I have found that I am too selfish.

Dr. Robert Sokol: What about the use of conjoint therapy as a preparation for analysis?

Dr. Grotjahn: I often do that—people begin to know that I am interested in family therapy and they come to me in families. For instance, I am seeing a man who has had a coronary occlusion; he has the feeling, perhaps rightfully, that his wife has her hands around his heart and every once in a while she squeezes it and he comes down with an angina attack. So I started with both simultaneously. Since it was shortly after the patient's coronary he had to be in limited therapy—which I can handle better with the wife there. It is possible that after a while I will let the man retire from treatment and will hold on to the wife and show her what she is doing.

Conjoint therapy is popular today! It is easier to go to a psychiatrist's office together rather than to send "the other one," which was the usual technique.

Let me add a few words about how to treat Dr. Morgan's group of psychiatrists. You may try a different way to get the wives into treatment. Perhaps you could call these sessions a study group or "work shop" and insist that you will come only when the ladies are invited.

You have a better chance when you establish a group outside of your own home ground. For instance—I have just returned from two days in a city 150 miles from here. In this way you are not "one of the boys." It is as if you came from outer space. You are not involved in their professional reality.

How to get families into the doctor's office? When I have a family in which I am really interested, I tell them that I'll come to them. Families are easier to keep together in their own home, which you then enter.

Dr. Gordon Saver: The difficulty Dr. Morgan is having with the group of psychiatrists has, I believe, to do with their narcissism. One of the major problems we have with our individual analytic patients has to do with this area. Wives are the most magnificent interpreters of the male's narcissism; they are the best supporters and defenders and the most efficient destroyers of their husbands' narcissism. Your group of psychiatrists have an investment in keeping their wives out of the group. They are protecting their own narcissism.

My group therapy experience has impressed me with this insight: insufficient working through in individual psychoanalysis may not necessarily or directly relate to transference but perhaps toward either the patient's or our own narcissism. We actually facilitate a narcissistic gratification in psychoanalysis. The patient gets an enormous amount of almost daily pleasure out of being listened to for years. I have arrived at the point where I put many analytic patients into a group concurrently. I never cease to be amazed, if not sometimes shocked, at how many years I have wasted, focusing on inconsequential matters with the patient rather than upon what goes on between him and other human beings in the world outside the therapeutic dyad.

Not too long ago I had a woman in psychoanalysis who was simply delightful as a patient—she charmed and entertained me for several years. She adored me as well. It was a marvelous analytic case. She reached the point where she would complain of the one real unpleasantness in her life: her husband never made love to her. I thought for a while of seeing them jointly, but he was in analysis with someone else and I had heard he was making progress. I finally decided to put her into a group. I soon discovered that one of the reasons her husband avoided her was because of her incessant talking. I never knew this before, inasmuch as I had been seeing her for years and was enjoying her talk. I must say I learned something about my narcissism in the process.

Dr. Saul Brown: I feel that what presents itself to us now, and I am sure will continue increasingly, is that the diagnostic procedure must come first with the field—not with the individual member of the field; that out of an appraisal of the total field comes a decision and the clarity with which one then goes ahead to say this one or that one or another one should be now involved in analysis, perhaps for several years, or this one should be involved in child and play therapy, or these two should be involved in a period of clarification of the recurring issues that go on between them. At some point then perhaps one or both, or each or all—depending on the financial resources, the sociological placement, the self-image of the family therapy—should begin with an appraisal of the field, which is turning the whole thing upside down from the way it used to be.

Dr. Harvey Strassman: When I had a seminar with Max Sherman I learned one does individual therapy in groups. The same thing is now done in family therapy; we do individual therapy with families—echoing what Walter Briehl said. The most important part of family therapy is the ability to be flexible and use dynamic knowledge in terms of every member of the family.

Dr. Grotjahn: You do not practice individual therapy in families. You apply the same dynamic-technique to both.

Dr. Sigmund Gabe: I find myself dizzy from the tremendous spectrum of therapies which have been touched on this morning; it is all very interesting, and healthy. However, these therapies are not analysis. They are additional therapies to analysis. When we start mixing up therapies we come out with a hodgepodge. It will take a long time before the specific indications for these various modalities are worked out.

I would like to rise in defense of keeping analysis distinct. I am afraid that the amount of enthusiasm for new modalities leads us to disregard some of the fairly proven procedures which analysis has given us and which we know are effective in bringing about not only temporary symptomatic changes in patients, but actually are effective in fundamental structural changes in the patients. In conjoint family therapy a field is created which is so complex that I am afraid none of us is astute and knowledgeable enough to know what is really going on.

Dr. Morgan interrupts: Have you tried conjoint interviewing? I find it simplifies the field. In my experience it makes the field less complex and perplexing.

Dr. Gabe: There have been some occasions when I had to have some interviews with members of the family because of certain crises and I noticed a very complicated situation.

For example—in defense of keeping our concept distinct—Dr. Rogawski tells us that in the terminal or the finishing phase he develops a three-way relationship—and tries to work through the final phase. That is a different type of therapy than psychoanalysis. The essence of the analytic procedure, as I see it, is to establish a transference relationship in which the patient projects his internal life onto the analyst and relives it with him. One of the fundamental things for bringing this process to a conclusion is to allow the patient to realize that these projections on to the therapist are inappropriate in the situation, that this is a repetition of an earlier situation, and when this insight is attained by the patient, he may then be ready to give up this fantasy which he has carried with him.

Dr. Morgan: There are many secret and silent relationships to which we never have access in a one-to-one situation. I cannot study these relationships in analysis—but they become suddenly clear and obvious in long family therapy interviews. It is another dimension of the patient which we simply don't see in a one-to-one relationship. It only emerges in the group analytic situation.

Dr. Gabe: If you interpret the transference relations, the patient will be able to handle his reality relations himself.

The great importance of the transference-neurosis has to be established during the analysis. Unless that phase is brought to a satisfactory conclusion, the treatment is really not adequately terminated. Because of difficulties in bringing this phase to a satisfactory conclusion, Alex Rogawski applied these parameters. It seems to me these parameters would preclude doing the very thing that Dr. Rogawski wants to achieve.

The terminal phase is primarily a phase in which the patient is supposed to work through the mourning of having to give up the infantile object, which the analyst has become. This cannot be done if at the same time you introduce a reality situation where the spouse is brought in. How can the patient allow himself under such circumstances to ventilate freely the intense experience he has developed over the years and which is now coming to a terminus?

To bring this process to a satisfactory conclusion the patient must go through a period of mourning as if he had actually lost a dear person. This process must be allowed to be worked through adequately or the transference is never fully terminated and the patient will continue to defend himself against the pain of this loss. It may be through developing hate for the analyst, which may be overt or covert—and may go on for many years and lead to all kinds of difficulties in the patient's life. Or the patient may develop a projective identification with the analyst and for the rest of his life be a satellite of that analyst; whether the patient is in the analyst's environs or not he is still attached and tied to him—still longing for the gratification that he did not obtain in the analysis.

So it seems to me that a strictly one-to-one relationship has to be maintained during this terminal phase. After that has been worked through you can leave it to the patient—if he has a fairly good ego. We are not dealing with children with whom we always have to use parameters, we always have to juggle reality and then project the techniques we are using. But we are dealing with adults here and you can depend upon the adult part of the patient's ego to make the necessary adjustments.

Dr. Rogawski: In 1814, when Stevenson developed the locomotive, there were many articles written stating that nobody could possibly stand the speed with which he would be propelled with such a steam engine, that men couldn't survive it. There was one way to prove it and that was to try it.

I can only say there are many situations the results of which cannot be predicted until they are tried. I agree with many points Dr. Gabe has made but the proof lies in the pudding. We must experiment. Even Freud had serious doubts about analytic therapy when, in 1937 he wrote his paper on "Analysis, Terminal and Interminable." So, perhaps it might be more terminable when we try certain finishing modalities.

Dr. Albert Schrut: I saw a suicidal girl about twenty years old, who wanted me to see her father and mother and how they manipulated her and forced her to various acts. I saw the parents and their interaction. What I did see more clearly was how the daughter manipulated her parents. At the next individual session I pointed out not only what she wanted me to see but what she did not want to see: how she threatened the parents, how she cajoled them, how she whined, how in effect she said: you made me neurotic, now you have got to suffer and do whatever I want you to do—it is all your fault—I have a doctor to prove it.

Dr. Rogawski: I wish to thank the participants in the discussion. It is 12:00—time to end for today.

Alexander S. Rogawski, M.D.
416 N. Bedford Drive
Beverly Hills, California 90210

Saul Brown, M.D.
8727 W. Third Street
Los Angeles, California 90048

Martin Grotjahn, M.D.
416 N. Bedford Drive
Beverly Hills, California 90210

Discussant

Carl A. Whitaker, M.D.
Madison, Wisconsin

I changed from treating patients by individual therapy first to couples therapy and later to family therapy. I do not think family therapy is group therapy, nor do I think of couples therapy as family therapy. Family therapy involves two generations. Couples therapy is the therapeutic intervention in a well-stabilized two-person peer relationship.

Conjoint sessions, as used by Doctor Rogawski, seem to me a kind of intervention in order to decathect the setting and make ending less painful. The spouse comes in as a way of ending the one-to-one relationship. This is certainly feasible but seems strategically difficult. The therapist is, in effect, the mother-in-law of the visiting spouse and the whole triangle is grossly off balance.

My pattern is to have another therapist see the spouse; when they have established a relationship, we then move to four-way interviews with two therapists and two patients. It's difficult for the "mother" of the patient—the therapist—to be marriage counselor in his own child's marriage. I believe the dynamics of an individual are inextricably interwoven with those of his spouse, and that all movements on the part of the individual patient are preplanned by the couple. Thus it is hard for me to see how the non-patient can be an occasional visitor. If we use the spouse as a source of information to better manipulate the patient, we imply a capacity for understanding the patient's life that I don't have.

I admire the therapist acknowledging his countertransference but am dubious that it can be worked through, understood, or assumed to be controllable. The only way I can visualize this process would be first to see the couple, then have an individual interview with each partner, and subsequently arrange alternate individual and joint interviews at frequent intervals. My preference is to see the couple from the first interview and never to see either alone. Therapy is just as effective this way as any other. Certainly I am more alive in this kind of relationship. I agree with Dr. Rogawski in assuming the therapeutic experience is similar to Franz Alexander's "corrective emotional experience."

During the conference, the idea was mentioned of couples continuing the therapy at home. I disagree. In fact, I make strict recommendations that each of them contain his own inner experience between interviews. Thus, all the discussion about their growing takes place where I can be in on it. This is a deliberate effort to mobilize anxiety within each person. It often prevents the usual fight or fusion which precedes each interview and cuts down on the pain and stress of the triangular setting.

If a one-to-one analytic relationship makes the relationship of that therapist to that couple impossible, I wonder whether the precipitous ending in Case 2 was not a flight into health. The couple agreed to fight it out by themselves and not let the therapist in on the marriage. Thus, we must treat that third patient, the marriage.

We also neglect the needs of the non-patient who I believe to be equally disturbed, equally powerful, and equally involved in everything that goes on between patient and therapist. I am increasingly convinced that in the one-to-one therapeutic process, the non-patient carries on the treatment of the patient between interviews, making for a very uncomfortable and distorted kind of treatment process.

I am amazed at how much the analyst permits the patient to be in charge of the therapeutic process. My patient may run his life, but I run my office.

I do not agree with Dr. Brown that couples therapy is headed towards objectivity and tolerance. Mine is not. Couples treatment is just as profound and painful as individual therapy. If tolerance occurs, it is based on a new integrity in each of them, and on a decision that this marriage is one they can fight in rather than merely endure.

I am particularly delighted over the notation that couples or group, or even family therapy is seen as a way of helping the therapist to work through his own distortions.

Dr. Brown speaks of the sadomasochistic relationship between couples as complementary. The dynamics are not just complementary but reciprocal, reversible—a kind of seesaw. I doubt that we can discuss couples psychotherapy with the same dynamic words we use for the discussion of individual therapy. We need a new language. Dr. Brown hints at this when he speaks about "crossover" to denote a negative relationship between two marital partners. It might also be used to describe the positive, supportive aspects of each for the other and, possibly, the dynamic force which makes marriage itself greater than the sum of the two persons.

I agree with Dr. Grotjahn's suggestion to try couples therapy in the beginning and middle phase. Such experiments are exciting, educational and growthful.

I applaud Dr. Grotjahn for his remarks on the difference between group and family therapy. Family therapy is difficult, complex and a power-packed situation in a two-generation setting.

I would suggest that only one with extensive experience with couples treatment should try to do family psychotherapy. For others, the dynamics become too powerful. I myself believe we should engage the family only with a team of two therapists. I agree with Dr. Grotjahn that couples treatment as a triangular relationship changes the bilateral manipulation that goes on in my one-to-one relationship, but I am not sure this always benefits us. At times, therapy becomes more confused, and the multiple loyalties and dynamics within the therapist and within the couple may bring the constructive process to a grinding halt.

I disagree with Dr. Grotjahn that the family should take over the therapeutic work between interviews, for this keeps the therapist out of the situation and makes him less useful.

I concur with Dr. Briehl that the use of the spouse as adjunct transference figure is not conjoint family therapy.

I like Dr. Morgan's idea of using a group to get rid of the therapist's own residual affect toward his patients, and I agree with Dr. Saver's conclusions that the psychiatrists don't bring their wives because the psychiatrists don't want them there. Furthermore, the psychiatrists don't want them there because the therapists don't want them there. If I were to get cornered like this, I would suggest that the wives work with another group therapist. After the group is established, then both groups could come together with both therapists. If this were not possible, I would put an end to the group and let the psychiatrists and their wives go for couples treatment to a third therapist. The therapist as the "mother-in-law" to the spouse is rarely more obvious than in this kind of setting.

I do not agree with Dr. Grotjahn that we can treat the well member of the couple where the husband has had a coronary, because the dynamics of the marital relationship will not be in the office. When the husband is not so involved, therapeutic competence cannot be brought to bear on their relationship. Taking the wife's hands away from her husband's heart and holding her hands in his may not solve the problem as well as seeing them both together continually. Thereby, the husband can warm the hands and the heart. There is danger in manipulating the marriage from either side.

Finally, a comment on Dr. Strassman's remark that Max Sherman taught him to do individual therapy in groups: not all of us do it this way. My group work consists mainly in being an expert patient and trying to activate the group's movement. I do not treat any individual in the group; although in family therapy when I have parents and children, I may work with an individual in the presence of the rest of the family, trying to expand this into treating the family group at every chance.

I like the honesty with which this seminar has been presented.

Discussant

Don D. Jackson, M.D.
Palo Alto, California

Dr. Rogawski's comments are frank, interesting and take into account the many problems for the analyst who would also do family therapy. I am sorry that he had to bring Sigmund Freud into the picture since such comments seem atavistic. Freud has done more than any of us can hope to do and it seems the matter could rest there without implying Freud might have been a family therapist had he lived.

Dr. Saul Brown's comments were penetrating and I have no quarrel with them. However, it is sad for the state of our art that only the term "sadomasochistic" in all of our psychoanalytic lexicon seems to fit the marital interaction. Perhaps we see sadomasochism more often than it exists simply because we have no other term!

As usual, I found Martin Grotjahn worth attention, and I suspect that the maternal feminine identification in physicians he speaks of has been too long neglected in their therapy —even in the therapy of those in training analyses!

The comments of Dr. Sigmund Gabe remind me of my mother and therefore I cannot comment on them cogently. For example, his most astonishing statement: "If you interpret the transference relations the patient will be able to handle his reality relations himself." My mother used to make certain recommendations for action based on her concepts of reality. Unfortunately, it often turned out that this was not someone else's concept of reality and I felt caught in the middle.

The results of analytic therapy would seem to indicate that merely interpreting the transference is an expensive, over-long and unproductive method of therapy. Unfortunately, the individuals who are afraid that change will disturb or distress are the very ones who do not try it and their own reality misses this particular experience.

Discussant

Albert J. Solnit, M.D.
New Haven, Connecticut

Dr. Rogawski's observations and formulations seem to have a serious internal inconsistency which Dr. Gabe alludes to in his discussion. This inconsistency is most clearly indicated in the assumption that the patient can continue to use his analytic understanding and thinking after the analysis is terminated; at the same time it is assumed that the terminal phase of the analysis should be conducted in a manner which prevents the patient from working through the transference-neurosis.

It is my impression that Dr. Rogawski's conduct of conjoint interviews with his patient and the patient's spouse constrains and distorts the transference process. This constriction and distortion is such to make it almost impossible for the patient to work through the transference-neurosis and to analyze those reactions evoked in the terminal phase of an analysis.

There are many other questions raised by this mixture of analytic treatment and conjoint therapy which time does not permit me to discuss fully. Such a mixture confuses and/or distorts: (1) The focus and influence of analytic treatment on autoplastic and alloplastic processes; on external reality and intrapsychic (inner) reality; (2) The patient's ability to use the working through processes characteristic of Freudian psychoanalysis; (3) The characteristics and findings of conjoint therapy (see Dr. Briehl's remark); (4) Who is the patient? (5) The degree of the patient's effective self-understanding as measured against the therapist's zeal.

Discussant

Terry C. Rodgers, M.D.
New York, New York

I have had some experience with conjoint therapy with different therapeutic aims under a variety of circumstances. In some instances the aim and technique bear no relationship to the psychoanalytic method, even though psychoanalytic theory (especially object-relations theory) is the frame of reference. An example would be conjoint sessions with father, mother and adolescent child where the aim is clarification of disturbed metacommunication between the various family members.

More frequently I have conducted conjoint analytic psychotherapy with husband and wife with therapy of the marriage as the primary focus and when formal psychoanalysis of one or both partners was not practical nor indicated.

More closely related to the focus of the present panel is conjoint therapy as an addendum or supplement to psychoanalysis. This may be instituted in the terminal phase of an analysis of one marital partner or after termination of analysis proper.

In this instance and as a parameter of psychoanalytic therapy, I would make a distinction between such a procedure and that of individual or conjoint interviewing of the spouse of an analysand, because the conjoint therapy is an addendum or introduced as a method of termination.

As an addendum, it may be desirable to have such therapy conducted by a therapist other than the original analyst, especially when the transference images which the unanalyzed partner and the analyst have formed of each other are so fixed as to become mutually reinforcing and self-fulfilling. This, too, depends largely on the personality and experience of the original analyst.

Not long ago, a colleague who was moving to another city referred a forty-three-year-old woman to me. He felt that, despite an otherwise successful analysis, she still needed support in dealing with the "reality" of an inadequate husband. In our first session this woman let drop a remark which caused me to think her "inadequate" husband was in large part a myth shared by the patient and her former analyst and perpetuated by a shared narcissism. I saw the husband and found him not at all the "shlimazl" he was purported to be. Then I saw them jointly and for the next ten months witnessed an extraordinary example of two people learning communication with and discovering the grossest distortions in their conceptions of each other.

I think the true parameters of psychoanalytic therapy are the conjoint and/or individual therapeutic interviews with the spouse of an analysand. These are introduced to overcome a specific resistance in the analysis of the primary patient and are not designed for therapy of the marriage or even of the spouse. They are indicated only when acting out within the marriage has so reinforced the patient's intrapsychic resistance as to create a therapeutic impasse.

The pathogenic transferences of patients with severe marital problems tend to be drained off in extra-analytic attachments; especially so when the neurosis of a patient and the neurosis of his spouse complement each other, making the spouse a suitable object onto which the patient can project a rejected introject—an unconscious self-representation that is ego-dystonic. Unconsciously they chose each other because of their mutual suitability for such projections.

When their interactions constitute what Giovacchini has called a "character object relationship," and when this involvement is based on early conflictual and destructive object relationships, that relationship is intensely symbiotic and vital to the psychic equilibrium of each partner.

At the moment the analyst effectively intrudes into this previously closed unit, the marriage neurosis acts as a resistance to treatment. The spouse reacts so as to sabotage the analysis; the patient reacts so as to encourage this behavior, and then utilizes the "reality" as a resistance to analysis.

The analysis of such patients does not necessarily call for conjoint or collateral interviewing of the sabotaging spouse. Such a parameter is chiefly determined by the degree of ego distortion in the analysand. When this is significant, conjoint interviews with the spouse will often provide sufficient insight to make effective interpretations possible. The split-off portion of the transference may then be brought into the analytic relationship and a workable transference-neurosis established.

In regard to Dr. Robert Sokol's question about the use of conjoint therapy as a preparation for analysis, I am coming to think this is the procedure of choice when marital discord is the reason for seeking analysis. A series of individual and conjoint interviews with both partners is essential to a diagnostic evaluation of the field in which our future analysand lives and within which we must work. These initial interviews may provide insight into the complementary neurotic interaction and forestall the need for introduction of any parameter into the future analysis of one or the other partner.

Moderator's Response

Alexander S. Rogawski, M.D.
Beverly Hills, California

Dr. Solnit's assertion that my "observations and formulations seem to have a serious internal inconsistency" puzzled me. I did not advocate that the "working through" of the transference-neurosis be replaced by conjoint interviews. I study, interpret and "work through" the transference-neurosis of my patients from the beginning and throughout the course of their treatment. The most conscientious working through often fails to *resolve* the transference-neurosis. In such situations and in the finishing phase of the treatment, conjoint sessions have proven most useful.

I also do not share Dr. Solnit's concern that this technique confuses and distorts "the focus and influence of analytic treatment on autoplastic and alloplastic processes." Long ago I lost my belief in the immaculate separation of these categories. In his brilliant "Notes on the Reality Principle" Heinz Hartmann exposited the intricacies of this problem better than I myself could attempt.

Dr. Jackson's generous encouragement is much appreciated. I am sorry that I gave the impression of assuming that Freud would have eventually become a family therapist. Nothing could be further from my mind. But I did wish to point out that Freud—contrary to some latter-day analysts—did not shun a meeting with the relatives when the occasion arose.

Though Dr. Rodgers structures his experiences in somewhat different ways they seem to resemble in essential aspects the experiences of the panelists.

Dr. Whitaker's spirited reply reveals that he is quite at home with analytic terms. I understand his concern that the analyst may appear to the spouse as a protective and interfering "mother-in-law." In actual experience I have found that by carefully posting myself in equal distance to both participants in the conjoint session I am soon perceived as doctor of both partners. The experience of the past analysis is now used for the understanding and in the interest of both spouses and their mutual transactions.

The patient in Case 2 did not end his treatment precipitously. He set the date himself six months in advance. If he indeed "escaped into health"—a notion which I view often with skepticism—then he has remained quite comfortably in this hide-out for the two years since his treatment ended. He has continued to grow personally, professionally and in his marriage.

I do aim to achieve eventually a therapeutic partnership with my patients but I do not see this an evidence that I let my patients "run my office."

It was instructive and enjoyable to read the stimulating responses to our panel reflecting the varied experiences others have in their offices. "The Forum" has provided an excellent format to shake us out of our solipsism and compare our thinking. I wish to express my appreciation to the discussants and to this original publication.

The Forum

Title A Patient and Her Cats

Author Beryl Sandford

Member and Training Analyst of the British Psychoanalytic Society. She studied psychoanalysis in Paris with the late Dr. Rene Laforgue and worked with families and family interaction in London during World War II. She has been particularly interested in problems of projection and reprojection within the family unit.

Discussants

Harold F. Searles, M.D.

Supervising and Training Analyst in the Washington Psychoanalytic Institute. He was on the staff at Chestnut Lodge for nearly fifteen years, is a Consultant in Psychotherapy at the Sheppard and Enoch Pratt Hospital, and has written *The Nonhuman Environment in Normal Development and in Schizophrenia*, and *Collected Papers on Schizophrenia and Related Subjects*.

Milton Rosenbaum, M.D.

Professor and Chairman of the Department of Psychiatry of Albert Einstein College of Medicine. He has many publications in the fields of clinical psychiatry and psychoanalysis, psychosomatic medicine and medical education. Dr. Rosenbaum is a Member of the New York Psychoanalytic Society. He says you really have to be an "animal" psychologist to discuss this paper.

H. Michael Rosow, M.D.

Associate Clinical Professor of Psychiatry at University of California, Los Angeles, and Lecturer at the Los Angeles Psychoanalytic Institute. He has been a Consultant to the V.A. Mental Hygiene Clinic, the Veterans Administration Psychiatric Hospital and to the Department of Corrections, supervising individual and group therapy. Dr. Rosow has participated in an ongoing research project at Mt. Sinai Hospital, "The Nature of the Therapeutic Process."

Dorothy Semenow Garwood, PH.D.

Holding Ph.D. degrees in chemistry and psychology, she is engaged in psychotherapeutic practice and is on the Sensitivity Training Staffs of the University of California at Los Angeles and National Training Laboratories. She does consultation and treatment with students of the Claremont Colleges, and is the author of many publications. Her current research efforts involve attempts to interrelate psychoanalytic principles and the biochemical basis of behavior.

David W. Morgan, M.D.

Associate Clinical Professor of Psychiatry at the University of Southern California and on the Faculty of the Southern California Psychoanalytic Institute. He has worked with many doctors and their families in therapy projects.

Marshall S. Cherkas, M.D.

Assistant Clinical Professor of Psychiatry at University of Southern California and Consulting Psychiatrist, Los Angeles County Department of Mental Health. He works with addicts and late adolescents.

Arnaldo Rascovsky, M.D.

Honorary President of COPAL (Co-ordinating Committee of the Latin American Psychoanalytic Organizations), Founder, Former President and Training Analyst of the Argentine Psychoanalytic Association. He is the Founder and Former Editor of the "Revista de Psicoanalisis"; the author of two books, *Psychosomatic Pathology* and *Fetal Psychism* and co-editor of another book, *Mania and Psychopathy*, to be published.

A Patient and Her Cats

Beryl Sandford

London, England

Most analysts are familiar with patients who bring material about their pets which can be interpreted as projected parts of themselves, but we do not often have the chance to see the effect of these projections on the pets.

A well-defended psychotic patient of mine gave me the opportunity to observe at close quarters how she uses her cats to people her lonely worlds, both inner and outer, and to serve as receptacles for her projected impulses and feelings.

The first opportunity to see this in action occurred when the patient brought her cat to analysis. Later during a rather severe crisis in her life, I went to her home three times, and had tea with her and her cats.

I will call my patient "Elsie." She first came to me for analysis in 1951 when she was thirty-five years of age, a worthwhile, likeable, intelligent and witty person who was, at that time, about eighty per cent mad. This percentage varied a good deal; sometimes the sane part would be almost completely submerged.

She was born to a psychotic mother and an ineffectual, and often absent, father. Her mother—a severe asthmatic—was mentally and physically too ill to cope with a baby, and Elsie was left to starve for a good part of her infancy. Later her mother beat her unmercifully nearly every day "for her own good," as Elsie dryly remarked.

She cannot remember ever having any toys but on two occasions she had a kitten, which her mother got rid of as soon as the child grew fond of it. Elsie, however, made friends with the cat next door and carried on a secret and close friendship with this cat until it died.

When Elsie was six years old, a brother was born. Whatever she may have felt of envy and jealousy was completely overshadowed by the fact that she now had someone who loved her devotedly. From a very early age, he protected her and stopped mother from beating her.

Elsie did well at school and went to the University, but while there, disaster overtook her. She suffered a double loss; both her brother and her fiancé were killed within a few months of each other during the war. Elsie, whose equilibrium was no doubt always precarious, suffered a severe breakdown.

She left college without taking her degree and after living alone trying to "keep the bits together," she spent a year in a mental hospital, where she was given no treatment beyond a little occupational therapy. She improved sufficiently to leave the hospital and a psychiatrist referred her to her first analyst.

I think she gained much from this analysis although she broke off after two years, in a state of paranoid anxiety, and once again shut herself up in her room. She told me that during this time (called by her "my brain storm") she smashed a good deal of furniture including a kitchen sink, after which she felt better and found a job as a shorthand-typist. Gradually, however, the persecutory fears returned and the psychiatrist who had referred her to her first analyst sent her to me.

The picture she presented at her first interview was not unlike the photo she later showed me of herself as a little girl. She was white-faced, big-eyed and terribly emaciated. Her clothes looked as though they had been found in a dustbin and it later transpired this was actually true of the coat she was wearing. She was not eating at all and existed solely on an occasional glass of beer and a little milk. She was living in what was little better than a coal-hole, gas-lit and damp. An important aspect of her second analysis was that she was paying for it; her first analysis had been free. In the early months of her analysis with me, the first thing I used to see of her was her hand holding the money, coming round the door; she would refuse to come in until I had taken it.

The cat which played such an important part in her life did not appear in the analytic material until almost two years had passed.

It was necessary at first to find a framework within which Elsie could function. She liked lying on the couch but made it into a home away from home, surrounding herself with all sorts of impedimenta such as newspapers, books and knitting, unconsciously arranging a situation from which I was excluded. Interpretations terrified her and before I said three words she would cry "Stop!" in a state of acute anxiety. I finally made the suggestion that I would first say "I have an interpretation—shall I give it to you?" She agreed to this and usually said "Yes" until one day when I asked the usual permission to interpret, she answered tartly, "Of course you may, what do I pay you for?"

It was after this that she began to tell me about her cat. The cat, whom I will call "Spooty," was a handsome tom. Elsie had rescued him a year before from some boys who were tormenting him, had taken the injured animal home and nursed him back to life.

It was soon clear that Spooty was the receptacle of all Elsie's emotional needs. She would cook a rabbit, making it so toothsome that her mouth watered—and then give it all to the cat and be upset if he could not finish it. Spooty also had to live her sex life for her. She would urge him out on to the tiles, round up lady cats for him and, if the weather was bad and he could not go out, she would supply him with a bit of an old fur rug "to have fun and games with." She gave him the best of everything; he had soft cushions and warm blankets while she covered herself with a threadbare coat or newspaper.

Now that Spooty had been brought into the analysis there was ample material for interpretation. But for Elsie just to be given interpretations was not enough, and she started bringing the cat to analysis.

For the first three sessions Spooty behaved in the most exemplary fashion; he lay in front of the fire with his back to me or joined Elsie on the couch, where she fed him fish and chips. But on the fourth day things were different. Elsie arrived, complete with fish and chips and a huge bundle of newspapers. She was in a jumpy, giggly mood and Spooty was decidedly ill at ease. Instead of lying in front of the fire as usual, he began trying to get out of the door. After running frantically around in circles and meowing dismally, he urinated copiously in a corner of the room. Elsie, with a yell of laughter, leapt from the couch and armed with the newspapers she had brought, proceeded to mop up the floor, getting herself very wet in the process. She then returned to the couch with the cat and an armful of soaking newspapers and lay there laughing, saying, "Of course I don't know about you, but I *like* the smell of cat's pee."

Perhaps because I found the smell almost unbearable, I gave her some rather negative interpretations along the line that she was attacking and messing me inside and out. I did not realize I had missed the positive aspects of what had happened until after the next session, when she arrived without the cat saying Spooty was ill. She had taken him to the Cats' Hospital and asked them to keep him for the night, but the hospital declined as there was nothing wrong with him. Furiously and tearfully she said, "No one wants my lovely cat," rushed out of the room and banged the door.

After she missed four appointments I phoned her and was greeted with the curt remark, "You're no good. You didn't understand." I said I thought I understood better now, and reluctantly she agreed to come back. When she returned the next day, I interpreted what had happened, not only as an attack but also as a love offering. She had brought me her "lovely cat"—that is to say, her "lovely mess" —and I had rejected it.

From then on during the next two years, the analysis really moved. Elsie started eating and put on weight; she bought new clothes and moved from the "coal-hole" to a top floor two-room flat, with access to the roof for the cat. She was, in fact, coping quite well. She decided to stop analysis, at least for the time being, as it was a drain on her finances now that she was spending money sensibly on rent, food and clothes. She no longer projected all her needs onto Spooty, but my fear was that if he died, she might have a breakdown. She agreed to keep in touch with me and from time to time phoned or sent a postcard.

A year later, the veterinarian told her Spooty was not likely to live much longer. As in the past Elsie tried to protect herself from disaster. After hearing the vet's verdict she promptly acquired a female cat, a poor flea-bitten stray, whom she cossetted and nursed and then mated with Spooty, personally supervising the mating. The result was one female kitten. Six weeks later Spooty died—a catastrophe for Elsie despite her well-laid plans to cope with the loss.

She came to see me at once and lay on the couch crying helplessly, saying she did not think she would have the courage to go on living as there was nothing to live for now that Spooty was dead. She wondered whether she had ever had anything to live for except her brother, her fiancé and Spooty. Her despair seemed so well-founded that all I could do was to agree. This made her feel less desperate; she had found someone who could accept her despair and she was able to face life again. In her own way she tried to cope with her loss, first, by bringing the dead cat to me to photograph; and second, by having him stuffed.

During the next three months it became clear that her grief and despair were being expressed mainly through her flat which, she kept telling me, was becoming more and more of a pigsty. Often she had found it difficult to tidy her room when depressed, but now the chaos got out of hand: the mess was suffocating her and she felt helpless. She could talk of nothing else and my interpretations seemed to get lost in the chaos, and she could do nothing with them. Her continual cry was, "It must be seen to be believed," and finally she despairingly asked me if I would come see it. I said I would. She invited me to come for tea, but at the same time she insisted this was to be a professional call. She sent a note: "I must stress that Saturday will be no normal social occasion but more in the nature of a visiting consultation, or is this where I could talk of extramural research?" Looking back at the three tea parties, I think the latter is a very good description of them.

The day I was to visit, she phoned and said she could not let me come until she had cleaned things up a bit. After she put me off three times I asked why she could not trust me to see the mess—after all she had been saying it had to be seen to be believed and if she tidied it up before I came she was defeating my chances of believing it. She said, "That's reasonable, I'll risk it."

The chaos was unbelievable. She took me into a small room which she used for eating, sleeping, washing and cooking. Elsie had cleared a narrow path through the room, which was covered with heaps of junk to a height of about three feet. Two clothes lines, one on each side of the pathway, were hung with every kind of dirty garment and old bits of sheets and blankets. In the fireplace were close to fifty empty tins of cat food; the place smelled strongly of cats and old boiled fish. It was alive with fleas which Elsie said were cat fleas and would not bite humans. Despite this, I was badly bitten.

In the midst of this squalor and chaos was a small spotlessly clean table, on which were unopened packets of tea, butter, bread and an unopened bottle of milk. She asked me to sit on the divan and the two cats—whom I will call "Queenie" and "Kitten"—sat on each side of me. I had given some thought as to how I would conduct this visit and finally decided to act on an *ad hoc* basis. I would observe what happened and accept any role demanded of me, in a state of free-floating receptiveness.

Elsie immediately started making tea, saying, "At least everything you eat and drink here will be clean." When she came to pour milk for my tea she said, "I will give you all the cream from the top of the bottle." I replied, "But what about you? You will leave yourself only skim milk." She looked up in surprise saying, "But I *always* give the cream to the cats." One could have immediately given an interpretation, but I felt to do so at that moment would have shattered her delusion before it had been lived through, so I thanked her and drank the cream. Elsie ate and drank nothing. She hovered at the other end of the room waiting on me and the two cats.

After tea I was taken into the other room, which was coldly tidy. As I thought how chill and dead it was, Elsie suddenly opened a wooden box; inside it was Spooty, stuffed. I was then taken back into the first room and Elsie asked me to help her start tidying up, adding, "I can't cope with it, it is stronger than I am." I suggested starting with the heaps on the floor, and began to lift things from the pile nearest me. Elsie, apparently enormously relieved, said, "That's all right, *now* I can get on with it," and sat me on the divan while she set to work clearing the floor. Oddly enough there was little that was junk on the floor. Most of the things were worth keeping: half-knitted jumpers and cardigans, books, handkerchiefs, scarves and stockings. At the bottom of the heap she found a one-pound note, which she handed to me as part of my fee.

The finding of the money coincided with the end of the session; I had been there just under an hour. As she brought me my coat she said, "This has been the most valuable session I have ever had. Will you come again next Saturday? It is *very* important." I agreed, since it was obvious that something very dynamic was being worked through.

On my next visit the small room was much tidier—though still flea-ridden. I was taken at once into the other room which was still chill and comfortless. The two cats which were on the roof came in when Elsie called them. They seemed nervous; they arched their backs, jumped away from me and refused to be friendly. Again she had the unopened packets of tea, butter and milk, but also a jar of cream and some raspberries. Elsie kept washing the raspberries saying "I don't want you to get any maggots." She made me sit in a large armchair in the middle of the room; again she ate and drank nothing. In addition to the raspberries, there was a plate piled high with pastries. I ate as much as I could of raspberries and cream and pastries but I could sense Elsie's hostility because I did not eat them all. When I refused a third helping of raspberries she said testily, "Don't worry, there aren't any maggots in them."

When tea was finished, the cats came in again, but only for a moment. Queenie arched her back and Kitten spat at me and both went out on the roof again. Elsie then brought in a plant which she wanted me to transplant from one pot to another. As I did so, I spilled some wet earth on the carpet, making a small brown stain. Elsie rushed to wipe it up. Although protesting vigorously that she did not mind, she was obviously upset and angry. The atmosphere was tense and hostile and quite unlike that of the week before. I stayed about fifty minutes; as I left she agreed to come to my consulting room Monday as I felt that I could now begin to interpet what had been happening.

I suggested the untidy room represented Life and the tidy room Death. In this connection, the fleas were significant. When Elsie brought the dead cat to be photographed, she remarked, "Dead cats don't have fleas—only live ones do." At the first tea party I was Spooty, alive and well—and flea-bitten—and being fed with cream; a good cat who helped her clear up her internal chaos and to cope with the mad mother whom she felt was inside her suffocating and overwhelming her. At the second tea party I was the cat she overfed, whom she stuffed both in life and in death, and who she feared would get maggots as a result.

Her reply was most illuminating. She told how she had tried to feed Spooty his favorite foods when he was dying, but he couldn't eat anything; then, just as he died, he defecated, making a small brown stain on the carpet. Now she was able to express her fury with Spooty for dying and refusing all her efforts to "feed" him back to life. Also, the vet warned her Spooty might get maggots because she had delayed having him stuffed. This was followed by a memory of herself having worms when she was small, and of mother spending hours deworming her. At the end of the session she asked me to come for *one more* tea party, saying "It is *very* important."

The third and last tea party can be quickly described. There was a marked change in the flat. "The once chaotic room was reasonably tidy; there was no odor and no fleas. The other room, formerly so dead and chill, looked warm and pleasant; there were flowers around and the tea was laid on a small table in front of the fire with an armchair on each side. Instead of hovering at the other end of the room, Elsie sat in the armchair opposite me. She made tea, toasted crumpets and ate as many as I did. The cats did not escape on to the roof, nor arch their backs and spit. Queenie sat on my knee and Kitten sat on Elsie's knee, both cats purring contentedly. After this visit the analysis continued in the ordinary way for nearly a year until Elsie had worked through her mourning for the loss of Spooty and was able to eat, sleep and work again.

There are several questions I would like to discuss in regard to Elsie's relationship with her cats. For example, what type of relationship was it? Was Spooty a "transitional object"? Was this a narcissistic relationship? Why the need for all the massive projective-identification and acting out not only of patient, but also of analyst?

In light of material from Elsie, and observation of her behavior at the tea parties, I suggest she always had to carry the burden of projections which her mother was unable to re-introject. Elsie was always struggling to find objects who could take both her own and her mother's projections and cope with them for her. When these receiving objects were lost, psychosis threatened to overwhelm her completely. So long as she had Spooty, the chaos in her room, though sometimes menacing, could be kept within bounds. When Spooty died she could not battle alone with the mad mother who overwhelmed and suffocated her. She had to turn me into Spooty and not only use me to work through her mourning, but also to deal with her mad mother's projections. The moment I started tidying up her room for her, she was able to take over and do it for herself. I think in that moment, when she tackled the heap on the floor, I had, for Elsie, accepted her reprojection and given her the chance to cope with her own internal problems, free of the burden of her mother's madness.

I now come to the question of object choice. Why did Elsie choose a cat? For Elsie, it seems to me to have been the perfect choice. A dog, dependent and object-seeking, would have been a continual threat to Elsie's internal world, but a cat would not as it makes a relationship but does not impinge, nor does he allow you to do so. A cat is faithful, but comes and goes in his own time; he may stay away for days yet expects to be accepted on his return, on his own terms. He will be pleased if you feed him and offer him a warm fire, but if you do not, he will finally go off and manage for himself.

Elsie's independence seems to have been inbuilt from the beginning of her life. She and others who have similar problems of very early and severe deprivation, are independent because they are still, as it were, one with the universe. They cannot be dependent because, until they have achieved a state of differentiation from the external world, there is no "not-me person" on whom to be dependent. This is different from the baby whose mother is inconsistent, close to the baby one day and withdrawn the next. This person will not dare to be dependent on anyone for fear of being dropped. For Elsie, the question of being "dropped" did not enter because there just wasn't anyone there to drop her, as all external objects were part of herself. This state of oneness with the universe was carried into Elsie's everyday life and everyone with whom she came into contact was unconsciously felt —and used—by her as part of herself.

For this type of relationship, cats were the perfect choice. This was clearly demonstrated in the analytic sessions and at the three tea parties, where I watched the cats accepting roles assigned to them and playing their parts in a most remarkable way. Also, by allowing myself to accept the role of the cat—alive, dying and dead—and thus becoming part of Elsie's deluded world, I was able to help her to emerge from her delusion and become more nearly a separate person than she had ever been before.

The more I study her case, the more I realize how like a cat Elsie is. I have always alluded to her in my notes as "the cat girl," but only since I started writing this paper have I appreciated how well this describes her. She has all the cat's ability to manage for itself under all circumstances; she has all the cat's capacity to isolate itself; she has, in fact, all the proud independence of a cat. Both for the cat and for Elsie this independence is their strength—but for Elsie it is also her tragedy.

51 Queen Anne Street
London, W.I. England

Discussant

Harold F. Searles, M.D.
Chevy Chase, Maryland

In this wholly delightful paper we have a fascinating picture of a therapist who possesses a remarkable capacity to appreciate the individuality, intelligence and creativity of a very psychotic woman. Mrs. Sandford goes to lengths of therapeutic devotion which put most of us, her colleagues, to shame.

The importance of the cats in the patient's life parallels that of pets in the lives of schizophrenic patients whom former colleagues at Chestnut Lodge and I have treated. Of particular interest to me was Mrs. Sandford's discovery that she had come to possess the transference meaning to her patient, of the latter's beloved cat. My monograph on the nonhuman environment reports many clinical examples of this variety.

I presume Mrs. Sandford is correct in her belief that the cats served as transitional objects for the patient—as objects midway, in their significance for this woman's primitive ego-functioning, between "me" and "not-me." But I would emphasize that the cats may often have not merely given vicarious expression to this woman's unconscious needs, but may have had a genuine impact upon her as separate and real initiators of various "interpersonal" processes. My monograph quotes Louis Linn as observing, regarding dogs, that:

". . . Clearly, the dog is no inanimate repository of symbolic meaning, but a living being that eats and bites and destroys and urinates and defecates and can lavish affection and has a sex life and, finally, is subject to illness and death . . . In short, dogs are capable of entering into human emotional relationships which seem almost as complicated bilaterally."

One of the few basic lessons I have learned

about schizophrenic patients is the extremely significant degree of positive feeling between the patient and the mother— even in those instances, as in Mrs. Sandford's case-description, where it appears to us that the mother was unrelievedly hostile to the child. My surmise is that Elsie's mother was the first "cat," for whom the real cats later came to serve as substitutes, and that with the development of Elsie's transference to Mrs. Sandford, the "cat" reacquired its human personification. My surmise is, further, that just as Mrs. Sandford found this patient to have redeeming features despite the blatant craziness, so, too, had Elsie's mother possessed redeeming features in her daughter's eyes.

To hypothesize, further, I suggest that Elsie's craziness sprang in large part from an introject of her psychotic mother who not only had caused Elsie grievous suffering, but whose own suffering the daughter had tried desperately to relieve. I believe the patient unconsciously recreated, *via* her psychosis, the situation with her ill mother. As a result, Mrs. Sandford, who with the help of the patient was able to cope effectively with the psychotic process, personified Elsie's own child-therapist strivings to save her mother from psychosis. "Her mother . . . was too ill mentally and physically to cope with a baby" forms a striking parallel to Elsie's saying, of her own flat, "I can't cope with it; it is stronger than I am."

Lastly, I suggest that Mrs. Sandford's starting to tidy up Elsie's apartment meant to Elsie that her therapist no longer needed for Elsie to be crazy. We develop an immense emotional investment in our patients' craziness. Here, Mrs. Sandford was showing, in action as well as in words, that, much as she appreciated the patient's craziness, she valued sanity more.

Discussant

Milton Rosenbaum, M.D.

Bronx, New York

I enjoyed reading this delightful manuscript which was more of a poignant human story, well told, than a "scientific" paper. Parts of it, especially the "tea party," bring up pleasant memories of similar tea parties of Alice and her "friends."

The main defect of this paper is that the author does not give enough of the raw data of the "analysis" (such as dreams, associations, etc.), which perhaps though not too important in this type of communication, nevertheless does not permit critical discussion of some of the issues.

The particular significance of the cat in the life of the patient is of course overdetermined. The author emphasizes the identification of the patient with the cat's "proud independence" and capacity to isolate itself within a continuous pet-master relationship. I agree, but in addition to the use of the cat for projection there must be particular significance in the fact that Spooty was a tom. The identification of Spooty with Elsie's brother and the use of Spooty in the patient's penis envy conflict was not emphasized.

The most fascinating aspect of the case was the therapy. Was the patient in psychoanalysis as it is usually defined? I would say no, but would consider the patient to have been treated by a psychoanalyst in "relationship" therapy. This leads to the transference implication. The author mentions she was identified with Spooty, but perhaps the good therapeutic benefits resulted from the analyst being a human being who cared and was concerned (as she certainly was) for this patient rather than a "proud, independent and isolated" cat who does not have the capacity to care for and be concerned.

The author speculates that patients suffering from severe early deprivation are "independent" because they have never experienced a meaningful object relationship, and she differentiates such people from those who remain dependent because of fear of loss of objects as the result of inconsistent mothering. I do not think the term "independent" really describes the major or basic difference between these two groups, because in the latter the "independent" behavior is a defense while in the former it is a severe and serious ego defect.

Discussant

H. Michael Rosow, M.D.
Beverly Hills, California

Most striking, in this moving clinical paper, is that the patient comes through as a likeable, even admirable, very real three-dimensional personality. This reflects Mrs. Sandford's respect and genuine concern for Elsie as a person. That such a severely traumatized patient was willing to accept the therapist's admission of error in rejecting her "gift" and return to therapy speaks well for the rapport the analyst was able to establish with her.

I question the therapeutic value of analysis when for Elsie it was not enough to give interpretations. One cannot work through resistance and transference feelings, i.e., work analytically, with a patient for whom interpretations are not enough. Since the therapist was aware of this, why play the "May I give you an interpretation" game? How can one expect a patient who cannot differentiate herself from the outside world (from the "not-me" person) to possibly utilize transference interpretations which require the capacity for such differentiation.

I suspect analytic uncovering technique would be antitherapeutic for such a patient, and may have been responsible for her psychotic paranoid-anxiety break after two years of analysis. I believe Elsie wisely defended herself from analysis by bringing her "impedimenta" to the couch (thereby misusing it, and negating its analytic function). She sensed that she needed a meaningful encounter with the therapist and converted her enforced position on the couch into a real relationship by shouting "Stop!" whenever the therapist would "interpret" instead of being such a real person.

The parameters introduced by the therapist at the patient's insistence were the therapeutically effective modalities. Elsie could only master her traumatic memories by reenacting them with the therapist. For example, only by the analyst "becoming" Spooty and allowing herself to be overstuffed, i.e., by a non-verbal reexperiencing in action, could any meaningful resolution be accomplished. Similarly, the therapist had to express her concern and her dedication to do whatever was necessary to help Elsie through action for it to be meaningful for Elsie. This, Mrs. Sandford did by initiating the tidying-up of Elsie's room, by her willingness to subordinate her own comfort in braving the flea attacks and the patient's psychotic behavior, and by being there when she was needed. The actions were effective because they were emotionally packed, meaningful and properly timed empathic nonverbal communications.

Similarly, Elsie could only discharge her rage and really be aware of it through action (smashing her furniture) with resulting effective therapeutic results; perhaps these proverbially traumatized patients can only "remember" through such actions. This would not be mistaken for the "acting out" which serves as a resistance to avoid remembering.

The therapist's consistent emotional presence, the availability of her physical presence, and her tuning in on Elsie's emotional needs converted a tenuous therapeutic alliance into a meaningful encounter. Elsie's recognition that Mrs. Sandford really knew and felt and accepted Elsie's despair is, I believe, what enabled her to dare trust the analyst enough to try to cope with life again.

Projective identification is undoubtedly a useful concept of a type of mental functioning. However, I have an uneasy feeling that in the examples given, this mental mechanism becomes an almost palpable structure. I refer, for example, to the author's remark, "The cats served as receptacles for the projected impulses and feelings of her own."

Anyone who ever owned a pet knows how sensitive such creatures are to the owner's moods. Do we really need such elaborate explanations to account for the cats being nervous and running off when Elsie behaved irrationally?

It would be more convincing if we were given more material to support the formulations that she used Spooty and later the therapist as reprojection receptacles.

Nor do I believe one is justified in saying her independence is due to her inability to distinguish herself from a "not-me" person on whom to be dependent. (This implies early fixation as opposed to regression.) I believe her narcissistic withdrawal and psychotic reactions were regressive responses to the simultaneous loss of her brother and fiancé. Her near-catastrophic reaction to the loss of Spooty indicates considerable capacity for dependence.

I believe this paper is a fine example of the art of therapy. With the right ear and the right heart, the theoretical formulations of the therapist seem to assume a secondary importance.

Discussant

Dorothy Semenow Garwood, PH.D.

Beverly Hills, California

Mrs. Sandford presents a fascinating story and a deeply moving communication of an analyst's profound respect for and commitment to her patient. She demonstrates uncommon intuitiveness and clinical acumen in fathoming "the cat girl" and, what is rarer, remarkable courage in translating her perceptions into action which was at once effectively therapeutic and exquisitely human.

Elsie struggled for what should have been her birthright—the right to live as a *separate* person. The analyst expertly navigated a precarious course replete with such crucial milestones as her patient's needs to pay a "good" fee, to control interpretations, and to have her tea parties despite the "risk." In each event the analyst delivered Elsie from the Scylla of invasion and the Charybdis of abandonment, and thereby ultimately earned interpersonal mutuality with Elsie—a mutuality which freed Elsie to begin to achieve her individual separateness. The "cat pee episode" could have proved disastrous, but was turned to therapeutic advantage. The analyst admitted and corrected her error, thus delineating herself as an autonomous person who, unlike Elsie's mother, took responsibility for her wrongs (and projections) toward Elsie.

For the psychotic "Elsies," and for others who suffer from very early and severe deprivation and yet elude psychoses, the traumatic roots extend back beyond words. Refusal to visit Elsie in her home, and there to receive her deepest non-verbal symbolic communications, would have been refusal to "see" (and "it must be seen to be believed") and hence the ultimate negation of Elsie.

The tea parties had important therapeutic

significance in addition to their crucial role as a means of expression for Elsie. Here we may find it instructive to utilize concepts from learning theory as a framework within which to consider the function of the tea parties and to compare it with other therapeutic methods.

Thus, while most therapists of a variety of persuasions utilize learning principles in their treatment of less severely disturbed patients, many become rather alarmed at the malignant regressive potential inherent in their application to cases such as Elsie's. Therapeutic circumspection is, of course, indicated, but the voice of the patient's needs must be heeded and answered. Elsie, in rock-bottom despair, yet clung to a thread of hope in her conviction that if she could take the analyst back with her to the point where things went wrong (the pathological stimulus constellation), the analyst could help her (a new positive reinforcement) with her demons and she could find the beginnings of a separate existence for herself (a new response or solution). Indispensable to Elsie's learning and a different solution to her critical situation was the concrete presence of certain cues: her home, her "mess," her food, her Life Room, her Death Room, her cats, *and* her analyst.

Optimal learning conditions are characterized by the closest possible association in time between the stimulus events and the new desired responses. In Elsie's case this would dictate that the analyst's interpretations be given during the tea parties. However, for patients like Elsie, such on-the-spot interpretations seem contra-indicated. Somehow, at that moment, interpretations interfere with the patient's feeling of freedom to live out her symbolic truth; perhaps to be allowed to "show" without interference is an essential initial corrective emotional experience. Later, once the analyst had proved herself in the living room of action, the patient became increasingly involved in the verbal interpretive work.

Severely deprived, yet non-psychotic, patients may find it necessary to voice their needs through similar symbolic action. A Jewish woman patient, in the throes of an intensely ambivalent transference, brought matzos to her hour and clearly had in mind to "break bread" with her therapist. The patient was well aware of usual therapeutic procedure and the defiance of "the rules" that her act entailed. Yet the therapist responded, by eating the matzos, to her patient's deeper plea for the therapist to join in a pact to help her out of bondage. The patient was relieved and moved by the therapist's acceptance of her offering; she herself interpreted the negative aspects of the matzos episode, the immediate therapeutic impasse was resolved, and the usual therapeutic work was continued.

These patients for whom at times "words are not enough" find themselves other roads out of despair.

Discussant

David W. Morgan, M.D.

Pasadena, California

This sad and beautiful clinical report on the Cat Girl reminds me of an enchanting book by E. B. White, *Charlotte's Web*. To have given this lonely girl the mother she needed is the remarkable achievement of her analyst. The careful interpretive work and the intuitive seeking for material from Elsie's cats and her home are indicative of this analyst's willingness to search for meaningful cathexis wherever she can find it.

I assume the dream material was barren and rarely useable. The living death of Elsie stalks us throughout this report. Elsie literally rescues herself from death by using the reliable childhood object, "the cat next door." Then Elsie, in the presence of her benevolent new mother, builds a cat family that provides a reenactment of her past, makes restitution and offers more positive maternal introjects. I would guess that "the cat next door" died before the pregnancy and birth of Elsie's brother. The brother temporarily gave tremendous relief for Elsie from her destructive wishes towards the unborn brother and the pregnant mother. The maggots and berries scene seems to be a distorted reenactment of feelings toward the pregnant mother.

Finally, the cat family included the resurrected mother and child, the new mother (analyst), and her daughter (Elsie). These scenes with the cat in the office and the visits to Elsie's home resemble a critical sequence of dreams which illuminate a more traditional working through of the transference to a more tenable human relationship.

To say that cats are not very dependent on their masters is to reveal either the prejudice of a dog lover, or ignorance of cat behavior. Elsie's cats performed precisely in a well-structured intimacy. Then too, we know that domesticated animals are used by man to represent and gratify various aspects of his inner world. Cats in our times often represent the sphinx mother, the daughter of the witch, the cold bitch, or the distant, destructive, howling "nut." Cat worship is still with us in "pussy cat a-go-go." Cats will perform their roles in obedience to the master's unconscious demands.

Be that as it may, Elsie would not have survived a sphinx therapist. An analyst willing to become a cat's mother leads this sick girl to a more humane and less dissociated way of being. To quote a beat friend: "Shrink, that pussy-cat analyst played it real cool. She's great. She turned that square cat on." Case studies like this renew my pride in being an analyst.

Discussant

Marshall S. Cherkas, M.D.

Beverly Hills, California

Mrs. Sandford's paper was read by me with glee and horror—the glee springing from her fascinating description of her patient's psychotic life so beautifully interwoven with the cat; the horror, because of the objectless, cold aura of the world as it must have been perceived by Elsie. I am afraid I cannot deal with Mrs. Sandford's "reprojections," "re-introjections," and "transitional objects"; they sound too much like Elsie's stuffed Spooty (artificial and unsatisfying), but I certainly understand what she intends to convey concerning Elsie's need to find some living thing into whom she could pour her feelings.

The character of this patient reminds me of Horney's description of the "withdrawn" personality who harbors deep unconscious longings for closeness. Might Elsie's erotic devotion to Spooty represent her "often absent" father and lost brother fused into one? Perhaps she reaches out so tentatively with her money because she must first give to another to assuage what must be an overwhelmingly punitive superego growing out of the inner rage against such a mother. (How close the pussycat is to the tiger!) This may also account for her internal "mess" and also explain her need to have an analyst who would see, touch and feel her at this level.

One sees a real beginning of transference with the anger over the analyst's refusal of her "gift" (the cat and its urine). For the patient to accept the analyst as a meaningful person, she must convey to the patient a real demonstration of receptivity at such an infantile level. I admire Mrs. Sandford for her clinical skill and her willingness to meet Elsie in her world (however masochistic this might seem).

I seriously doubt that one can work with such psychotic patients without this openness and zeal. I laughed when I read how Mrs. Sandford's countertransference broke through by "accidentally" dropping the dirt on Elsie's carpet in retaliation for Spooty's office deed.

If we are to understand and emotionally contact such patients, I think we must courageously "act out" by entering the tiger's cage as Mrs. Sandford did. Only then can we be the "participant observer" and return the gift through "the corrective emotional experience."

Discussant

Arnaldo Rascovsky, M.D.
Buenos Aires, Argentina
Received as "The Forum" went to press

Beryl Sandford's vivid and original essay leads us to clarify the relationship between the individual and the animal object, specifically the cat, the last tamed feline. The displacement towards the animal as a substitute object appears in a large range of situations going from totemism to bestialism.

In the case presented, the intense projective identification is of such outstanding significance that the problem is stated in terms of the possible psychosis of the cat itself or its receptiveness of and identifications with the projections of the patient's psychotic parts.

I fully agree with Mrs. Sandford that the specific animal choice is based not only on the historical relationship with cats in the patient's childhood, but more basically on the structure of the cat itself as an object able to receive in absolute independence the split-off parts of the patient as well as on the patient's incapacity for an adequate splitting and therefore integration of these parts.[1]

I had two important experiences with patients and their cats. The first was a women who had to interrupt her treatment because she was forced to settle in another country for a period of years. She then returned home and resumed her analysis. During the period she was away, an intense depressive process was reactivated. It was related to serious traumatic and surgical situations at a very early age which prevented her from working through the infantile depressive position and all separations in later life. In the country where she settled, she started a very intense relationship with a kitten which she brought home and reared when she was pregnant with her first child. This kitten became a substitute object representing her mother and her analyst, as well as her own parts identified with these objects. A year later a peculiar phenomenon occurred: the cat used to be in heat simultaneously with the menses of the patient. This was so obvious that, when the cat started its heat mewing, her husband would ask his wife if her menses had started. The cat made such an intense identification with her and her child that the infant's anxiety in demanding its mother was perceived by the cat who went in search of the mother to care for the baby.

The second patient is more interesting from a psychopathological point of view. He was a markedly autistic schizoid subject, having a complex family history because of his parents' frequent quarrels and divorce and the fact that he was the only son, closely and submissively attached to his eldest sister. When he came for

[1]As Thevenin says (*Origine des Animaux Domestiques*, Presse Universitaire de France, 1947): ". . . of all our domestic animals the cat is the only one not living in herds or at least in groups in freedom. It is surprising that, even when its interest is not at stake, it shows towards man frank affective feelings, whilst such feelings are not shown to the individuals of its own race, and solitary life seems to be the most appropriate."

treatment, he had just broken up his marriage as a result of his paranoid and manic aggravation. The disparagement of the object's importance and his contempt for it had rendered marital life impossible. He had never achieved an internal separation from his parents which would enable him to live independently with a woman. Denial of this factor was based on his keeping a family of cats at home, which had the function of preserving the idealized family organization of his childhood and the manic reparation of his wish to destroy his parents' union and his early objects. One reason for his divorce was that he slept with all the cats in the marital bed, thus objectifying the persistent relation with his parents and preventing his marital life. One of the pathetic episodes during his analysis occurred when the mother cat died: the patient fell into an acute process of mourning which was not adequately worked through because another cat was substituted.

I have not had the unique and most rewarding experience of coming directly in contact with the cats, as Mrs. Sandford did, and observing the effect of the patient's massive projective identification on them.

Mrs. Sandford puts forth the question as to what type of relationship Elsie had with her cats. Was it a transitional object? It seems, rightly enough, that Elsie had not achieved an adequate differentiation from the external world and that her external objects played the exclusive role of being her primitive internal ones. The cat was an entirely narcissistic object in the sense that it was a projected internal object, having no re-introjective modifications. It is likely that the intensity of the massive projective identification is the main basis for the patient's acting out and her inducing the analyst's acting out. The persecutory nature of the early object is the cause of the impossibility of its adequate re-introjection and healthy splitting. Therefore, idealization is increased, thus falling on a displaced object liable to receive it, namely, the cat. In such an idealization all positive goods are bestowed on the object who must thence eat all the food, use the best blankets and have the best sexual possibilities, while Elsie stands as the persecuted object with no possibility whatsoever and subject to all sufferings. The three sessions with the cat are followed by a fourth in which the projection of the idealization on the cat returns to her own self and the cat is now the persecuted, ill and sad object which she felt as her own bad parts rejected by the analyst. She therefore missed the next sessions.

This intense splitting still prevails in the episodes in the rooms of her flat and in her behavior with the analyst during the tea parties.

Her persistency in this object relationship and her incapability to relate with more organized human objects seem to be directly connected with the extreme paranoid nature of the initial human object, i.e., the mad mother, which forces the displacement towards the cat.

We could consider the cat as Elsie's double on which the unacceptable split-off parts are projected, thus enabling the internal split union in the outside world: Elsie and the cat. The peculiar feature in this relationship is that the cat is the idealized part. Elsie keeps to herself the negative part and reproduces to a certain extent the longed-for union with her mother, her desire to have been taken care of as she takes care of the cat. This union is very regressive and exclusively on a fetal level, denying in this way the extreme paranoid aspect of her relationship with her mother.

Two elements are suggested but not emphasized in Mrs. Sandford's material. They are guilt and reparation with reference to the death of her brother and fiancé, repeating the more archaic working through. I consider they are essential elements in her care and rearing of the cats.

The union with the cat also permits the splitting-off of the ideal and bad object, of the sexual wealth of the cat and her own misery.

The ideal object is thus preserved by the projection on the cat, there being no possibility of contamination with the bad aspects within her submitted to the mad mother.

On the other hand, the analyst at the tea parties obviously assumes the patient's projections to such an extent that it might be supposed that the analyst stained the carpet repeating what Spooty had done when dying, i.e., defecating on it. On the other hand, the maggots that the analyst and the cat might get are associated with the reparatory aspects of the mother who appears in a memory deworming her as a small child.

Another point of considerable importance is her need to find real receiving objects for her projective identifications. When early anxieties are too intense, in order to avoid psychosis, the projection must not be made *in vacuo* (as in dreams and hallucinations) but on the receiving object. This is one of the important functions carried out by the animal object which is nearest to the human one.

Author's Response

Beryl Sandford

London, England

I would like to thank the discussants for their appreciative and interesting comments.

Dr. Morgan is correct about the dream material—it was rare and of a primitive type, mainly concerned with bodily sensations which terrified the patient and had a nightmarish quality. I do not seem to have made myself clear as Dr. Morgan suggests that I have "the prejudices of a dog lover or ignorance of cat behavior"! When I say that cats are not very dependent on their masters what I really mean is that cats do not accept us as their "masters" in the way that dogs so readily do. One might say that one does not own a cat —the cat shares one's home. I would only agree that "cats will perform their roles in obedience to the master's unconscious demands" if it is expressed as follows: "Cats will perform their roles in response to their companion's unconscious demands."

A cat will only come on one's knee if he decides this for himself and this was characteristic of Elsie; any attempt on my part to, as it were, take her on my knee would have been repulsed. Availability was the keynote of the situation. This is opposite to the behavior of a patient whom I might well call my "dog-girl" (she once owned three dogs and fourteen puppies). This girl was forever trying to force me to satisfy her demands in a very desperate and pathetic attempt to control me completely. Elsie, on the contrary, was extremely undemanding, which I think arose from her having coped with early deprivations by the mechanism of "denial of the need."

Dr. Rosow asks why I played the "May I give you an interpretation game?," knowing this was not sufficient. At the beginning of her analysis, although I realized a special framework was necessary, I could not at first know the best way to handle the situation. The "interpretation game" was a stepping-stone and did, as I pointed out, enable Elsie to accept many interpretations until the death of Spooty produced a crisis calling for different handling. The tea parties arose from this crisis and I do not think they would have been possible without the preliminary period when we played the "interpretation game." Elsie's first analysis, broken off after two years, had been rigidly "classical" and the analyst who conducted it told me she realized that Elsie needed something different. This analyst died about six months after Elsie started her analysis with me. Elsie was heartbroken and feared she had caused the analyst's death. Elsie's first remark to me, at the preliminary interview, was, "What would you do if I smashed up your room?" I said, "I would stop you," and she answered with relief, "*That's* all right then!"

Spooty certainly stood for everything mentioned by the discussants—the often-absent father, the brother, the fiancé, her own genitals, but I agree with Dr. Searles that the mother was the first "cat." I also agree with his hypothesis that there were positive feelings hidden behind the mother's apparently perpetual hate and that Elsie was unconsciously striving to relieve her mother's sufferings. This was expressed by Elsie when she rescued Spooty and the Sandy Mother Cat from the results of ill-treatment and nursed them both back to life.

Since the cat's tea parties described in my paper, Elsie's mother has died. This called for a few more extremely interesting tea parties. I would like to describe very briefly the behavior of the mother just prior to her death and Elsie's behavior at the funeral. Both actions seem to reveal the hidden love which must always have existed between them. Telling it to me as a sardonic joke, Elsie described how she had taken a huge wreath of roses to her mother's funeral and had written the following message across it in large letters:

"With Christ which is Far Better." Behind the sardonic joke was Elsie's despair at not being able, as Dr. Searles puts it, to be the therapist-daughter to the suffering mother, and she was sadly consigning her mother to someone who could do it "far better."

Elsie's remark, "Mother could never give me a present—except beatings," helped us toward understanding an apparently very hostile action on the part of the mother who, at her death, left all her money to a home for orphan girls. It seems as though she could not give her love/money directly to her own "orphan" Elsie—she had to give it to as many substitute "orphan" Elsies as she could. A previous example of the mother's indirect way of showing her positive feelings occurred during Spooty's lifetime. Elsie took him with her on one of her rare visits to her mother. She told me next day with great delight that her mother had said, "That's a very nice cat indeed," whereupon Spooty jumped on the mother's knee and had been stroked and made much of. Characteristically, Elsie made an amusing and witty anecdote of the incident, but she could not hide the great happiness she derived from this indirect love offering.

It is possible that it was her unconscious appreciation and acceptance of her mother's indirect love offering which made her almost fanatically refuse her solicitor's attempts to get her to contest the will. When I said to her, "You are the 'orphan girl' your mother is leaving her money to," she said very quietly, "I know."

The Forum

Title — **Manic Depressive Cycles of the Poet Shelley**

Author — **Milton L. Miller, M.D.**

Professor of Psychiatry at the University of North Carolina at Chapel Hill and Chairman of the University of North Carolina-Duke Psychoanalytic Institute. He is engaged in the teaching and training of psychiatrists in psychoanalytic training and is the author of numerous articles on psychoanalytic topics, psychosomatic disorders, and a book, *A Psychoanalytic Study of Marcel Proust.*

Discussants

George Frumkes, M.D.

Associate Clinical Professor of Psychiatry at University of Southern California and a Training Analyst of the Southern California Psychoanalytic Institute. He has been interested in the application of psychoanalysis to literature and, conversely, the influence of philosophic attitudes on the theory and techniques of psychoanalysis, as illustrated in two of his papers, "The Oedipus Theme in the Stories of the Opera," and "The Impairment of the Sense of Reality in Psychoneurosis and Everyday Life."

Louis Fraiberg, PH.D.

Professor of English and Chairman of the Department at the University of Toledo. He received his Ph.D. from the University of Michigan with a dissertation which became his book, *Psychoanalysis and American Literary Criticism.* He has also contributed to scholarly and scientific journals on the relation between literature and psychoanalysis, his special field being the modern age which, defined flexibly, includes the time of Shelley. He has taught courses in the Romantic Period and is an admirer of the poetry of that age. He has also been a special lecturer in the New Orleans Psychoanalytic Institute.

Maurice N. Walsh, M.D.

Associate Clinical Professor of Psychiatry at the University of California at Los Angeles and on the Faculty of the Los Angeles Institute for Psychoanalysis. He has published papers on psychiatric aspects of the lives and works of Leonardo da Vinci and Pietro Aretino, on ego psychology, on the psychopathology of Nazi leaders, and on unconscious motivations for war.

Fred Feldman, M.D.

Member of the Faculty of the California College of Medicine (University of California) where he is in charge of psychosomatic and comprehensive medicine. He is on the Faculty of the Southern California Psychoanalytic Institute where he has taught a course in the psychoanalytic aspects of music and art. Dr. Feldman has conducted seminars at the University of California at Los Angeles on "Criticism in the Arts."

Manic Depressive Cycles of the Poet Shelley

Milton L. Miller, M.D.
Chapel Hill, North Carolina

Shelley recommended the study of dreams, and hoped one day to create a complete psychological theory. Without being explicit, Shelley, together with his paramour Mary Godwin who later became his second wife, often indicated that they had an important psychological contribution to offer. I believe they did, and that it was to expose certain imagery of manic-depressive cycles.

Shelley often thought of himself as a frail, innocent child, or else as an almost omnipotent force in nature, like the West Wind, or a star. He admitted being unable to identify himself with flesh-and-blood, everyday people. Although he was the father of many children and was preoccupied with infants and children in his imagery, fatherhood as experienced by ordinary men was alien to him. He felt, instead, a grandiose identity typified by Job, Prometheus, or Ahasuerus, the Wandering Jew—all figures persecuted by God's tyranny. He feared not only his own father, but all priests, governments, man-made laws, customs and traditions. To fight back against these overwhelming adversaries, he identified with the omniscient, supreme force of good in perfected verbal imagery. He felt that poetry must eventually conquer evil without doing evil. He very often solved his personal problem of non-aggression by considering that the conquest of the evils of life lay beyond death. He felt, while in his enthusiastic states, that he was a fountain of goodness with Messianic mission for mankind. The liquid character of musical sounds was often emphasized in his poetry.

He experienced heights and depths of emotion, sometimes in daily cycles. When depressed, he wrote, as in 1820, a two-line poem on "Torpor":

> "My head is heavy, my limbs are weary,
> And it is not life that makes me move."

The characters he created were frequently subject to madness, their psychosis due to lack of love, mistreatment, and persecution. Through self-understanding, some of them regained sanity. In his own life, he repeatedly overcame gloom by mobilizing intense enthusiasms. His elations combined rage at tyranny, a sense of mission to rescue the weak, a feeling of being rescued, and a world-wide demonstration of enormous potency, rectitude and genius. He evaded household problems and financial distress by dwelling on eternal, universal imagery.

There are many gaps in Shelley's biography. Even critical writings about him teem with paradoxes because certain stereotyped images in his poems make objective criticism confusing.

To quote again from Shelley:

> "Some said that he was mad; others believed
> That memories of an antenatal life,
> Made this, where now he dwelt, a penal hell"
> (from "The Daemon of the World")

Bertram D. Lewin, in 1950, outlined the course of psychoanalytic theory regarding manic-depressive swings. He started with Kraepelin's and Mendel's descriptions, and then covered psychoanalytic theories of mood swings up to modern psychodynamics based on dream theory. In addition to case histories of his own, Lewin analyzed certain theoretical points which dealt with the early months of life. Lack of adaptation to the infantile nursing phase, and the infant's consequent fears regarding sleep and the sense of repletion which is accompanied by a feeling of extinction—as if melting away and being devoured at the breast—are apparently related in some infants to a dread of merging with the mother. This leads to lasting or recurring anxiety about sleep in infancy and later life. Then the wish to sleep, to be devoured, to merge with the mother, as part of the urge to nurse to satiety, becomes interfused with anxiety. Future development in the infant's emotional life is impeded.

The infant's defense of denial, which makes a fiction of unpleasant elements wherever possible, may interfere with reality-testing in the nursing phase, and persist in later life. There is a tendency, then, to test later situations as sources of anxiety or security, rather than truth or falsity. What is anxiety-provoking seems evil; therefore, a small child develops strong fear of what is felt as wrong. His sense of right and wrong is secondary to a sense of safety and danger.

Fear of sleep at the breast, as Lewin described it, may create in fearful infants a similar fear of passive sleep. The manic mood, in a young child, and then in an adult, may become a substitute for sleep at the breast, to escape the fear of death there, as Lewin described elation. Manic action takes the place of repose; the search for what is good, a source of security, then, leads away from repose. Repose is danger—hence the manic flight into activity.

Ten years after Lewin's book was published, Myer Mendelson surveyed psychoanalytic contributions to the theory of manic-depressive cycles. He referred particularly to the following: Karl Abraham treated manic-depressive disorders in which ambivalence toward love-objects was a determining factor. Freud described the narcissistic type of person whose love-object is so like himself as to permit introjection; this fusing of self and love-object may then possibly be followed by vilification of part of the depressed patient's ego. Rado stressed narcissism and dependence in the melancholic, involving deep shame at dependence, and consequent attempts at rebellion to build up lost self-esteem; when rebellion fails, loss of self-esteem is followed by melancholia.

Few psychoanalytic case histories are available for corroborative study of theories regarding manic-depressives. Frieda Fromm-Reichmann, in 1959, described intensive psychotherapy of manic-depressive patients by a group of Washington psychoanalysts. Robert Cohen, Grace Baker, Frieda Fromm-Reichmann, and Edith Weigert had previously published on the same subject. Edith Weigert, in 1961, discussed the difficulty of manic-depressive patients in feeling ordinary mourning or repentance. Typically, they experienced deep loneliness and searched for love. The kind of love they sought was an absorbing one, as if melting into an ideal, beloved person as Shelley described so well in "Epipsychidion."

Though loquacious and seemingly confidential, manic-depressive patients are mainly manipulators of others, including their therapists, and are not completely candid. There is much that they deliberately withhold, or cannot express, and their biographical accounts tend to be stereotyped. Therefore, the content of their mood swings is difficult to trace in detail. Probably there are many types of manic-depressives with varied somatic components in their swings of mood. Hypochondria, real illnesses, or tragedies in life, may either mark or mask their depressive phases.

A further impediment to understanding manic-depressive types, if such definite categories exist, is that many successful people learn to live with, and disguise, their fluctuating emotional cycles.

Shelley is challenging, because although he

has baffled his biographers, he labored to disclose many of his fantasies to the fullest. In fact, in a letter to Godwin, he described his chief gift as an ability to "apprehend minute and remote distinctions of feelings." He said that his poems were pictures of his mind at various times. He expected that only a handful of people would ever decipher the mystery of what he really meant. Although he was a master of words, his aim was to go beyond words to imagery, and even beyond images to the "deep truth" that was "imageless."

Much of the theory regarding manic-depressive cycles, and the core of what Lewin has written about elation—based largely on dream analysis—is illustrated throughout Shelley's writings.

In his description of the "oral triad" Lewin states that Freud has already described the oral drive, the wish to devour. Lewin emphasizes the wish to be devoured, to fall asleep at the breast, and the fear of death there. The wish to be devoured is less understood because it is more subtle. This is precisely what Shelley very often conveys. For example, in his poem, "A Vision of the Sea," he depicts a blissful infant at its terrified mother's breast, on a sinking ship.

During his early childhood Shelley seems to have had unusual capacity for making himself the center of attention. His curiosity about magic and other awesome phenomena aided him in this drive. He learned to become master of the nursery by imaginative tales, such as stories about a headless spectre in the woods, an alchemist in the attic, a giant tortoise in the pond, a dragon, and a giant snake. Four younger sisters and then a little brother were not enough audience for him. He wished to adopt a child himself, and tried to purchase a little gypsy tumbler. As a mark of his precocious intellect, we see him at the age of six, arousing his father's admiration by reciting Latin verses.

He also had high enthusiasm about scientific experiments. One time he had his sisters dress as fiends, and he ran ahead of them with a flaming stove, saying they would construct a hell. Later he almost set fire to his school, and at college, he performed chemical experiments without caution, so that his best friend feared the dormitory might be blown up, or that they might be poisoned.

Ordinary boyish games of competitive skill were unknown to Shelley. At the age of ten he was sent away to school where he was treated with howls of derision by his schoolmates. He was flogged, beaten and shamed. He was apparently capable of aggression in those days, but he gave up violence, and determined to become a great poet and altruist. His next school, when he was almost twelve, was Eton. Here, too, there was much flogging and a rigid fagging system, which Shelley defied. He stood apart from other boys, gentle and provocative at the same time, a Promethean object of vicious teasing. Sometimes he fled from his persecutors; at other times he shrieked in a paroxysm of anger as he held his ground. "Mad Shelley," he was called.

His early works may still be read. His horror novels are interesting as expressions of typically paranoid imaginings and grandiose pronouncements about free love. Perhaps the outstanding function of his early books was to help crystallize a personality which might have been flung into fragments, under stress of anxiety.

In his lonely existence, he learned to create followers, companions who were shadows of himself, bands of Shelley-worshippers whom he could manipulate. He organized his groups, not only through his wildly imaginative power, but also by imposing his sense of rectitude.

The economic conditions of the early nineteenth century in England evoked only too well Shelley's need to help the destitute. Similarly, England's lack of free speech and freedom of the press at that time justified his sending money to those writers with liberal opinions, who were in danger of being jailed or were actually in prison.

After Shelley's views on atheism broke up his romance with his cousin, while he was at Oxford, Shelley wrote a tract on religion entitled "The Necessity of Atheism." He had it printed and sent copies of it to various bishops, to the Vice Chancellor of Oxford, and the Heads of the Houses at Oxford. He strewed copies about in the leading bookstores. He might just as well have entitled his pamphlet "The Necessity of Being Expelled." To his dismay, he was expelled from Oxford, and his chum, Hogg, insisted on sharing the guilt and the expulsion with him. Shelley's father demanded public retraction of the atheistic position Shelley had taken, but Shelley's attitude became still more fixed and rigid. Along with losing his father's affection, Shelley lost financial security, as well as the most consoling defense against all his woes of early years—the troupe of younger sisters who had shared his imaginary exploits and admired everything he did and said (and no doubt unconsciously fulfilled his need for restitution).

As if he had foreseen such a catastrophe, he was already bolstered with the close friendship of Hogg. His fear that his father might have him declared insane, and threats by bailiffs and creditors, remained an enduring problem. There were times when he hallucinated attacks upon himself, but his provocativeness evoked real threats. The theatrical peril in which he placed himself most of the time gave him logical grounds for his fears of attack. His biographers still cannot quite unravel some of the real and some of the imaginary assaults upon him, physical and legal. He was also an enigma regarding his morals. He sacrificed himself for ideals, was altruistic to the point of giving away his needed money and his bread—and yet he was the originator of disasters to people close to him.

Not long after his expulsion from Oxford he involved a very young girl in his atheistic and political rebellion. This was Harriet Westbrook, who was mistreated at school because of her friendship with Shelley. During the months when Shelley encouraged this girl to be his disciple, he, himself, was both pupil and teacher to a twenty-nine-year-old school teacher, Elizabeth Hitchener. Both of these ladies came to grief, through Shelley. Harriet eloped with him and became his first wife. Elizabeth Hitchener came to live with them in an unsuccessful alliance that wrecked her career. Shelley's first long poem, "Queen Mab," shows us an idyllic version of Shelley's position in regard to both Harriet and Elizabeth Hitchener, that of combined pupil and teacher, on a cosmic scale.

Before the birth of his second child he eloped with Mary Godwin and her sister, Claire. Mary was intellectually and artistically able to keep up with him. Mary, very depressive, and Shelley, exalted, shared ambitions and illusions.

From letters of both Shelley and Mary we see that he later fostered a love affair between her and his friend Hogg when she was late in illegitimate pregnancy. At this time, to further complicate matters, Shelley was dependent on Hogg for funds. In February, 1815, Mary's first baby fathered by Shelley was born prematurely. Only two weeks later the infant girl died.

Shelley began to write his next important poem, "Alastor," in August, 1815. The poem deals with a virtuous poet who turns from rebellion in the real world to search for complete happiness in his own imagination. Cradle and tomb become one, for him.

Shelley voiced intense curiosity about the secrets of birth, life and death. The image of the alchemist, carried over from childhood, is referred to in "Alastor." Curiosity about where children come from is expressed as an urge, in many of his writings, to go—toward death and toward bliss. In fact, Shelley once startled an actual mother, a stranger, by asking such questions of her infant.

Often in an enthusiastic state, he felt impelled to seek out truth from the devil or from magical sources. He wished, in his own turn, to give out oracular truths.

He was so hypersensitive about suffering that when he lived with Mary and Claire Godwin at Marlow he could not even bear to see live crayfish hawked on the streets of the town, and used to send out his manservant to buy the crayfish and dump them back into the water. No meat was eaten in his household.

One night at Villa Diodati, Byron's home, Mary, Claire and Shelley were sitting beside the fireplace listening to Byron quote from Coleridge's "Christabel," lines describing the witch's deformity. When Byron said, "Behold! her bosom—," Shelley ran shrieking from the room. He later confessed he had imagined he saw eyes instead of nipples on Mary's breasts —an image based on an old Sussex fable. Years later, in his poem, "The Witch of Atlas," he used the same image of breasts with eyes as nipples when he described a procession of creatures resembling abortions that came to wonder that the "enwombed rocks" could have produced anything so marvelous as the birth of "The Witch of Atlas." Among those who gazed at the birth of the "Witch" were:

"Wet clefts, and lumps neither alive nor dead,
Dog-headed, bosom-eyed, and bird-footed. . ."

From Shelley's life and work, one keeps getting the impression that seeing so many nursing babies when he was a small boy, and precociously deducing what details he could gather about repeated births and a baby's death in the household may have helped determine the forms his imagery was to take. His denial of hostility toward his sisters took the form of exaggerated, almost caricatured tenderness, domination, and seductiveness. He ruled his sisters, and later ruled other women by fusing his personality with theirs. This suggests a combined acting out and reversal of what may have been an early desire to merge with his mother.

On October 8, 1816, a half-sister of Mary's and Claire's, Fanny Imlay, committed suicide by taking laudanum, apparently because of frustrated love for Shelley. Then on December 10th, Harriet Shelley's body was found drowned in the Serpentine River. Shelley went through a marriage ceremony with Mary Godwin, December 30, 1816—just a few weeks later—and sued for custody of the two children whom he had had by Harriet. He was ruled an unsuitable parent, and the children were denied to him, largely on the basis of his poem, "Queen Mab." His response to being accused publicly of incapacity to bring up his boy and girl properly may be reflected in Laon's instruction to Cythna, who then becomes Laone, in "The Revolt of Islam."

In the year 1818 Shelley made a sudden decision to leave England a second time, for Italy. In addition to his urge to be near Byron, in Italy, there was the practical necessity to arrange with him for bringing up Allegra, the baby daughter Claire had with Byron. Shelley journeyed ahead with Claire to discuss matters about Allegra with Byron. Mary, now his legal wife, had an infant girl, Clara, in addition to the toddler, William. While Mary was traveling alone with the two children, the infant, Clara, sickened and died.

Probably a few weeks before little Clara's death, Shelley had begun to write the poem he considered his greatest—"Prometheus Unbound." Depressed and ill as Shelley was, he suffused this poem with an astonishing sense of omnipotence. In a preface to the poem, he says that when the world appreciates men of genius, great changes are brought about in the public's way of living. The future, he tells us, is foreshadowed in the minds of great men, and is mirrored first in poets' minds.

Jupiter, ruler of the universe, is depicted in the poem as the supreme force of cruelty. Prometheus, through strength of will and hope, conquers evil. Prometheus rejects what his teachers have taught him and draws upon a secret store of knowledge.

In "Prometheus Unbound" an ideal woman who is a goddess, a sister, as he calls her, is separated from Prometheus during his ages of torture, and reunited with him at the time of his final triumph. Differing from the original myth by Aeschylus, Shelley's Prometheus never compromises with Jupiter, and is never reconciled with the father image. In Shelley's version, Jupiter's offspring, Demogorgon, who Jupiter hopes will destroy and enslave Prometheus, causes the downfall of Jupiter instead. When Demogorgon is yet unborn, its foetal image floats between Jupiter and his bride, unbeheld and awaiting incarnation. Instead of taking Jupiter's side in the struggle with Prometheus, Demogorgon betrays his own father, and casts Jupiter eternally into an abyss. Prometheus then becomes monarch of the world.

Around the time Shelley wrote "Prometheus Unbound," Mary finished her novel, *Frankenstein*, subtitled *A Modern Prometheus*. In her novel, a young girl falsely confesses murdering the little boy, William, although he was really killed by Frankenstein's monster. Real life soon produced a parallel event. In the spring of 1819, Mary feared that if they stayed in Rome the heat there might kill her son, William. She urged Shelley to leave, but he insisted on staying at Rome, because of his own ill health. Little William sickened with dysentery and died. Mary's depression after her son, William, died has been described as psychotic. Shelley did not dare voice his own grief.

Politically, Shelley had extreme views. He demanded total and complete bliss and security—or else he predicted destruction and overwhelming evil. Later in life, he called on rebels to resist passively and be mowed down.

At times he gave contemporaries the impression of having a mind of great strength and the character of a martyr. Others, including the majority of literary critics of his day, considered him confused, dishonest, chronically unreliable, perhaps insane.

His sleep was filled with nightmares. He suffered from sleepwalking from the time he went away to school up until the very end, when he had some terrifying sleepwalking episodes. For example, he fled screaming in his sleep to Mary's room when he dreamed of the sea flooding his household. He saw himself strangling his pregnant wife, Mary, toward the end of his life.

Mary had her second miscarriage not long before he drowned. One of Shelley's waking hallucinations, shortly before this, was of seeing little Allegra, Claire and Byron's dead girl, rising from the sea, clapping her hands happily. Around that time he also thought he met his own image walking on the terrace.

Defenses may not have worked so well in his daily life, but he always fell back on them in his literary work, especially his fantasies of flight to far places, and to other worlds.

Mingling of truth and fantasy seems to be characteristic of violent mood swings. Certainly, in Shelley and his wife, perceptions, illusions, falsifications and profound insights alternate strangely with shocked denials and flights. They both had a genius for distracting attention from what was going on in current life, while at the same time they dealt with prophetic truths. They were able to accomplish what they did because they externalized the feelings they could not bear to face in personal circumstances.

Helene Deutsch has described mania and paranoia as alternate defenses against dangers to the ego stemming from melancholia. Shelley quite consciously fought Mary's melancholic disposition with his verve and energetic calls to combat persecution. Sometimes he insisted that his own light-hearted mask, particularly after the loss of various children, was a deliberate disguise of his feelings, lest Mary become dangerously melancholic.

After he drowned, Mary said she preserved as many of Shelley's writings as possible so that his mind's development could be studied.

Summary

The events of Shelley's life and his imagery epitomize many of the essentials that psychoanalytic theory has outlined regarding manic-depressives. Shelley's unrealistic approach to right and wrong, real and unreal, seems to be rooted in a very early tendency to deal with security and anxiety-provoking fantasies as if security were the source of truth and righteousness and fear the source of evil. This was at the root of his dwelling at such great length on free love, atheism, and defiance of law and custom, which kept his life in turmoil. His unique approach to right and wrong confused his associates, critics, and biographers, and had a profound effect on his imagery.

Denial of jealousy, grief and hostility helped him maintain an enthusiastic, elated state, which, in turn, often helped him avoid some of the deadly torpor which was associated in his imagery with drowning and cannibalistic fantasies. His defenses and Mary Godwin's tended to be reciprocal—she the depressed, and he the elated one. Yet he courted drowning with eventual success.

His genius enabled him to externalize his conflicts and to manipulate others in the best sense when he was most successful, by becoming the verbal fountain of love which was his ideal. He combined a messianic and childlike role, aerial and insubstantial. At the same time he encouraged incestuous fantasies and deathly oedipal defiance—and seems to have fled in sleep and waking life from fears of retaliatory persecution by his father and authorities of all kinds. His attempts to apply his intellect to political problems was hampered by confinement to stereotyped patterns of inner conflict. The integration he could not achieve in his own life shines, instead, from his successful poetry.

Bibliography

1. Abraham, K. (1911). "Notes on the Psychoanalytic Investigation and Treatment of Manic-Depressive Insanity and Allied Conditions." In *Selected Papers on Psychoanalysis.* London: Hogarth Press.
2. Benedek, T. (1956). "Toward the Biology of the Depressive Constellation." J. Amer. Psa. Assn., Vol. 4.
3. Bibring, E. (1953). "The Mechanism of Depression." In *Affective Disorders* (Ed. Phyllis Greenacre). New York: Int. Univ. Press.
4. Cohen, M., Baker, G., Cohen, R., Fromm-Reichmann, F., and Weigert, E. (1954). "An Intensive Study of Twelve Cases of Manic-Depressive Psychosis." Psychiatry, Vol. 17.
5. Deutsch, H. (1932). *Psychoanalysis of the Neuroses.* London: Hogarth Press and Inst. of Psa.
6. Fromm-Reichmann, F. (1959). *Psychoanalysis and Psychotherapy* (Ed. D. Bullard). Chicago: Univ. of Chicago Press.
7. Freud, S. (1917). "Mourning and Melancholia." In *Collected Papers,* Vol. 4. London: Hogarth Press and Inst. of Psa.
8. Grabo, C. (1935). *The Meaning of the "Witch of Atlas."* Chapel Hill: Univ. of North Carolina Press.
9. Hoch, P. and Rachlin, H. (1941). "An Evaluation of Manic-Depressive Psychosis in the Light of Follow-up Studies." Amer. J. Psa., Vol. 97.
10. Jackson, D. (1958). "Guilt and the Control of Pleasure in Schizoid Personalities." British J. of Medical Psychology, Vol. 31.
11. Jacobson, E. (1957). "On Normal and Pathological Moods." *Psychoanalytic Study of the Child,* Vol. 12.
12. Jones, E. (1912). "The Theory of Symbolism." In *Papers on Psychoanalysis.* Baltimore, Md.: Williams & Wilkins Co. 5th ed. reprinted 1950.
13. ———. (1956). *Sigmund Freud: Four Centenary Addresses—The Nature of Genius.* New York: Basic Books.

14. Kanzer, M. (1958). "Image Formation During Free Association." Psa. Quart., Vol. 27.
15. Kubie, L. (1958). *Neurotic Distortion of the Creative Process.* Lawrence, Kansas: Univ. of Kansas Press.
16. Lewin, B. (1958). *Dreams and the Uses of Regression.* New York: Int. Univ. Press.
17. ———. (1950). *The Psychoanalysis of Elation.* New York: W. W. Norton.
18. ———. (1953). "Reconsideration of the Dream Screen." Psa. Quart., Vol. 22.
19. Lewis, N. and Hubbards, L. (1931). "The Mechanisms and Prognostic Aspects of the Manic-Depressive-Schizophrenic Combinations." Assn. for Research in Nervous and Mental Diseases, Vol. 11.
20. Lewis, N. and Piotrowski, Z. (1954). "Clinical Diagnosis of Manic-Depressive Psychosis." In *Depressions* (Eds. P. Hoch and J. Zurbin). New York: Grune and Stratton.
21. Mendelson, M. (1960). *Psychoanalytic Concepts of Depression.* Springfield, Illinois: Charles C. Thomas.
22. Nunberg, H. (1938). "Homosexuality, Magic and Aggression." Int. J. Psa., Vol. 19.
23. Rado, S. (1928). "The Problem of Melancholia." Int. J. Psa., Vol. 9.
24. Rapaport, D. (1953). "On the Psychoanalytic Theory of Affects." Int. J. Psa., Vol. 34.
25. Read, H. *In Defense of Shelley, and Other Essays.* Supplement to British Book News (Published by British Council of the Nat. Book League), London, New York and Toronto: Longmans, Green and Co. (Published by Wm. Heinemann, Ltd., London, Toronto: 1936.)
26. Rennie, T. (1942). "Prognosis in Manic-Depressive Psychosis." Amer. J. Psa., Vol. 98.
27. Rogers, N. (1956). *Shelley at Work: A Critical Inquiry.* Oxford: Clarendon Press.
28. Shelley, M. *Frankenstein or the Modern Prometheus.* Garden City, N.Y.: Halcyon House.
29. Shelley, Percy Bysshe. *The Complete Works* (Ed. by R. Ingpen and W. Peck). 10 vol. Julian Edition, London: 1926-1930.
30. Stovall, F. (1931). *Desire and Restraint in Shelley.* Durham, N.C.: Duke Univ. Press.
31. Weigert, E. (1961). "The Psychotherapy of the Affective Psychosis." In *Psychotherapy of the Psychoses* (Ed. A. Burton). New York: Basic Books.
32. White, N. (1945). *Portrait of Shelley.* New York: Alfred Knopf.
33. Zilboorg, G. (1933). "Manic-Depressive Psychoses." In *Psychoanalysis Today* (Ed. S. Lorand). New York: Covici-Friede.

Department of Psychiatry,
University of North Carolina Medical School,
Chapel Hill, North Carolina

Discussant

George Frumkes, M.D.

Beverly Hills, California

Dr. Miller's paper is an interesting and scholarly study correlating the biography of the fascinating Romantic genius, the poet Shelley, with a psychoanalytic study of his life and works. Dr. Miller believes Shelley and Mary Godwin contributed to psychological knowledge by exposing certain imagery during manic-depressive cycles. Shelley thought of himself as a frail innocent child or else as an almost omnipotent natural force like the West Wind. He identified with legendary figures persecuted by God's tyranny, e.g., Job or Prometheus. He feared his own father and revolted against priests, governments and customs. He identified with the omniscient and supreme force of Good. He experienced heights and depths of emotion, sometimes in daily cycles. The characters in Shelley's poems were frequently subject to madness induced by persecution or lack of love. As a school boy, Shelley was nicknamed "Mad Shelley."

Dr. Miller summarizes elements in Lewin's book, *The Psychoanalysis of Elation*—the effects of maladaptation on the infantile nursing phase, fears of sleep, repletion and the feeling of extinction while being devoured by the breast. Miller cites material from the poems which can be interpreted in terms of the "oral triad," e.g., in the poem, "A Vision of the Sea," he depicts a blissful infant at its terrified mother's breast on a sinking ship. Shelley referred to breasts frequently and Miller correlates this interest with the biographical history of four younger nursing sisters. Shelley once confessed he saw eyes instead of nipples on Mary Godwin's breasts, and a line in "The Witch of Atlas" reads: "Dog-headed, bosom-eyed, bird-footed." Shelley was sensitive, generous, and altruistic, yet he was a cause of disaster to his wives, children, and relatives. His wife's half-sister committed suicide and his first wife, Harriet, drowned herself in the Serpentine sometime after he divorced her; he was refused custody of the two children by Harriet, and Mary's two children died partly because Shelley refused to leave Rome during a hot season. At the age of thirty, he drowned in the sea near Leghorn where his schooner, the *Ariel*, had been run down by another vessel.

The term "manic-depressive" is technical in the sense of "manic-depressive" psychosis. Shelley was often subject to mood swings, but I don't think the term "manic-depressive" is accurate even if there are similarities between the psychoanalytic content of manic-depressive cycles and mood swings of elation, excessive optimism, enthusiasm, wishful denial of unpleasant facts, frustration, pessimism, dejection. The term "manic-depressive" to me means something more technical, classificatory, and diagnostic. The inspired generous enthusiasm of his poetry cannot be used as evidence of psychosis.

In *Recollections of the Last Days of Shelley and Byron* by E. J. Trelawny (who was with Shelley at Leghorn before he was drowned), there is a chapter "Hellenism: The Ideal versus the Reality." Trelawny had induced Shelley to visit a Greek ship and compare the real Greeks with the "ideal" Greeks of his poems. Shelley left the ship in disgust. Trelawny offered to show Shelley an American clipper (representing another republican ideal), and Shelley said, "I had rather not have any more of my hopes and illusions mocked by sad realities." This insight illustrates my contention that the illusions in the poem are not manic.

As for the psychoanalytic study of the rebelliousness and the struggle against the government's customs and institutions of his time, it should be emphasized that Shelley was expressing an important phase of the spirit of his age. He was part of Romanticism. Although the French Revolution had apparently been defeated, it was not yet undone; Rousseau and the Age of Reason, and the necessities of political and economic life demanded a change in the social order. The adverse criticism of Shelley by his contemporaries is not evidence of Shelley's madness but of a political difference. More friendly critics characterized him as an "ineffectual angel" in his lifetime. Others referred to him as a poet of the new era, unexcelled in his ideality, unexcelled in his music and unexcelled in his importance.

Discussant

Louis Fraiberg, PH.D.

Toledo, Ohio

Dr. Miller's suggestive and revealing paper opens up for study an aspect of Shelley which holds promise for further understanding of the relation between the man and his work. Shelley's imagery is usually analyzed for poetic and philosophic clues, for the development of his technical skill or his private brand of Platonism. I am not aware that very much attention has hitherto been given to what it might tell us about his psychic life or about the effect of this on his poetry, although biographical studies deal with the obvious influences of his personal connections. Dr. Miller has entered this potentially fruitful field and emerged with a number of interesting insights which both illuminate and tantalize.

Since the paper speaks for itself, I shall not repeat his findings but rather record my regret that the material is so sketchy and essentially a summary. No doubt this is due to the necessity of compressing a great deal into a small space for publication. I wish it were more detailed because the material is so interesting.

For example, Dr. Miller remarks in one place that Shelley "evaded household problems and financial distress by dwelling on eternal, universal imagery." This seems to be perfectly valid, but it stops there while my mind runs on to the thought that there is also another side to this behavior. Shelley exhibited a repetitive pattern: he twice brought third parties (female) into the house where he was living with his wife; he married Harriet Westbrook and he championed Emilia Viviani, both of whom he regarded as oppressed; he alienated his father (the source of his money), and he repeatedly borrowed against his expectations, at ruinous interest in order to lend large sums to his friends, including his father-in-law.

I cite these to suggest that, while I agree with Dr. Miller's stress on Shelley's evasion of unpleasant responsibilities, it is also worth considering that the poet brought some of his difficulties upon himself, that he must have had strong unconscious motives for doing so, and that signs of these troubles are worth looking for in the imagery, too. Shelley appears to have taken an unusually active part in constructing and nurturing his own neurosis.

There is no doubt that Shelley suffered from manic-depressive mood swings, as Dr. Miller amply demonstrates. I hope that he or someone equally qualified will go on to provide more examples and to show their place in the total pattern of Shelley's life. Obviously, this is more than a short paper can accomplish; what I am proposing is no less than a critical psychic biography, and I am grateful to Dr. Miller for arousing my appetite for it. Among the problems to be treated is the fact that Shelley's art developed notably—though not with chronological consistency—throughout his life. How can the oscillating mood swings be reconciled with a fairly orderly progression of poetic skills? With a higher philosophical achievement more in touch with reality than his youthful idealism? With at least a partial maturing of his own psyche? Of course this progress is relative and incomplete; after all, he was drowned just before his thirtieth birthday.

I should also add one of the most striking of Dr. Miller's topics, namely Shelley's use of symbols which are commonly regarded as evil but used by him to represent good, e.g., the serpent. Why this reversal, in the particular circumstances where it occurs?

These are only a few of the avenues which Dr. Miller's richly suggestive paper opens for exploration.

Discussant

Maurice N. Walsh, M.D.

Beverly Hills, California

It is evident that the making of an exact psychiatric diagnosis on a person who lived before the age of scientific psychiatry is apt to be most difficult, even though he wrote voluminously. As Freud demonstrated, authors' literary productions subjected to critical scrutiny by a psychoanalyst will yield information concerning the author's unconscious motivations and conflicts. This information, when supplemented with biographical data, may permit certain conclusions regarding his character structure and predominant ego defenses.

Psychoanalytic authors since Freud's time have not hesitated to use the writings and biographical material of literary men and women long dead as material possessing diagnostic value. They have been able to demonstrate that the basic structure of the human psyche is essentially unchanging with time. The type of neuroses from which humans suffer is a different matter. The character neuroses seen today were seen much more rarely a generation or two ago, while the so-called classical neuroses so commonly observed then are rare now.

These factors make exact diagnostic conclusions regarding the type of psychopathology from which Shelley suffered difficult. There can be no doubt that elation and feelings of depression were prominent features of his psychiatric illness. When we try to speak of a cyclic alternation between episodes of manic excitement and depression the situation becomes less clear.

Miller has clearly demonstrated the use of denial as an ego defense in Shelley's works and in his actions. Miller seems to indicate that the defense of denial is responsible for the absence of a clearly cyclical character in Shelley's mood shift. Was Shelley a manic-depressive? As the Italians say, "One swallow does not make a summer," and evidence of moods of elation and excitement together with more or less alternate moods of depression can be observed in certain schizophrenic syndromes as well. Nor do the existence of hallucinations and delusions, such as Miller calls attention to, as occurring in Shelley, necessitate, by themselves, a diagnosis of schizophrenia. The fact is that the psychopathology demonstrable in the literary and biographical material regarding Shelley which has survived presents a confusing variety of psychiatric data.

As Miller notes, there are large gaps in the biographical data available in the case of Shelley. He has elucidated the various factors which appear important in the elation and depression so clearly expressed at various epochs in Shelley's life, as well as the reciprocal defenses manifested by Shelley and his women companions. This is particularly clear in his association with Mary Godwin in which she was the depressed and he the elated one.

A brief consideration of the nature of artistic creativeness as manifested in Shelley and the influence of his genius on his pathography might be of more interest. Several authors including Rickman, Kris and Fenichel have called attention to the importance of restitutive phenomena in artistic creation, the mechanism of projection serving for the reparation and restitution of introjected, lost objects. The loss has taken place through fantasy destruction by the individual himself and the restitutive effort then constitutes an attempt to undo the destruction and control aggressive impulses. Something like this seems to have taken place with Shelley, both in his artistic work and in his life. His production of numerous children, to whom he could not be a parent, suggests that these children represented merely attempts to reconstitute aspects of himself.

Freud once wrote: ". . . when an instinctual trend undergoes repression, its libidinal elements are transformed into symptoms and its aggressive components into a sense of guilt. Even if this statement is only accurate as an approximation, it merits our interest." The restitutive theory of artistic creativeness necessarily has a close relationship with a sense of guilt. Miller notes that Shelley early was capable of aggressiveness, but that this was given up in favor of the goal of becoming a great poet or an altruist. It seems that he is referring here to the vicissitude of the aggressive instinctual drive. This is confirmed by Shelley's apparent substitution of masochistic tendencies for sadistic ones—he was savagely beaten in his school days apparently without being able to effectively defend himself. His sadistic treatment of a series of women and children certainly appears, as Miller suggests, like a belated attempt to master infantile situations.

What can be said about the influence of Shelley's genius on his psychopathology, or vice versa? As Jones noted, up to the present we have little reliable psychoanalytic data as to the true nature of genius. Jones suggests that one prominent characteristic feature of genius is "this remarkable capacity for perceiving with somnambulistic sureness what is absolutely and universally true. It transcends the simple love of truth itself, essential though this may be. I think it must occur at special moments when there is an unusual, and often only temporary, fusion of all the elements in the mind in a peculiar degree of harmony. The sureness arises from the completeness with which the ego is receiving in an unquestioning fashion the message from the preconscious. At that moment there is a complete coincidence between the striving of the id, the permission of the superego, the acceptance by the ego and the external perception of the problem being studied."

Jones also noted that there is every reason to suppose that men of genius possess exceptionally strong emotions and usually a correspondingly strong capacity for containing them. In this connection it is relevant to recall that the Sterbas hypothesized that aggressive energy was indispensable for great artistic creativeness and for the impact of the creations of great artists in any field, who seem to have the unique gift of neutralizing aggressive energy in circumscribed areas of creative activity, but not sufficiently so as to diminish its impact. They pointed out that great works of art are not conflict-free but conflict-accepting.

Could it be that the common notion that artistic creativeness or genius depends upon adult neurosis really refers to the necessity for specific types of childhood neuroses which predispose to the occurrence of certain vicissitudes of the aggressive instinctual drive?

If this could be demonstrated to be the case, then one might think of the possibility that non-neurotic regression might be an important factor in artistic creativeness and possibly in genius, rather than purely neurotic regression. Further study will be necessary to validate or invalidate this hypothesis.

Discussant

Fred Feldman, M.D.

Beverly Hills, California

Dr. Miller has a valuable, creative and new idea in matching Shelley's imagery to psychoanalytic concepts. Students of literature know Shelley well; psychoanalysts know him too little. Miller makes a fresh start, by reaching back 150 years to the most impassioned and modern mind among English poets.

Did Shelley in truth have manic-depressive cycles? Did he have them in a pathological sense, or only to the extent that all of us do?

Shelley seems to lie outside the orbit of our psychiatric nomenclature. He was not a poet of escape like the other romantics who wrote perfect lyric poetry—Keats, Wordsworth and Coleridge. They fled into their verbal imagery, whereas Shelley fought back against the forces of evil with his every act. His great lyric poems are but one side of him. His long poems and his prose are founded on his lifelong study of the great writers of every period. His reason told him that the world was an unreasonable, imperfect place—that man was irrational, cruel, deceitful. He was no armchair philosopher. He fought the world, crying out for kindness, openness, generosity, order. His writings still inflame the minds of men today, more than Keats, and more than Wordsworth.

R. M. Smith, in *The Shelley Legend* (1945), noted that no definitive biography was possible, since vital source material was still being withheld from examination. In addition, he documented the many forgeries about the life of Shelley and felt there had been too much covering up and angelicizing of him. He recommended following the spirit of Shelley who all through his life wrote, "Let us see the truth, whatever that may be."

In *Flight of the Skylark* (1954), Norman

wrote: "There was always activity where Shelley was . . . He was too bent on reforming evils and playing the knight-errant to unhappy souls for his life to take the quiet course of a conformer's. Wherever there is action, criticism follows." He too says there is no way of determining whether Shelley was responsible for Harriet's drowning (three years after he left her), and that the reasons for Fanny Imlay's suicide are not known.

The "free love, atheism and defiance of law and custom, which kept his life in turmoil," may also be seen as expressions of independent thinking. They were, in any case, mainly the expression of his feelings before he was twenty-one or twenty-two. After that, his ideas became so much more complex that these phrases do not seem to describe him.

Perhaps the most obvious clinical finding in manic-depressive cycles is the prevalence of the one mood, the absence of the other. The manic has (consciously) lost sight of life's tragedies, the depressive has forgotten its joys. Shelley, in his later poems, never seems all joy or all sadness—he shows the mingling of the two which is exactly what the manic-depressive does not.

In one of his most beautiful poems, "The Two Spirits: An Allegory," he intertwines the two sets of feelings. He seems to know the infinitude of desire, but simultaneously the realistic limits of life.

Shelley was "atheistic" in the early years, but later sought a deity in thought itself. His god, or identity, was of the most complex sort. One of his poems perhaps sums up the essence of what psychiatrists have tried to explain as insight. His "Hymn to Intellectual Beauty" sought to depict those moments of joy in which feeling and thought are mingled. He did not euphorically hope for many of these moments, or that they would replace the ordinary work of life.

Norman sums up that Shelley himself did not demand hysterical adulation, but only hoped for vision. "Returning from this many-colored clamor, we may submit that Shelley, at the peak of his mature production, does touch a truth beyond argument."

If we assume that Shelley, or any other great poet, does have manic-depressive swings, how does his poetry illuminate the basic dynamics of elation and depression for the psychoanalyst?

The imagination of the great poets certainly throws some light on psychopathology. The images not only express what we see in everyday life, but express it in a new way. Many of our psychoanalytic concepts stemmed from these images. However, poets go further. Their ideas are more complex and yet more simple, more beautiful and more touching. Our formulas, in comparison, seem to be only formulas.

I am not sure that Shelley's writings corroborate Lewin's theories of manic-depressive cycles. Shelley does not convey to me the wish to be devoured. He does not, most of the time, seem fearful of the breast, or of any kind of "thing," since he lived for ideas, for knowledge. His mind was influenced by the philosophies of everyone from the Greeks on, and instead of being devoured by this knowledge, he constantly reordered it.

The oedipal conflict is present in Shelley's images, but his poem on the death of Keats ("Adonais") is relevant. Here was his one great rival, his only peer and perhaps superior. Yet his praise gave birth to one of his most moving and profound poems. "Adonais" seems to show a man beyond conflict for a moment, postambivalent, pouring out his heart in mature sorrow. It is also a tribute to thought, and to the idea that feelings informed by thought mean everything in life. He saw the essence of Keats suspended in this mixture of intellect and beauty.

Is Shelley best understood by an examination of possible pathological conflicts which stand behind his writings, or is he best studied in terms of the growth of his autonomous ego strengths, which overcame the ordinary conflicts of life, and led him to sublime realms? In other words, should we be more interested in the creative process he had in extraordinary degree, or in the psychopathology which was perhaps not really very marked in his case?

The question may be raised whether conflict, or ego strength, explains the imagery of the great poets. In many lesser poets, pathology is perhaps the better index. In the great poets, it seems that the conflict is not central. Shelley's enthusiasm was for that exercise of the mind which finally found its highest pleasure in reasoning and fruitful imagining. His images do reveal his fears of death, for example, but his real work lies in the resolution through thought of this universal fear.

Miller refers to the image of breasts with eyes as nipples, in "The Witch of Atlas." That imagery is there, but also, "The Witch of Atlas" represents man's hope for immortality, and simultaneously the realization that it cannot exist. Shelley's bitter agnosticism appears in the lines:

"We, the weak mariners of that wide lake
Where'er its shores extend or billows roll,
Our course unpiloted and starless make
O'er its wild surface to an unknown goal."

This is followed by a typical expression of hope.

The more one reads Shelley, the more sane one feels, not in the sense of the conventional grasp of reality, but in that breathless wonder of the mind's fullest use of itself.

His "A Defense of Poetry" is considered an epic work of philosophical and psychologic insight. He said that the moral content of a poem is identical with its power to show an ordered universe, in which human actions express law and reason. He cites Milton in "Paradise Lost" for his power of exhibiting such a picture of the universe, combined with his "bold neglect of a direct moral purpose."

If we want to, we can find in Shelley precursors of the death wish, of many things Freud felt about the source of "evil." In his early works, Shelley blamed the church and economic dictators, but in his later writings he spoke of an *intrinsic* source of evil, of a class of actions which derive "from a profounder source than the series of our habitual conduct, which derives from without. There are the actions . . . which make human life what it is." In his later works, Shelley seems "modern"—he seems to say that we are destroyed by our inability to integrate the good and bad within all of us.

I close with a note the twenty-two-year-old Shelley wrote to his publisher about his early poems (age eighteen and nineteen):

"My poems will little stand the criticism even of friendship. Some of the later ones . . . are faithful pictures of my feelings at the time of writing them. But they are, in a great measure, abrupt and obscure . . . These defects I do not alter now, being unwilling to offer any outrage to the living portraiture of my own mind, bad as it may be pronounced."

Author's Response

Milton L. Miller, M.D.
Chapel Hill, North Carolina

There seems to be no disagreement with the idea that the creative process in man is a subject greatly in need of understanding. It is a constant source of fascination for the psychoanalyst in his daily work. Because of the need for brevity and the fact that I condensed this Shelley paper from a much larger study, a false impression may have been created that diagnosis was emphasized. I actually wanted to demonstrate how conflicts based on early experiences found their way into Shelley's poetry. Varied beauty, aesthetic importance, philosophic implications, and even political reflections were influenced by repressed conflicts and by the nature of preconscious activity in Shelley's creative process.

I agree with Dr. Frumkes that the diagnostic term, "manic-depressive," is a harsh one to use in conjunction with poetic genius, but I do so, in a condensed way, to stimulate thought about both madness and poetry.

Evidence of Shelley's psychotic tendencies occur in his hallucinations, and delusions, such as the fear he had of having contracted elephantiasis from a woman on a bus, and also in his insistence on attempting to drown, while boating with Mrs. Williams. He induced real persecutions and troubles, such as pursuit by bailiffs for his debts, so that biographers had difficulty disentangling real from imagined persecutions. However at one time he drew a picture of his assailant, and the drawing can be seen in reproductions. It is not of a man but of a devil. As Louis Fraiberg mentions, strong unconscious urges to bring about situations of persecution were created by Shelley and justified such acts as fleeing from his residences.

He developed poetic symbols over a lifetime, as a result of much study. It was after his poet friend, Peacock, insisted that he read the ancient classics that he achieved the most balanced artistic sense. His symbolism, traceable in his notebooks, eventually delineated his personality with all its strengths and weaknesses, his neurosis, and its somewhat psychotic underlayer. He liked the symbolism of the serpent and identified with it. He thought that in the eventual perfection of the world the serpent would be harmless; an infant could then play with it in safety. The symbolism of the bird and snake that fought each other in the air was not original with him, but he assigned a role of importance to it.

It was Shelley's famous biographer, Newman Ivy White, who diagnosed him as manic-depressive, and wondered why.

When Shelley was a boy a book by Robert Paltock, *The Life and Adventures of Peter Wilkins*, about glumms and glowries and winged children destined to improve the world, impressed him immensely. The imagery of children being rescued and leading people to happy realms runs through his work, especially winged children. I certainly agree with the restitutive impulse which Dr. Walsh mentions. The vicissitudes of Shelley's aggressive drives are very markedly like Dr. Walsh's description of them. It is likewise true that Shelley remained very much a child, and thought that children were poets but lost this gift when they grew up.

As to Dr. Feldman's question whether Shelley had manic-depressive cycles to the extent that all of us do, I think the answer is we could not get by with what he did. He described his own feelings during the exalted phase—when even the stimulus of looking at a blade of grass was too intense—and the torpor in which he could scarcely move.

Poems which show a good mingling of the exalted and saddened phases are his best, most famous poems. His notebooks and unsuccessful fragments show his least integrated moods.

I recommend the poem about Laon and Cythna, "The Revolt of Islam," for a study of raw impulses.

To study the growth of Shelley's ego it is necessary to estimate the challenge to it by brutal forces of hostility and disintegration pitted against courageous creativity. Here his genius shows most clearly. His ego is a fulcrum between positive forces, with manic overtones, and extremely sadistic, destructive forces with depressive slants. He wished to be a fountain of messianic hope. He reassured both himself and his readers about life's purposefulness, its beauty, its possibilities. Therefore I agree with Dr. Feldman that one feels more sane while reading him.

Forum

Title Sigmund Freud on Suicide

Author Robert E. Litman, M.D.

Clinical Professor of Psychiatry at the University of Southern California and on the Faculty of the Southern California Psychoanalytic Institute. For the last eight years, he has been Chief Psychiatrist of the Suicide Prevention Center in Los Angeles. He has published numerous articles on suicide, accidents, sexual perversions, and other aspects of self-destruction.

Discussants

Angel Garma, M.D.
Founder of the Argentine Psychoanalytic Association and on the Faculty of the Buenos Aires Psychoanalytic Institute. He has been in private psychoanalytic practice since 1930 in Berlin, Madrid, Paris and Buenos Aires. He is the author of *Sadism and Masochism in Human Behaviour* and several other books concerning the theory and practice of psychoanalysis, dreams, peptic ulcers and headaches.

Edwin S. Shneidman, PH.D.
Professor of Psychiatry (Psychology) at the University of Southern California and Co-Director of the Suicide Prevention Center in Los Angeles. Recently, he was appointed national Special Consultant to the newly-established NIMH Suicide Prevention Center in Bethesda, Maryland. He has just completed an edited volume entitled *Essays in Self-Destruction* which will be published later this year. He is co-editor with Norman Farberow of *Clues to Suicide* (1957) and *The Cry for Help* (1961), and is the author of many articles and chapters on suicide and death.

Bettina Warburg, M.D.
Assistant Clinical Professor of Psychiatry at Cornell University. She is a Member and on the Faculty of the New York Psychoanalytic Institute and was a Member of the Committee for Study of Suicide during its operation. She has published a paper entitled "Suicide, Pregnancy and Rebirth."

Lilla Veszy-Wagner, PH.D.
Member of the British Psychoanalytic Society and Imago group, author of the chapter on Ernest Jones in the *Psychoanalytic Pioneers*, and many other contributions to the history and technique of psychoanalysis and anthropology.

Justin Simon, M.D.
Assistant Professor of Psychiatry at Downstate Medical Center of the State University of New York in Brooklyn. He is a member of the Psychoanalytic Association of New York and is a Contributing Editor of the *Annual Survey of Psychoanalysis*. As former Co-Director of the California Medical Clinic for Psychotherapy in San Francisco, he had experience with suicide prevention activities. He is director of research on a recorded analysis in progress at the Downstate Medical Center.

Sigmund Freud on Suicide[1]

Robert E. Litman, M.D.

Beverly Hills, California

In this essay I will review the clinical experiences and theoretical steps which led Freud to his various conclusions about suicide. My purpose is to abstract from the totality of Freud's writings his pertinent observations and to evaluate the contributions they make to the understanding of suicide and of suicide prevention in our own time, a full generation after Freud's death.

It would be a mistake to assume that Freud's encounters with suicide were only theoretical or philosophical. To the contrary, Freud had considerable clinical experience with suicidal patients. There are, for example, references to suicidal symptomatology in all of the case histories that Freud published, except that of Little Hans, a five-year-old child.

Suicidal behavior was an important aspect of the symptoms of Josef Breuer's patient, Fraulein Anna O. Breuer discovered the cathartic method of treatment, an approach that Freud later developed into psychoanalysis. Anna O. became suicidal after the death of her father. On the doctor's recommendation, and against her will, she was transferred to a country house in the neighborhood of Vienna (in June, 1881) because of the danger of suicide. "The move was followed by three days and nights completely without sleep or nourishment and by numerous attempts at suicide by smashing windows and by other methods." After this she grew quieter and even took chloral at night for sedation. (5)

Very early in his career as a psychoanalyst, Freud was aware of the importance of guilt for hostile impulses against parents in causing symptoms, especially after the parents' death. In May, 1897, in a letter to Wilhelm Fliess, Freud wrote: "Hostile impulses against parents (a wish that they should die) are also an integral part of neuroses. . . . They are repressed at periods in which pity for one's parents is active—at times of their illness or death. One of the manifestations of grief is then to reproach oneself for their death . . . or to punish oneself by putting oneself into their position." (2)

After his father died (October, 1896), Freud was moody, anxious and depressed for some time. (1) He worked his way back to health through his self-analysis and his writing. There is no evidence that Freud was suicidal during this period, although a possible guiding fantasy was that of death and rebirth. In a letter of June, 1897, he wrote, "I have been through some kind of neurotic experience, with odd states of mind not intelligible to consciousness—cloudy thoughts and veiled doubts, with barely here and there a ray of light . ." Freud continued the letter with a paragraph describing a new case, a nineteen-year-old girl whose two older brothers shot themselves, and then concluded, "Otherwise I am empty and ask your indulgence. I believe I am in a cocoon, and heaven knows what sort of creature will emerge from it." (3) During this whole period, Freud was struggling most particularly with painful feelings of guilty rivalry with his father and with Fliess.

Possibly Freud's most intense personal experience with suicide occurred in August, 1898. "A patient over whom I had taken a

[1]This is a shortened version of the paper which will appear in *Essays in Self Destruction*, E. S. Shneidman (ed.) New York: Holt, Rinehart and Winston.

great deal of trouble had put an end to his life on account of an incurable sexual disorder." The suicide of the patient stirred up in Freud certain painful fantasies connected with death and sexuality, which he more or less successfully repressed. Several weeks later, still under the influence of these unconscious fantasies, Freud was unable to recall the name of Signorelli, creator of magnificent frescoes about the "Four Last Things"—Death, Judgment, Hell and Heaven. Freud tried to visualize the frescoes and the artist and felt the inadequacy of his associations as a source of inner torment. With great effort he reconstructed his conversation with a traveling companion immediately before the forgetting. The topic was foreign customs, the Turks, their confidence in doctors, their resignation to fate, even death. Freud had thought of telling an anecdote. "These Turks place a higher value on sexual enjoyment than on anything else, and in the event of sexual disorders, they are plunged in a despair which contrasts strongly with their resignation toward the threat of death."

A patient (Freud's?) once said, "Herr [Signor], you must know that if *that* comes to an end, then life is of no value." Feeling suddenly uncomfortable, Freud suppressed the anecdote, deliberately diverted his own thoughts from death and sexuality, and changed the subject to the famous frescoes. But in his unconscious effort to continue to forget the suicide, Freud now forgot the painter's name, which joined the memory of the suicide in Freud's repressed unconscious, until someone else suggested the correct name. Freud recognized it instantly and used it to recall the repressed fantasies and reconstruct the mechanism of forgetting. Freud reported the episode immediately to his friend, Fliess, (4) and published an account of it several months later. (6) He omitted in these first two reports, however, that the specific unpleasant news which precipitated the forgetting was a patient's suicide. Later, when Freud rewrote the material as the first example in his book, *The Psychopathology of Everyday Life*, he included the fact of the suicide. (7) Unfortunately, we know nothing more about the patient nor the details of his treatment.

As far as I know, Freud's only overt suicide threats occurred during his long, passionate and stormy engagement. In 1885, he wrote to his fiancée, Martha, whom he eventually married, his decision to commit suicide should he lose her. A friend was dying, and in this connection Freud wrote, "I have long since resolved on a decision [suicide], the thought of which is in no way painful, in the event of my losing you. That we should lose each other by parting is quite out of the question . . . You have no idea how fond I am of you, and I hope I shall never have to show it." (26) So Freud could understand how someone, like the Turks of the censored anecdote, or his deceased patient, could turn to death when frustrated sexually. "One is very crazy when one is in love." (2) Many years later, Freud was to comment that the two situations of being most intensely in love and of suicide are similar, in that the ego is overwhelmed by the object. (12) In his early theory the claims of love (libido) and self-preservation were opposed, and he consistently maintained that to love is dangerous (acknowledging always that not to love poses an even greater peril).

Freud's psychoanalytic material contained numerous accounts of suicidal behavior. For example, the only sister of Freud's most celebrated patient, the Wolf Man (so called because of his childhood phobia of wolves), committed suicide by poisoning herself. The patient's strange lack of grief over the sister's death aroused Freud's special interest until the psychoanalysis clarified the complicated processes of displacement of the mourning reaction in this patient. (14) The dramatic case of Dr. Schreber's paranoia (1911) included descriptions of Schreber's longing for death. "He made repeated attempts at drowning himself in his bath and asked to be given the 'cyanide that was intended for him.'"(11)

The first of Freud's longer case reports (1905) described fragments of the analysis of an eighteen-year-old female hysteric whom he called Dora.(8) She pressured her parents into obtaining treatment for her by writing a letter in which she took leave of them because she could no longer endure her life and leaving the letter in a place where they would be sure to find it. Dora was not the first person in the family to talk of suicide. Her father once told the story that he had been so unhappy at a certain time that he made up his mind to go into the woods and kill himself. From this case, we learn about suicide as a communication, attention-getter, cry for help, method of revenge, and as a partial identification with the father.

Additional insights appear in Freud's 1909 case history of a man with a severe obsessional neurosis, in whom one dramatic feature was a special fantasy about rats.(9) The patient's many obsessions and compulsions included suicidal impulses and commands. In the analysis, numerous examples of these suicidal commands were identified as punishments for rage and jealousy toward rivals. Freud said, "We find that impulses to suicide in a neurotic turn out regularly to be self-punishment for wishes for someone else's death." Freud was well aware that suicide is not a great danger in obsessive neurotics. The patient said that he might actually have killed himself on several occasions except for consideration for the feelings of his mother and sister.

In April, 1910, the Vienna Psychoanalytical Society discussed suicide. Adler and Stekel talked at great length and in great detail, emphasizing the aggressive aspects of suicide. Freud was unconvinced and elected to suspend judgment and await further experience. (10) Despite his many clinical observations concerning suicide, Freud was unable to organize them systematically into his psychoanalytic theory of instincts. In his early theory, the basic conflicting instinctual drives were thought to be libido (sensuality, sexuality) and self-preservation (hunger, aggressive mastery). How could suicide satisfy the needs either of sexuality or self-preservation? Eventually, Freud revised his theory of the instincts in order to provide appropriate recognition of the importance of self-destructiveness.

In *Mourning and Melancholia* (written in 1915, published in 1917), Freud took as his starting point a special type of patient, melancholics who express great guilt and self-reproach. "We see how in him one part of the ego sets itself over and against the other, judges it critically and in a word takes it as its object. Our suspicion that the critical agency which is here split off from the ego might also show its independency in other circumstances will be confirmed by every other observation."(12)

How does this splitting-off occur? The explanation in terms of psychic energy (libido) is quite complicated. Energy withdrawn from a lost object of love is relocated in the ego and used to recreate the loved one as a permanent feature of the self, an *identification* of the ego with the abandoned object. "Thus, the shadow of the object fell upon the ego, and the latter could henceforth be judged by a special agency as though it were an object, the forsaken object." "Shadow" objects existing as structures in the ego (identifications) obviously are not fully integrated into the total personality. A demarcation zone or fault line remains, along which ego-splitting occurs.

Also significant was Freud's speculation that certain ways of loving are less stable than others. Narcissistic love of another, for example, is especially vulnerable to disorganization and regression toward immature and primitive stages of the libido, especially sadism. "It is this sadism alone which solves the riddle of the tendency to suicide which makes melancholia so interesting and so dangerous. . . . We have long known it is true that no neurotic harbors thoughts of suicide which he has not turned back upon himself from murderous impulses against others, but we have never been able to explain what interplay of forces can carry a purpose through to execution. The analysis of melancholia now shows that the ego can kill itself only if, owing to the return of the object-cathexis, it can treat itself as an object—if it is able to direct against itself the hostility which relates to an object and which represents the ego's original reaction to objects in the external world. Thus, in regression from narcissistic object-choice, the object has, it is true, been gotten rid of, but it has nevertheless proved more powerful than the ego itself. In the two opposed situations of being most intensely in love, and of suicide, the ego is overwhelmed by the object, though in totally different ways." (12)

The above excerpt is quoted frequently in the literature concerned with suicide, most often with misplaced emphasis on the aspect of the original hostility and murderous impulses. In my opinion, the more important creative concepts are those of regression, disorganization, and ego-splitting, pathologic processes which allow a portion of the ego to initiate action disregarding the interests of the remainder.

The last of Freud's longer case reports, "The Psychogenesis of a Case of Homosexuality in a Woman," was published in 1920. The patient was an eighteen-year-old girl who was brought to Freud by her father about six months after she made a suicide attempt. What disturbed the family was not so much the suicide attempt as the girl's homosexual attachment to a woman about ten years older. The woman had not greatly encouraged the girl, and when one day they were walking together and met the father who gave them a furious look, the woman told the girl now certainly they must separate. Immediately the girl rushed off and flung herself over a wall down the side of a cutting onto the suburban railway line which ran close by. Although, fortunately, little permanent damage was done, the girl was in bed for some time, and Freud felt that the attempt was undoubtedly serious. After her recovery, she found it easier to get her own way than before.

It seemed to Freud that much of the girl's behavior was a reaction to the birth of her third brother three years previously. It was after that event that she turned her love away from children toward older women. Concerning the suicide attempt, Freud said, "The analysis was able to disclose a deeper interpretation beyond the one she gave (despair over loss of the woman). The attempted suicide was, as might have been expected, determined by two other motives besides the ones she gave. It was the fulfillment of a punishment (self-punishment) and the fulfillment of a wish. As the latter it meant the attainment of the very wish which, when frustrated, had driven her into homosexuality —namely the wish to have a child by her father, for now she fell through her father's fault. From the point of view of self-punishment, the girl's action shows us that she had developed in her unconscious strong death wishes against one or the other of her parents —perhaps against her father out of revenge for impeding her love, but more probably against her mother, too, when she was pregnant with the little brother. Analysis has explained the enigma of suicide in the following way: Probably no one finds the mental energy required to kill himself unless, in the first place in doing so, he is at the same time killing an object with whom he has identified himself and, in the second place, is turning against himself a death wish which had been directed against someone else. Nor need the regular discovery of these unconscious death wishes in those who have attempted suicide surprise us (any more than it ought to make us think that it confirms our deductions), since the unconscious of all human beings is full enough of such death wishes against even those they love. Since the girl identified herself with her mother, who should have died at the birth of the child denied to herself, this punishment-fulfillment itself was once again a wish fulfillment. Finally, the discovery that several quite different motives, all of great strength, must have cooperated to make such a deed possible is only in accordance with what we should expect." (16)

The most significant of the ideas expressed above is the discovery that suicide is multiply determined by the interaction of several motives. The emphasis is on ego-splitting and identifications. The suicidal act is explained as a reenactment—by a split-off ego identification with mother—of the delivery of the brother. The murderous look the father gave the girl is mentioned. Allusion is made indirectly to the theme of death and rebirth (rescue). The effect of a suicidal act as a communication which changes the environment is recorded. Erotic and masochistic elements of the suicide attempt are specially noted. Death wishes are described as the source of the energy required for suicide, yet death wishes are not limited to suicides but are typical of all human beings.

Freud continued to feel that his theoretical explanations were incomplete for several major clinical phenomena associated with self-destructiveness. These included "negative therapeutic reaction," sadism, masochism, and the "enigma of suicide." In 1920 Freud proposed for speculative consideration that there might be an instinctual drive toward death. (15) His arguments were partly on clinical grounds (traumatic neuroses, repetitive actions) and partly biological and philosophical. Although at first the new ideas were advanced tentatively and cautiously, Freud soon came to accept them fully and with increasingly complete conviction. (28)

The death instinct concept was a major theoretical construction. It has, however, received relatively little acceptance among psychoanalysts. Why was Freud so convinced of its usefulness? Ernest Jones suggests that there were subjective motives, and reports insightfully on Freud's intense, complicated, personal, daily fantasies about death. (28) However, Freud's own explanation is logically consistent. Freud said he accepted the death instinct theory because he needed it to explain masochism (and suicide). (22) How then do suicide and masochism appear from this viewpoint?

"If we turn to melancholia first, we find that the excessively strong superego which has obtained a hold upon consciousness rages against the ego with merciless violence . . . What is now holding sway in the superego is, as it were, a pure culture of the death instinct and in fact it often enough succeeds in driving the ego into death . . ." (17) In melancholia, the ego gives itself up because it feels itself hated and persecuted by the superego instead of loved. To the ego, therefore, living means the same as being loved by the superego so that the death by suicide symbolizes or reenacts a sort of abandonment of the ego by the superego. It is a similar situation to separation from the protecting mother.

The original quantity of internalized death instinct is identical with masochism. The individual tries to externalize this energy as aggressiveness or sadism. Where there is a cultural suppression of the instincts, the destructive instinctual components are turned back into his superego. We see a helpless, masochistic ego in relationship with a sadistic superego. The modality of the relationship is punishment. In order to provoke punishment, the masochist must do what is inexpedient, must act against his own interests, must ruin his prospects, and perhaps destroy himself. But since there is always some fusion of the erotic and destructive instincts, there is always an obvious erotic component in masochism, so that even the subject's destruction of himself cannot take place without libidinal satisfaction. (18)

Due to the prolonged, extreme biological and social helplessness of the human infant who cannot, unaided, satisfy his vital needs or regulate his own destructive instincts, each individual must incorporate controlling, coercing, and punishment components into his superego. (19) (20) By this process the instincts are tamed and the child can participate in family life and education. By an anthropological analogy, Freud viewed civilization as a group superego development. In civilized man, extra aggression is channeled into the superego and turned against the ego. It is now felt as unconscious guilt, masochism, a need to be punished, or an obscure *malaise* and discontent. The price we pay for our own advance in civilization is a loss, to some degree, of the possibilities of happiness. (21) "We owe to that process (civilization) the best of what we have become, as well as a good part of what we suffer from." (23)

To Freud, suicide represented a symptom of what we suffer from, a product of man and his civilization, a consequence of mental trends which can be found to some degree in every human being.

Summary

There are, according to Freud, *general features* of the human condition, at least in Western civilization, which make each individual person somewhat vulnerable to suicide. These general features include: (a) the death-instinct with its clinical derivatives, the aggressive instinct directed outward and the destructive instinct directed inward; (b) the splitting of the ego. This is inevitable because of the extreme helplessness of the human ego in infancy when it is unable to master its own instincts and must conform to the parents or parish; (c) the group institutions, family and civilization, which require guilty compliance from every member of the group.

The above general features only begin to account for any individual suicide. Individual suicides involve certain *specific suicide mechanisms*. All of them involve a breaking down of ego defenses and the release of increased destructive, instinctual energy. Examples are: (a) loss of love objects, especially those who have been loved in certain dangerous ways; (b) narcissistic injury, symbolically through failure or by direct physiological injury through fatigue or toxins; (c) overwhelming affect: rage, guilt, anxiety, or combinations; (d) extreme splitting of the ego with decathexis of most elements and a setting of one part against the rest; and (e) a special suicidal attitude and plan, often based on an identification with someone who was suicidal.

Finally, there are a great number of *specific predisposing conditions* that more or less favor suicide, although they are not precipitating mechanisms. These include: (a) a disorganized or disharmonious ego structure which splits up under relatively low conditions of stress; (b) a tendency of the libido to be fixated at pre-oedipal positions, especially strong tendencies toward sadism and masochism; (c) disease of the superego due to cruel parents, dead parents, parents that wished you were dead; or due to some constitutional, inherited superego trait of excessive destructiveness; (d) a strong attachment of the libido to death, dead loved ones, or a fantasy of being dead; (e) vivid erotic fantasies which symbolize and cover up death wishes, for example, the fantasy of bearing a child by father, symbolically actualized as a fall from a height; and (f) a chronically self-destructive living pattern expressed, for example, as gambling addiction or homosexuality.

Experience has confirmed Freud's statement that each suicide is multiply determined by the interaction of several motives. My observations as chief psychiatrist in a multidisciplinary project of research, training and clinical service for suicide prevention (Suicide Prevention Center) are in agreement with Freud's general schematic view. Deep down there seems to be a suicidal trend in all of us. This self-destructiveness is tamed, controlled and overcome through our healthy identifications, ego defenses, and our constructive habits of living and loving. When the ordinary defenses, controls and ways of living and loving break down, the individual may easily be forced into a suicidal crisis. At such times he feels helpless, hopeless and abandoned, and may or may not be aware of a great deal of unexpressable, aggressive tension.

Most of the therapeutic actions of therapists at the Suicide Prevention Center are aimed at reinforcing the ego defenses, renewing the feeling of hope, love and trust, and providing emergency scaffolding to aid in the eventual repair and healing of the splits in the patient's ego. Direct psychological techniques for turning aggression outward have not been particularly successful in our experience. Rather we try to deal immediately with the feelings of deprivation.

Many of Freud's perceptive inferences have been explored and consolidated by later workers. For example, Freud often referred to certain dangerous ways of loving in which the ego is "overwhelmed" by the object. Typically, the psychic representations of the self and others are fused, and the other is experienced as essential for survival. Modern writers have termed these attachments "symbiotic," making explicit the analogy to the primitive, dependent relationship between a baby (or fetus) and its mother. Freud's observation that symbiotic love is a potential precursor of suicide still holds good.

Freud's dictum that suicide starts with a death wish against others, which is then redirected toward an identification within the self, has been overly accentuated by some psychotherapists and has become a cliché. Freud is quoted to support a relative overemphasis on aggression and guilt as components of suicide with underemphasis of the helplessness, dependency and erotic elements. In other words, the suicidal drama often reproduces not so much guilt for the unconscious wish of the child to murder the parents, but rather a reaction of abandonment on the part of the child to the parent's unconscious wish for the child's death. The mechanisms of regression and ego-splitting, and the themes in suicide of helplessness, constriction and paranoid distrust, have made the deepest impression on me.

Freud pointed out that infantile helplessness is the essential circumstance which creates masochism. Freud was accustomed to using his concept of the oedipal complex as his reference point for psychopathology. From that viewpoint, guilt over rivalry with parents, especially the father, looms large. In our suicide prevention clinic, we are more accustomed to using the mother-child, pre-oedipal relationship as a reference concept. Further research, hopefully, will clarify this issue.

It is remarkable that Freud said so little about the all-important attitude of the mother in instilling into a child the desire for life. It is remarkable because Freud was well aware of the influence of his own mother in instilling into him a feeling of confidence and a zest for living. (25) Moreover, he had found in his patients and in himself, as a reason for continuing to live, the idea that his premature death would be painful to his mother. When Freud's mother died in 1930, age 95, Freud noticed in himself a feeling of liberation. "I was not allowed to die as long as she was alive and now I may." (27)

Freud's personal attitude toward death, according to the sharp eye of his biographer, Jones, was altogether a rich and complex one with many aspects. "In the world of reality he was an unusually courageous man who faced misfortune, suffering, danger and ultimately death itself with unflinching fortitude. But in fantasy there were other elements." There was at times a curious longing for death. "He once said he thought of it every day of his life, which is certainly unusual." (28)

In three essays on war and death, Freud expressed himself as a cautiously hopeful realist. Horrified and depressed by the cruelty, fraud, treachery and barbarity of World War I, he tried to extract some value out of discarding his illusions about civilization and facing disagreeable truths (1915). "To tolerate life remains, after all, the first duty of all living beings. Illusion becomes valueless if it makes this harder for us." And, characteristically, he added, "If you want to endure life, prepare yourself for death." (13) Freud described himself as a pacifist (1933). "We pacifists have a *constitutional* intolerance of war . . . whatever fosters the growth of civilization works at the same time against war." (28)

Freud was well aware of the difference between philosophic speculations about the general causes of man's misery and the requirements of practical life to do something about it. In a letter to Einstein (1933) on the problem of preventing war, he commented, "The result, as you see, is not very fruitful when an unworldly theoretician is called in to advise on an urgent practical problem. It is a better plan to devote oneself in every particular case to meeting the danger with whatever means lie at hand." (23) Freud applied the same advice to his own clinical endeavors. In 1926, discussing a young patient, Freud wrote, "What weighs on me in his case is my belief that unless the outcome is very good, it will be very bad indeed; what I mean is that he would commit suicide without any hesitation. I shall therefore do all in my power to avert that eventuality." (24) No doubt many psychotherapists whose work exposes them continuously to affects of violence, sadism and death gain in confidence and flexibility by partially identifying with the complex personality of Freud.

Bibliography

1. Freud, S. (Nov. 2, 1896). *The Origins of Psycho-Analysis.* New York: Basic Books, Inc., 1954, pp. 170-171.
2. ———. *Ibid.* (May 31, 1897), p. 207.
3. ———. *Ibid.* (June 12, 1897), p. 221.
4. ———. *Ibid.* (Sept. 22, 1898), pp. 264-265.
5. ———. (1893-1895). "Studies on Hysteria." *Standard Edition of the Complete Psychological Works.* London: Hogarth Press, 1953-1965, Vol. 2, p. 28.
6. ———. *Ibid.* (1898). "The Psychical Mechanism of Forgetfulness." Vol. 3, pp. 290-296.
7. ———. *Ibid.* (1901). "The Psychopathology of Everyday Life." Vol. 6, pp. 1-6.
8. ———. *Ibid.* (1905). "Fragment of an Analysis of a Case of Hysteria." Vol. 7.
9. ———. *Ibid.* (1909). "Notes Upon a Case of Obsessional Neurosis." Vol. 10.
10. ———. *Ibid.* (1910). "Contributions to a Discussion on Suicide." Vol. 11, p. 232.
11. ———. *Ibid.* (1911). "Psycho-Analytic Notes Upon an Autobiographical Account of a Case of Paranoia." Vol. 12, p. 14.
12. ———. *Ibid.* (1917). "Mourning and Melancholia." Vol. 14, pp. 247-252.
13. ———. *Ibid.* (1915). "Thoughts for the Times on War and Death." Vol. 14, pp. 289-300.
14. ———. *Ibid.* (1918). "From the History of an Infantile Neurosis." Vol. 17, pp. 21-23.
15. ———. *Ibid.* (1920). "Beyond the Pleasure Principle." Vol. 18.
16. ———. *Ibid.* (1920). "The Psychogenesis of a Case of Homosexuality in a Woman." Vol. 18.
17. ———. *Ibid.* (1923). "The Ego and the Id." Vol. 19, pp. 53-58.
18. ———. *Ibid.* (1924). "The Economic Problem of Masochism." Vol. 19, pp. 169-170.
19. ———. *Ibid.* (1926). "Inhibitions, Symptoms and Anxiety." Vol. 20, pp. 154-155.
20. ———. *Ibid.* (1930). "Civilization and Its Discontents." Vol. 21, pp. 124-128.
21. ———. *Ibid.*
22. ———. *Ibid.* (1933). "New Introductory Lectures on Psycho-Analysis." Vol. 22, p. 104.
23. ———. *Ibid.* "Why War?" Vol. 22, pp. 213-215.

24. ———. *Psychoanalysis and Faith.* New York: Basic Books, Inc., 1963, pp. 101-102. (Letter to Rev. Oskar Pfister.)
25. Jones, E. *The Life and Work of Sigmund Freud.* New York: Basic Books, Inc., 1953-1957, Vol. 1, p. 5.
26. ———. *Ibid.* p. 122.
27. ———. *Ibid.* Vol. 3, p. 153.
28. ———. *Ibid.* p. 275-280.

2521 West Pico Boulevard
Los Angeles, California 90006

Discussant

Angel Garma, M.D.

Buenos Aires, Argentina

In 1937, "Imago" published a paper of mine on the subject of suicide, in which I indicated that the principal determining factors were the loss of an important libidinal object and aggressive wishes towards an object, both secondarily turned against the ego. Other determinants I mentioned were the recovery of the lost libidinal object and the carrying out of aggressive wishes.

Over the years I became convinced aggressive wishes turned against the ego were less important. Further psychoanalytical experience confirmed for me Freud's theory in "Beyond the Pleasure Principle" that "masochism is older than sadism" and not the reverse.

For this reason I completely agree with Dr. Litman that in the psychoanalytical literature on the subject of suicide, "most often there is a misplaced emphasis on the aspect of the original hostility and murderous impulses" and that "Freud's dictum that suicide starts with a death wish against others . . . has been overly accentuated among some psychotherapists . . . and has become a cliché."

The existence of intense sadistic wishes in suicides is not to be doubted, but these are frequently the result of their masochistic reaction to external and internal objects. They arise more from the need to provoke masochistic guilt feelings with which to justify the act of suicide, rather than from the desire to satisfy sadistic feelings. This is the situation described by Freud in "Criminals From a Sense of Guilt" with the difference that the suicide directs the criminal act against himself.

Freud occasionally shares the misplaced

emphasis on sadism as an explanation of pathological behavior patterns. Thus, in describing the Oedipus complex, he lays much more stress on parricidal wishes than on the foregoing filicidal behavior of Laius and Jocasta. Masochism was present in Oedipus before the appearance of sadism, and in fact was the cause of it. The name Oedipus means "swollen feet" and thus in his very identity we perceive the masochistic traces of his parents' sadistic aggression against him.

Analytic candidates generally tend to interpret in this way. It becomes evident that this accentuation of sadism occurs because the severity of their psychoanalytical training recalls earlier submissions of an infantile, scholastic or religious nature. In the latter case, the guilt-ridden individual interprets that he himself, on account of his criminal and sadistic tendencies against God is the cause of all his misfortunes. Actually he is masochistically submissive to his parents, teachers and rulers. This type of guilt-laden submission may persist even after the analytical training and cause psychotherapists to make interpretations with undue emphasis on sadism, resulting in guilt feelings in their patients.

Oedipus does not commit suicide, although Jocasta, whom we may consider to be a part of him, does. Oedipus blinded himself, which may be interpreted as partial suicide. Following this reasoning, and as Dr. Litman expresses it, it is very probable that "suicidal drama often reproduces not so much guilt for the unconscious wish of the child to murder the parents but rather a reaction of abandonment on the part of the child to the parents' unconscious wish for the child's death." However, in the case of Oedipus, his parent's filicidal wishes were his own parricidal desires; on the contrary they (his parents) made a very conscious attempt to carry them out.

Discussant

Edwin S. Shneidman, PH.D.
Los Angeles, California

My interests in suicide and suicide prevention over the past seventeen years, building first on the theoretical structure of Freud, and later on the (to me) more viable and meaningful formulations and outlooks of Murray, have moved from an initial focus on suicide on to an intermediate interest in death, and now currently to a concern with the wider area of self-destruction in man.

This current interest encompasses the topic of self-imposed death (cessation) as well as related conditions such as temporary or permanent cessation of a part of the psychic life —the cessation of affect (feeling almost dead), or the cessation of an orientation of conscious life, such as the cessation of social life, or of spiritual life (what Murray refers to as "dead to the outer world" and "dead to the inner world," respectively). These have to do with a variety of psychic states characterized by marked diminution or near cessation of affect.

In my opinion an interest in self-imposed death must perforce include an interest in partial deaths and in the attritions, truncations, and demeanings of life—the whole range of inimical or maladaptive behavior. Dr. Litman's chronological exegesis of Freud's thoughts on suicide provides the student and the therapist of self-destruction with a baseline of fundamental understandings from which a variety of useful and meaningful conceptualizations can be made.

The popular notion of Freud's concept of suicide as solely lethal hostile impulses turned against the introjected love object (which I have called "murder in the 180th degree") is currently shared by lay person and professional alike.

Dr. Litman has done a notable service in explicating the various psychodynamic elements: love (including its shades and nuances of different kinds of love), the need for communication, anguish, revenge, self-punishment, and especially helplessness and dependency elements which occur in self-destruction, in addition to and even in lieu of the ubiquitous hostility suggested by the earlier psychoanalytic formulations of suicidal dynamics.

One can hardly fault Freud for his univalent approach to the concept of suicide—treating the multiplicity of suicidal phenomena as though they were a single (albeit multiple-determined) phenomenon. Part of the difficulty of Freud's exposition on this topic was that he was searching for the psychodynamic formulation of "it," whereas most of us (Litman in the forefront) realize we have long needed to think in terms of the cultural, social, psychodynamic, dyadic, adventitious, and other components of "them"—i.e., the varieties of psychological and behavioral patterns often over-inclusively labeled as "suicide."

Discussant

Bettina Warburg, M.D.

New York, New York

A formal discussion of this article would imply reviewing the literature, for which time is lacking. However, there are two points which I would like to make:

1. In his paper, Dr. Litman refers to "identification." It is true that Freud discusses identification, but in *Mourning and Melancholia* on page 160 of the old English 1925 edition, he also states: "The ego wishes to incorporate this object into itself and the method by which it would do so, in this oral or cannibalistic stage, is by devouring it . . . We should not hesitate to include among our special characteristics of melancholia a regression from object-cathexis to the still narcissistic oral phase of the libido."

In omitting this concept from his description, Dr. Litman consequently also omits the idea that patients with this mechanism are unconsciously killing the introjected object rather than themselves when they commit suicide, and that here the gratification of this unconscious wish is accompanied by the talion punishment of self-destruction.

2. Freud discusses the concept that in certain types of suicide the unconscious wish is to rejoin some loved person in the hereafter, but he does not emphasize that death in this sense is not conceived of as dying, but rather as entering a more desirable life in which the lost object is regained, and that suicide is conceived of as being reborn rather than as dying.

Discussant

Lilla Veszy-Wagner, PH.D.

London, England

This is a scholarly paper, enjoyable as well as instructive. Freud's thoughts about suicide are fairly well known by now; thus the quest into his possible subjective sources and his own "suicidal" ideas are far more fascinating.

It is good to be reminded of the possible connection between the repression of the suicidal thought, and forgetting (such as Freud's forgetting the painter Signorelli's name) as a symptomatic action. Freud sensed its importance because he introduced a whole volume on parapraxes with this anecdote. (It must, however, be noted that it was not one of Freud's patients, but a patient of a colleague—a Bosnian Turk—who said to his doctor that life is of no value when sexual enjoyment has come to an end.)

Freud diverted his own uncomfortable thoughts from the topic, suppressing the anecdote not only at that point but later by placing a great emphasis on the libido as life instinct when setting up his theory of the death instinct holding the balance. Earlier, he would not tolerate libido having to do with anything other than sex.

An interesting speculation by Sabine Spielrein went almost unnoticed by Freud. Following his first instinct theory granting that sexual (love) instincts are opposed to life instincts (self-preservation), she contended that instincts represent a kind of suicidal tendency (a pull towards the "little" or temporary "death" in orgasm). This must have displeased Freud who, by then, had turned more and more toward his second instinct theory which encompassed the idea of a separate death instinct. Certainly it also influenced his attitude against acknowledging any kind of libidinal strivings in what he regarded as a final and unadulterated life-destructive goal—the ultimate extinction of life.

However theoretical his deductions, there must also have been subjective factors involved. These, in my view, were not only his pride (accepting the terminal steps in life as self-willed), but also his refusal to accept the hidden libidinal, incestuous lure in the suicidal bent. Freud's subjective "longing for death" certainly had something to do with his death instinct theory. Suicidal ideas, however, are *not* always (or not only) self-punishments for someone else's death. As Dr. Litman rightly points out, they sometimes conceal libidinal desires.

A suicidal patient of mine who was unable to get an erection once dreamt he "was waiting in a prison to be hanged." He remembered that men experienced an erection at the moment of hanging. After the interpretation of this dream—that he wanted to be hanged in order to get an erection—he had another impulse to end his life by poison. This represented the oral longing for his mother whose poisonous milk would be better than anything he could receive from others. After that he had fantasies of having to kill himself to take revenge on his mother who loved his sister more than she loved him. After the analysis of these moods, his depression abated and his suicidal wishes receded.

Dr. Litman is most perspicacious to notice Freud's hesitations on the occasion of the Vienna discussions about suicide (1910). Would it be too daring to assume that Freud, a man with both depressive and obsessional character traits, hesitated to decide upon the origins and sources of his own depressive reactions to suicide?

I do not think it unlikely that Freud's rare moments of longing for death were connected with his reluctance to analyze his oceanic feelings towards his mother. After her death he said that he noticed in himself a feeling of liberation. "I was not allowed to die as long as she was alive and now I may" sounds very much like a rationalization, i.e., "I could not die as long as she lived because I still unconsciously hoped to be reunited with her, but now I may—or must—because only this way could I be reunited with her."

The cessation of the incest taboo through his mother's death gave Freud a feeling of liberation, however transitory. Because he regarded tolerating of life the first duty of all beings, it is probable this meant tolerating the status quo of the incest taboo which, however, is lifted in death. Hence the longing for death, the liberator from this status quo.

When Freud regards being intensely in love and suicide as opposites, he also condemns his own desires—which certainly persisted unconsciously in connection with his mother throughout his life—to be overwhelmed by the object. These desires showed themselves in his fainting attacks in connection with Jung toward whom he felt a deep and ambivalent attraction.

It is noteworthy that Freud, in dealing with the "Rat man," did not point out the loopholes in the suicidal commands which, in the obsessional, make us doubt their sincerity. Similarly, he did not interpret the alternative (the wish to kill "the old woman" instead of himself) as directed, unconsciously, against the patient's own mother.

Freud's indecisions about the problem of suicide show even more clearly in his evasiveness in "The Psychogenesis of a Case of Homosexuality in a Woman." It seems unconvincing that the eighteen-year-old girl should have turned her love "away from children towards older women" as a reaction to the birth of her third brother. More likely, she looked for a mother substitute in the ill-chosen "lady," and her suicidal attempt was an act of despair over "the lady's" unreliability—a repetition of the experience of being "jilted" by mother for baby brother.

Too, she resented brother and father as obstacles preventing her from keeping mother. Freud preferred to think the self-punishment stemmed from the girl's failure to woo her father successfully and get a child from him; and, unable to identify with mother, wished her to die in childbed.

Freud apparently did not feel that father was regarded as an enemy rather than as a love object, nor that the girl's suicidal attempt represented a desire to be reunited in death with the "lady," symbolic of the original mother.

Perhaps Freud's undisclosed or denied similar feelings prevented him from seeing the stronger (pre-oedipal) pull to the mother over the weaker oedipal one to the father.

The girl's despair and suicidal desire originated in her realization that she could never satisfy her mother as could father or brother, nor could she so satisfy the "lady" as to make her allegiance durable. Similar feelings must have haunted Freud although he was mother's favorite—or perhaps *because* he was her favorite.

In my view, these feelings caused Freud's dissatisfaction with his theoretical explanations as incomplete for a full explication of suicidal temptations. He saw, especially in melancholia, that these feelings represented a situation similar to the separation from the protecting but also loving-mother, which even the favorite has eventually to face.

I certainly agree with Dr. Litman—that the helplessness, dependency and erotic elements in the suicidal syndrome have not been sufficiently emphasized in today's analytical literature.

I also agree there is (based on Freud's tenets) an overemphasis on aggression and guilt as components.

Freud was aware that his mother obviously gave him his self-confidence and zest for living. What he was not conscious of was his clinging to her. He therefore acknowledges his debt to her while minimizing the importance of this factor (through the almost desultory tone) and of the strength of his own unresolved incestuous feelings towards her.

Discussant

Justin Simon, M.D.
Brooklyn, New York
Received as "The Forum" went to press

The dual approach of presenting psychoanalytic metapsychology of a topic and at the same time reviewing the historical development of that metapsychology is shown by Dr. Litman to be a felicitous exercise and a stimulating one. The viewpoints illuminate each other, juxtaposing Freud's unfolding concepts against an emergent appreciation of the complexity of the problem of suicide. One can forgive both Freud and Litman for failing to achieve theoretical synthesis in attempting to explain a symptomatic act which occurs across a wide spectrum of psychopathology.

The paradox in Dr. Litman's paper is that in his task as critical reviewer he touches the epistemological-philosopher frontier of psychoanalytic theory which is the death instinct, but in his role as original contributor he focuses so sharply upon the therapeutic-prophylactic issues as to blur the main province of psychoanalysis which lies between psychotherapy and philosophy.

Dr. Litman cannot be accused of omitting from his discussion any possible psychodynamic consideration in suicide. But the thrust of his own contribution is to criticize Freud's "overemphasis on aggression and guilt as components of suicide with underemphasis of the helplessness, dependency and erotic elements."

Dr. Litman rightfully shows how Freud's continuing focus upon id psychology and the central role of the Oedipus complex in psychoneurosis led him to ignore, relatively, the ego aspects of severe depression and the value of those ego aspects in psychotherapy. He is to be commended on his role in the pioneering work which has forged new psychotherapeutic tools in dealing with suicidal risk. Dr. Litman should not, however, with the illumination to which he has made a significant contribution, commit the opposite error and lose sight of the instinctual issues which enter into that complex act of suicide. In the service of emphasizing the ego aspects of "the suicidal drama" Dr. Litman evidently feels that it is necessary to challenge the significance of the more comprehensive metapsychology.

While Dr. Litman may be correct that Freud has overemphasized the aggressive instinctual issues in suicidal ideation and action, still one would expect that the balanced evaluation of the complex of forces is more likely to issue from the data derived from a thorough psychoanalytic case study than from the emergency psychotherapy clinic.

At Downstate Medical Center we are doing research on a recorded analysis. One of the goals of this study is to provide direct and reproducible clinical psychoanalytic data upon which to validate or modify various psychoanalytic propositions. This study, as yet, involves only a single patient, nor are we yet in a position to deal with the question of whether or not a genuine analytic situation can develop under research conditions. Nonetheless, the data we have from almost two hundred audio-recorded psychoanalytic sessions may be relevant to this question.

The analysand in this research is an obsessional psychoneurotic woman, and although suicidal ideation has not been an issue, serious depressive episodes have. It is in rather striking conformity with Freud's "overemphasis on aggression and guilt" that severe depressive reactions have not followed as a general response to frustration, anxiety or disappointment, all of which she suffers in abundance. The significant depressive responses have followed upon specific transference frustrations which have reactivated powerful aggressive impulses against both parents about which she felt guilty and turned back upon herself. Therefore, she weathered a long interruption of the analysis because of the analyst's illness rather well, but following a period when she thought that the analyst had lied to her (as her parents had), she was in a state of severe agitated depression and threatened to break off the analysis. A later revival of this transference reaction brought out clearly the ego aspects which Dr. Litman emphasizes. She felt hopelessly abandoned and distrustful. But the underlying issues in every depressive reaction seem always to be aggression, object loss and introjection of the hated object. At these times the patient suffers the fate of feeling unloveable because she feels incapable of loving. This very schematic presentation is in lieu of a fuller exposition which would be out of place here.

In summary, then, Dr. Litman valuably extends the applications of psychoanalytic theory, especially ego psychology, to the treatment of suicidal patients. While it may be therapeutically valuable to de-emphasize aggression in the suicidal patient, the metapsychological validity of that shift has yet to be demonstrated.

Author's Response

Robert E. Litman, M.D.

Beverly Hills, California

The discussions contained a number of important contributions. Dr. Warburg's two points are brief but most significant. Freud was convinced that in the unconscious there is no conception of self-death or suicide. For this and other reasons, psychoanalysts feel that concepts of suicide are represented quite differently in the id, superego and ego.

Of course, the act of suicide is executed by a portion of the ego. In the moments preceding suicide, the ego typically is fragmented and the perplexing problem of which fragment is the executor and which fragment is the object can only be settled by direct observation under special circumstances. I have the impression that often the powerful *introjected object* captures the avenues that control motility and kills the self.

Dr. Garma, who has written extensively on all aspects of self-destructiveness, emphasizes the primary role of masochism and gives us a brief illumination of the Oedipus drama in its sadomasochistic aspects. Very little has been written about suicide recently in the North American psychoanalytic literature. But this is not true for the South Americans, who have contributed some dramatic theoretical reformulations. For example, Mauricio Abadi (Suicide: A Psychoanalytic Approach, Acta Neuropsiquiat. Arg. 5:366-374, 1959) states boldly that every self-murder is a psychotic act; that it is an ultimate and triumphant ego defense mechanism to escape paranoid anxiety and persecution; but the death is not a real one but a *magic death*, with fantasies of resurrection; and, finally, the compulsion to suicide implies a deep regression to the schizo-paranoid position.

Dr. Shneidman reminds us of the intimate connection between suicide and the whole wide area of self-destruction in man. I agree that the psychoanalytic view of suicide is only one of many avenues to increased understanding of this most complex and multiply-determined group of phenomena.

The clinical vignette reported by Dr. Veszy-Wagner is most appropriate, for it reminds us of a whole taboo area of bondage perversion in which it is necessary to be bound, degraded and hanged as a preliminary to orgasm. Dr. H. L. P. Resnik and I are preparing a report on a number of such individuals, some of whom died "accidentally" while practicing their perversion.

I wish we knew more about Freud's patient who committed suicide. The news of this "melancholy event" set the stage for the "Signorelli" incident. In his biography of Freud, Ernest Jones said, concerning that incident, "As I hope to expound in a revised edition of Volume I of this biography, it was connected with a significant episode which must have played an important part in the inception of Freud's self-analysis." Unfortunately, Jones died before revising the biography. Not only are we left with an intriguing biographical mystery but also with an important scientific problem concerning the patient of Freud who committed suicide. Who was this patient? What happened in that analysis? Did Freud describe fragments of the case, heavily disguised, somewhere in his writings? Or was the history of the patient totally repressed from the memory of science? Why did Jones, who has so much to report about Freud's work and his patients, choose to postpone the illumination of the suicide incident? The important scientific problem is this: Is the taboo on suicide so intense that even psychoanalysts are reluctant to expose their case material and personal experiences in this area?

Sigmund Freud as a Consultant and Therapist: From Sigmund Freud's Letters to Edoardo Weiss[1]

Martin Grotjahn, M.D.
Beverly Hills, California

INTRODUCTION

The correspondence between Sigmund Freud and Edoardo Weiss shows Freud in the light of a psychoanalytic consultant. This aspect of Freud has rarely been described in detail and the recently published correspondence between Sigmund Freud and Karl Abraham[2] shows little of such advisory activity, with the exception of one letter written to Karl Abraham early in the correspondence (January 9, 1908).

One of the first things which startles the reader of the Freud-Weiss correspondence in relationship to discussing technical aspects of psychoanalytic practice is Freud's outspoken and undisguised judgment between worthwhile and not so worthwhile patients. In the privacy of his correspondence Freud used sharp words, including the word "scoundrel"; and he was generally skeptical about the therapeutic efficacy of analysis in such cases.

Freud gave advice freely and generously from his immense clinical experience; for instance, he said: The patient who talks too much about his analysis prepares a betrayal or hostile exposure of analysis. At another time he explained with great kindness and patience, which characterized all of these letters to his younger colleague, that the therapist in question is perhaps too young in order to invite the necessary father transference. At all times Freud was very careful not to be overwhelming with his advice and whatever he said was meant "without obligation" to the recipient of the letters.

Freud was writing to a colleague so much younger—Edoardo Weiss was thirty-three years his junior—but he was always careful, almost protective and anxious to guard his student's self-respect.

Again and again Freud sounded a warning against excessive therapeutic ambition, impatience, or pressuring the patient. This does not necessarily indicate therapeutic pessimism. It seems to represent the general early European attitude of skepticism and guarded expectancy towards psychoanalysis or any kind of therapeutic approach as a method to treat mental illness or to change personality. The original attitude of using psychoanalysis as a method of study, more than as a form of treatment, shines through the words of Freud.

Another warning is expressed in the words: Go slow with teaching more liberal views on sexuality; they could shock and harm the inhibited patient.

The many different aspects of an analyst's therapeutic attitude are represented in various colors and shades. Freud knew what it meant to win a patient, to interest him in his analytic work, to enthuse him; words like "conquest" and "overwhelming" were used. Once he almost pleads with Edoardo Weiss not to leave the patient to his "demon." Edoardo Weiss explained recently that the "demon" referred to is the demon of the repetition-compulsion.

Most striking in all of these letters on psychoanalytic therapy is the superb, simple, straightforward and convincing reconstruc-

[1]Published with the agreement of Edoardo Weiss, M.D., Chicago, Illinois and Ernst Freud, Director of the Sigmund Freud Copyrights, Ltd., London.

[2]*A Psycho-Analytic Dialogue*. The Letters of Sigmund Freud and Karl Abraham. 1907-1926. (Eds. H. Abraham and E. Freud). New York: Basic Books, 1966, p. 20.

tion of psychodynamics. To the recipient of these letters they must have amounted to a training in psychodynamic reasoning. Such deepening of analytic understanding is more important for a student than help in a specific situation; it is difficult to give, easily misleading and always asks for a mature student who is willing to listen and to learn, but who is also on his way to stand on his own feet, in this case almost alone in all of Italy.

There are many informal hints and clues about the therapeutic attitude: at one time Freud warned against the setting of termination dates. At another occasion he recommended talking with the parents of a patient. He surprisingly suggested interruptions in psychoanalysis with a promise to resume after several months. In other places he emphasized the importance of predicting events in order to cushion the impact of negative reactions in the transference-neurosis. He proposed warning parents and predicting things to come in order to safeguard the position of the therapist and to forestall the intensity of disappointment for therapist, patient and parents.

Through all the letters goes the admonition that we have to be glad to learn something in the understanding of people and their unconscious. There is still so much to learn for young colleagues and experienced teachers alike.

Twice repeated is the reassuring word that many a patient has "cussed" his way to health. Even if the analytic process activates an underlying psychosis, self-accusations are not necessarily justified; it can happen to anybody and it is probably unavoidable in our clinical work.

Freud was willing to see patients and therapists together in a consultation. On one occassion, however, before agreeing to see the doctor and his patient in Vienna, he asked if the patient also desired it, feeling the interview would otherwise be pointless and even harmful.

The first half of the letter dated April 12, 1933 is known from its publication in Ernst L. Freud's "Letters,"[3] and the translation follows the one given there. It is published here again to show the hitherto unknown last paragraph which shows Freud's habit of seeing his colleague's patients in person, together with the therapist.

One of the early letters (October 3, 1920) contains the unusual term *leidens-conflict* —translated as "suffering from conflict." It implies that only a conflict causing suffering can be expected to originate enough energy for the necessary therapeutic effort in psychoanalysis. Where such suffering is not present the therapist has lost. In one such case, Freud drily considered a drastic step: send the patient to South America, let him seek and find there his destiny. Such brief, simple, classical, psychodynamic vignettes are typical of Freud letters and make them so alive like drawings quickly sketched by a master's hand.

The letter with the corrected date from the 3rd of March, corrected to the 3rd of April, 1922, shows an analytic dilemma known to any analyst: how to navigate under a heavy, perhaps too heavy burden of patients. By then Freud seemed to have turned to a greater extent to training physicians by analyzing them. Avoiding the term "candidate," he spoke of nine people and one patient.

In a remark about his own patient [Mrs. L. M.] whom Edoardo Weiss knew well, he was guarded, but at the same time spoke frankly about the necessary new educational effort in combination with analytic interpretations.

Here are the letters, first in German transcript and then in English translation:

---

[3]Letter No. 269 in *Letters of Sigmund Freud*, Selected and Edited by Ernst L. Freud and translated by T. and I. Stern; New York: Basic Books, 1960.

Prof. Dr. Freud 3. Okt. 20

Wien IX, Berggasse 19

Lieber Herr Doktor

█████████████████████████████████████[4]

Da Sie heute ein richtiges Gutachten ueber ihn von mir verlangen, will ich mit meiner Meinung nicht zurueckhalten. Ich glaube es ist ein schlechter Fall vor Allem fuer die freie Analyse nicht geeignet. Es fehlt ihm zweierlei dazu, erstens der gewisse Leidenskonflikt zwischen seinem Ich und dem was seine Triebe verlangen denn er ist ja im Grunde mit sich sehr zufrieden u leidet nur an dem Widerstreben aeusserer Verhaeltnisse, zweitens ein halbwegs normaler Charakter dieses Ichs der mit dem Analytiker zusammen arbeiten koennte; er wird im Gegenteil stets danach streben diesen irre zu fuehren ihm etwas vorzuspiegeln u ihn bei Seite zu schieben. Beide Maengel treffen im Grunde in Einem zusammen, in der Ausbildung eines ungeheuer narzisstischen selbstzufriedenen, der Beeinflussung unzugaenglichen Ichs das sich zum Unglueck auf alle seine Talente und persoenlichen Gaben berufen kann.

Ich meine also, es haette keinen Nutzen wenn er zu mir oder einem anderen zur Zeit in Behandlung kaeme. Seine Zukunft kann sein, dass er in seinen Ausschweifungen verkommt, es ist auch moeglich, dass er wie Mirabeau von dessen Typus er sein mag, sich von selbst noch aufrafft u unter Beibehaltg aller seiner Laster zu einer besonderen Leistung kommt. Aber das ist wol nicht sehr wahrscheinlich.

Ich sehe dabei ganz davon ab, dass er ein homosex ist. Er koennte das bleiben u doch geordnet u verstaendig leben.

Ich verstehe aber auch, dass die Mutter ihn nicht ohne weiteren Versuch aufgeben will. Der Mechanismus ist ja auch bei ihm ein neurotischer und die dynamischen Verhaeltnisse einer Aenderung unguenstig. Ich schlage also vor, ihn zu einer ueberwaeltigenden therapeutisch wirksamen Person in eine Anstalt zu schicken. Als solche habe ich Dr. Groddeck in Baden–Baden (Sanatorium) kennen gelernt. Er muesste natuerlich von der Eigenart des Pat. verstaendigt werden. Will er ihn nicht nehmen, so kaeme noch Marcinowski in Heilbrun bei Toelz (Baiern) in Betracht aber der wird ihn wahr-scheinlich von vorne herein abweisen. Im unguenstigsten Fall schifft man solche Leute wie ████ mit etwas Geld ueber den Ozean, sagen wir nach Suedamerika u laesst sie dort ihr Schicksal suchen and finden.

Wenn Frau ██ die Absicht hat dies Gutachten zu honoriren, so lassen Sie sie Lire 100 ██████████████████████████

Ich werde mich freuen, von Ihnen persoenlich u von der Uebersetzung zu hoeren.

Herzlich gruessend

Ihr Freud

4.4.21.

Lieber Herr Doktor

Ich antworte zuerst auf Ihre Frage nach ████ auch darum, weil ich es gerne tue. Sie ist mir ungemein lieb, es geht vorlaeufig sehr gut, ihr Ernst und ihre Intelligenz sind sehr erwuenschte Helfer. Natuerlich stehen grosse Schwierigkeinten irgendwo bevor sie sollen uns aber nicht schrecken. Die Vorbehandlung bei ████ hat ihr gewiss nicht geschadet, wenigstens habe ich den Nutzen davon, denn sie hat viel Verstaendnis mitgebracht. Die Behandlung konnte nicht gelingen 1) weil ██ ein junger Mann ist vor dem sie sich zuviel genierte 2) weil er den ganzen ersten Rueckstoss des Widerstandes auszuhalten hatte 3) weil sie eine zur Vateruebertragung geeignete Person brauchte. Viel-

[4]All blacked out areas deleted by editors for purposes of discretion.

leicht hat er ihr auch zuviel in zu kurzer Zeit eroeffnet.

Aus der theoretisch ausgezeichneten Schilderung Ihres Patienten kann ich nur entnehmen, dass er als "einfache Depression" aufgefasst werden darf. Die Affliction ist wenig studiert muss aber der Analyse zugaenglich sein. Versuchen Sie's geduldig weiter. Als Vermutung moechte ich's aussprechen, dass es sich um einfache Mutterfixierung hohen Grades handelt, die er zeitweilig von sich weist, so dass er dann gar nichts hat. Die Schwierigkeit Ihrer Stellung liegt wohl darin, dass er diese Beziehung vor Ihnen—als Mann, Vaterersatz—geheimhalten muss. Technisch wird das so gemacht, dass der Patient sich einen Einfall *absichtlich* zurueckbehaelt, womit dann die Analyse stillsteht. Lassen Sie sich durch kein Leugnen von seiner Seite von diese Behauptung abbringen; es kommt haeufiger vor, als wir erwarten. Es wird mich interessieren zu erfahren, ob Sie aus diesen Andeutungen etwas machen konnten.

Es freut mich, zu hoeren, dass die Publikation der Vorlesungen gesichert ist.

Mit herzlichem Gruss

Ihr Freud

4.

Prof. Dr. Freud 3. 3. 22[5]

Wien, IX. Berggasse 19.

Lieber Herr Doktor

Ich antworte Ihnen u bitte Sie █████ Mitteilung zu machen.

Ich weiss was ich █████ versprochen habe, u war gewiss bereit es zu halten. Ich war aber nicht gefasst darauf bis zu welchem Ausmass mich die aus der Fremde zustroemenden Schueler—ich habe unter 9 Personen jetzt nur 1 Patienten—beschaeftigen wuerden dadurch dass einige von ihnen laenger geblieben sind als sie beabsichtigt hatten bin ich in solches Gedraenge gekomen, dass zB. A. F. Meijer der bekannte hollaendische Ana-lytiker seit Sept vergeblich auf seine Einberufung zur Analyse wartet.

Es waere mir also eine grosse Erleichterung gewesen wenn ich gehoert haette, dass █████ bei Ihrem Freund die Endbehandlg gefunden hat. Da dies nicht der Fall ist, bleibt mein Versprechen aufrecht, dass ich sie nehmen werde sobald sich eine freie Stunde ergiebt. Ich kann ja weder meine Arbeitsleistung steigern noch Verabredungen die ¾ Jahre alt sind rueckgaengig machen. Wenn diese naechste Zeit—ich schliesse am 1 Juli—keine unerwartete Luecke bringt so will ich hoffen, dass ich sie am ~~1 Okt~~ (30 Sept)[6] in meinem Warte-zimmer finden werde.

Mit besten Wuenschen fuer Sie Beide

Ihr

Freud

Prof. Dr. Freud 7.1.23.

Wien IX, Berggasse 19

Lieber Herr Doktor

Wie Sie aus dem Brief der Frau Dr. G. wissen hat sie ueber die Erkrankung ihres Mannes auch an mich geschrieben. Ich theile durchaus Ihre Ansicht, dass die Diagnose an u fuer sich nicht von der psycho-analyt. Behandlung abschrecken soll vorausgesetzt es sei uebhpt ein psychogener Fall was hier sicherlich zutrifft. Ich denke dabei an einige Erfahrungen der letzten Zeit. Natuerlich wird man eine guenstige Phase der Erkrankung abzuwarten haben.

Auch prognostisch halte ich an der frueher geaeusserten Erwartung eines guten Ausganges fest. Die Bewunderung Stekel's ist allerdings als Zeichen eines schwachen Urteils u perversen Geschmacks bedenklich mag mit seinem Misbrauch der Selbstanalyse zusamen-

---

[5] As corrected in original.

[6] As corrected in original.

haengen. Es ist gar nicht so selten, dass die Beschaeftigg mit der Analyse wenn sie nicht durch analysirt werden korregirt wird, die Krankheitsdispositionen weckt wie sie anderseits die schlechten Seiten eines Charakters zur Entwicklung bringt.

Die beiden Briefe der Frau G. folgen eingeschrieben in besonderem Couvert.

████ hat diesmal wieder sehr viel gelernt ich hoffe auch dauernd profitirt. Einer gruendlichen Erledigung der Neurose steht wol die unerfreuliche Realitaet im Wege. Ich bin darum auch ueber ihre Zukunft nicht ganz ruhig. Neuerziehung, und ihren graulichen Sadismus u ihr exzessives Wesen zu baendigen schiene durchaus moeglich aber wuerde dauernde Beeinflussg durch lange Zeit beanspruchen.

Mit Befriedigg denke ich an Ihre unerschuetterliche Ueberzeugung, Ihre Opferwilligkeit u Ihren rastlosen Fleiss u wuensche Ihnen befriedigenden Erfolg im neuen Jahre.

Herzlich Ihr Freud

Prof. Dr. Freud Wien IX, Berggasse 19

30.IX. 26.

Lieber Herr Doktor,

Ich danke Ihnen für Ihre Nachrichten über die italienische Gesellschaft, die allerdings günstiger lauten könnten, die man aber so annehmen muss wie sie sind. Es kommt ja oft vor, dass die Form früher da ist als der Inhalt und ich freue mich, dass Sie nicht die Absicht haben, diese Form jetzt zu zerstören. Hoffen wir, dass sie sich mit der Zeit mit Inhalt erfüllen wird und wenn dies geschieht, wird es Ihr Werk und Ihr Verdienst sein. Ueber B. ████ denke ich genau so wie Sie. Ich habe seine Schwächen und seine guten Seiten immer so so beurteilt wie Sie es in Ihrem Briefe tun. Ihre Morsellikritik ist durchaus was wir gewünscht haben. Wo sie hart scheint, hat Morselli diese Härte wohl verdient. Man hat mir erzählt, dass die Redaktion der Zeitschrift Ihren Aufsatz um etwas verkürzt hat. Umso befriedigter bin ich, dass Sie ihn in italienischer Sprache unverkürzt publizieren konnten.

Ihre Anfrage betreffs meiner Aeusserung in der Einführung des Narzissmus ob es Neurosen gibt, bei denen der Kastrations-komplex keine Rolle spielt, bringt mich in Verlegenheit. Ich weiss nicht mehr, woran ich damals gedacht habe. Heute wüsste ich allerdings keine Neurose zu nennen, in der nicht dieser Komplex anzutreffen wäre und würde jedenfalls den Satz heute nicht niedergeschrieben haben. Aber wir übersehen das ganze Gebiet noch zu wenig, ich möchte mich lieber nach keiner Seite endgültig binden.

Mit herzlichem Gruss

Ihr
Freud

---

12. 4. 1933

Prof. Dr. Freud Wien, IX., Berggasse 19

Lieber Herr Doktor

Der italienische "Moses" hat mich besonders erfreut. Ich habe zu dieser Arbeit eine Beziehung wie etwa zu einem Kind der Liebe. Durch drei einsame Sept.-Wochen bin ich 1913 alltaeglich in der Kirche vor der Statue gestanden, habe sie studiert, gemessen gezeichnet, bis mir jenes Verstaendnis aufging, das ich in dem Aufsatz doch nur anonym auszudruecken wagte. Erst viel spaeter habe ich dies nicht analytische Kind legitimirt. Es ist eine schwer ertraegliche Folge meines reduzirten Zustandes dass ich nicht mehr nach Rom kommen kann. (Zuletzt 1923).

Was F. ███ u Ihre Patientin anbetrifft, so bin ich zu allem bereit, was Ihrer Behandlung Nutzen bringen kann. Aber Sie wissen, das ist imer nur zu erwarten, wenn sich die Pat. selbst den Besuch lebhaft wuenscht. Wenn sie sich nur mitnehmen laesst und mich dann ebenso behandelt wie jetzt Sie, so stiften wir hoechstens Schaden.

Also fuer den positiven Fall erbitte ich Ihre genauen Auskuenfte.

Mit herzl Gruss

Ihr Freud

---

3. October 20.
Vienna IX, Berggasse 19

Lieber Herr Doktor:

Since you are asking me today for a professional report on him, I shall not hesitate to give you my opinion. I believe it is a bad case, and one that is most particularly not suitable for free analysis.[7] For this, he lacks two things: first of all, that certain suffering from conflict between his ego and what his drives demand, for he is basically very well-satisfied with himself, and suffers merely from the struggle against external circumstances. Secondly, he lacks a half-way normal character of that ego which would be able to cooperate with the analyst. On the contrary, he will always strive to lead the analyst astray, to deceive him and to push him aside. These two defects basically amount to the same thing, namely, the development of a tremendously narcissistic, self-satisfied ego that is inaccessible to being influenced and that, unfortunately, can boast of all his talents and personal gifts.

Accordingly I believe that there would be nothing gained by having him come into treatment right now with me or with anyone else. It may be that in his future he will deteriorate through his excesses; it is also possible that, like Mirabeau, whose type he may resemble, he will yet pull himself together by himself, and while continuing all his vices, accomplish some outstanding achievements. But that is not very likely.

In all this, I disregard completely the fact that he is a homosex[ual].[8] He could continue to be one and yet live a well-ordered and sensible life.

I also understand that his mother does not want to give him up without further efforts. The mechanism, even in his case, is a neurotic one, and the dynamics are unfavorable for a change. Accordingly I suggest that he be sent to an institution with an overwhelmingly effective therapist. I know Dr. Groddeck in Baden-Baden (Sanatorium) to be such a person. Naturally he would have to be informed of the patient's peculiarities. If he does not wish to take him, Marcinowski in Heilbrunn near Toelz (Bavaria) might still be considered, but he will probably turn him down from the start. If worst comes to the worst, one ships such people across the ocean with some money, let us say to South America, and lets them there seek and find their destiny.

If [Mrs. F.] intends to pay for this report, have her send 100 lire

I would enjoy hearing from you personally and also about the translation.

With cordial regards,

Your Freud

4.4.21
Vienna, IX Berggasse 19

Lieber Herr Doktor

First I answer your questions about [Mrs. L. M.] because I do that gladly. I am very fond of her; she feels very well for the time being; her seriousness and her intelligence are very welcome helpers. Naturally great difficulties are awaiting us somewhere but they shall not frighten us. The preparatory treatment with [F.] did certainly no damage, at least I have the benefit of it for she arrived with much understanding. The treatment could not succeed

---

[7]Free analysis means free associative, classical psychoanalysis, according to an explanation given by Edoardo Weiss.

[8]Words in [brackets] are added by the translators.

1) because [F.] is a young man and she felt too embarrassed 2) because he had to endure the entire first recoil of resistance 3) because she needed a person fit for a father transference. Perhaps he also had opened up too much in too short a time.

From the theoretically excellent description of your [patient] I can only conclude that the case can be considered as a "simple depression." The affliction is little studied; it should, however, be accessible to analysis. Keep trying patiently. I should say, as a surmise, that it is a matter of a simple fixation of high degree on the mother, whom he rejects from time to time, so that then nothing is left to him. The difficulty of your position may lie in the fact that he has to keep this relation hidden from you as a man, a father substitute. Technically, what happens is that the patient holds back intentionally some association through which the analysis then comes to a standstill. Do not let yourself be dissuaded by any disavowal on his part; it happens more often than we suspect. It will interest me to learn whether you can make anything out of these hints.

I am glad to hear the publication of the lectures is assured.

With cordial greetings

Your
Freud

April
3. March 22[9]
Vienna, IX, Berggasse 19

Lieber Herr Doktor:

Here is my reply, and I would like you to pass it on to [Mrs. L. M.]

I know that I promised [her], and was certainly ready to keep my promise. However, I was not prepared for the extent to which my time would be taken up by the students who came to me from foreign countries in a steady stream—out of nine people, I now have only one [who is a] patient. Through the fact that some of them remained with me longer than they had anticipated, there has been such pressure on me that, as an example, A. F. Meijer, the well-known Dutch analyst, has had to wait in vain since last September to be called into analysis.

Accordingly, it would have been a great relief had I heard that [Mrs. L. M.] had been able to complete her treatment with [F.]. Since this is not the case, I shall abide by my promise that I will take her as soon as a free hour is available. I simply cannot increase my work load nor can I fail to keep commitments that were made three quarters of a year ago. If the near future—I lock the doors on July 1— does not bring an unexpected vacancy, I shall hope to find her in my waiting room on ~~Oct. 1~~ (September 30). [10]

With best wishes to you both,

Your
Freud

7.1.23
Vienna IX, Berggasse 19

Lieber Herr Doktor

As you know from the letter of Frau Dr. G. she wrote to me too about the sickness of her husband. I agree absolutely with your opinion that the diagnosis in itself should not frighten you away from psychoanalytic treatment, under the assumption that this is a psychogenic condition which seems certainly to be the case. I think here of some experience of recent time. Naturally one would have to wait for a more favorable phase of the illness.

---

[9]Corrected in the original.

From this letter a quotation in different translation has been published in: "Clinical Aspect of Depression," Edoardo Weiss, The Psychoanalytic Quarterly, Volume 13, 1944, page 451.

[10]Corrected in the original.

Concerning the prognosis I stand by my earlier stated expectation of a good outcome. His admiration of Stekel is, however, a worrisome sign of poor judgment and of perverted taste, and it may be connected with his abuse of self-analysis. It is not so rare that the preoccupation with analysis awakens the disposition for sickness, if it is not thoroughly corrected by analysis, as it also may help to develop the bad aspects of a character.

The two letters of Frau G. follow by registered mail in separate envelope.

[Mrs. L. M.] has again learned much this time and I hope with lasting benefit. Unpleasant reality stands in the way of a thorough dissolution of the neurosis.

Therefore, I am not quite reassured about her future. New education and taming of her gruesome sadism and of her excessive behavior seem really possible but would ask for continuous influence over a long time.

I think with satisfaction of your unshakeable conviction, your willingness for sacrifice and your restless industriousness, and I wish you fulfilling success in the new year.

Cordially,

Yours, Freud

Vienna IX, Berggasse 19
30. IX. 26.

Lieber Herr Doktor,

I thank you for the news about the Italian Society which however could have sounded more favorable, but which one must accept the way it is. After all it happens frequently that the form is there earlier than the content and I am glad that you do not have the intention to destroy this form now. Let us hope that it gets filled with content in time, and after this has happened it will be your work and your merit. I think about [B.] exactly as you do. I always evaluated his weaknesses and his good sides as you do in your letters. Your criticism of Morselli is exactly what we wished. Where it appears harsh, Morselli deserved this harshness. I was told that the editors of the Journal have shortened your essay somewhat; therefore I am especially satisfied that you can publish it unshortened in the Italian language.

Your question, in connection with my assertion in my paper on Narcissism, as to whether there are neuroses in which the castration complex plays no part, puts me in an embarrassing position. I no longer recollect what it was I had in mind at the time. Today, it is true, I could not name any neurosis in which this complex is not to be met with, and in any case I should not have written the sentence today. But we know so little of the whole subject that I should prefer not to give a final decision either way.[11]

With cordial greetings,

Yours, Freud

12.4.1933
Vienna IX, Berggasse 19

Lieber Herr Doktor

The Italian "Moses" has given me particular pleasure. My relationship to this work is something like that to a love child. Every day for three lonely weeks in September of 1913 I stood in the church in front of the statue, studying it, measuring and drawing it until there dawned on me that understanding which in the essay I only dared to express anonymously. Not until much later did I legitimize this nonanalytic child.

One of the consequences of my failing health difficult to bear is that I can no longer come to Rome (the last time was in 1923).[12]

---

[11]The last paragraph from footnote to page 93 in: "Sigmund Freud." *Standard Edition*, Vol. 14, 1914. "On Narcissism: An Introduction."

[12]The first two paragraphs published as letter 269 in *Letters of Sigmund Freud*, Selected and edited by Ernst L. Freud and translated by T. and J. Stern. New York: Basic Books, 1960.

Concerning F. and your patient, I am ready to do anything that could be of benefit for your treatment [of the patient]. But you know it [benefit] is only to be expected if the patient herself desires a visit wholeheartedly. If she only allows herself to be brought along [with you] and she treats me then the way she treats you now, we would cause damage at best.

In case of a positive decision, please give me exact information.

With cordial greetings

Your, Freud

The Continuing Forum

The Continuing Forum is open to all readers so that they may send their reactions, suggestions, criticism and contributions to the topics which are presented in The Psychoanalytic Forum.

Cannibalistic Impulses

To the Editors: I am in full agreement with Dr. Devereux's contention that cannibalism is for adults only. His evidence culled from biological, anthropological and psychoanalytical data reduces infantile cannibalism to a "counter-cannibalistic," reactive function. Devereux argues convincingly that the very complexity of the anthrophagic pattern prevents the child from being parcntivorous, and that even without the necessity of the cannibalistic know-how puppies and piglets have no apparent appetites for their mothers. In fact, their capacity to react defensively to noxious stimuli from birth on may be speculatively ascribed to their innate fear of oral incorporation by natural enemies including the older members of their own species. (2)

The widespread existence of cannibalism of eggs and young by older individuals can be viewed "not as a strange and exceptional development in eccentric environments among lower organisms, but seemingly as part of the order of things to the organisms themselves." (1) There are many reports which confirm these general statements by specific examples documenting the practice of cannibalism from the lowest to the highest form of life including that of man. According to Sumner and Keller, "man-eating was once no isolated phenomenon. It has been practiced very widely over the earth [and] there is not a people that has not practiced this custom at some period or other in its history." (3)

Inferring that the human animal shares with his phylogenetic ancestors the same basic fear of being eaten by the older and stronger (2) and adducing this fear as another circumstantial proof for Devereux's postulate, we must come to terms with the question of why the cannibalistic impulse does not manifest itself before adulthood. I believe that the answer is relatively simple. If we strip the concept of cannibalism, animal as well as human, of its social and ethical connotations, we find in it nothing but the usual drive to procure food no matter from which source. There is no cannibalistic impulse per se—there is only an impulse to eat. The prohibitions and taboos came later as safeguards against the consumption of human flesh as just another nutrient or an object of pure gluttony. (3)

Would it, therefore, be of no benefit to debate whether cannibalistic tendencies remain masked as oral sadism until they become overt at maturity, not unlike genitality, or whether they develop on an extrinsic basis? The child with teeth is not more and not less cannibalistic than the adult who shares with him a humanoid meal. The difference lies not in genetic predisposition, dormancy of drive or maturation of impulse, but solely in the assumed prerogative of practice. The adult is not only stronger than the child, but has intuitively through cogent demonology conditioned the child against parricide. Not at all relying on that powerful deterrent, i.e., the child's dependency on his parents, the elders, perhaps partly motivated by their own oedipal rumblings, have intimidated their young by severe sanctions; the brutal initiation rites serve as stern, unforgettable warnings.

Gert Heilbrunn, M.D.

(Dr. Heilbrunn's discussion was received after The Forum went to press. Dr. Heilbrunn is Associate Clinical Professor of Psychiatry at the University of Washington and the author of 60 papers, one of which dealt with cannibalism. He wishes it known that to date he has not yielded to anthrophagic urges in spite of his comments and attendance at certain professional meetings.)

Bibliography

1. "Cannibalism as a Factor in Natural Selection." (1916). Current Opinion, Vol. 61.
2. Heilbrunn, G. (1955). "The Basic Fear." J. Amer. Psa. Assn., Vol. 3.
3. Sumner, W. and Keller, A. (1927). "Antecedent of Human Sacrifice," *The Science of Society*. New Haven: Yale Univ. Press, Vol. 2.

Sudden Death

To the Editors: We welcome Dr. Saul's interesting report, "Sudden Death at Impasse" and commend the author's courage in writing it and the Forum's courage in printing it. Having devoted more than 15 years to an attempt to understand better the settings in which illness (and death) occur, we can fully support Saul's suggestion that what he calls "situations of impasse" represent circumstances in which illness and even death may occur. (3)

From the study of many hundreds of patients with all varieties of illness, including fatal illness, we have been led to delineate a psychological complex, which we are calling "giving up-given up," as a non-specific onset condition in which illness develops. (2) It has the following characteristics: (a) It has an unpleasant affective quality, expressed in such terms as "it's too much," "it's no use," "I can't take it anymore," "I give up," and so on, sometimes ascribed to failures on the part of the environment and sometimes to failures of oneself. (b) The patient perceives himself as less intact, less competent, less in control, less gratified, and less capable of functioning in a relatively autonomous fashion. (c) Relationships with objects are felt to be less secure and gratifying, and the patient may feel himself given up by objects or he may give himself up. (d) The external environment may be perceived as differing significantly from expectations based on past experience, which no longer seems as useful a guide for current or future behavior. (e) There is felt to be a loss of continuity between past and future and an inability to project oneself into the future with hope or confidence. Hence, the future may appear relatively bleak or unrewarding. (f) There is a tendency to revive feelings, memories, and behavior connected with occasions in the past which had a similar quality. Though the data reported by Saul are sparse, his account of the settings in which these three fatal episodes occurred would seem to fit well with the "giving up-given up" complex.

Saul's emphasis on death as the outcome, while correct, is somewhat misleading. It would be more correct to say that the "impasse situation" precipitated or accelerated illness in already vulnerable persons, illnesses which in these cases happened to be characterized by a propensity to sudden death. Yet it remains a fact that given the development of illnesses with a potential for fatal outcome, the balance between survival and death undoubtedly is significantly influenced by the psychological state of the victim at the time.

As we have learned from long—and sometimes painful—experience, the proposal of such a relationship between psychological factors and serious or fatal illness tends to provoke highly irrational reactions. This is certainly the case in the responses to Saul's report. Apparently, even analysts, who are comfortable with the notion of a powerful unconscious, find it difficult to embrace the notion of the psychobiological unity of the organism if it includes the possibility of psychological decompensations contributing to fatal somatic decompensations. Thus, we find Philip Solomon inappropriately invoking statistics to explain these three cases as the "operation of chance" even though we know such statistics have little bearing on the single case.

If Solomon will forgive a bit of tongue in cheek, when an analyst resorts to statistics to disprove the single case, that is really a case of "man bites dog." Let us try out his statistics on another example. Let us say one man shoots another in a fit of anger. Each year a great number of men are shot and an even greater number have fits of anger. Hence, from a statistical point of view, the likelihood that the two phenomena will occur together by chance is appreciable. Yet we doubt that anyone would invoke coincidence to explain such an occurrence (though the murderer may well hope the jury will!). The inappropriateness of using statistics in this manner also becomes clear when one acknowledges that the overwhelming majority of angry men never shoot anyone (as the great majority of men at impasse do not die). This only serves to demonstrate that anger (and impasse) are not simple unitary phenomena and cannot be dealt with statistically as digital functions or be adequately represented by frequency of occurrence. They represent highly complex variables, and it remains to be clarified which components can justifiably be handled in this manner. Until this is accomplished, such statistical efforts cannot be used either to prove or disprove the thesis.

Solomon also speaks of "huge numbers who do die of these disorders while in a joyful state or peacefully asleep in bed." The hyperbole, "huge numbers," is most interesting. If it reflects his carefully documented experience, he should report it. We are not familiar with any such data in the literature. In our experience with patients with these conditions, some of whom died and some of whom survived, we have as yet to encounter one whose attack occurred during "a joyful state." Even "peacefully asleep" is an unjustified assumption. The most recently studied case of a coronary occlusion occurring during sleep was that of a man whose son had just been assigned to duty in Vietnam. Before retiring, he was listening to the war news on the evening broadcast and was by no means tranquil when he went to bed.

White and Kaufman both stress the preexisting disease, and correctly so, but in so doing tend to downgrade the important implications of Saul's report, namely, why did these people die at the exact point in time that they did? This question brings up another statistical issue. If one is to estimate probabilities, it is not sufficient to pose the question in terms of how many men will die of coronary disease in their 45th year and how many episodes of impasse (or "giving up-given up" complex) will occur in their 45th year, but rather what is the likelihood of these two events occurring in a single day (out of 365), or even in a single ten minutes, to use Saul's first case. Such probabilities are truly infinitesimal.

And to Dr. Saul's concluding comment "that the history of medicine shows that suggestive clinical observations have stimulated our observation and increased our knowledge, and may still do so," we can only say "Amen!" (1) Such case reports do not constitute proof, but they do provide the justification to pursue the issues raised with all the scientific skill we can muster.

George L. Engel, M.D.
Arthur H. Schmale, M.D.

(Drs. Engel and Schmale are Professors in both the Departments of Psychiatry and

Medicine at the University of Rochester Medical Center.)

Bibliography

1. Engel, G. (1965). "Clinical Observation. The Neglected Basic Method of Medicine." J.A.M.A., Vol. 192.
2. Engel, G. and Schmale, A., Jr. "Conversion, Specificity, the Onset Situation, and Biological Defenses. Some Considerations of the Psychoanalytic Theory of Somatic Disorder." Read at Amer. Psa. Assn., N.Y., Dec. 4, 1965.
3. Schmale, A., Jr. (1964). "Object Loss, 'Giving Up,' and Disease Onset. An Overview of Research in Progress." In symposium on "Medical Aspects of Stress in the Military Climate." Walter Reed Army Inst. of Research, Washington, D.C., U.S. Govt. Printing Office, 1965.

Reflections on Training

To the Editors: I should like to be permitted a few comments on Dr. Kubie's proposal regarding a "new profession," medical psychology or psychological medicine. Inevitably, this issue becomes a discussion on "lay analysis," and draws a great deal of fire from different factions; participants feel indignant, angry, self-righteous, and virtuous, and nobody changes his mind or his entrenched stance. I do not want to embark on a polemic in favor of "lay analysis" (a term, by the way, abhorrent to non-medical analysts): it would be presumptuous to think that I can add appreciably to the arguments in Freud's monograph, (2) Dr. Kubie's (4) numerous articles, and Dr. Eissler's giant opus, (1) among others.

I do want to describe the effect, as I see it, of the opposition to "lay analysis" by the American Psychoanalytic Association and its affiliates on the actual practice of "lay" psychoanalysis and psychotherapy.

The tremendous need for practitioners, the more and more rigidly enforced certification requirements for psychologists, and the tacit assent of a large percentage of the psychiatric community all make the practice of psychotherapy (psychoanalytic and otherwise) by non-medical professionals a widespread reality. Dr. Kubie writes that, if medical psychiatry refuses to make even pilot tests of a plan to train non-medical behavior scientists, the psychologists will go it alone. They have already done so.

In 1962, New York University began a postdoctoral program for clinical psychologists leading, for the first time, to a certificate in psychoanalysis and psychotherapy granted to non-physicians under the auspices of a university. Adelphi University started a similar program one year later. Setting aside these programs which are still in flux and too recent to be evaluated, let us examine the plight of a clinical psychologist who has acquired the basic principles of scientific method, personality theory, psychiatric nosology, diagnostic methods and psychotherapeutic procedures and has had a clinical internship and further clinical experience, has met the certification and licensure requirements of his state, and who then wants training in psychoanalysis and psychotherapy in the context of the only currently viable theoretical system, viz., the Freudian (or "freudian," as "The Psychoanalytic Quarterly" insists on calling it).

The institutes with the best organized training curricula and the best teachers, training analysts and supervisors (many of whom are "lay" analysts) are automatically closed to him. He is aware of a small loophole: if he has made substantial contributions in his field and if he commits himself to research rather than practice, he may be admitted for conditional training. However, he wants training because he sees in himself the possibility of making substantial contributions in his *chosen* field and *in order to* make substantial contributions to that field; after all, his medical colleagues are accepted on the basis of demonstrating such promise rather than having fulfilled it. Furthermore, he considers a pledge to use his skills in research rather than in practice to be co-operation in a humiliating maneuver; besides, this is the one field where research and practice are absolutely inseparable as Freud himself discovered, and there is no way of identifying in advance patients who will turn out to be "good research subjects."

He now has to choose between "private" training and institutes which are not affiliates of the American Psychoanalytic Association. If he is conscientious, he can go into analysis with a training analyst of a legitimate institute, buy supervision from an eminent analyst who is a member of such an institute, and perhaps form a study group with a few colleagues and organize seminars under the direction of a number of qualified senior analysts—rules and regulations notwithstanding, the "tacit assent" to which I referred makes this a very real possibility. And he can read Freud and the psychoanalytic literature, the circulation of which no one has yet decided to restrict!

But he is deprived of the stimulation of most of the eminent teachers and of the tremendously enriching contact with a large number of colleagues whose thinking is congenial to him. If he is indeed talented, he has to work in relative isolation and make the best of it and, for comfort, he can think of the "Wednesday meetings" where ability and goodwill were considered the only criteria for admission to learning. (Admission to learning need not imply the eventual granting of an imprimatur for practice, the criteria for which should be determined on the basis of relevance rather than pre-training status.)

If our hypothetical psychologist has a strong affiliative need, as well as economic worries which make him feel that belonging to groups is a good insurance policy, he looks around for a training facility which does not *a priori* rule him out. He has a choice of a whole array of institutes which admit physicians as well as psychologists. There are institutes which have been set up in healthy defiance of orthodox arrogance and which have become havens for pedestrian minds and opportunists, both in their faculties and student bodies. There are culturalist schools where the cultural fallacy reigns supreme and the physicians vie with their "lay" colleagues in their vehement rejection of man's biological givens. There are schools where fallacy cannot reign, since a logical structure is neither a value nor a goal: scientific method is ridiculed, phenomenology is idolized, "existence" is the password for acceptance, and nobody is concerned with the ordering of experience—both the process of psychotherapy and the training process are seen as occurring through mystical communion in an atmosphere tinged with the chrysanthemum colors and green-tea aroma of Zen monasteries. He either gives up in disgust, or decides on the institute which gives him the best passport to respectability, and tries to take what is best and not to let himself be affected by what is worst.

Both he and the psychoanalytic community are thus deprived of the best the other has to offer.

If relief comes, it will have to come not from Medicine, not from Psychiatry, but from the American Psychoanalytic Association. And the response will come from individuals with zeal and ability, not from Psychology or Clinical Psychology. Dr. Gabe (3) correctly points out that there is no ground swell of support on the part of psychologists for Dr. Kubie's plan for a new profession which, incidentally, is not the "upgrading the training of the clinical psychologist by incorporating into it some exposure to clinical medicine and medical ethics so long as the clinical psychologist is going to attempt [*sic*] to treat patients." Is it any wonder that there is no ground swell of support from Psychology which largely speaks with the voice of organization officers who are experimentalists and academicians? Was Medicine more receptive to psychoanalysis some decades ago? Should Psychoanalysis reject non-physicians for the sake of the acceptance it has received from medicine?

Michel Radomisli, PH.D.

(Dr. Radomisli is a Certified Clinical Psychologist in New York.)

Bibliography

1. Eissler, K. (1965). *Medical Orthodoxy and the Future of Psychoanalysis.* New York: Int. Univ. Press.
2. Freud, S. (1926). "The Question of Lay Analysis." In *Standard Edition.* London: Hogarth Press, Vol. 20.
3. Gabe, S. (1966). Disc. of Dr. Kubie's paper "Reflections on Training." Psa. Forum, Vol. 1.
4. Kubie, L. (1966). "Reflections on Training." Psa. Forum, Vol. 1.

Response

To the Editors: Dr. Radomisli's excellent comment does not discuss my underlying argument, nor the various plans which I have suggested from time to time. It is primarily a discussion of the destructive consequences of the official opposition which psychoanalytic organizations exhibit to any systematic training of non-medical behavioral scientists in psychodiagnosis and psychotherapy, and even to any systematic pilot testing of such training. With this part of his argument I am in complete agreement.

There are, however, a few points of disagreement which may be worth noting. For instance, when Dr. Radomisli says that Freud "discovered that research and practice of psychoanalysis are absolutely inseparable," I am afraid that he is not doing justice to Freud as a scientist; since in the very nature of things this cannot be true of any professional discipline. It is not and cannot be true that every practitioner of medicine, of clinical psychology, of surgery, or of electrical engineering is an investigator. In the application of facts or theories, one may make observations which others can use as a basis for new investigations. But that does not make the clinical observer an investigator, not unless he changes roles and turns from application to investigation. Furthermore, in every field of medicine many men are fine investigators yet not good physicians and therapists, and many excellent therapists and physicians are not good investigators. The same is true in psychoanalysis, whether this is carried out by a man who has been through the full medical discipline or by a man whose basic training is in clinical psychology or in psychiatric social work. The two roles are not one and inseparable and never will be. Furthermore, the argument itself has been misused as an excuse for the absence of basic research in psychoanalysis and on psychoanalysis, which is both possible and urgently needed. So I deplore Dr. Radomisli's misuse of this inaccurate and defensive argument.

Again, I would point out that in this field there are problems of strategy as well as problems as to goals. We must first agree on the goal we want to reach. Then comes the question of how to reach it. It is this strategic issue which accounts for the fact that I have sometimes urged the desirability of creating a new profession, sometimes a new subdiscipline within the medical profession, sometimes a new doctorate. These suggestions are not inconsistent. They are efforts to think through the advantages and disadvantages of the various alternative approaches to the same goal.

Finally I have one point of serious disagreement which focuses on his last paragraph. What Dr. Radomisli calls "relief" must come not from any one of these interrelated disciplines or organizations alone, but through the mutually respectful cooperative efforts of all. This is precisely where the strategy of the situation demands consistent objectivity, and generosity. Because some doctors use shallow arguments against the training of non-medical behavioral scientists in psychodiagnosis and psychotherapy, this does not mean that all such arguments are shallow. For example, there are at least two which are serious and require careful thought. One raises a question of human maturity; will we lose or gain if we shorten materially the period of preparation so that the graduate will be several years younger than the medical psychiatrists? The other has to do with the importance of not driving a wedge between somatic and psychological medicine. Their close rapport has been a special feature of American medicine and should indeed be jealously guarded.

Nothing can drive as deep a wedge between medicine and psychiatry as our persistent inability to supply the help we advocate and promise for lack of enough trained personnel. In other writings I have repeatedly explained how the development of a doctorate in medical psychology under joint medical and behavioral auspices will tend to bring the two fields closer together, and not to drive them apart. Considerable evidence in support of this can be adduced. But this misgiving must not be brushed aside as unimportant or trivial.

Lawrence S. Kubie, M.D.

Fatal Accidents

To the Editors: To comment on Dr. Harold Marcus' discussion—he and others indicated that a greater amount of case material would be valuable in passing critical judgment on the hypotheses we presented. Such material is available in three additional publications: "A Comparative Psychiatric Study of Accidental and Suicidal Death" [Arch. Gen. Psych., Jan., 1966]; a chapter in the about-to-be published *Essays in Self Destruction* on fatal accident, and a soon-to-be published article in "The Psychoanalytic Quarterly" entitled "Fatal Traffic Accidents."

In regard to Dr. Marcus' point that "information from friends and relatives is superficial, subjective, biased—and not reliable as a scientific tool," I would not agree. I think information from informants is subject to various kinds of biases, even as information from the accident victim himself is. A critically thinking scientist-observer takes neither at face value but attempts to judge the biases so that his impression as to what is probably going on takes into account those biases. In addition, there has been published work to indicate that the impressions and judgments of relatives and other informants concerning subjects in psychiatric studies in at least some circumstances bear a striking correlation with the independent observations and impressions of social scientist-observers.

Dr. Marcus does not believe that the impulsive activity which we hypothesize is a regression, but on the contrary that its purpose is to discharge extreme anger. Interestingly, later on he states: "The impulsive act is akin to a childhood temper tantrum." Our feeling is that it is not necessary to choose one or the other of these two alternatives. It is possible that anger is sometimes expressed in the impulsive act. However, what we are attempting to emphasize without excluding the other possibility is that the impulsivity is very much an ego issue and that the expression of anger or other impulses takes place because the ego is not operating at its usual and highest state of adaptation. Thus, the crucial issue is not whether or not the person is angry or has other of those many feelings to which human beings are heir. The point is that the individual is not able to deal with these feelings in a state of functioning which more effectively would preclude the possible occurrence of an accident.

Finally, I think it should again be stated that research in accident has not proceeded to the point where it can be looked upon as a syndrome with definite psychological precursors and attributes which would be universal for all kinds of accident. Our impression is that at this point in accident research, it is most valuable to hold open the idea that accidents may be arrived at by an interaction of many variables, psychological and others.

Norman Tabachnick, M.D.

(Dr. Tabachnick, the co-author of "Character and Life Circumstance in Fatal Accident," responds to Dr. Marcus' discussion which was received as The Forum went to press.)

The Psychoanalytic

FORUM

Table of Contents Vol. 1, No. 3, Autumn, 1966

continued

The Forum

Title **Psychodynamics of the Depressive Character**

Author **Bernhard Berliner,** M.D., PH.D

Charter Member, former President and Training Analyst (retired) of the San Francisco Psychoanalytic Institute; now in private practice. Dr. Berliner has lectured and written numerous papers on the psychology of the masochistic-depressive personality and on brief psychoanalytic psychotherapy.

Discussants

Eli Marcovitz, M.D.
Training Analyst and Chairman of the Educational Committee of the Philadelphia Association for Psychoanalysis and Attending Psychiatrist at the Albert Einstein Medical Center. Dr. Marcovitz is Senior Consultant at the Philadelphia Psychiatric Center and author of several papers on addiction.

Albert J. Lubin, M.D.
Clinical Professor of Psychiatry at Stanford University. For several years he has been studying the creative aspects of Vincent van Gogh's depressive-masochistic personality.

León Grinberg, M.D.
Head of the Training Committee of the Latin-American Psychoanalytic Institutes (C.O.P.A.L.) and former President and Training Analyst of the Argentine Psychoanalytic Association. *Culpa y Depresión (Guilt and Depression)* and other books are among his many writings on depression, guilt and mourning.

Edith Weigert, M.D.
Chairman of the Faculty of the Washington School of Psychiatry where she has participated in research projects on manic-depressive psychoses and in a study of pregnant women. She is a Training Analyst of the Washington Psychoanalytic Institute and former President of the Washington-Baltimore Psychoanalytic Society.

Stanley Goodman, M.D.
Teacher and Training Analyst at the San Francisco Psychoanalytic Institute and currently Chairman of its Education Committee. He is in private practice in Berkeley, and his interest includes both theoretical and clinical aspects of psychoanalysis.

Psychodynamics of the Depressive Character[1]

Bernhard Berliner, M.D., PH.D.

San Francisco, California

Our psychoanalytic knowledge of depression goes back to the investigations of Freud (9) and particularly Karl Abraham. (1) Their findings have remained valid with regard to the instinctual functions involved, but today we see the problem more from the point of view of the adaptive functions of the ego and of object relations. This presentation is limited to the dynamics of the depressive character, which is the matrix of any depressive illness and therefore basic for our understanding of depression.

The depressive character is immensely frequent, at least in Western civilization. There is general agreement that a depressive state of mind in later life is a continuation or a reproduction of a primal depression in childhood. In my experience, every one of these patients had an unhappy childhood. He was—or at least had reason to feel—unloved or rejected or mistreated. Unhappy events, such as disruptions of the family, may have had traumatic effects. In other cases the child was unable to fulfill the expectations which the family held for him and was confronted with critical and punitive attitudes which hampered the development of his self-esteem. (6) Some parents cannot love their children because they are depressives themselves. For this information we need not rely on childhood histories alone; it is amply verified by men and women who in their analyses reveal their often unconscious hostilities against their children.

Frustrations and traumatizations in childhood, which may weaken the child's survival potential, are so numerous that the great frequency of depressive conditions *seems* to be fully explained. However, such childhood situations cause the disposition to depression only if they coincide with a particular *constitutional factor*.

The depressive patient had, or still has, a great need for gratification by way of mouth and body surface. His oral and skin erotisms are constitutionally stronger and more demanding than average. The infant is absolutely dependent on his mother or mother substitute. His personality is conditioned by his need for being loved, and he receives gratifications of this need through his mouth by being nursed and through his body surface by the warm contact with the mother's body. In the normal course of maturation these earliest gratifications lose their predominance but they never disappear.

Orality does not in itself predispose to mental pathology, but a high degree of it makes a person vulnerable. If these earliest oral and skin erotisms are strongly frustrated, or if they are constitutionally so demanding that they cannot be gratified by any amount of love, or if they are reinforced by pampering and then frustrated, a *fixation* on this early need for being loved takes place. A dynamic pattern is established in the personality, causing a constant readiness for regression. The frustrated need may never stop claiming its gratification; it will never disappear and *never cease to be frustrated*, and the development to more mature stages of development is blocked.

The fixation on *frustrated* early oral and skin erotic needs is the basic substratum of de-

[1]Condensed from a paper presented as the Frieda Fromm-Reichmann Memorial Lecture at Palto Alto Veterans Administration Hospital, April 17, 1961, and at the Fourth Western Divisional Meeting of the American Psychiatric Association, Salt Lake City, Sept. 23, 1961.

pression. In the absence of adequate love, the vital need for being loved can be gratified vicariously and pervertedly by frustration, by nonlove which comes from the person whose love is needed. Through his demanding and incorporating oral libido and the need for bodily contact, the child absorbs—and later unconsciously seeks—displeasure, sadness and suffering in the place of being loved, and he assimilates these feelings into his personality.

The love-seeking tendency and the assimilation of frustrations are blended into the striking picture which makes the patient appear as if he loves his suffering. Consciously he does not, and we do him injustice if we imply it. He is actually unhappy and his suffering is very much unwanted by him. But it is *libidinized* and *introjected*; it takes the place of being nursed and cuddled, while the traumatic nature of this process is repressed or denied. This adaptation—taking suffering for love—seems in many cases the only way in which a child in his dependency and powerlessness can stand his deprivation: it is a *defense mechanism in the service of survival.* However, it is an unsuccessful defense. The original conflict with the outer world continues within the personality. In depression the infantile injury is constantly relived and reenacted, though in an ever changing frame of circumstances and with ever changing co-actors, but the essential inner mechanism remains the same. Depressive suffering has a positive libidinal motivation.

We see here the principal difference between normal mourning and depression. The "work of mourning" (9) is not possible for the dependent child. He cannot give up the frustrating love object and withdraw his libido from it. Instead he preserves it within his personality, and he remains dependent on it and in love with it. Freud said: "So by taking flight into the ego love escapes extinction."

Starting in earliest infancy, the introjection of love objects and experiences connected with them is the most important factor in the formation of the *superego.* Freud has shown that the superego originates from libido. Its commands and prohibitions are accepted and incorporated in the name and for the sake of love. The infantile superego is potentially malignant. The superego of the depressive is actually malignant because of the strength and durability of the introjects.

With the development of oral and anal aggressive drives, the experience of hate is added to the picture of early orality, and *ambivalence* and *feelings of guilt* appear. Both are prominent in the depressive character.

The analysis of guilt feelings in the depressive reveals its relation to libido. Guilt is a complex affect, consisting of the need to be loved, the awareness or expectation of having forfeited love by one's own action, a loss of self-esteem and the expectation of rejection or punishment. The latter, when accepted, may restore love and esteem. A *need for punishment* or self-punishment is the need for the love of a person who punishes.

The feeling of guilt can grow spontaneously out of these elements; or, more often it seems, it is planted in the child by external educational influences and is in the nature of an introject. It develops from the subject's own aggressiveness as well as from the aggressiveness of love objects.

The basic understructure of the depressive character is that state of mind in which the subject loves passively, i.e., needs and seeks the love of those objects who hate or ill-treat or frustrate him. *It is the libidinal reaction to the experience of hostility from the environment.* The experience is introjected, it enters into the superego and it remains an unconscious direction-giving pattern within the personality, either as an overt fixation or as the unconscious base for regressive revival.

I have devoted many years to the study of that immensely frequent condition known as "moral masochism," (3,4,5) and I have come to the conclusion that this term is a misnomer. What is meant by it is nothing else but the depressive character. The name is a matter of history. (2) The sexual perversion described by Krafft-Ebing in 1882 under the name of "masochism," in which a person responds with genital libido to being mistreated by a sadist, was a fascinating pattern to apply to a frequent nongenital mode of behavior. While for Krafft-Ebing masochism was a form of object relation, later authors, including Freud, saw in it a component sexual drive of a congenital order, or even a manifestation of the "death instinct." The nonsexual, so-called moral form of masochism was then considered a desexualized form of a sexual instinct, and the point of view of object relations was lost.

Today we know that every sexual masochist is at bottom a moral masochist in whom the comparatively rare sexual perversion grew as the result of special situations in psychosexual development. The difference, as I see it now, is that the sexual masochist submits to the sadism of genital love objects, the moral masochist to the sadism of pregenital love objects who are reexperienced in transference representations. The depressive personality is what makes masochism possible. Masochism is a symptom, not a nosological entity.

One of the older concepts about depression and moral masochism is that they are the manifestation of a sense of guilt and a need for punishment. But guilt and punishment for what? The Oedipus complex has been most often cited as the source.

Depression does not start with the Oedipus complex; it originates much earlier. Analyzing a depressive patient we regularly find that his Oedipus complex already bears the stamp of preoedipal pathology.

Freud conceived the Oedipus complex after Sophocles' play *King Oedipus*. He assumed that the Oedipus complex is a universal phenomenon which for phylogenetic reasons develops in every child out of his instinctual constitution. This view puts the responsibility for the complex upon the child and ignores the participation of the parents in it. (7)

But let us have another look at the Oedipus story as Sophocles tells it. King Laius and Queen Jokasta decided to get rid of their newborn son. The reason, or rather rationalization, was that the Delphian Oracle had told them that this son would kill his parents.

Doing away with unwanted children was in those days a popular procedure. The Greeks had a word for it: *chytrizein*, which means "to put a child out in a pot." (*Chytra* is a pot.) It seems that the pot symbolized the womb; putting the child in it may have meant undoing the birth.

Laius and Jokasta followed the custom and, to make the job more effective, the father crippled the baby's feet by piercing the ankles and pinning them together, whereupon he was to be thrown on a trackless mountain. The child was rescued, adopted by a childless royal couple and brought up as a prince. When grown he consulted the Delphian Oracle and learned that it was his destiny to kill his father and marry his mother. Greatly disturbed he flees from home, believing that his adoptive parents are his real ones. At a crossroads the proud young prince meets another traveler, an overbearing old man in a carriage with a retinue of servants. They try to force him off the road. A quarrel ensues in which the old man attacks the young one with a deadly weapon. Oedipus parries the attack and, *in self-defense*, slays the old man not knowing that he is his natural father who for the second time, though unknowingly, has attempted to kill his son. After this, Oedipus becomes the hero who frees the city from the murderous Sphinx, is elevated to the vacant throne of Laius, and, as an act of state, given the widowed queen in marriage.

As the tragedy unfolds, the poet makes it clear that the real culprit is Jokasta, the mother. She had handed her child to the servant, who now appears as witness, with the order to kill him. She becomes aware of the truth prior to Oedipus. Indeed, the spectator is made to feel that she had always known it. She kills herself. Then Oedipus, after he had destroyed his eyes, cries out: "Apollo has done all this!"

The god, the super-father, who treats his human children as human parents treat theirs, creates their guilty fate. Oedipus, who calls himself "the sinners' sinning child," had no intention or knowledge of any crime; but society, the super-parental authority, holds him guilty and punishes him.

In Sophocles' Oedipus drama the instinctual processes in the son play no overt part. The real principals are the parents and, above them, the gods who preordain a man's destiny which he unknowingly is bound to live. There are older versions of the Oedipus legend in which Oedipus kills his father in self-defense against a homosexual assault. (7) Here, too, we see the hostility between father and son originate in the father.

Freud, in his anthropological orientation, assumed the sense of guilt connected with the Oedipus complex to be an inheritance from the archaic Oedipus deed in the primal horde. He says in *Moses and Monotheism* that "men have always known that once upon a time they had a primeval father and killed him." (11) If we accept this statement, I think we are justified in adding a corollary: namely, that men have always known that once upon a time (and still in historic times) it was customary and legally permitted to kill unwanted children.

Our culture no longer allows parents to put a child out to die. However, it cannot be ignored that there are innumerable psychological equivalents of this action which for the dependent child mean a threat of annihilation. The deepest meaning of the Oedipus legend, beyond parricide and incest, is *infanticide*, not only in the simple form of killing a child but also by burdening it with guilt—a guilt without conscious wrongdoing. The guilt of Oedipus is decreed by the god: the city is visited by a plague which, so says Apollo's oracle, will only cease when the unknown killer of Laius is expelled. The god is on the side of the father. Children are made to feel guilty by parents as a technique of education as in adult proportions humans are guilty in the face of the gods. By that they are partially killed—that is, driven to self-destructive living. True, this is a cultural inheritance, but certainly not an inborn one.[2]

The severe forbidding superego which is a prominent characteristic of Western culture and is most powerful in depression is, it seems to me, more the extension of the rejected and crippled child than of the murderous rebellious one. And if there is in the depressed a need for punishment, we should not forget that such need can only exist after it has been impressed upon the child by punishing parents, either individual or collective. There is in society a universal *drive to punish* (4) as part of man's sadistic instinctual endowment. This drive, introjected by the child through his instinctual need for love, appears in him as self-punishment or asceticism or self-destruction. The child has learned to execute on himself an order that grows in him out of a troubled matrix of introjects. Suicide is sometimes deferred infanticide.

Sometimes it appears that the accusations a patient raises against a parent are projections of his own oedipal hostility. Depressives project hostility, of course, often to a paranoid degree, but they show also a kind of projection which is quite different. Freud has made the important discovery that the self-criticisms and self-accusations of the depressed are covert

---

[2]A. J. Levin, in a paper, "The Oedipus Myth in History and Psychiatry" (Psychiatry, Vol. 2, p. 283, 1948), came essentially to the same conclusion. Dr. Levin's paper came to my attention after the present paper was written and presented.

accusations against another person who is, or was, a frustrating love object. (9) The depressed, in his adaptation to the object, represses his own sense of loveworthiness. As he needs the object and its love he does not accuse it—he exonerates it as if saying: "I am the bad, the guilty one, not you." He projects goodness and loveworthiness upon the object as part of the libidinization of the experience of hate. This phenomenon has also been described as "borrowed guilt." (10)

It has been said that depression means a desperate cry for a good mother to come and give love and comfort. This need makes the patient appear as if he were constantly presenting an old unpaid bill. The need for affection is rarely gratified, the introjected frustration is reenacted simultaneously. The need becomes a demand which is either directed toward persons who are not inclined to fulfill it, or it is expressed in such form that the other person is repelled. There is often a hidden invitation in the attitude of the depressive to which people unconsciously respond, to treat him as he has learned to see himself treated. The depressed needs love, but what he finds is unhappy, frustrated love. He hangs on, symbolically, to a breast which is not there and which he would have to repudiate if it were.

The permanent frustration is partially the automatic function of introjects, partially it is engineered by the patient's aggressive behavior. Many authors believe that the subject's own aggressive drive is the primary motivating force in depression. This point of view results partially from a confusion of depression with compulsion neurosis in which defenses against aggressive impulses play the major part. (4) There are, of course, mixed forms. In a pure depression, however, the interpretation of the subject's own aggression as the causal factor is not only empirically wrong but is therapeutically detrimental. The typical depressive does not use aggressive trends for hostile action; he uses them as tools for the operation of the central process in depression, namely the need and the bid for affection. Aggressiveness is guarded against and repressed because it may cause loss of love, and it is also unleashed for the libidinal purpose of gaining love and avoiding its loss.

The depressive person inflicts himself upon his love objects either by professing guilt and badness and playing upon sympathy or with bribing and blackmailing attitudes. He tries to extort love. He is insatiable in his demands, possessive, reproachful, faultfinding. His object relations are more "against" than "with." It is more important for him to be in the right against others than to be happy with others. The need for being loved makes him unaware of the hostility which is thereby expressed. He feels and acts as if it were the partner's duty to love him: the partner becomes a frustrating parent figure in transference. He is incapable of loving; only being loved counts. Active outgoing love could not develop because of the fixation on the frustrated need to be loved. And in endless arguing with the past, endless rehearsing of what he should have done or said on some occasion but could not, he magically tries to force his past to change, to make "them" change their minds, make amends and give him more love. The belated mastery which he thereby seeks he never finds because of the introjected frustration that accompanies his efforts.

Although the depressive appears narcissistic, he can love himself as little as others. He cannot conceive of being loved by anybody. His self-esteem, too, is low, often in contrast to the actual esteem his environment has for him. He is allergic, so to speak, to any sort of praise. He is modest, often immodestly so. The narcissism of the depressive is of the nature of auto-erotism—a retreat from inadequate object relations, and it retains the quality of inadequacy.

As the depressive cannot love, he cannot hate either. Any attempt to hate or to assert himself invites punishment, as a reenactment of the old pattern in his superego. His behavior may appear hateful, but a closer look shows that there is a reservation to hate: it is not employed to fight an enemy or to change external conditions. The inner reservation is that the hated person must be appeased and preserved as a love object, at least in the imagination. Therefore, when hating or acting destructively, the depressive suffers feelings of guilt which make him return to a love-begging submissive attitude. What looks like hate is only irritation with a love object. The incapacity for outgoing love or hate results in a weakness of all object relations, to persons as well as to inanimate objects.

The use of aggression for reinforcement of the bid for affection is impressively revealed in manifold threats ranging from showing oneself hurt to active self-destruction. "You will be sorry" is the keynote. Making someone sorry means both making him concerned for the subject, who ought to be loved, and simultaneously punishing him by making him guilty.

The drive to punish operates in the depressive against the love object—to get back at, to get even with a past object in a new representation. Passivity is turned into activity. This can be a potent defense against suffering; however, in the depressive it is not true aggressiveness. Under the guidance of the introject the depressive identifies with the punishing parent or a transference surrogate, and the punitive attitude remains subordinated to the passive demand for love. This "identification with the aggressor" is, as Anna Freud (8) and Spitz (13) have shown, an important mechanism in the formation and the functioning of the superego. We should keep in mind that the identification has originally occurred because the other person was needed and expected to be loving but happened to be an aggressor.

The identification with the unloving parent appears in two ways. Aggressive trends are directed against the self, causing self-produced suffering and self-punishment; and they are directed against the external world reproducing the way the original love object has treated or might treat external objects.

The constant need for the affection of once-rejecting, introjected love objects leads into the characteristic self-depreciating attitude of the depressive. The analysis regularly reveals a powerful unconscious feeling that he is *supposed* to suffer, or to be inferior or to be guilty. He feels that he is supposed to satisfy and to accommodate those who hate or resent him, so that he will be accepted by them. He feels that he has to make sacrifices and to scale himself down in numerous ways, to reconcile the world with his unwanted existence. Even by being offensive, or in some cases delinquent, he means to lower his value as a love object so that the hater will be justified in not loving him. He pays the price of self-depreciation or self-destruction to gain love or a semblance of it.

On the other hand, with submission to the hostile parental power the depressive borrows the authority for his own drive to punish. This imitation out of his love attachment gives him the feeling that he is right—that by being aggressive, too, he is the way he is supposed to be. This aggressiveness is only very partially the subject's own. In the main it is imitation, it is the introjected and libidinized aggressiveness of an early love object. The subject's own aggressive instinct is the source of energy, from which the identification with rejecting objects is set into action. Or it is steered by the introjected sadism of the object against the self and against outside objects.

The turn of aggressiveness against the self under the command of the superego reaches its highest degree in the suicidal tendency. There are two motivating forces in this tendency: the wish to die and the wish to kill. In the wish to die the libidinization of suffering reaches its ultimate degree. Death may mean the reunion with a lost object or it may mean the liberation from the guilt of existence and of being a burden to others. There may be the narcissistic motive of self-glorification, but little aggressiveness. The wish to kill oneself usually includes the more or less unconscious wish to kill another who is reached in the form of an introject within the self; the intrapsychic representation of a frustrating love object. Or it means (to quote from a letter of the painter Van Gogh, who committed suicide later) turning "friends into murderers."[3] (12)

"The ego," Freud says, "can renounce its self-preservation for its own egoistic motives." Among these motives, that of revenge—the drive to punish—is outstanding. The other person is in any case a real or an imaginary love object. In this wider sense all suicides are committed out of unhappy love; they are irrational attempts at relatedness. (6) It is the need for love and for self-preservation that gives the irrational motivation for self-destruction. The motive of self-preservation is particularly evident if the lost object is not a person but such issues as honor, fortune, health and the like, which fundamentally mean a state of being loved. When all hope is gone, suicide is the ultimate expression of the bid for affection.

We can now arrive at a brief conclusion: The psychology of depression, its genesis as well as its symptomatology, can be fully understood in terms of pathogenic object relations. The condition is an adaptation to influences that cripple the vital urge to self-preservation and pervert it into self-negation. However, self-preservation is the goal, through all the self-denying, self-destructive and destructive forces that constitute the clinical picture. The function of depression is to preserve the libidinal attachment to a lost or frustrating love object or to seek a restitution of a lost relationship. To that end libidinal forces incorporate aggressive ones into their structure. Depressive suffering derives from a person or persons who once caused it, who survive in the subject as introjects, which are permanently reprojected into the external world. The depressive reaction, being itself a manifestation of regression, seems to prevent further regression into total object loss, i.e., schizophrenia. (6) The regression is halted at a point where libido, facing the danger of annihilation, still holds on to life, though in a crippled state, using aggression, which is likewise crippled, for reinforcement. Love neither succumbs to destructive forces nor overcomes them; it capitulates to hate and forms an alliance with it.

[3]The whole quotation follows: ". . . can't you see that similarly self-sacrifice, living for other people, is a mistake if it involves suicide, for in that case you actually turn your friends into murderers."

Bibliography

1. Abraham, K. *Selected Papers. International Psychoanalytical Library*, No. 13. London: Hogarth Press.
2. Berliner, B. (1942). "The Concept of Masochism." Psa. Rev., Vol. 29.
3. ———. (1940). "Libido and Reality in Masochism." Psa. Quart., Vol. 9.
4. ———. (1947). "On Some Psychodynamics of Masochism." Ibid., Vol. 16.
5. ———. (1958). "The Role of Object Relations in Moral Masochism." Ibid., Vol. 27.
6. Cohen, M., Baker, G., Cohen, R., Fromm-Reichmann, F., and Weigert, E. (1954). "An Intense Study of Twelve Cases of Manic-Depressive Psychosis." Psychiatry, Vol. 17.
7. Devereux, G. (1953). "Why Oedipus Killed Laius." Int. J. Psa., Vol. 34.
8. Freud, A. (1946). *The Ego and the Mechanisms of Defense*. New York: Int. Univ. Press.
9. Freud, S. "Mourning and Melancholia." In *Standard Edition*. London: Hogarth Press, 1953-1965, Vol. 14, p. 237.
10. ———. "The Ego and the Id." Ibid., Vol. 19, p. 3.
11. ———. (1939). *Moses and Monotheism*. New York: A. A. Knopf, p. 159.

12. Lubin, A. (1961). "Vincent van Gogh's Ear." Psa. Quart., Vol. 30, p. 368.
13. Spitz, R. (1958). "On the Genesis of Superego Components." In *The Psychoanalytic Study of the Child*, Vol. 13. New York: Int. Univ. Press.

120 Commonwealth Avenue
San Francisco, California 94118

Discussant

Eli Marcovitz, M.D.
Philadelphia, Pennsylvania

There is much to be learned from this distillate of Dr. Berliner's years of interest in the problems of depression and "moral masochism." However, it seems that in the zeal of stressing factors which are undoubtedly signifcant (the pathogenic influence of disturbed object relations based on the hostility of parents toward children), he has made sweeping absolute statements which, in a discussion group, he would probably modify.

For example, how would he define "depression," "depressive illness," "depressive reactions" and other related terms and diagnostic labels? Would there necessarily be general agreement on which of these are born out of "the depressive character, which is the matrix of any depressive illness"? Should the word "any" be modified? Is there "general agreement that a depressive state of mind in later life is a continuation or a reproduction of a primal depression in childhood"? How early does a depression have to occur to be called "primal"? Is it universal experience "that every one of these patients had an unhappy childhood"?

(In my own experience I have found to my surprise that sometimes the patient remembered only a happy childhood in which he had been the most loved or admired member of the household; apparently significant traumata had not occurred until mid-latency or beyond. In these instances it seemed that the depressive reactions were related either to the disappointment of the unconscious expectation that he was about to recapture the lost satisfactions of a very "special" childhood or to the conviction that he would never regain them except in death.)

Is there a qualitative difference which distinguishes all people who have experienced depression from all others, or is there a universal potential for depressive experience? Is Dr. Berliner attempting to define those in the extreme group in terms of the factors tending to produce their greater vulnerability? What are the differences in the history and character structure of various types of depression? What constitutes the "constitutional factor"? How does one measure the "strength" or "demandingness of innate oral and skin erotisms," and what evidence is there that these are significantly greater in the infancy of later depressive characters?

Although it is appropriate for the author to stress the adaptive ego purposes of depression, we should not dismiss the importance of depression as a manifestation of superego function or of the development of initially unpleasant experiences as means of pleasure, not only in terms of the perversion of masochism but also in such a general experience as the development of taste—e.g., for the tart and bitter.[1]

We can agree that the depressive does not consciously love his suffering and that we do him injustice if we so imply. However, Dr. Berliner states that the depressive "later unconsciously seeks displeasure, sadness and suffering in place of being loved." This must mean that the depressive experience is accompanied by discharge phenomena or affects or by ideation which ordinarily accompanies the experience of being loved, and this must include affects which we would call "pleasurable." Therefore do we not also do the depressive injustice if we fail at some point to help him recognize the element of pleasure of which he is unaware, as well as the components of control, revenge or guilt of which he may also be unaware? The interpretation of the subject's own aggression as *the* causal factor is not only empirically wrong but is therapeutically detrimental.

Dr. Berliner attempts to explain the process whereby the child's experience of suffering at the hands of a love object becomes part of the permanent character structure. He mentions "identification with the object" as one of the methods used and states that through incorporating oral libido and the need for bodily contact, the child absorbs suffering in the place of being loved and then assimilates these feelings into his personality. I think he is describing what I have called "auto-identification,"[2] a process which involves the introjection of and identification with a part, a product, a function or an experience of the self, especially an intense and/or repeated affective experience, first for defense and mastery and secondarily leading to the establishment of a self-image which then exerts its self-perpetuating autonomy. The relationship to the object may be part of the total experience which is then introjected and becomes a factor in the tendency toward the repetition of similar object relationships.

An adult in depression generally has a component of guilt, which may be unconscious, a sense of having unjustifiably hurt someone who loved him, of having betrayed a person, group or ideal; therefore he deserves punishment which either has already occurred or is anticipated. Perhaps we can assume that the anaclitic depression of early childhood is the direct result of neglect, rejection and abandonment, lacking the component of guilt; for guilt requires the awareness of separateness from an object toward which hostility has been experienced or expressed. When awareness of separation occurs—at whatever age—it must also be the time of some awareness of ambivalence of feeling toward the object as well as of

[1]Waelder, R. (1965). *Psychoanalytic Avenues to Art.* New York: Int. Univ. Press.

[2]"Auto-Identification in the Development of the Self-Image." Paper presented at the American Psychoanalytic Association Meeting, Dec., 1964.

pleasant and unpleasant feelings "caused" by the object.

The instinctive wish to incorporate the object has inevitably both preservative and destructive aspects which simultaneously combine the earliest precursors of love and guilt, and therefore of depression. Then the child who experiences trauma, frustration or rejection attributes it to the mother. He often reacts with hostility, but he may also react with depression, depending partly on the degree of guilt he feels. Just as the infant needs loving mothering to avoid anaclitic depression, he also needs loving parental care and interest to counteract the depression of guilt which otherwise accompanies a feeling of deserved punishment or rejection. The author mentions "man's sadistic instinctual endowment" but then treats it as if it exists chiefly in adults toward children and only insignificantly in children toward adults.

The author seems to deny entirely the occurrences of depression related to oedipal guilt except as they are manifestations of depressive tendencies from earlier experiences of insufficient love. In fact, he seems to repudiate the usual concept of the oedipal experience as an innate developmental process of the human species and to see it rather as a manifestation of the parental wish to abandon or to kill the child. The validity of Freud's oedipal concept is not challenged by the debatable possibility that the Oedipus legend has more to do with infanticide than with the child's sexual and destructive impulses toward the parents. This is another example of an extreme attitude which I expect Dr. Berliner would modify or clarify. In any case, guilt and depression for oedipal hostility toward the father are not uncommon among men and are not necessarily always part of a depressive character. In women the combination of oedipal and preoedipal guilt toward the mother frequently presents a more complicated problem.

One can also question statements such as that a need for punishment "can only exist after it has been impressed upon the child by punishing parents," "Children are made to feel guilty by parents as a technique of education . . . True, this is a cultural inheritance, but certainly not an inborn one," and "Depressive suffering derives from a person or persons who once caused it."

It seems to me we must recognize both innate and learned components in guilt, in the need for punishment and in depression, elements both from the child's innate drives and maturational potentials as well as from the parents' attitudes, whether overindulging, overhostile or both. For example, instead of the second statment just quoted, I think it more accurate to say, "Parents may affect the child's innate potential for guilt, either diminishing or enhancing it." (Incidentally, what about those instances where guilt and depression are increased by the giving of love in place of punishment or rejection?)

It almost seems as if the author advocates the abolition of guilt and thereby of depression and that he believes it possible to attain this goal if only parents would or could get over their hostility to their children. This is another impression I am sure he would modify or clarify. Is the elimination of guilt really to be desired? Besides a very rational basic self-protective interest which may not be sufficient, what else is there to limit the potentially limitless intra-species destructiveness which distinguishes the human from other species?

In my opinion the statement, "The inevitable wish to destroy the love object is the root of guilt and depression," should be a necessary preliminary to Dr. Berliner's conclusion that "the function of depression is to preserve the libidinal attachment to a lost or frustrating love object or to seek a restitution of a lost relationship." These are complementary statements. Even in his conclusion, he implicitly acknowledges the presence of love toward the child in the parent of the depressive. One has no guilt about separation from or destruction of a completely noxious stimulus or object. Guilt comes only with the conflict of ambivalence, hostility toward an object which has provided pleasure as well as pain, toward whom one will feel the pain of betrayal and the loss of pleasure as well as the relief from pain.

There is no question that Dr. Berliner's description of the depressive character is masterful and that his views should be part of our thinking with every depressive patient, but we should also be aware of the presence of other important etiological considerations in the total picture.

Discussant

Albert J. Lubin, M.D.
Woodside, California

Bernhard Berliner's thesis that masochism is a bid for the affection of a hating love object has proved to be of great value, both theoretically and therapeutically. Now he extends his ideas by bringing masochism into the realm of depression. The reasons for this are so compelling that it is difficult to understand why the relation between them has not always been recognized. It is this aspect of the paper that I will discuss.

The complaining, the suffering and the feelings of being humiliated and tormented are characteristic of both depression and masochism. Clinical experience suggests that whenever masochism is manifest, depression is to be found nearby, even though it is not overt. But this does not mean that they are the same. I prefer, perhaps more than Dr. Berliner, to differentiate between the two, even though the distinction in individual cases is relative and arbitrary. I would suggest that a continuum exists between theoretical "pure" depression and "pure" masochism.

Broadly speaking, the depressive suffers and the masochist exhibits suffering. Though he complains bitterly of his misery, the masochist tends to minimize or deny to himself the affect of depression. The affect is distilled out of the depressive mixture, leaving behind a residue of depressive ideation. Depression is infectious; gloom spreads in its wake. But, partly because of this dissociation between affect and thought, masochism stirs resentment and recrimination, and the masochist is sometimes condemned as a fraud who exaggerates his woes. Analysis, however, discloses profound unhappiness.

The depressive feels the misery inside himself and blames himself for it. Using provocative behavior, the masochist manages to cause others to bring it on him. This helps him to to deny the inner unhappiness. Through externalizing it, he can exhibitionistically appeal for help and sympathy, righteously express anger toward his persecutors and absolve himself of guilt. These safety valves are not available to the depressive. The expression of anger in itself is an antidote against depression.

"Pure" depression in this view is a state of hopelessness, whereas masochism is an attempt to preserve or resurrect hope through a display of suffering which appeals for love. It is this masochistic display, rather than the archetypal depressive suffering, which has libidinal motivation. Hence, I would modify Dr. Berliner's statement, "Depressive suffering has a positive libidinal motivation," to read "Depressive suffering takes on a positive libidinal motivation in the masochist."

At one end of the depression-masochism continuum, the depressive is paralyzed by hopelessness and isolates himself by cutting off his attachments. At the other end, the masochist makes the most out of depression by using it exhibitionistically in order to preserve or inaugurate libidinal attachments; he is on stage, dramatically portraying his tragic role without the necessity of feeling it as part of himself, expecting applause.

In addition to the varying combinations of depression and masochism, one sees alternating cycles of depression and masochism, similar to manic-depressive states, though less obvious. In both, hopelessness alternates with hope. In masochism, in contrast to mania, however, hope emerges in a climate of complaint and humiliation.

Vincent van Gogh, whom Dr. Berliner quotes, exemplifies this relationship between depression and masochism. He swung back and forth between paralyzing depressive states and productive masochistic-creative states. He voiced aloud the advantages of the masochistic state and sometimes was even proud of it. His favored expressions during a deeply religious period included "Sorrow is better than joy," "Sorrowful yet always rejoicing," "By the sadness of countenance the heart is made better," and "Passing through great tribulations leads to greater joy."

Here, sorrow referred not to paralyzing depression but to the masochistic use of depression to stimulate hope and anticipate love. The use of this device, encouraged by Christian ideology and myth, enabled him to accept unhappiness as a means of attaining eternal joy in heaven as well as the approbation of his fellow men. With the glorification of grief, the thought of grief remained while the feeling diminished or disappeared. He appeared to accept the cruel demands of the rejecting, punishing, shaming world by rejecting, punishing and shaming himself; but, at the same time, he defied and rejected this world and asserted his intimacy with God and heaven. He made a compact with the sadists, but he also defied them. He became a martyred hero, as many masochists see themselves in their minds' eye. He turned guilt into innocence and shame into pride.

Such masochistic defenses (or adaptations) are usually built upon identifications with masochistic-appearing parents and cultural institutions. The more the institution glorifies martyrdom, the more effective it may be in this regard.

If masochism is considered a function of depression, the relationship can be expressed in a graph. Everyone, in theory, has a characteristic "masochism-depression diagram," for everyone uses masochistic defenses against depression in varying degrees and circumstances. This is not, however, a continuous straight line function. When depression is at its maximum, it is paralyzing, and masochism becomes impossible; when depression recedes to zero, masochism is unnecessary. Hence, the masochism peak lies in the area between.

This, it need be noted, is a simplified view, purged of other variables. To be complete, many other continua would have to be considered. These would include the transition between depression and anxiety, depression and manic denial, depression and compulsive activity, and depression and paranoid thinking. All of these factors influence the shape of this depression-masochism graph. Manic denial and compulsive activity, for example, diminish the need for masochism.

Much is made of guilt in the genesis of depression and masochism. Little, however, is said of shame. In "Mourning and Melancholia,"[1] Freud stated that feelings of shame in front of other people "are lacking in the melancholic, or at least they are not prominent in him." And yet the melancholic feels humble, ugly and inferior; that is, he feels full of shame. For shame is the affect in which one feels looked down upon and desires to shrink from sight. Further, when the depressive character is not in a state of depression, he

---

[1]Freud, S. (1917). "Mourning and Melancholia." *Standard Edition*, Vol. 14, London: Hogarth Press, 1957.

tends to be vulnerable to shaming; indeed, he probably has a low threshold to it.

Why, then, is it not obvious in the state of depression? The answer is twofold and paradoxical. First, he has withdrawn attachments from others; therefore, they cannot shame him. Second, he shames himself as no one else can, thus anticipating all the others who are eager to do so. As he internalizes the sadism of the object and hurts himself to please the object, so does he internalize the shaming tendency of the object and shame himself to please the internalized shamer.

The masochist, on the other hand, not only shames himself but also induces others to shame him, similarly to the clown who induces others to laugh at him. These others are not the real object he fears. This, of course, is easier to tolerate than the original shaming because the shamer is selected and the shaming self-induced. It is under the control of the masochist, not the shamer.

Exhibitionism and shame are related. Exhibitionism is associated with a desire to be seen and shame with a desire to drop out of sight in order to be unseen. Exhibitionism in the masochist is not inhibited as W. Reich[2] suggested. Rather, masochistic exhibitionism is an attempt to show off one's worthlessness and ugliness, a point stressed by T. Reik.[3] The masochist shames himself, counterphobically, in a caricature of humiliation and provokes shaming from others. But it is not for purposes of degradation as it was originally, but for love; in anticipation of this love, he feels better. The masochistic artist—Van Gogh being one example—may paradoxically regard the ugly as beautiful and portray his own ugliness for all the world to see and admire, as well as angrily confront the world with what it has done to him and all sufferers like him.

[2]Reich, W. (1949). "The Masochistic Character." In *Character Analysis*. New York: Orgone Institute Press, 3rd ed.

[3]Reik, T. (1941). *Masochism in Modern Man*. New York: Farrar & Rinehart.

Discussant

León Grinberg, M.D.
Buenos Aires, Argentina

I have read Dr. Berliner's paper with most interest. I have found some aspects thoroughly convincing. There are others, in my opinion, which could be approached differently. It is my purpose to refer to both and to add some of my own views on the subject.

I think Dr. Berliner is correct in first stating the basic assumption that an adult depressive state is a reproduction of a primal depression in childhood and in stressing that parental hostility impairs the development of self-esteem, a feature that is often neglected.

I also believe that his emphasis on the quality of the depressive character's object relationship is equally important, thus the need to take into account the infanticide aspect within the Oedipus complex.[1] Although Dr. Berliner mentions the role of the constitutional factor as another crucial element, he does not pursue this line. I think it is worth pointing out that this constitutional factor is also related to the aggressive drives and fantasies directed toward the objects of the preoedipal and oedipal relationship. Those

[1]Dr. Arnaldo Rascovsky has pointed out in "The Scope of Aggression in Mania" (read at the sixth Latin-American Psychoanalytical Congress in Montevideo, July 1966) that parricide is the result of Laius's and Jokasta's filicidal tendency against Oedipus. He adds that the split between the bad father and the good one ceases when depression is established, as shown by the fact that when Oedipus learns that the man he slew was his father, he is also told about the death of Polybos at Corinth.

drives are, in fact, the content of many conflicts underlying depression. Abraham was the first to indicate the connection between feelings of guilt and cannibalistic wishes, thus stating the significance of sadistic pregenital factors, particularly oral-sadistic, in the emergence of depression.

Dr. Berliner holds that the superego originates from libido through the introjection of love objects, adding that the infantile superego is potentially malignant. Drawing on Abraham's description, M. Klein has shown that the early superego images are invested with intense sadism as a result of the projection of the child's own drives. Freud himself said that the demands of the superego sometimes spring from the child's own hostility turned against himself.

Regarding the technical aspect raised by the question of interpreting the patient's aggressiveness, I firmly support the view that the latent component of the manifest material should be interpreted in any analytic situation. If the latent content of transference fantasies is aggressive, the patient should be made aware of this through interpretation. Otherwise, we encourage denial and repression of the hostility, and we prevent him from freeing himself from the vicious circle that frequently makes the depressive patient, prompted by an unconscious sense of guilt, continuously seek punishment and behave in a masochistic way.

On the other hand, if the analyst does not interpret the patient's aggressiveness, the patient may feel the analyst believes him to be worse than what he really is and does not accept his aggressiveness because it is thought to be dangerous, thus increasing the patient's belief in his own destructive omnipotence. It may be suitable to remember Freud's words on this issue, that to become conscious of what is unconscious is the first step toward cure. This is to be completed by adequate working through.

Another point Dr. Berliner rightly touches on is the dynamics of a perverse object relationship, in the sense of seeking suffering (moral masochism) instead of love gratification. I wish to add to the reasons singled out by Dr. Berliner the working of the guilt feelings underlying aggressive fantasies and the hate felt for objects. Dr. Berliner himself talks about "man's sadistic instinctual endowment," even though he does so in reference to "the universal drive to punish."

Moreover, Dr. Berliner presents guilt as stemming both from the aggressiveness of love objects and as a result of the subject's own aggressiveness. I have suggested a solution to this double view by formulating the existence of two kinds of guilt:[2]

A *persecutory guilt*, often reinforced by the aggressiveness of the object, prevails during the earliest stages of life. It is this guilt which determines masochistic attitudes as well as extreme submission to the object. It may also lead either to crime or suicide, depending on whether the aggressiveness is directed toward the outer object or the inner object. Freud's description of "criminals from a sense of guilt" belongs to this category.

On the other hand, there is a *depressive guilt* which calls for a more mature and integrated ego. This guilt gives rise to grief and responsibility for aggressive fantasies or for the damage felt to be done to the object and strives for reparation. M. Klein has described this as guilt under the influence of the "depressive position."

I believe that feelings of guilt are experienced not only in reference to the object but to the own self as well; they are part of the mourning reaction for the loss of the object and also for the lost parts of the self.[3] I am inclined to think that these depressive feelings

---

[2]Grinberg, L. (1964). *Culpa y Depresión* (*Guilt and Depression*). Buenos Aires: Ed., Paidos.

[3]*Ibid.*

for the self occur more often than is generally recognized, and constitute to a certain extent what Dr. Berliner describes as the experience of an impaired, deprived self that badly needs to be given libidinal nourishment to make up for its losses. Due to persecutory guilt, it also endeavors vicariously to turn the need for being loved into suffering. Some feelings among the phenomena of the psychopathology of everyday life can be postulated as micro-depressions or micro-mournings.

I hope this contribution helps round off the picture of the depressive character that Dr. Berliner gives us.

Discussant

Edith Weigert, M.D.
Chevy Chase, Maryland

Dr. Berliner published a series of papers on masochism between 1942 and 1958 in which he maintained Freud's distinction between erotic masochism, feminine masochism and moral masochism. According to Freud's early instinct theory, erotic masochism, particularly in the male, is a sexual perversion due to the sadomasochistic component of the sexual drive. After the introduction of Eros and Thanatos, erotic masochism was understood to result from a preponderance of aggressive over libidinal drives, the erotic masochist seeking a sadistic partner who fulfills his sexual wishes only under the condition of more or less painful or humiliating punishment, while in the moral masochist the erotic gratification may be missing. The image of frustrating parents is internalized in the superego whose punishing functions are in later life projected on a partner who is provoked and manipulated into acting out the punishing functions in the hope for reconciliation.

In his present paper Dr. Berliner considers "moral masochism" a misnomer and replaces it with "depressive character," a form of character widespread in our culture and an ingredient of many psychoneurotic conditions. The libidinal goal is not missing in the life of the depressive character, but gratification cannot be reached because of the compulsion to repeat an original traumatic situation of childhood frustrations. Dr. Berliner sees the original trauma in a lack of oral and skin erotic gratifications in the early phase of childhood, but this lack of gratification is only a partial aspect of the original trauma; the depressive character seems to be insatiable in his demands for nutriment.

The voracious eater and the addicted patient are depressive characters who never reach the point of satiation. The depressive character who refuses food, in extreme cases reaching the state of *anorexia nervosa*, suffers from such despair that no intake of food will squelch his sense of deprivation.

He is equally insatiable in demands for reassurance and comfort, accompanied by skin contact, stroking and caresses, but no endeavor to meet the patient's needs can fill the bill.

Dr. Berliner aptly describes the depressive condition as one in which unfulfilled bills of the past are presented. Beyond frustration of oral and skin erotic needs, the patients have experienced a trauma that threatened their whole existence. They may have received from dutiful mothers the appropriate amount of calories and adequate physical hygienic care, but they sensed they were not welcomed by spontaneous loving care. Many depressed characters have depressive mothers who were not able to express active love and fathers who were unable to compensate for this lack. The children were expected to gratify the parents' insatiable demands. The lopsidedness in the parent-child relation does not permit the child to outgrow the symbiotic tie. Differentiation of parent and child, which allows a development of a phase-adequate, integrated competence is, for constitutional or environmental reasons, impaired, and in partially persistent symbiosis the child holds on to the demands for narcissistic supplies, his lack of trust in his own competence corresponding to his level of ego development, and without confidence in the mutuality of give and take relations.

The insatiability of the depressive character makes him appear overconcerned about himself, but not in the sense of a healthy narcissism. The depressed character compensates for the defects in his self-esteem by exploiting the sympathy of others, depending on pain and suffering to elicit narcissistic supplies from them. But this dependency on pain is an inefficient defense against the dangers of frustration, since the very insatiability of demands inevitably discourages the willingness of even the most generous partner and turns him away with feelings of futility and disgust. The disgust increases the despair and the frequently vengeful, though repressed, hatred against the partners in adult life.

Dr. Berliner has not overlooked this vicious cycle in the interpersonal relations of the depressive character, but his emphasis lies on the original traumatic experience and the repetition compulsion of the frustrations in the oral phase. According to Dr. Berliner, the roots of the Oedipus conflict reach into the preoedipal phase.

Dr. Berliner reexamines the Oedipus legend from the standpoint of the original traumatic experience. Oedipus was an unwanted child. Due to the tragic predictions of the oracle that Oedipus would kill his father and marry his mother, his parents exposed him to almost certain death, hanging him to a tree after piercing his ankles. Oedipus was saved and escaped from his parents' infanticidal intentions. He lived to kill his father, ignorant that it was his father who barred his way and provoked him to fight and kill him in self-defense. Oedipus saved his father's kingdom and his mother from the distress of widowhood, producing four children with her.

In the psychoanalytic literature the infanticidal intentions of Oedipus' parents remain mostly unmentioned, and the universal Oedipus conflict is mostly used to illustrate the unconscious patricidal intentions of the son and his incestuous attachment to the mother. The tragedy of Sophocles emphasizes the *hubris* or compensatory narcissism of the tragic hero. He was not consciously guilty, but destiny burdened him with what Freud spoke of as "borrowed guilt feelings"—originally not his, but stemming from his parents' desertion of parental responsibilities, causing the tragic guilt.

Dr. Berliner concludes that the guilt of the depressed patient, in general, stems from parental insufficiency in active loving care. This insufficiency condemns the child to a failure of development in which aggressive self-centered demands defy the integrative functions of Eros.

Dr. Berliner's conclusion has an important impact on psychoanalytic theory. According to his interpretation of the depressive character, the Oedipus conflict is not necessarily universal but the result of a miscarried parent-child relation, a partial persistence of the symbiotic dependency which has not been outgrown in the phases of pregenital development.

Parental maturity is not necessarily identical with genital maturity. The unconscious infanticidal impulses of parents are relatively infrequently treated in psychoanalytic literature, though the study of postpartum psychoses allows us some glimpses into the infanticidal impulses in narcissistic mothers who have not reached the level of personality integration in which a surplus of erotic energies winning out over aggressive energies is available for responsibilities of parenthood and the spontaneous loving care of an expanding family.

We are grateful to Dr. Berliner for having stimulated this discussion.

Discussant

Stanley Goodman, M.D.

Berkeley, California

Dr. Berliner's provocative paper stimulated reflection on at least two relevant issues: first, the matter of nosology, and second, the question of the relation between interpersonal and intrapsychic factors in development and pathogenesis.

Psychoanalysis has inherited from predynamic psychiatry descriptive diagnostic categories which do not really lend themselves to satisfactory translation into the psychoanalytic frame of reference. The traditional terms provide us only with relatively gross and approximate abbreviations rather than with precise meaningful illuminations of complex psychopathology. Dr. Berliner has performed a most useful service in calling our attention to the need for clarification and more exact definition of two widely applied diagnoses: "moral masochist" and "depressive character." However, it is just because we do not yet have a systematic analytic nosology that it is difficult to arrive at a dependable judgment of his thesis, namely, that these terms are essentially identical and that "the term masochism should apply only to the special character of object relations . . . to which the depressive character is prone."

Masochistic behavior can be observed in persons who have been assigned a wide variety of the usual diagnostic categories, and our clinical experience does not, in fact, lead us to conclude that a depressive substate is an invariably necessary and sufficient factor for all of them. I agree that depression may frequently be important in the genesis of masochistic behavior, but for the present I hesitate to restrict the use of the term to the object relations of the depressive. Dr. Berliner's problem, and ours, resides in the difficulty of achieving an exact dynamic vocabulary for the differentiation of pathology while utilizing rather crude and static, albeit "classical," labels.

The author's reappraisal of the Oedipus myth and the oedipal situation in personal development is particularly interesting. His thesis is that we must understand the child much more as the passive victim than as the active aggressor in his relations with the adult world. This question of the origins of psychological conflict in infancy has, of course, been much studied and discussed through the years. As we know, there is a wide spectrum of opinion on the matter.

At one extreme are those who view the effects of the environment, which include real object relationships, as essentially negligible. They feel that the constitutionally given, including a complex and relatively inflexible fantasy life, is the predominating factor in mental development and pathology. At the other extreme are those who consider the infant an essentially blank slate, to be written on almost exclusively by the external environment.

The former attitude has the practical implication that the real behavior of the parents is relatively unimportant in pathogenesis. The latter attitude implies that parents may regularly and justifiably be accused of actually causing the child's neurosis. The main body of psychoanalytic opinion seems to have taken a middle ground position, suggesting that both intrapsychic as well as interpersonal conflict and adaptation are always operative, and that one or the other may have crucial significance in the history of a particular individual.

Early in the paper, Dr. Berliner clearly indicates the importance of the infant's instinctual endowment, its constitutional variation, and the undoubted significance of fixation at the oral stage of psychosexual development for depression. He also reviews the consequences to ego development of the introjection of the lost or threatened love object. The external struggle becomes internal, contributing to the model for later depressions, and may be externalized once again, contributing to the model for masochistic behavior. However, later in the paper, while there is an appropriate emphasis on the relative helplessness of the infant in its initial object relations and on its vulnerability to intentional and non-intentional trauma, I feel that the intrapsychic forces and structures are unduly minimized.

My own position would differ from Dr. Berliner's in that I would want to attempt to specify much more precisely the intrapsychic dynamics in both the child and the parent. The infant is relatively helpless, but I question the validity of ascribing to it a complete passivity. The weight of evidence suggests rather that the powerful instinctual drives of sexuality and aggression are active from the beginning of life and significantly influence, as well as being influenced by, the actual object relations. We assume also that the drives are modified and influenced in their expression in response to innate maturational factors which are independent of the external environment.

Over and over again the author implies that we do depressive persons an injustice if we consider them to be reacting only to their own aggression. One might say also that we do their parents an injustice if we dismiss them as "hateful and unloving." Perhaps we should give up looking for the villain in the Oedipus play, myth, or situation. Laius consulted the oracle and received a message derived from his own impulses. But then presumably the same would hold true for Oedipus. Both could be accused as villains; both could be defended as victims; both could represent us all.

Author's Response

Bernhard Berliner, M.D., PH.D.
San Francisco, California

Dr. Lubin raises the question of why the relationship between depression and moral masochism has not always been recognized. The reason, it seems to me, was that for a long time moral masochism was considered a derivative of a sexual perversion and treated from the viewpoint of the id. The growing interest during recent decades in the ego and in object relations brought the condition into the focus of the ego and of character formation. Wilhelm Reich (1933) was particularly instrumental in this turn.

Looking for the differences between masochism and depression, Dr. Lubin rightly points to the exhibitionistic behavior in moral masochism. His descriptions, including the brief review of his beautiful studies on Van Gogh, are most interesting and convincing. They corroborate my view that moral masochism is a symptom in the frame of the depressive character structure. The symptom shows varying appearances according to when and how much it is needed for defense. The defense is directed against the original conflict between the instinctual need to be loved and the experience of nonlove. I must maintain my basic thesis that depressive suffering has a positive libidinal motivation. This thesis refers not only to the important events in the psychogenesis of the depressive character but also to intrapsychic factors the importance of which I do not underestimate.

Dr. Grinberg finds my consideration of the constitutional factors incomplete. I referred only to the high degree of oral and skin erotisms and to the process of introjection which starts the superego formation. Other constitutional determinants, e.g., biochemical ones, are suspected but not known. The role of the aggressive drives as a constitutional etiological factor in the depressive character is difficult to assess. At first sight the patient's aggressiveness appears to be of low intensity. One feels tempted to speak of a "weak ego." Possibly we have here a constitutional element, but I am not sure. With the progress of the analysis it shows that aggression largely operates in response to introjects. The superego orders its expressions as well as its repression and the turn against the self. The cases in which strong aggressiveness conditions the development of depression do not seem to belong in the category which I described but rather to the obsessive-compulsive group. I have dealt with this differentiation in two previous papers (4,5)[1] in which I quoted a statement by Freud referring to the attitude of passivity toward another person, which attitude is absent in obsessional neurosis but present in masochism. Abraham found that manic-depressives in the interval between attacks show an obsessional character structure. The type which I described is quite different.

Concerning the turn of the subject's aggression against the self—it has never been shown before why and how such turn occurs. I have tried to show here and previously that the aggression which is turned against the self is a blend, in various proportions, between the subject's own aggressive drive and the introjected and libidinized aggression of early love objects. The latter steers the subject's own aggression against the self.

The depression that accompanies guilt for oedipal hostility might deserve a different name: remorse. That does not exclude, however, that in such cases an underlying depressive character may also be present. We may find it necessary to distinguish between different forms of "Depression." Perhaps I will then have to modify my statement that the depres-

[1]See Bibliography, p. 250.

sive character is the matrix of any depressive illness.

The theories of Melanie Klein, profound as they are, I am unable to accept. They do not give sufficient consideration to the ego and to object relations. Depressive character formation, I feel, cannot be explained from id functions alone.

I am glad to see that the colleagues in Buenos Aires, Dr. Grinberg, Dr. Rascovsky and Dr. Garma (in his discussion remarks in Vol. I, No. 2, of "The Forum," p. 214) share my view of the significance of the infanticide in the Oedipus legend. It feels good not to be alone when one proposes a novel aspect in psychoanalysis.

Dr. Marcovitz raises so many questions that to answer or discuss them one would have to write a volume. Some answers I have given in the foregoing. Space demanded a limitation of my subject as well as a condensation of my thoughts which may have made my statements appear more "sweeping" than they were meant.

I, too, have seen patients who initially described their childhoods as happy, sometimes in such glowing terms that they stumbled over their defensiveness. Further analysis uncovered the flaws. Furthermore, traumatic frustrations and losses are harsher when they occur after prior overindulgence, which, on the part of parents, may have covered up an underlying hostility which the child sensed.

I had no intention to repudiate the oedipal experience as an innate developmental process of the human species. I only wanted to stress the parental participation in addition to the filial oedipal conflict (see also my references to G. Devereux and A. J. Levin). I am well aware of the guilt and depression for oedipal hostility which need not be part of a depressive character. My concept of the depressive character need not be invalidated thereby. On the other hand, why do many children emerge from the Oedipus situation unharmed, some even with an enhancement of their creative abilities, while apparently only a few develop depression and very few of these as a lifelong character structure? There must be additional causes.

How can we differentiate between innate and learned components of guilt? I believe that a potentiality for guilt reaction is present in every human being. It becomes activated into manifest feelings of guilt through the likewise universal need for affection, as I tried to describe in my paper.

Is it true that "the inevitable wish to destroy the love object is the root of guilt and depression"? Was Oscar Wilde right with his generalization: "Each man kills the thing he loves"? Or do statements of this kind refer only to severely neurotic persons? Future work on depression might give an answer.

I am far from advocating the abolition of guilt and thereby of depression, and I do not believe it possible to attain this goal if only parents would or could get over their hostility to their children. I am no crusader. This problem, I believe, must be left to the general progress of civilization in which, however, psychoanalysis has its share.

Dr. Weigert, drawing on her own rich experience, generously exemplifies and expands on my views. However, I did not mean to dispute the universality of the Oedipus complex. I meant to say that the depressive character originates prior to the Oedipus complex and that in the depressive the Oedipus complex already bears the stamp of the preoedipal pathology. The depressive child in the Oedipus situation can neither love and desire his mother nor hate his father (vice versa in the girl) with the intensity which we find at the root of other neuroses. Love-hungry submissiveness toward both parents dominates the picture. That could possibly mean (to answer also Dr. Marcovitz) that in the preoedipally depressive child the impact of the Oedipus situation is mitigated.

Dr. Goodman calls attention to the semantic difficulties in our nosology. Names can clarify and names can confuse. These difficulties are increased by the fact that we have no vocabulary with which to describe unconscious processes in other terms than those used to describe conscious ones. Until a systematic analytic terminology will be developed we have no better way than to describe as minutely as possible what we can observe, without sticking rigidly to old names or making deductions from time-honored theories. The fact that many conditions are mixed forms, e.g., depressive reactions accompanying various neurotic conditions, makes this all the more necessary.

The differentiation between the relative importance of intrapsychic and interpersonal forces in forming conflicts seems to me greatly overrated. The subject as a nature-given organism is always there before the outside experience. Interaction both ways and in innumerable forms is part of the very essence of life. An "either-or" makes no sense.

Looking for the villain in the Oedipus play, myth or situation has a theoretical and a therapeutic aspect. Dr. Goodman seems to refer to the former only. I agree with him there. Regarding analytic therapy I have previously (5) proposed a technical principle which experience has proven to be right. (This may also be an answer to Dr. Grinberg.) The moral masochist (or the depressive) appears in a twofold light: he is a victim and he is a troublemaker. I give the analysis of the victim and his need for affection priority. An initial or early reference to the troublemaker can create an unsurmountable resistance. One should wait with this confrontation until the transference can support it. Then of course the patient's hostilities have to be analyzed.

My warm thanks to all the discussants for their very valuable additions to my paper.

The Forum

Title

Of Divers Things: Preliminary Note on the Dynamics of Scuba Diving

Author

Roderic Gorney, M.D.

Assistant Professor of Psychiatry at the University of California at Los Angeles. He is Staff Psychiatrist at the Neuropsychiatric Institute, California State Department of Mental Hygiene. Dr. Gorney is a scuba diver.

Discussants

Louis Jolyon West, M.D.

Professor and Head of the Department of Psychiatry, Neurology, and Behavioral Sciences at the University of Oklahoma School of Medicine. He has made many contributions to experimental psychopathology and research on problems of consciousness, including studies of hypnosis, brainwashing, sleep, dreams, sensory isolation, dissociative phenomena and hallucinations.

George L. Engel, M.D.

Professor of Psychiatry and Medicine at the University of Rochester and a Career Research Awardee of the U.S. Public Health Service. He is a member of the Western New York Psychoanalytic Society and the American Psychoanalytic Association. He has published numerous papers on high altitude decompression sickness and many more in the general field of psychosomatic medicine. Dr. Engel is the author of two books, *Fainting* and *Psychological Development in Health and Disease.*

Robert Howard

Biotechnical Engineer in Litton Space Sciences Laboratories, Beverly Hills, California. Since his academic training in the biological sciences he has worked more than ten years in the field of underwater research and commercial diving with experience as Chief Diving Officer in the evaluation of deep diving equipment and underwater construction. He is currently certified as an Underwater Instructor by principal undersea operating agencies, and as Divemaster in the Los Angeles County Advanced Instructors Program, he teaches the instructors course. He is a member of the Marine Technology Society, the International Oceanographic Foundation and the American Geophysical Union and has authored two books and many papers dealing with diving techniques and hydrobiophysics.

Leo Goldberger, PH.D.

Associate Director of the Research Center for Mental Health at New York University's Graduate Psychology Department as well as Research Associate Professor. Dr. Goldberger has been a Research Candidate at the New York Psychoanalytic Institute for the past four years and holds a National Institute of Mental Health Research Career Development Award. Since 1956 he has been engaged in research on perceptual isolation and has published many papers on that topic. He is an avid spear fisherman but only an occasional scuba diver.

Of Divers Things: Preliminary Note on the Dynamics of Scuba Diving

Roderic Gorney, M.D.
Los Angeles, California

The ocean's fascination is attested to by eight million Americans who have tried various phases of diving. With scuba (self-contained underwater breathing apparatus) it has become possible to learn quickly to explore the ocean floor in freedom.

Instead of the fear he expected, the novice scuba diver is often surprised to find himself feeling a peaceful complacent euphoria when first submerged in the ocean. Psychological factors alone do not explain this inappropriate confidence sufficiently. Physiological changes produced by submersion must be analyzed and correlated with psychological factors. Thus integrated, the two aspects of the diving experience display an illuminating synergism.

Man has always been fascinated and frightened by the mystery of the ocean. The siren-myth (5) is a typical personification of the ocean as a seductive and destructive woman or mother. The sirens exhibit their charms to lure unwary sailors into shipwrecks.

With the advent of satisfactory diving equipment, the mystery of the ocean has been decreased. But man's emotional relationship to the ocean has been potentiated. It remains a mixture of desire and fear.

Physiological Aspects

Though corroborated by experts and related literature (1,9,11,12,13), the following formulation is considered only a working hypothesis in the absence of controlled experiments. A diver exercises strenuously on the surface. He swims heavily weighted and develops exertional dyspnea. As soon as he submerges even to such shallow depths as 10-40 feet he is suspended effortlessly and weightlessly in a silent world. He feels smaller due to magnification of his surroundings by light refraction, and abdominal compression elevates the diaphragm permitting more complete pulmonary ventilation. Because the compressed air he breathes is under increased pressure, the exchange of respiratory gases is accelerated, and any previously incurred oxygen debt is repaid rapidly. Various factors improve venous return to the heart, such as horizontal posture, peripheral vasoconstriction due to cold, and a pressure gradient between the lungs and the periphery due to the dorsal location of the lung regulator. The consequence is a comforting slowing of rapid pulse. As a result of all this he feels fresh and relaxed despite his exhaustion a few moments before. This change which can be recognized as physiologically initiated, I call "shallow water euphoria."

This shallow water euphoria (not to be confused with "nitrogen narcosis" occurring at great depths) is one cause for the common addiction to diving. The other is the unconscious symbolic equation of the concepts "mother" and "love" to the concept "ocean."

Shallow water euphoria blunts awareness of physiological dangers: (*a*) exhaustion resulting from moving through a medium 800 times the density of air. (*b*) drowning. (*c*) dangers due to pressure changes such as ear-drum rupture, pulmonary embolus and "bends" resulting from diving or ascending too quickly.

Psychological Aspects

Widely different people are amazed by their own diving reactions and subsequent lyric or mystic reports. A lumber merchant, when asked how long he'd been diving, replied, "As normal time is reckoned, four years." Phillippe Diolé (4) writes that the diver ". . . moves about the sea the way one flies in dreams. I have perhaps lived a miracle . . . I have swept away all my anxieties as a man . . . the solitude of diving lulls and stays a deep-rooted dissatisfaction. . . . Down below . . . man feels for a moment in tune with life." Of particular interest are the many references by divers to the psychic relation between diving and dreams of flying. Captain Jacques Cousteau (3) reports he dreamt of flying all his life, but these dreams ceased after his first dive with his invention, the Aqua-lung. He believes the dreams stopped because the experience of "flying" was his thereafter in reality. Considering our knowledge of the meaning of flying dreams, (8) it seems strange that "ocean flying" should eliminate the need for dream flying. A possible explanation emerges when we examine the diving experience in terms of certain aspects of infantile sexuality and ego development. (6,8)

The diving experience is intimate and sensual, an escape from the complexities of earthbound relatedness. A shy, polylingual foreign patient expressed it in a punning daydream: He came to a pair of doors. Both had signs in French. The right one read *L'affaire d'amour*. The left one read *L'affaire d'meer*. *(Meer:* German for ocean.) He went through the left door. His first association to *L'affaire d'meer* was the French word for mother, *mère*. His daydream, like the siren myth, further reveals the well-known symbolic connections between the concepts "mother" and "ocean," and their mutual relation to the concept "love."

What transpires emotionally when one chooses *L'Affaire d'meer?* Despite obvious healthy ego mastery elements, one is struck immediately with the counterphobic factor in diving. (2) The diver deliberately forsakes the safe and familiar land for the dangerous alien world of the "ocean mother" to which he is barely adapted. Despite the physiological dangers—and stingrays, moray eels, sea urchins, sharks, killer whales, live coral infections—he is not afraid! Perhaps he arrives at the diving area exhausted. He may consider returning to shore, but, his heart pounding and chest heaving, he inserts his mouthpiece and inhales hopefully as he sinks. He thrills to the sight of the ocean's life at first hand. Now begins his shallow water euphoria. He is startled to realize that in less than 30 seconds all his anxious distress has disappeared. He feels weightless, reduced in size, comfortable in a silent dream, rocked in the ocean-mother's surge. He feels utterly and inappropriately safe against all dangers. He feels he could continue forever, at one with his whole environment. Perhaps this reaction is one variety of the "oceanic feeling."[1]

To understand this ocean-mother fantasy better, let us retrace the diver's steps from the developmental viewpoint. Once before he has experienced the weightlessness of fluid support in a near-silent world; (7) but let us move on to the period of infancy, lest these amniotic reflections take us too close to Rank speculation.

Much is done during infancy to duplicate the womb. The baby is held, supported against gravity, kept in a warm quiet environment and, ideally, spends many hours in contact with his mother's body, rocked by her respiration, if not her arms. Tensions build up and are relieved by mother. The infantile psyche has no limits, and the whole world with mother in it is part of the baby's self—the "oceanic feeling." In her care he feels safe against all dangers. Soon he learns how inappropriate this feeling is. Maturation draws boundaries separating himself from mother and sketches the increasingly tedious techniques he must employ to please and influence her. Ordinarily she guards him against her own and the

---

[1]Compare marked psychological changes produced by other disruptions in patterning of sensory input.

world's most instantly destructive menaces. He discovers, however, that her powers and good will have limits. From that point the long history of psychological growth is, in one sense, a gradual reluctant recognition of the necessity of relinquishing the addiction to maternally-administered pleasures. His craving shifts to the sanctioned active mastery of nonmaternal reality, but he retains a perpetual wistful glance over the shoulder at the magic past in which total bliss through reunion with mother beckons seductively.

It is this wishful fantasy which synergizes with the physiologically initiated euphoria. Thereby diving mobilizes many pregenital and genital derivatives, including scoptophilia, impulses to devour, pregnancy and rebirth fantasies, castration fears, and impulses toward mastery. We will consider here certain particularly prominent phallic elements in the "mother-ocean" equation.

Shallow water euphoria is the siren song of the ocean-mother. She offers return to infantile pleasures: weightlessness, quietude, rocking, and quick passive relief from dyspnea, tachycardia and anxiety. She allows him the supreme ecstasy of reentering mother's body. Then once again active satisfactions preempt the diver's energies, but with this difference: the ocean-mother invites exploration and mastery of her own contents. As he acts on this invitation, the diver's more primitive strivings may be brought under genital primacy, or at least be integrated in the service of phallic activity. In so doing he has been taught to "fly" in reality—but only within the reality of the ocean-mother. It is these phallic libidinal impulses, combined with ego-mastery strivings from corresponding levels of development, which are expressed in dreams of flying. In actual flying and diving the entire body is endowed with a phallic role. Perhaps it is this erotization of generalized muscular activity in the reality of "ocean flying" which made Cousteau's dream-flying unnecessary.

Submersion in mother-ocean recapitulates the risks as well as satisfactions of infancy. Here the relation to the siren story becomes clear. While untold pleasures are seemingly offered the diver, forsaking of his vigilance can result in final reunion with the ocean-mother with irreversible erasure of his separate existence. The seduction thus would end in death.

An essential safeguard is the diving partner who becomes invested disproportionately with confidence and affection. There is a conscious need for the other's protection against dangers sensed as being primarily external. But unconsciously the diving partner is looked to as a bulwark against yielding altogether to the seductive blandishments of the ocean. I believe this strong cathexis may be a partial displacement from mother to a beloved sibling with whom one decides to share mother in exchange for help in resisting the temptation to surrender one's identity to her permanently. In any case, this safeguard becomes the more necessary when we recall that unlike the original actual or imagined mother, despite all her apparent soothing promises, the ocean-mother takes a disturbingly neutral attitude toward those real external dangers which menace her child. Not only will she permit the diver to smother while in her lap, but he and his partner are on their own in defending themselves from shark or stingray.

In addition to her nonpartisanship in this defense, mother-ocean lays down strict rules for conduct which the diver may not violate on pain of disaster. For example, in escaping a shark, he may not follow his primitive urge to dash to the surface. He must control panic and ascend slowly or risk lethal air embolism or the "bends." So at least with respect to her unwillingness to have her filial ties severed abruptly, the ocean-mother does resemble uncomfortably many of her land-bound sisters.

If the diver has safely executed the permitted gradual leave-taking and arrives at the surface intact, mother-ocean has one last ordeal for him to surmount in escaping a shark. As a scavenger the shark is most prone to attack an object splashing or floating on the surface. So the diver's final farewell at the ocean-maternal boundary is made still more poignant for him by the increased risk of assault by this incarnate maternal Id impulse.

That the dangers are approached with such equanimity may confirm our insight into the dynamics of manic elation. In the diver's experience, the idealized ocean-mother seems to symbolize and promise, not only the magic pleasures of infancy, but the psychotic triumph over death through reunion with mother beyond life and death in eternal peace. (10)

Summary and Conclusions

The diver responds to the ocean-mother who lures him with promises of ineffable pleasure and mastery of the fascinating and frightening mysteries of her body and domain. But he must not become tied to her apron strings too tightly or he will never return to his own world. Conversely, he may not flee from her in haste. For this transgression she may exact a more terrible vengeance than even her earthly sisters and thrust him back into his own world, broken on the rack of hers.

Finally, he must remember to avoid the risk of lyrical prose in conveying this experience to his friends and colleagues. As a diver, I fear I have so far obeyed all but the last of these warnings.

Bibliography

1. Behnke, A. "Physiological Effects of High Pressure Atmospheres." Summarized in a table: "Effects of High Air Pressures on Psychological Tasks." From "Narcotic Effects of Gases." Pers. communication.
2. Bond, D. (1952). *The Love and Fear of Flying.* New York: Int. Univ. Press, Inc.
3. Cousteau, J., with Dumas, F. (1953). *The Silent World.* New York: Harper and Brothers.
4. Diolé, P. (1953). *The Undersea Adventure.* New York: Messner.
5. *Encyclopaedia Britannica* (11th ed.). (1911). "The Lorelei." Vol. 17.
6. Fenichel, O. (1945). *The Psychoanalytic Theory of Neurosis.* New York: W. W. Norton.
7. Ferenczi, S. *Thalassa.* New York: Psa. Quart., 1938.
8. Freud, S. *General Introduction to Psychoanalysis.* New York: Garden City Pub. Co., 1943.
9. Goff, L. (ed.). "Proceedings of the Underwater Physiology Symposium." Pub. 377, Nat. Acad. of Sciences-Nat. Research Council, Washington, D.C., 1955.
10. Grotjahn, M. (1960). "Ego Identity and the Fear of Death and Dying." J. of the Hillside Hospital, Vol. 9.
11. Lambertsen, C., Stroud, M., Gould, R., Kough, R., Ewing, J., Schmidt, C. (1953). "Oxygen Toxicity. Respiratory Responses of Normal Men to Inhalation of 6 and 100 percent Oxygen under 3.5 Atmos. Pressure." J. of Appl. Physiol., Vol. 5. Summarized by Behnke, A., in a table, "Physiological Effects of High Pressure Atmospheres." Pers. communication.
12. Lanphier, E. (1957). "Diving Medicine." The New Eng. J. of Med., Vol. 256.
13. Shilling, C., Hawkins, J., Hansen, R. (1936). "The Influence of Increased Barometric Pressure on the Pulse Rate and Arterial Blood Pressure." U. S. Naval Med. Bull., Vol. 34.

760 Westwood Plaza
Los Angeles, California 90024

Discussant

Louis Jolyon West, M.D.

Oklahoma City, Oklahoma

Dr. Gorney has given us a vivid and personal discussion of some psychodynamic aspects of scuba diving. He describes a characteristic "shallow water euphoria" (as distinguished from the "rapture of the depths" caused by nitrogen narcosis in deep-sea divers) in terms of a combination of physiological changes (including sensory, postural, circulatory, and biochemical factors) and psychological effects of submersion. The latter are interpreted in terms of regressive mobilization of infantile affects. One might raise an eyebrow at some of the author's comparisons between the life of the human infant and the subsurface life of the diver; nevertheless, in general, this portion of Gorney's hypothesis for shallow water euphoria as "the siren song of the ocean-mother" is attractive. Even if the appeal were only a literary one, we should be tempted to accept it for its romance and its charm.

Certain of the author's derivative propositions (e.g., the camaraderie of diving partners as partial displacement from mother to beloved sibling) are a little more difficult to accept. No special data—even anecdotal—are provided to characterize the relationship between divers, or to differentiate it from other companionships among sportsmen. Additional postulates are offered which cannot be seen to derive at all from the basic formulation. For example Gorney defines a "synergism" of wishful fantasy (to return magically to blissful reunion with mother) with physiologically initiated euphoria. "Thereby diving mobilizes . . . scoptophilia, impulses to devour, pregnancy and rebirth fantasies, castration fears. . ." We are not told about any such experiences; indeed it is suggested that, through the "synergism" proposed above, diving reinforces counter-phobic defenses rather than mobilizing castration fears.

Without gainsaying the author's basic contention, I would like to point out that states of euphoria are not uncommon in adventuresome sports, from skiing to sailing, in which a major escape from the tensions and preoccupations of everyday life is accomplished. The feeling that is commonly experienced on reaching a mountain top can be just as "oceanic" as in diving—and the euphoria of the mountaineer is sometimes attributed to *diminished* oxygen tension, as contrasted with the increased oxygen tension of the scuba divers' air (or at least the rapid repayment of oxygen debt on submerging).

If one begins to make comparisons with other sports, an issue arises which is not treated in Dr. Gorney's paper. Mallory wanted to climb Everest "because it is there." The sea, like the mountains, has always been there, but what factors impel individuals to choose scuba diving as an avocation, with so many other possibilities available to those who possess the time, money, and physical qualifications? It would be interesting to know what Gorney thinks about initial motivation among scuba divers, and perhaps learn whether he has observed personality differences between those who become enthusiasts and those who do not.

Although Gorney does not go into detail regarding the psychophysiological side of his formula, a word might be said about underwater experiments in sensory isolation—the "hydrohypodynamic environment" employed by Shurley in his experiments.[1] Many of the factors, including shallow water submersion in a mask, are similar to scuba diving, and other aspects of Shurley's tank are even more womblike than the sea (water at 94°F; a very

[1]Shurley, J. (1960). "Profound Experimental Sensory Isolation." Amer. J. Psa., Vol. 117.

peaceful, dark, quiet setting; an "umbilical cord" air-hose from the mask, etc.). However, while some euphoria is reported by certain subjects, it is by no means universal, nor does it usually develop until a fair amount of time has passed—an hour or more. Of course these subjects are breathing room air rather than a scuba-type mixture.

A final interesting point might be to consider some implications of recent research on the "diving reflex," or "oxygen-conserving reflex," for the psychophysiology of scuba diving. It has been shown that a complex adaptive metabolic response is initiated in creatures who frequently submerge (the duck, or the seal), with a remarkable counterpart in man.[2,3,4,5,6] Simply submerging a man's face in a bowl of water will initiate this response which includes bradycardia, increased arterial pressure, decreased blood flow to skin and viscera, fall in blood pH, and rise in blood CO_2, potassium, lactic and other organic acids. Most interesting is the finding by Wolf, *et al*, that while the diving reflex is "monotonously predictable in the duck," in man it is subject to considerable cerebral influence and can be initiated even by anticipation of diving. Wolf also points out "that this fundamentally protective mechanism, involved as it is under both appropriate and apparently inappropriate circumstances, may, when not adequately balanced by opposing forces, provide a mechanism of sudden death."[7]

[2]Olsen, C., Fanestil, D., and Scholander, P. (1962). "Some Effects of Apneic Underwater Diving on Blood Gases, Lactate and Pressure in Man." J. Appl. Physiol., Vol. 17.

[3]Scholander, P. (1962). "Physiological Adaptation to Diving in Animals and Man." *The Harvey Lectures* (Series 57). New York: The Academic Press.

[4]Scholander, P., Hammel, H., LeMessurier, H., Hemmingsen, E. and Garey, W. "Circulatory Adjustment in Pearl Divers." (1962). J. Appl. Physiol., Vol. 17.

[5]Andersen, H. (1963). "The Reflex Nature of the Physiological Adjustments to Diving and Their Afferent Pathway." Acta. Physiol. Scand., Vol. 58.

[6]Wolf, S. (1964). "The Bradycardia of the Dive Reflex—A Possible Mechanism of Sudden Death." Trans. of Amer. Clinic. and Climat. Assn., Vol. 76.

Discussant

George L. Engel, M.D.

Rochester, New York

This is one of those delightful and fascinating essays psychoanalysts enjoy writing as well as reading. It probably will appeal to the popular imagination and no doubt will be snared by the wire services for newspaper distribution—though not without some tongue in cheek derisive commentary.

Dr. Gorney's thesis *may* be entirely correct, but it is neither good science nor good psychoanalysis. He provides no information as to the source of his data and the mode of its acquisition. Is this a personal experience? Did he analyze a series of scuba divers? (He cites the daydream of one diver.) Did he interview a group of divers? Did he interview diving instructors for their observations on the scuba novice? No such information is provided.

What is the distribution of the data? Are we to believe there is merely one pattern of reaction—that all divers respond with a mixture of desire and fear? Or does Dr. Gorney refer only to those who experience "shallow water euphoria"? From what material does he generalize?

Dr. Gorney does not clearly define his terms. What is meant by "euphoria" in operational (data-derived) as well as in conceptual

[7]Wolf, S., Schneider, R., and Groover, M. (1965). "Further Studies on the Circulatory and Metabolic Alternation of the Oxygen-Conserving (Diving) Reflex in Man." Trans. Amer. Assn. Phys., Vol. 78.

terms? To move from exhaustion to feeling "fresh and relaxed" hardly qualifies as "euphoria." Nor does the reference to "lyric or mystic reports" satisfy the requirements of a phenomenologic or operational definition any more than does the account of the hypothetical diver setting forth with his diving equipment.

A daydream of one patient (about whom we know nothing other than that he is shy and polylingual) constitutes the sum total of manifest content reported. We do not even know what relation the daydream had to his diving experience or even, for that matter, that he did scuba diving. At this point the author may protest he has more data and I certainly trust he does—to which my response can only be "I only know what I read in the paper[s]." He generates broad and sweeping generalizations which would be equally applicable to a host of life experiences, from falling asleep, swinging in a hammock, viewing a magnificent scene after an arduous and dangerous mountain climb, post-orgasm, and what not.

With one grand sweep from womb fantasies to active mastery of nonmaternal reality, the author focuses on the "perpetual wistful glance over the shoulder at the magic past in which total bliss through reunion with mother beckons seductively" as the central wish underlying the euphoria. Then, as if that formulation constituted observed data, he continues, "Thereby diving mobilizes many pregenital and genital derivatives. . . ." Once again there is no documentation. Certainly they are plausible formulations if for no other reason than that their generalizations make it difficult for them not to be. Plausibility, however, is not synonymous with validity. It merely provides the justification systematically to test validity; it does not justify a paper.

Discussant

Robert Howard

Beverly Hills, California

I must preface my remarks by stating that I am not a psychiatrist nor a psychologist, but a physiologist. As such, I believe it would be impertinent and presumptuous of me to comment on the psychoanalytic accuracy of Dr. Gorney's statements. I do feel, however, that as a professional Diving Officer, Master Diving Instructor, and an individual who has spent the greater portion of his professional career in, on, or under the waters, I can comment on the accuracy of some of the conclusions drawn by Dr. Gorney in his paper.

Over a period of the last eight or nine years I have worked with, trained, and supervised hundreds of divers. These divers have covered the entire spectrum of skill, ranging from the young would-be sports diver-in-training, to the older experienced professional diver with a background of 15 to 20 years under water.

I cannot recall one individual who, entering the water for the first time (with diving equipment), appeared relaxed, euphoric, or even reasonably comfortable in his or her new environment. As a matter of fact, every novice I have talked to recalled feeling "scared stiff" during the first few exposures to the underwater area. It is common to note a condition of extreme body rigidity, altered breathing pattern, and low-grade coordination loss during the first few exposures to the aquatic environment. It is most certainly the exception rather than the norm to find a diver who is comfortable or even partially acclimatized to being under water in less than 20 or 30 hours of diving time.

When the diver had gained enough experience in his new environment and with his equipment to allow him to relax, only then could he begin to appreciate and emotionalize within the scope mentioned by Dr. Gorney. In the fields of commercial diving or military diving, any diver who exhibited the type of almost manic elation ascribed to all divers in the article would never even be allowed to complete his initial qualification training. The best military and commercial divers seem to be those who possess an emotional equilibrium and almost stoic personality traits. As a matter of fact, these traits are stressed in the initial interviewing of diver candidates.

I do not feel at this time we know enough about the various aspects of man-underwater relationships, either physiologic or psychologic, to be able to set forth in "lyrical prose" or otherwise a working hypothesis for evaluating the emotional response of underwater personnel.

Discussant

Leo Goldberger, PH.D.

New York, New York

In the mushrooming literature on man's adaptation to "unusual environments"—be it above or below the earth's surface, simulated or "for real"—only slight attention has been paid to the psychodynamic implications, let alone to the evocation of fantasies. The first order of business generally has been the determination of man's physiological adaptive capacity, secondly his performance efficiency and, only as a kind of afterthought, has there been concern with the psychological meaning, the affective and motivational impact of the situation on a given person. In his timely contribution Dr. Gorney provides us with a psychoanalytic hypothesis concerning the impact of one class of unusual environments—the ocean as experienced by the scuba diver.

Starting with the observation that, despite a host of reality dangers, the diver typically experiences a state of "peaceful complacent euphoria," Dr. Gorney posits a synergic relationship between the physiological changes that occur in a hypodynamic environment and the wishful fantasies it triggers, the wishful fantasies presumably being mediated by the symbolic ocean-mother equation. In other words, the substantial similarities between the scuba diving experience and the mother-infant experience (both physiologically and symbolically) revive impulses and fantasies pertaining to the latter. Essentially, then, the mother-infant experience is viewed as standing in a kind of prototypic relationship to the subsequent diving experience. The specific psychosexual contents of these fantasies would of course be determined by the individual diver's unique history and character structure. Also they conceivably might involve revival of imagined constructions pertaining to intrauterine existence without invoking the dubious assumption of prenatal memory traces.

This sort of hypothesis is consistent with analytic theory as applied to other phenomena, in which we speak of revival or reactivation of earlier fantasies as a function of some similarity between a current situation and its prototype. Frequently the similarity is simply a fleeting, primitive sense impression—for example, proprioceptive or olfactory. In diving we are dealing with massive similarities, as Dr. Gorney so vividly details. It would seem reasonable to assume at least some positive correlation between degree of similarity and probability of reactivation.

Dr. Gorney's paper stimulated me to think of other situations that share situational or experiential similarities with aspects of early mother-infant experience. Three observations in the literature seem to dovetail with Gorney's scuba diving hypothesis:

(*a*) Some findings suggest disordered reality-contact (as produced in sensory deprivation and perceptual isolation experiments) facilitates regression to primary process modes of ideation, e.g., fantasy material. The many infantilizing aspects in the isolation situation are thought to be important determinants for this regression.[1] Whereas isolation in a room with the subject lying supine on a bed did *not* generate "oceanic" feelings, exhilaration, or euphoria, the water-immersion technique (as used by Lilly and Shurley[2,3]) did elicit such affects, and possibly even some "addictive" tendency. Sensory deprivation would be a closer analog to the infant's state of primary narcissism, but the differential factor may be the water-immersion and weightlessness, etc., rather than sensory deprivation per se.

(*b*) The "break off phenomenon," not infrequently experienced by high altitude pilots (typically at around 30,000 feet), is a feeling of being detached, isolated or separated physically from the earth, often accompanied by the same peaceful, euphoric or exhilarated state that Gorney attributes to his divers.[4,5] The pilots describe this with the same mystical tone and often with omnipotent fantasies.

(*c*) There are the typical physiological effects of heroin on addicts—euphoria, exhilaration, and "oceanic" states—which also are found to "synergize" with wishful fantasies pertaining to early mother-infant relationship.[6,7] One author reports that to enhance the physiological effect many heroin addicts interviewed "prefer to sit in a dark room with soft music playing . . . while one boy preferred to take his 'shot' while lying in a bathtub filled with warm water."[8,9] One Rorschach study[10] found that "the heroin users produced a significantly greater number of responses with intrauterine implications than the controls."

It would appear that Gorney's hypothesis would have application over a wider range than simply scuba diving which is unique in its overlap with the prototypic mother-infant experience. Whether this similarity mobilizes ocean-mother mediated fantasies is an open question, subject to empirical verification. It would have to be tested in analytic situations by means of dream material, transference reactions, metaphors, etc., with patients who also happen to be "addicted" scuba divers. Another test could be similar to that of Silverman and Silverman[10] using the Rorschach (or the TAT) to gauge the fantasy-derivatives scuba divers manifest, compared to a matched control group. Certainly, there should be more systematic information-gathering to

---

[1]Goldberger, L. (1966). "Experimental Isolation: An Overview." Amer. J. Psychiat., Vol. 122.

[2]Lilly, J. (1956). "Mental Effects of Physical Restraints and of Reduction of Ordinary Levels of Physical Stimuli on Intact, Healthy Persons." Psychiat. Res. Rep., Vol. 5.

[3]Shurley, J. (1961). "Profound Experimental Sensory Isolation." Amer. J. Psychiat., Vol. 117.

[4]Bennet, A. M. H. "Sensory Deprivation in Aviation." In P. Solomon *et al.* (eds.) *Sensory Deprivation.* Cambridge, Mass.: Harvard Univ. Press, 1961.

[5]Clark, B. and Graybiel, A. (1957). "The Break-Off Phenomenon: A Feeling of Separation from Earth Experienced by Pilots at High Altitude." J. Aviat. Med., Vol. 28.

[6]Mannheim, J. (1955). "Notes on a Case of Drug Addiction." Int. J. Psa., Vol. 36.

[7]Savit, R. Unpublished paper presented at the 1958 Midwinter Meeting of the Amer. Psa. Assn. Cited by Silverman and Silverman (see footnote 10).

[8]Zimmering, P., Toolan, J., Safrin, R., Wortis, S. (1951). "Heroin Addiction in Adolescent Boys." J. Nerv. Ment. Disord., Vol. 114.

[9]———. (1952). "Drug Addiction in Relation to Problems of Adolescence." Amer. J. Psychiat., Vol. 109.

[10]Silverman, L. and Silverman, D. (1960). "Womb Fantasies in Heroin Addiction: A Rorschach Study." J. Proj. Tech., Vol. 24.

establish the significant presence of the phenomena Gorney uses—the shallow-water euphoria. In any event, I believe Dr. Gorney has made a good start.

Author's Response

Roderic Gorney, M.D.

Los Angeles, California

Objection that my brief paper[1] is unconvincing due to absence of detailed data must be accepted. I thought its modest intent was indicated in advance by title and tone. The flaw, only partially attributable to abridgment, is partially repaired below. But the ideas remain largely unproved.

What then justifies publication? Disregarding whatever weight alleged "literary appeal" or "charm" may carry, it has been suggested that the essence of science is art. First comes generation of ideas out of fragmentary experience. Later comes proof. The importance of testing hypotheses is not demeaned by designating that process the secondary aspect of science.

To my knowledge, this paper remains the only attempt to synthesize into testable hypotheses remarkable physiological and psychological changes associated with an activity said to have engrossed millions and killed thousands. Circumstances deny me opportunity to engage in rigorous verification. Others may or may not find the ideas useful or worthy of investigation.

Dr. Goldberger grasps my intent and offers excellent material on related experiences. Dr. West calls attention to the variable presence in man of the "diving reflex," which previously I thought confined to subhuman species. It offers alternative explanation of physiological changes I had attributed to increased pressures. As to personality differences, I've found that reflective, introspective

[1]Condensed from a Brief Communication read at the 1958 Annual Meeting of the American Psychoanalytic Association.

people more readily become diving devotees, whereas more outgoing assertive, nonpsychologically-minded counterphobes are as likely to withdraw as persevere.

Mr. Howard cannot recall one novice diver who exhibited euphoria during first scuba experience. I am at a loss to reconcile the discrepancy between his report and those of many certified instructors and divers who assured me they had seen numerous such reactions and considered them significant hazards to beginners. It was an error to allow this condensation to imply that all novices experience euphoria. I was disappointed that a physiologist made no appraisal of the specifically physiological aspects of my hypothesis, which I had hoped might have been elucidated in the intervening years.

Dr. Engel justifiably asks the source of my data. My own experience yielded initial observations of the physiological changes of shallow water euphoria, later substantiated by reference to experts and the literature. Work with one analytic and two psychotherapeutic patients revealed the symbolic aspects, partly substantiated in my own analysis, and in reactions, dreams and associations collected from friends who dive.

The Forum

Title **Omnipotence and the Avoidance of Pleasure: A Contribution to the Problem of Separation Anxiety**

Author **Richard P. Alexander, M.D.**

Assistant Clinical Professor at the University of Southern California and Associate in the Department of Psychiatry at Mount Sinai Hospital. He is on the Faculty of the Extension Division of the Southern California Psychoanalytic Institute. He has a particular interest in problems relating to separation anxiety and its psychosomatic correlates and has written a number of papers on these subjects.

Discussants

Arthur Malin, M.D.
Assistant Clinical Professor of Psychiatry at the University of Southern California and on the Faculty of the Los Angeles Institute for Psychoanalysis. For some years he has been part of a study group of psychoanalysts meeting to discuss object relations theory, identification, and related topics. He is co-author of an article entitled "Projective Identification in the Therapeutic Process," which just appeared in the International Journal of Psychoanalysis.

Elizabeth R. Zetzel, M.D.
Associate Clinical Professor of Psychiatry at Harvard Medical School and a Training Analyst of the Boston Psychoanalytic Institute. Her analytic training was received in London, where Melanie Klein was one of her teachers. She has published several authoritative critiques of the Kleinian approach and many other papers on psychoanalytic problems.

Norman A. Levy, M.D.
Clinical Professor of Psychiatry at the University of Southern California. He is President and Training Analyst of the Southern California Psychoanalytic Institute and has written on various aspects of psychoanalysis.

Edwin F. Alston, M.D.
Assistant Clinical Professor of Psychiatry at the University of California. He is on the Faculty of the San Francisco Psychoanalytic Institute and teaches at the Letterman General and Mount Zion Hospitals. Especially interested in the problem of anxiety and in superego function, he has given papers and seminars on these subjects.

George H. Pollock, M.D., PH.D.
Clinical Professor of Psychiatry at the University of Illinois and Director of Research and Assistant Dean of Education at the Chicago Institute for Psychoanalysis. He is Chairman of the Committee on Training for Research of the American Psychoanalytic Association. He has published various papers dealing with psychoanalysis, psychosomatic medicine, psychiatry and research methodology.

Omnipotence and the Avoidance of Pleasure: A Contribution to the Problem of Separation Anxiety

Richard P. Alexander, M.D.
Beverly Hills, California

In recent years, psychoanalysts have turned their interest to the infant's earliest years and to the infant's first object relation. In a certain group of patients severe anxiety consistently occurs in response to efficient functioning and/or some accomplishments which in the normal individual would evoke feelings of pleasure or self-satisfaction. Although Freud (8) described this phenomenon as being related to an oedipal conflict, I believe in many instances this problem has its roots in a much earlier period of development, i.e., that it is the anxiety of separation which is evoked and sets in motion a destructive regression. In analysis this state of affairs is apt to manifest itself in the form of a negative therapeutic reaction.

Reviewing some of the literature touching upon this problem lends credence to this position. For example, Bowlby (1,2) speaks of separation anxiety occurring in the infant when his instinctual responses are not properly or sufficiently responded to by the mother. Spitz (14) pinpoints such anxiety responses as occurring at about seven months of life when recognition of the face of the mother brings comfort, whereas others, who are experienced as strangers, evoke anxiety. As the infant's world enlarges, he is able to respond securely to others, and by the second year the relatively secure child can be observed to actively leave the parents for various periods of time to involve himself in the external environment, e.g., discovering and exploring new objects or playing with other children.

This capacity for interest in the new and unique is crucial because separation anxiety may overpower the satisfaction derived from this sense of adventure and mastery and bring about fear or panic. Winnicott (16) suggests that success here depends upon how well the infant has been able to include not-me objects and phenomena into his own body-scheme. Fairbairn, (6,7) however, believes that it is this very conflict between the progressive urge for separation from the object, and the regressive lure of identification with the object which explains phobic states and constitutes the primary deprivation and frustration which brings about destructive aims.

Expanding further, Winnicott (15) states that the capacity of the child to be alone is actually based on his experience of being alone in the presence of the mother. In this way, the child can develop a sense of security, arising from the realization that his mother is available if so desired, a condition made possible by the mother's ability to accept the child as a separate being. This ideal situation, requiring neither "too much" nor "too little" maternal influence, enables the child to discover his own self and mind. These "good mothering" experiences are internalized and form the matrix for a mature ego, and enable the child to tolerate longer periods of being alone. He then begins to experience pleasure at being able to function in an autonomous and spontaneous manner, which in turn increases his tolerance and even his desire for separateness. It is a goal of the psychoanalytic relationship to replenish the weakened ego by making available realistic good experiences which can be introjected.

Clinical Example

Mr. J., age 35, sought analysis for a variety of anxieties and phobias, the most debilitating being his fear of leaving home to go to his law office. The severity of this phobia was so great it became necessary for him to arrange an office in his home.

Mr. J.'s relationship with his mother was one in which infantile dependence played a prominent role. This was due, in part, to his mother's overprotective attitude toward him, and to her desire that he be her almost constant companion. Coupled with this was his desire to gain her devotion, intensified by the fact that, due to the need to provide for the family, his father was often out of the home. It also became necessary that his mother leave the home to work and the patient remembered feeling intense frustration and lonely sadness when, after school, he would return to an empty home.

Mr. J. was endowed with exceptional intelligence, and this was a source of great maternal pride, his mother often referring to him as "my brilliant boy." Unfortunately, his excellent grades primarily represented gifts to his mother rather than a source of self-satisfaction and potential for emotional growth. In his teens, Mr. J. did not behave as a "mama's boy." He engaged in a variety of activities with male friends and frequently strenuously resisted his mother's efforts to keep him home with her. His dating and sexual behavior were also somewhat precocious, although in these undertakings he was emotionally remote and furtive.

What appeared to be a healthy adult expression, however, turned out to be a protest against unconscious wishes to possess and be possessed. This became clear when he began to date his fiancée, during which time he first experienced the anxiety which eventually brought him into analysis. He was able to contain it during the early years of marriage until his mother's death immobilized him. He was unable to attend her funeral, and his anxiety soon prevented his leaving home for any activity. During analysis it became clear that one facet of this syndrome was an unconscious wish to deny mother's death and maintain an unconscious belief that they were still united in an unbreakable bond.

Excerpts from the Analytic Work

Mr. J.'s fear of being separated from the object of his fantasy was well demonstrated by his transference reactions. Possessive wishes projected on to me resulted in his protesting that I was "trapping him" and demanding that he remain immobilized on my couch. The origins of these claustrophobic sensations were derived from his fantasy to stake claim to and capture mother's breast. A corollary to this was his claustrophobic anxiety occurring while driving and which, as analysis progressed, became a particularly troublesome symptom. At other times frustration and rage, resulting from his inability to possess or have control over the breast-mother-analyst, brought about a form of retaliatory castration anxiety. As unconscious destructive wishes towards the breast mounted, he would, in panic, protectively reach for his genitals.

Behind these possessive wishes were the illusion of omnipotence and the denial of separateness to which he clung with great desperateness and tenacity. This refusal to accept the reality of his being was illustrated the night after the patient had demonstrated considerable ability and talent in handling a legal matter for a client. On his way to court, Mr. J. had been aware of anxiety as he anticipated a difficult hearing requiring all of his efforts. After he was successful in representing his client his uneasiness disappeared momentarily only to be followed by more intense anxiety. He then reported the following *dream*:

"I have stolen some merchandise from John [his client], then Mary [patient's wife] reminded me that I was to get $1,000. I became angry at her for saying this and countered by saying that I intended to give the stuff back. I knew that this was a lie and felt guilty. I asked John to forgive me, but he was silent. I then realized I'd have to resign."

Immediately, the patient's association was that the $1,000 somehow represented "a reward for stealing." He soon realized the $1,000 referred to money he actually earned. The rage at his wife referred to his refusal to accept himself as a competent attorney who could function in an adult manner—this would establish him as a separate individual functioning in reality. He preferred the "reward" to maintain the illusion of his omnipotence and preferred treating the other person as if he were "there only for the taking" (stealing); he was willing to pay the price of guilt and loss of justifiable self-esteem by resigning in order to maintain this unconscious belief.

It now became possible to point out to him that accomplishments brought about anxiety and were denied by incorporating them into the omnipotent system. Thereafter, Mr. J. soon realized that one of the reasons his analysis was prolonged stemmed from his refusal to work effectively because it threatened the omnipotent part of his personality. "I would rather be clever and devious and pick your brains," i.e., steal from the analyst and avoid recognizing their separate identities.

Following this insight, elements of the dream were lived out in the analysis. For example, frequently when he experienced pleasure over accomplishments, he would suddenly sit up in panic and lurch toward the side table, as an expression of his desire to deny his state of separateness. Thus, any such self-satisfaction was shortlived and replaced by the wish to intrude into the object so as to preserve the fantasy.

Simultaneous with his reluctance to realize his own worth was his inability to appreciate the object's value and experience feelings of gratitude. His difficulty in perceiving the analyst as realistically good had to be repeatedly pointed out and interpreted. In a like manner, he was unable to share his wife's satisfaction when she was offered an eagerly sought-after professional appointment. In an effort to abate his developing envy toward her, he attempted to depreciate and intimidate her by statements that he didn't think she was ready, emotionally or intellectually, to accept the position. This hostility was thinly veiled by a pretense of benevolence. When this failed, and after she left the house for her first day at work, the patient experienced great rage and anxiety.

During the analytic hour that day, he became conscious of fantasies that her breasts had dried up into two small desiccated masses. Further fantasies revealed his belief that if his wife enjoyed herself and gave herself to her work and the people involved in it, he would die of thirst as she would be drained by them. This projection only increased his possessive wishes and produced powerful feelings of guilt and further anxiety based on the belief that he had drained her, killed her and thus lost her. Denial of this hostile greed led to his feeling weak and debilitated, requiring help and soothing. This expressed both an identification with his sick complaining mother and a reliving of the hopelessness he experienced in childhood when his mother was not available.

Some Conceptual and Therapeutic Aspects

Freud's anecdotal concept of normality in terms of pleasure in work and love, expanded by Fromm (9) in his statement that spontaneous activity in love and work is the one way in which man can overcome the terror of aloneness without sacrificing the integrity of the self, expresses a therapeutic goal with regard to making the ego capable of coping with such experiences. Lichtenstein (11) uses the term "the subjective experience of the actuality of being" to denote the ego satisfactions available without reference to conformity.

In this context, Erikson (4) believes that the crucial organizing period in the life cycle takes place during the adolescent years. It is at this point that an identity crisis may occur and will be resolved either in a courageous, creative and progressive manner or through the safety of static conformity. This position is well illustrated in Erikson's biographical sketch of Freud (3) and in his larger study of Martin Luther. (5)

In our clinical work it is necessary to help patients work through the pain associated with giving up the idealized fantasy object and to reconcile themselves to reality. Segal (16) has pointed out that the loss of the love object represents a repetition of, and at the same time, results in a reliving of the giving up the original primary object, the breast.

The important ground work necessary to accomplish this step depends upon adequately dealing with the patient's idealized self-image. Rosenfeld (15) believes this over-idealized structure to be highly pathological, as it is based on the patient's omnipotence and denial of reality. Systematic interpretation directed both toward this omnipotent part, as well as toward the anxiety stirred up when this part is threatened by interpretation is necessary to expose the unrealistic beliefs and maintain the proper therapeutic alliance. Gradually, guilt, in relation to the patient's attempt to gratify this pathological part, can be brought into conciousness. It is then possible for the patient to contrast fantasy gratifications with the satisfactions available in reality. For satisfactory insight and working through it is essential that the specific fantasies which maintain the omnipotent belief be identified and isolated and exposed to the patient.

Through this approach, Mr. J. was able to tolerate well the autonomous actions of his wife, to look forward with joyful anticipation to her return, and to share with her the interesting experiences in which she was involved. This coincided with a reduction of the over-idealized transference in the analysis and an increase of positive feelings toward the analyst as a real person.

Oedipal Conflict Relative to Separation Anxiety

Until late in the analysis, Mr. J. maintained a contempt for his father on the grounds that he had abdicated his paternal role; he unconsciously believed his father and mother were sexually incompatible. These attitudes lent themselves to creating and maintaining the illusion of his omnipotence and a belief he had defeated father. Of course, such fantasies were maintained at the cost of considerable guilt, which contributed greatly to his immobilization at the time of his mother's death. He seemed willing to pay the price of oedipal guilt as well in order to preserve his illusions.

For example, late in the analysis, after his friendship with the analyst had been established, he had an impulse to break off the analysis and sacrifice the last few months of working through in the terminal phase. In a *dream* at this time, the hated, intrusive infantile part of himself, represented as a younger brother, interrupts a tender relationship between an older brother and a pretty young woman who was offering her beautiful breast. The young woman becomes grief-stricken, representing his belief that he had interfered with his mother's pleasure with his father, as well as his identification with the fantasied deprived mother. Similarly he fantasied that he had deprived father of mother and destroyed father's masculinity, a belief which prevented the maintenance of a sound masculine identity and the satisfactions it afforded. Following the analysis of this dream the next night's dream revealed his reconciliation to the real situation, i.e., that his father was capable of taking care of his mother and that they did share a love for each other He was now, at last, able to feel love for his father and in the analysis no longer feared destroying my maleness.

Thus his inability to resolve the first relationship with the mother in a realistic manner led to the oedipal conflict where the effort to reestablish his omnipotence was elaborated on this level. Klein (10) has shown us that the oedipal situation may be experienced by the child on the level of part objects as early as the first year where, for example, the rival penis of the father is experienced as intruding into the union of the infant and the mother's breast. In his regression to the paranoid-schizoid position, Mr. J. tended to idealize his mother whereas his father became a hated object.

Summary

Problems in the infant-mother relationship are presented with particular reference to symptoms of separation anxiety and related phobias seen in adult patients. A patient in psychoanalysis, illustrating the flight from progressive movement as it threatens unconscious omnipotent fantasies of union with the maternal object, is discussed and the successful resolution of this conflict is described.

Bibliography

1. Bowlby, J. (1958). "The Nature of the Child's Tie to His Mother." Int. J. Psa., Vol. 39.
2. ———. (1960). "Separation Anxiety." *Ibid.*, Vol. 41.
3. Erikson, E. (1954). "The Dream Specimen in Psychoanalysis." In *Psychoanalytic Psychiatry and Psychology*. New York: Int. Univ. Press.
4. ———. (1958). "Identity and the Life Cycle." In *Psychological Issues*, Monograph 1. New York: Int. Univ. Press.
5. ———. (1958). *Young Man Luther*. New York: W. W. Norton & Co., p. 254.
6. Fairbairn, W., Ronald, D. (1941). "A Revised Psychopathology of the Neurosis and Psychoneurosis." In *Psycho-Analytic Studies of the Personality*. London: Tavistock Pub., Ltd., 1952.
7. ———. (1943). "The War Neuroses—Their Nature and Significance." *Ibid.*
8. Freud, S. (1915). "Some Character Types Met With in Psychoanalytical Work." In *Collected Papers*. London: Hogarth Press, Vol. 4, 1949.
9. Fromm, E. (1941). *Escape From Freedom*. New York: Farrar and Reinhart, pp. 260-61.
10. Klein, M. (1957). *Envy and Gratitude*. New York: Basic Books.
11. Lichtenstein, H. (1963). "The Dilemma of Human Identity." J. Amer. Psa. Assn., Vol. 11.
12. Rosenfeld, H. (1964). "On the Psychopathology of Narcissism." Int. J. Psa., Vol. 45.
13. Segal, H. (1957). "Notes on Symbol Formation." Int. J. Psa., Vol. 38.
14. Spitz, R. (1957). "No and Yes." *On the Genesis of Human Communication*. New York: Int. Univ. Press.
15. Winnicott, D. (1958). "The Capacity to Be Alone." Int. J. Psa., Vol. 30.
16. ———. (1960). "The Theory of Infant-Parent Relationship." *Ibid.*, Vol. 41.

405 North Bedford Drive
Beverly Hills, California

Discussant

Arthur Malin, M.D.
Beverly Hills, California

Dr. Alexander offers the following formulation: to retain an omnipotent fantasy of union with the mother, the patient must avoid accomplishment and success which otherwise would lead to his separate existence as an adult. Success, therefore, gives rise to separation anxiety and destroys the omnipotence. The author gives an interesting clinical example.

Omnipotence is based on identification with the split-off, idealized object—the good breast-mother—and is normal in the earliest stages of life. An example is the hallucinatory wish fulfillment of the infant described by Freud.

Reactivation of omnipotence in later stages has to do with the development of the manic defense, as described by Hanna Segal and others. Dr. Segal states that manic defenses "are evolved in the depressive position as a defense against the experience of depressive anxiety, guilt, and loss. They are based on the omnipotent denial of psychic reality, and object relations are characterized by triumph, control, and contempt."

In my opinion, it is this important concept of the manic defense which unifies the ideas around the problem of omnipotence, separation anxiety and the avoidance of pleasure. Manic defenses deal very specifically with problems of loss, i.e., separation anxiety. The omnipotent behavior is a part of the manic defense. This broader concept helps the analyst interpret the material in the psychoanalysis of such patients in a more pertinent and effective way. The analysis of the omnipotence, which Dr. Alexander stresses in his clinical example, appears to be of major importance in allowing further manifestations of the manic defense and the depressive position to come into the psychoanalysis.

In such patients as described by the author, the mother, although a problem, is all he has within. She isn't much, but without her there is no good internal object. Separateness here means mainly a destruction of the internal object and subsequently of the self. In more normal circumstances, the child can internalize and identify with the mother who takes pleasure in both the growth and the development of separateness in her child.

Discussant

Elizabeth R. Zetzel, M.D.
Cambridge, Massachusetts

Although I have not attempted a detailed discussion of Dr. Alexander's paper, I have read it with particular attention first to its general soundness as an analytic contribution, and then to the relevance of specific Kleinian propositions to its basic argument.

The paper says little about the separation anxiety of phobic patients which could not be explained by references to the traditional literature; Helene Deutsch's contributions certainly point to the primitive sources of this type of anxiety in severely phobic patients.

I feel the Kleinian interpretations were brought in more for polemic reasons than for their special relevance to this patient. I would regard his symptom neurosis as a regressive response to the death of his mother which undermined his earlier counter-phobic character structure. There was little in the analytical material, other than the analyst's interpretations, which made Kleinian reconstructions placing oedipal conflicts "on the level of part objects" helpful or enlightening.

I do not think this paper merits the amount of discussion necessary to elucidate the weakness of its theoretical formulation. The bibliography is inadequate, even in respect to Kleinian literature. There is no reference to recent work of analysts such as Greenacre, Schur, Gitelson (and this writer) who have attempted to correlate different forms of anxiety with different levels of psychic development.

I am deeply interested in attempting to clarify possible areas of overlap and agreement between the contributions of Melanie Klein and the more traditional psychoanalytic theory. In general, these areas concern the significance of object relations to the analytic situation. Papers such as Dr. Alexander's, which utilize Kleinian reconstructions in the interpretations of material derived from the analysis of a straightforward neurotic, are in my opinion more likely to highlight differences. I believe this tends to impede rather than to further mutual understanding.

Discussant

Norman A. Levy, M.D.
Beverly Hills, California

Dr. Alexander's paper is difficult to discuss because there is little with which to disagree. With his main thesis I am in complete accord. It is my experience, too, that the anxiety of separation can evoke and set in motion a destructive regression. One not infrequently finds that an individual unconsciously strives to stay out of the adult (genital) role in order to maintain an infant-mother type of relationship (symbolically) both for the pregenital gratification involved and (and at times more importantly) to avoid the pain of psychological separation from the symbolic mother which is involved in the process of maturing.

Recently I described how individuation and strivings to develop as a separate and unique individual occur as a result of the normal narcissistic, aggressive and libidinal strivings, and express themselves as a need to establish an identity (second year). Part of the growth process is the development of this identity through a series of stages throughout childhood and adolescence (as Erikson has emphasized) until a final definite, crystallized, consolidated identity is achieved.

However, at the same time, there is also a need to maintain the original mutually reciprocal fusion-type relationship of the early infant-mother symbiosis. The unconscious wish to lose the individual self, to be merged with, be fused with a love object—or a symbolic one, a substitute for the original matrix—is always present and results in a wish to lose the very identity which man constantly struggles to maintain. This is in agreement with Alexander's references to identity and its role in dealing with separation and loneliness.

I agree with Alexander that "a goal of the psychoanalytic relationship is to replenish the weakened ego by making available realistic good experiences which can be introjected." I described this concept in somewhat different language in a paper reporting on some investigations of the psychotherapeutic process.[1] This was pictured as a learning process during which the patient lives through a series of emotional experiences with a new parent (substitute) who is significantly different from the original parents in that he is more consistently involved with the welfare and especially the growth of the patient, and in that he presents a more satisfactory figure for identification.

In his clinical case material, Dr. Alexander

[1] *Science and Psychoanalysis*, 1960, Vol. 4.

illustrates that the maturing process can be interfered with by the persistence of infantile strivings for and fantasies of omnipotence, by unresolved strivings for fusion with the mother, and by guilt associated with these narcissistic and aggressive patterns. He states that for satisfactory insight and working through it is essential that the specific fantasies which maintain the omnipotent self be identified, isolated and exposed to the patient. One can only agree with this: but often this statement is not sufficient, since insight into the defensive function of this regressive narcissistic armoring is also necessary, with exposure of the causes and underlying intense feelings of depression, hurt, inferiority, and loneliness. This is no simple task and usually involves slow and prolonged analysis, because these individuals are usually so deeply libidinally attached to and entrenched in their own ego-syntonic fantasy, magical thinking and denial systems and so isolated from any genuine interpersonal relationship with the therapist. In Dr. Alexander's presentation, the analysis appears deceptively simple, but I suspect this is due to the requirements of condensation and brevity.

Finally, I think the title of Dr. Alexander's paper is somewhat misleading, for although the paper provides a worthwhile discussion with a clinical example of an important psychodynamic constellation (fusion and separation) it does not represent an original contribution.

Discussant

Edwin F. Alston, M.D.
San Francisco, California

Dr. Alexander essentially makes two points: (*a*) anxiety associated with accomplishment may have roots other than the castration anxiety suggested by Freud; it also may be separation anxiety: (*b*) the threat is separation from fantasied omnipotence and total union with mother. The patient clings to an infantile ego ideal or its surrogate in the external world.

Dr. Alexander's patient reminded me of a very similar one who upon being offered an exciting academic opportunity turned it down with scorn and returned to his various nursing activities—sleeping, drinking and playing around with great ideas. His rationalization was that he "could not tolerate the idea of becoming a lesser light in the span of history." A more likely cause was that any challenge in reality was threatening to his fantasies of omnipotence and aroused anxiety which he could not endure.

The importance of the problem to which Alexander addresses himself goes far beyond "those wrecked by success" (to use Freud's term) or those who avoid success. There is always some resistance to change even in the face of chronic misery and even with high probability of self-realization and pleasure. No one ever experiences a change which is really significant for him without some associated anxiety. Certainly every analyst is familiar with resistances to change, even when it is ardently desired. We have a tendency to remain in ruts partly because it is so painful when we try to get out of them.

Alexander makes a significant contribution when he asks if the avoidance of success or gratification has roots other than castration anxiety. I agree also that separation anxiety often is a paramount factor. One need only think of the frequent patient who clings to the therapist, no matter what the cost, rather than endure the ordeals and uncertainties of separation.

I propose still another factor. Any significant change inevitably puts a strain on the psychic apparatus. It disrupts whatever balance has been developed between ego, id, superego, and the external world. There is resistance to this strain. The ultimate danger may be separation, castration, guilt, loss of self-esteem, instinctual flooding; but before the ultimate trauma there is strain. And there may be severe structural strain without the ultimate trauma. A common denominator in all the ultimate dangers is severe strain or disruption of structure.

The occurrence of structural strain depends upon the degree of stress and the nature of that psychic structure. A weak ego may be seriously strained whereas the same stress may stimulate a stronger or more flexible ego. A point to be scored here is that strain on psychic structure and associated anxiety may become operative and inhibitory long before the stressful significance can be detected by another person—and long before ultimate danger states such as separation or castration are evident in fantasy or reality.

For instance, Dr. Alexander's conceptualization is that his patient sacrificed achievement in order to cling to his fantasies of omnipotence and union with mother. Another conceptualization is that any departure from his established way of life had a disruptive effect upon his ego with consequent recoil or regression to his previous state.

For the sake of conceptual clarity, I would take exception to the title, "Omnipotence and the Avoidance of Pleasure," although Alexander is following a precedent set by Freud in his phrase "those wrecked by success." The fact is both Freud and Alexander recognize that the individuals in question are reacting to anxiety or unpleasure. The apparent reward is not the critical factor shaping the behavior. *The reaction is to the unpleasure, not to the pleasure.*

It is well to remember Freud's observation in *The Ego and the Id*: "Sensations of a pleasurable nature have not anything inherently impelling about them, whereas unpleasurable ones have it in the highest degree." In a similar vein, in "Analysis Terminable and Interminable," Freud says: "The psychical apparatus is intolerant of unpleasure; it has to fend it off at all costs, and if perception of reality entails unpleasure, that perception—that is, the truth —must be sacrificed."

Discussant

George H. Pollock, M.D., PH.D.
Chicago, Illinois

Separation anxiety has been studied by many analysts from different points of reference. A most rewarding framework has been provided by Margaret Mahler and her co-workers who have investigated the crucial separation-individuation phase of development. Some of her ideas have been developed to include the concept of the symbiotic neurosis.

Alexander tells us that in the separation-individuation phase, the child begins to leave the mother for "various periods of time to involve himself in the external environment, e.g., discovering and exploring new objects or playing with other children." I believe that when the mother cannot tolerate or allow the child to proceed in this separation experience, individuation and differentiation are impaired, fixation at the early childhood symbiosis occurs, and certain ego-object relationships remain distorted. This pathological state results in a symbiotic neurosis.

The maternal partner of the symbiotic dyad narcissistically over-invests the child and he becomes part of her. In some instances, this reflects the maternal phallic conflict, i.e., the male child becomes the maternal phallus. The mother becomes overly protective of this symbolic phallus, wishes to have it part of her, derives exhibitionistic pleasure from displaying it and cannot allow the child to become autonomous. The child, on the other hand, introjects this material symbiotic tie and experiences anxiety at its dissolution.

In the course of analysis, separation, individuation, differentiation, establishment of a stable self image and narcissistic investment of this self, including the body, occurs. These patients may exhibit pathological mourning reactions in treatment which include denial, anxiety or severe depression. When the symbiotic tie is dissolved during psychoanalytic treatment, these mourning reactions may appear for the first time, or may reappear depending upon the level of separation experience that previously occurred. Dr. Alexander's patient illustrates these propositions. (These mourning responses have been discussed previously in "Mourning and Adaptation" by me and by Fleming and her associates.)

Dr. Alexander's patient exhibited rage and anxiety when his wife (maternal transference object) refused to accept him as an adult, functioning as a separate individual, or when she left him to work on her own. Both of these responses related to his underlying anger with his mother about being left, particularly since he felt she had made him part of her. His anxiety stemmed from concern about functioning without her. The symbiotic union was threatened, as it was in the analysis when termination was in the offing. He may have sought to deny internal separation from the analyst by his impulsive thought of breaking off the analysis abruptly without working through the separation reaction in the terminal phase. He could thus keep the analyst alive internally and avoid the painful work of mourning.

This interesting clinical problem relates to the work of mourning, internal separation, individuation, differentiation and more mature functioning—a problem involved in many developmental progressions.

Author's Response

Richard P. Alexander, M.D.
Beverly Hills, California

I was gratified by Dr. Malin's excellent comprehension of the main premise of my paper. I agree that the fantasy of omnipotence is a manifestation of the manic defense characterized by control and triumph over the object, as for example, Mr. J.'s statement of picking my brains and stealing. I would like to clarify and expand Dr. Malin's last paragraph. It is my understanding that such patients have to destroy the *good* object because love for the object and regard for the self (including the good internal object and satisfying life experiences, e.g. successes) make the patient aware of the object and himself as separate beings. Of course, on the oedipal level successes also have to be destroyed when such strivings are dominated by omnipotent mechanisms and fantasies.

Conversely, I was disappointed with Dr. Zetzel's discussion because I don't believe she understood my basic orientation. I take as my fundamental frame of reference Freudian concepts enriched by certain of Melanie Klein's contributions. This frame of reference I utilize with all patients, be they neurotic, borderline or psychotic. Traditional explanations should always be open to modification and extension in the true spirit of scientific investigation. The writings of Greenacre, Schur, Gitelson and Zetzel are certainly of relevance as are papers of many other analysts which practical considerations precluded mentioning.

I believe Helene Deutsch's formulation regarding separation, anxiety, and phobia, is based on the concept that destructive wishes and fantasies against the object produce fears of destroying the object and result in the need to be constantly in the presence of the object to assure its being intact; and that identification with this object brings about an agoraphobia. For some time, interpretations on this level were given but had only limited beneficial effect.

It was only when the patient could be shown how he projected undesirable parts of himself onto important persons in the external world, including the analyst, that he could begin to get control of the claustrophobic symptoms and from here to master his guilt so as to make contact with the envious and possessive aspects of himself. Insight into this process of projective-identification is essential for a proper perception of the "significance of object relations to the analytic situation."

Dr. Levy's well thought out and clearly expressed remarks are appreciated. I am in accord with his comments relative to man's temptation "to lose his very identity which [he] struggles to maintain" so as to avoid dealing with the problem of separation. Space limitation prevents me from further discussing this interesting point. His drawing attention to patients of this type being "isolated from any genuine interpersonal relationship with the therapist" is extremely pertinent and, of course, related to the difficulty in dealing with the manic defense, previously mentioned.

In answer to his last point, I was not harboring the idea that the thoughts expressed in this paper were in any way original. However, I did believe that organizing and putting together the theoretical and clinical material in this systematic manner might represent a contribution to the literature.

Dr. Alston stresses both the concept of psychic pain and the need to avoid any "disruption of structure" as important factors interfering with growth and change. I agree completely. Since writing this paper, I have been more alert to other patients struggling with problems similar to Mr. J.'s and have been impressed by finding how often the pain of which Dr. Alston speaks is connected with anxiety relative to accepting one's state of separateness.

Also, the significant alteration of psychic structure the patient resists has to do with changes *within* the ego. This relates specifically to a shift in which there is an increase of introjection of good objects and experiences *into* the ego and a diminution in the projection of bad qualities *from* the ego. In this way the ego grows stronger and can both better *tolerate* the unpleasure of pleasure and *appreciate* the fruits of success.

Dr. Pollock's comment of the male child representing symbolically the maternal phallus is quite pertinent in the case of Mr. J. However, I believe the child's symbiotic attachment to the mother has its earliest and most significant roots in relation to the maternal breast which takes place in the infant's fantasies soon after birth. Mourning responses have their genetic origins in the giving up of or loss of the breast and the ambivalent responses to it.

The Forum

Title

The Clinical Handling of the Analyst's Responses

Author

Ian Alger, M.D.

Training Analyst at New York Medical College. He is co-editor of a forthcoming book, *Psychoanalysis and Marriage*, and is currently investigating the therapeutic use of videotape recordings in private practice.

Discussants

Samuel D. Lipton, M.D.

President-elect of the Chicago Psychoanalytic Society and a Training and Supervising Analyst of the Chicago Institute. At meetings of the Chicago Society and the American Psychoanalytic Association, and in his paper, "The Last Hour," he has contributed to the issues the author raises.

D. W. Winnicott, M.D., F.R.C.P.

Physician at the Paddington Green Children's Hospital, London, where his department gradually became a Department of Child Psychiatry. He became a psychoanalyst in the 1930's and is now President of the British Psycho-Analytic Society. His clinical and theoretical papers have been gathered together into six volumes.

Joseph M. Natterson, M.D.

Associate Clinical Professor of Psychiatry at the University of Southern California and a Training Analyst at the Southern California Psychoanalytic Institute. He is co-author of "Responsive Action in Psychotherapy," which deals with the issue of noninterpretive intervention by the therapist in psychoanalytically oriented psychotherapy.

Gerald Aronson, M.D.

Senior Faculty Member of the Los Angeles Institute for Psychoanalysis. He is Research and Teaching Consultant to several state hospitals and Consultant to the Rand Corporation.

The Clinical Handling of the Analyst's Responses

Ian Alger, M.D.
New York, New York

"There is almost universal agreement on the crucial importance of transference and counter-transference in clinical psychoanalysis, but far from unanimous agreement on how these concepts are to be understood and still less on how the phenomena themselves are to be dealt with in psychoanalytic treatment." With those words Douglass Orr concluded his paper on a comprehensive historical survey of the concepts of transference and counter-transference. (16)

I would like to present one point of view on how the analyst can deal with some of his own responses in the analytic relationship. I use the word "responses" because "counter-transference" is defined in so many different ways. The reference to "analytic relationship" acknowledges there are many types of therapy, but the one I wish to discuss is psychotherapy of a specific nature. The word "relationship" may give a further indication that my own orientation stems from an interpersonal and socio-cultural framework.

In "individual" psychoanalytic therapy there is a two-person system; exactly what each *thinks* he is doing with the other depends a great deal on the theory of the analyst. What is actually going on between them may be a very different story. Historically, with each discovery of new data, the theories have changed. Theories which have attempted to explain the human phenomena involved have, not unexpectedly, followed the general trend of scientific theories of the particular era. Furthermore, in all theories concerning the nature of psychopathology, philosophical questions concerning the nature of man, the nature of life, and the meaning of existence and the role of human values have had to be dealt with explicitly or implicitly.

In early analytic views (as noted by Wolstein) the patient was seen as a closed system in a state of internal psychic equilibrium, closely analogous to physical energy systems. The psychopathology was understood in terms of some disturbances in the distribution of the forces in this closed system. When a model of analytic therapy was constructed, the analyst, too, was seen as a separate enclosed system. (21) In 1899 Freud first recognized the phenomenon he called "transference," and at the same time he realized its importance in the actual therapy itself. Thus, the fact that is accepted by most analysts today, that the analysis of the transference is central to the psychoanalytic process, had early roots.

However, in the early theory, the reactions of the patient to the analyst were understood to originate entirely within the patient—within the closed system—and the analyst was depicted as a screen on which the patient could project his distortions. Thus, the *tabula rasa* model of the analyst was created. In *An Autobiographical Study* (1925), Freud wrote, "... In every analytic treatment there arises, *without the physician's agency*, an intense emotional relationship between the patient and the analyst which is *not to be accounted for by actual situation. ...*" (Italics mine.)

Although recommended as a technique, it was also realized that analysts were not blank screens, and, in 1910, Freud introduced the term "counter-transference" and strongly urged this be overcome in the analyst's personal therapy. (8) As the years progressed, more contributions to the literature were made by Ferenczi, Rank, Glover, Reich and others who recognized the presence of reactions in the analyst and what impact these had on the patient and on the nature of the therapeutic activity. In 1939 the Balints wrote, "Formerly belief in the absolute validity of the mirror-like attitude was so firm that contesting it was liable to be regarded as a sign of desertion. And now . . . the very possibility of such an attitude is challenged." (3)

Several writers noted how little had been written about the important and practical subject of the analyst's reactions. Fenichel felt that little was said because nothing could protect against it except the effectiveness of the analyst's own analysis. Through much of the literature runs the idea that counter-transference reactions are bad, should be somehow hidden, and analyzed away as soon as possible.

With the advent of newer theories emphasizing interpersonal relationships, more interest in the interaction between the patient and analyst was shown. When this material was used in conjunction with the older model of therapy, as occurring between two closed systems, one in the patient, and one in the analyst, some connection had to be made so that the two closed systems could interact, and everything could be referred back somehow to the inner dynamics of each. When a field theory taking into account the experiential factors was introduced, the data could be dealt with in an entirely different way. Communication theory is still another means of understanding human interaction and behavior.

It is interesting to contrast the change in theory by comparing Freud's early description of the patient's transference reaction as being not accounted for by the actual situation to the recent comments of Haley who writes, "Only recently have psychiatrists begun to include themselves in their description of a patient. Obviously they base their diagnosis upon how the patient responds *to them,* yet the report they write will include only inferred processes within the patient. A relevant question is always one like this: What was the psychiatrist doing when the patient behaved in such a way that the psychiatrist inferred he was delusional?" (12)

This view of the importance of the analyst's reactions and the impossibility of not having reactions is now being emphasized by analysts with varying viewpoints. Balint and Tarachow say, ". . . psychoanalytic technique is entering a new phase, rather reluctantly, to be true. It will aim at the counter-transference, the analyst's contribution." (9) Gitelson writes, "One must conclude that the analyst as a mere screen does not exist in life. He cannot deny his personality nor its operation in the analytic situation as a significant factor." (10) And Rioch states, "I believe that the personality of the analyst tends to determine whether the attempt at analysis will result in cure." (18)

I wish to discuss the manner in which the analyst deals with the following two points: first, that he indeed cannot avoid communicating his reactions to the patient, and second, that the analyst's reactions are intimately involved in both the expression of pathology by the patient and in the more happy outcome of improvement in the patient's behavior and feeling.

Let me try to define a dilemma which invariably arises for the therapist. It began when the importance of the therapist-patient relationship was accepted as a central part of theory and therapy. Patients began to reveal their feelings toward the doctor through words and action. They came late, they delayed payments, they developed headaches in sessions, they made sly and clever digs showing angry feelings and they fell in love with the doctor, etc. At that point the analyst handled these reactions by denying that they were directed at him. Thus far the dilemma was avoided. However, with the full realization that the analyst did indeed exist as a real person in the therapy situation, the importance of the analyst's reactions was admitted, but it was advocated that counter-transference be analyzed away.

Counter-tranference has had a multitude of interpretations. It has been called: (*a*) the analyst's reactions to the patient's transference reaction (11); (*b*) the analyst's own transference reaction to the patient (17); and (*c*) the total reaction of the analyst to his patient, including those reactions which have been called rapport, human understanding, empathy, and dedication. (13, 4) When it was advocated that counter-transference be analyzed away in the analyst's personal therapy, naturally these latter human qualities were not included. The dilemma became sharpened when it became apparent that, regardless of the amount of analysis, counter-transference reactions could never be completely changed.

Analysts discovered they continued to be irritated by some things their patients did with them, and some found that irritation was expressed in boredom, sleepiness, or forgetting; others found they were feeling frightened, or distant, or sexually aroused. Some analysts, including Bonime and Winnicott, attempted further refinements and tried to classify the analysts' reactions in terms of rational or realistic or appropriate responses to the activity of their patients with them. (5, 20) Once again, and as a rule, those reactions of the analyst which were judged inappropriate were slated for further work in a training analysis.

To restate the dilemma as it finally was focused, the analyst was left with a series of personal reactions to his patient; those reactions which were valued, such as compassion, and empathy and dedication, posed no problem. To many, those reactions which were judged appropriate, including irritation, and even at times fury, were also accepted and revealed openly and directly to the patient. Those other responses which, in spite of all personal analysis, remained and were considered irrational, inappropriate, neurotic, and harmful to the patient remained the hair on the analytical shirt. Often dynamism of denial and avoidance, inattention and insensitivity brought to some analysts a merciful release from having to face this problem. For others, however, the awareness gained in personal analysis allowed no such relief, and this awareness was often stimulated by perceptive, insistent patients who, accepting the dictum of being open and truthful about everything which came to mind, did not hesitate to include their perceptions and reactions to the analyst. Those of us who have treated patients who previously had worked with another analyst know that those who were reluctant to confront their analysts with their reactions certainly did not hesitate because of lack of perception.

The dilemma, then, is how the analyst can deal with these feelings of his which are often, at best, called inappropriate and neurotic and, at worst, sadistic and inhuman.

The suggestion offered here is that the analyst deal with these feelings differently than he deals with any other of his reactions: that he be willing to include all his reactions while he is with his patient as part of the analytic data of that particular situation. This approach is based on the assumption that the behavior of one person in a human situation can only be understood in the context of the total human experiential and interactional field involved, i.e., that the behavior of the patient in the session can be understood only if one includes the behavior of the analyst, and of course, the opposite is true as well. The analysis then becomes a joint activity in which the two participants attempt, by mutual effort, to assemble and share their perceptions, their concepts, and most importantly their own feelings openly with each other.

Clinical Example

The patient was a young unmarried woman in her 20's who was having difficulty holding a job, felt depressed, and seemed to feel very pessimistic and rebelliously sulky. One day she was my first patient after lunch and was already in the waiting room when I returned. A few minutes before our scheduled appointment I entered carrying a parcel containing something I had purchased a short time earlier. I greeted her in a friendly way and said I would be ready to start in a few moments. She smiled in a friendly way too, and I felt pleasantly surprised. She then said, "I see you have been out shopping!" I replied I had, adding I would be with her as soon as I put the parcel away. After a few moments I asked her to come into the office, and suddenly I was aware of a coolness, and quietness. I waited saying nothing, and she was silent as well. I was aware of my own feeling of discomfort because of her silence, and I, too, felt an urge to say nothing.

At this point I told her I felt tense and irritated by her silence and that I almost had not wanted to speak. I went on to say I felt her response in the waiting room had been friendly and now I sensed withdrawal. I was beginning to formulate an explanation to myself about her tendency to revert to an older pattern of suspicion as soon as she tried a new approach with more willingness to reach out, when I was taken up short by her response to what I *had* said. Openly irritated, she said that she *had* felt friendly in the waiting room, and then she had felt that *I* withdrew; from then on *she* felt cold and distant.

I was incredulous until it dawned on me that she was right about my own withdrawal, although until that moment I was unaware of it. I recalled that when she said, "I see you have been out shopping!," I had the feeling of clutching my package more closely to myself; now I could identify the accompanying feeling of not wanting to divulge more and some feeling of relief at being able to walk into my office. I admitted she was right about my withdrawal in the waiting room, told her my feeling about clutching the parcel and the relief I had felt because I could go into my office. I further remarked that apparently when I was urging her to be more open, I felt quite comfortable, but when she responded and wanted to move closer to me, I did pull back.

I speculated that her angry and depressed withdrawal had followed an attempt on her part to reach out (which was what it had seemed to her I was in favor of), and then when she did reach out and show some interest in what I had been doing while shopping, I grew distant and gave her the (contradictory) message that I didn't want this kind of behavior and interest from her. At this point it seemed that her anger and aloofness were no longer there. She began to talk about her fears of not being sure what people mean, and of her feeling of relief when I confirmed her perception that I had indeed become distant, though subtly, in a way that denied I was doing it—because I, myself, was unaware of my behavior.

One can speculate that she felt relief because she was no longer under pressure from me to respond to one of two contradictory messages (to be more open and friendly, or *not* to be so open and friendly), and that she no longer had to bear the burden of feeling she was sick or neurotic, because she resolved the dilemma by an angry withdrawal. The. explanation lay not just in *her* past, nor in mine, but in the complexities of the way the two of us were behaving with each other at that time and place. We both gained an understanding of the way we had affected one another. We felt excitement and gratification in the work we had accomplished together. And we were able to accept the responses we recognized in ourselves and in the other with no feeling of blame or accusation.

The issue of recent times, illustrated in this

example, pertains to the way in which one deals with behavior or responses of the analyst. The idea, while once taboo, that such responses should be exposed in the therapy now has much support although there is considerable difference on the degree and the timing. Several brief quotations from the literature will illustrate this: Berman (4) says that the problem is, "... how to integrate ... clinically, that the analytic situation is in a sense, a personal one for the analyst and most, if not all, patients either dimly sense this fact or have occasion to observe it quite directly." He says later, "In dealing with certain defenses, however, ... it may be necessary for the analyst to express himself verbally as to his feelings towards the patient." Little (15) believes that only harm can come from withholding counter-transference interpretations, and although she counsels on the importance of timing and the need to avoid a confessional quality, she emphasizes that the important thing is that the counter-transference reactions be recognized by *both* analyst and patient. Gitelson (10) gives a personal clinical example: "I did the only thing I felt I could do. I brought the whole episode into the open and admitted the irritation which I recognized I had produced." In a further important quotation, he says, "... An analysis can come to an impasse because the analyst does not realize, or misunderstands, or avoids, the issue of the patient's discovery of him as a person."

This brings us to a consideration of the suggestions I propose, which extend beyond those of the writers quoted, perhaps in part because the frame of reference is very different, and therefore the inclusion of the analyst's behavior in all its dimensions as part of the essential data of the analysis has different implications. Data about the analyst's behavior can be introduced either by the analyst or the patient, depending basically on which of them has some awareness of what is going on. An additional factor is the mutual understanding that the inclusion of such data is part of the process of analysis, and, as such, is welcomed by the analyst.

If the analyst really does not wish to permit such material, it will be quickly apparent and can either be challenged or ignored by the patient, and, depending on the choice, form the basis of analytic progress or the nucleus of a difficult impasse. In the example I have described, I introduced my feelings of irritation and my urge to stay silent and commented on the patient's distance and coolness. In turn she was the one to point out my own earlier withdrawal, of which I was unaware and could not have included without her help.

The analyst can be alerted to his own feelings if he is sensitive to signs of anxiety in himself. The usefulness of this as a clue has been commented on in detail by Cohen (6) and also by Tauber. (19) My experience has been that it is not only possible, but extremely helpful, to tell the patient that one feels some anxiety, and then, together proceed to examine just what is going on between analyst and patient at that time. Such a technique is also useful when feelings of irritation, or boredom, or withdrawal occur and disrupt the quality of immediacy or being-with the patient.

One might criticize this approach by claiming that an undue burden is placed upon the patient, that it is not the patient's job to support or to analyze the therapist. Indeed, in response to such an approach patients will often, at first, express indignation that "their" analysis is being taken up with the analysis of the doctor. However, I believe such criticism, from whatever source, is the result of a different view of the therapeutic and human process involved. In my experience most patients who make such objections soon come to welcome the possibility of a truly mutual and cooperative endeavor, and for the first time not only see the analyst as a human being in the process of continual change and striving to grow, but also see themselves in the light of the same possibilities.

If the patient does not introduce material concerning feelings toward the analyst, it is useful for the therapist to encourage him to express the feelings the patient has about the analyst as a person in the situation between them as it goes on. Merely mechanical methods will not achieve what is desired—a freedom of communication between the participants, in order that the data of the total experience become available for analysis. If the analyst is genuinely willing to be included in the relationship, this will become apparent to the patient in a way that no artifice can manage.

Recently, as a further development of this approach, I have used immediate playbacks of videotapes of therapeutic interactions between myself and a patient. We have watched our activity in the therapy session, each of us free to comment on the behavior of himself and the other. The inclusion of this additional objective data has supported the usefulness of the approach here described. This will be more fully elaborated in forthcoming papers. (1,14,2)

What are the advantages of this inclusion of the analyst in the analysis? First let us consider the disadvantages of other methods which are avoided by this process. In the case of the extreme "mirror-like approach," the disadvantage is lucidly described by Reich (17) when he states, "... it is a mistake to interpret the general analytic rule ... in such a manner that one assumes, always and in every case, an unalive, mummy-like attitude. Under such circumstances, few patients can thaw out, and this leads to artificial, unanalytic measure." On the other hand, disadvantages accrue from the approach wherein counter-transference is seen as a bad thing. English and Pearson (7) wrote, "... The good psychotherapist ... is able and willing to conceal any feelings he may have beyond desire to help the patient." I believe the difficulties in such an approach are evident. To the contradictions which exist because of his own unawareness, the therapist will be consciously hiding his true reactions. Because those reactions *will* be expressed in covert ways, in spite of all his efforts at concealment, this method serves to increase the double messages given to the patient, for example: I am interested in you and want to help you even though you may hear the quiet rustling of the pages of a book through which I happen to be glancing.

If, as I believe, there is any truth to theories of the importance of the double-bind pattern of communication in producing symptomatic behavior, then this behavior of the therapist is repeating the very kind of human relationship which elicited the troublesome patterns. There is a further damaging effect of this approach: when the analyst *is* at times confronted with the patient's perception of what is happening, he may turn it back on the patient by means of any number of analytic ploys such as, "If you were really involved in analyzing you would not be so ready to divert our work by criticizing me," or, "Apparently you want to possess me completely."

The advantages of the method of including oneself may be appreciated from the disadvantages (which can be avoided) of other methods. There are, however, positive advantages as well. The analyst's willingness to be open and to directly express his own feelings can be a most helpful example to the patient who may, as a result, develop an awareness of the possibility of expressing one's feelings and reactions honestly and directly to another human being. The analyst's revealing himself also indicates to the patient that in fact the analyst does trust him and considers him, to this extent at least, a worthwhile person. What might possibly be most important—the analyst's willingness to so involve himself in the relationship, and in such a very personal way —may be the act which convinces the patient someone can care for him, that he has meaning and value to someone. We speak of loneliness, and alienation, and detachment. Perhaps it is true that only involvement in a direct and real and total way can be convincing and can bring hope.

The method advocated here does not depend on one's "personality," but rather on one's activity as a therapist. It is not the therapist's "healthy personality" which can be helpful to another person; rather it is the analyst's behavior which will determine how much help he can be. What is advocated here is the attempt to join with the patient in a mutually cooperative endeavor to explore the relationship between each other. This can be a most human and involving experience. It can be one in which analyst and patient can help one another to grow. To accomplish this, I believe the analyst must be ready to include himself.

In the introduction of a widely acclaimed recent movie, "The Parable," life was described as a kind of circus, noting that some of us march in the circus parade, while others are spectators along the way. Wolstein has said in a similar vein, "[Analysts] seem to fall into two categories: those who would live and then try to understand what they have lived, and those who stand on the sidelines of life and understand what others have lived." (21)

In light of the "history" of psychoanalysis during which we are presently living, with the increasing universal acceptance of the importance of the analyst's reactions, it would seem the day has come when the choice must be made: will we *live* the analytic experience with our patients, or do we wish not to become that involved?

Summary

There has been universal agreement on the importance of transference and countertransference, but less agreement on the nature of these phenomena, and even less agreement on how they should be dealt with in psychoanalytic therapy. In earlier theories the analyst and the patient were seen as two separate yet self-contained systems, interacting in some way with one another. In newer field and communication theories the analytic situation is understood in terms of feedback systems. In this view, the analyst can not avoid communicating his reactions to the patient, and furthermore, the analyst's reactions are seen as intimately involved in determining the nature of the patient's responses.

It is advocated that the analyst attempt to openly include his own responses. In this way he can confirm the patient's perceptions and thereby clarify double-bind situations which might have been set up, and which duplicate similar binding situations in the patient's past. A further advantage of this procedure is the human closeness which develops from such a mutually cooperative endeavor. In brief, it is advocated that the analyst live the therapeutic experience with the patient as a mutually cooperative searching for an understanding of the patient in the context of the ongoing relationship between the analyst and the patient.

Bibliography

1. Alger, I., and Hogan, P. "The Impact of Immediate Videotape Playback on Involvement in the Group Process." Presented at Annual Meeting Amer. Group Psychotherapy Assn., Philadelphia, Jan., 1966.
2. ———. "The Use of Videotapes in Conjoint Marital Therapy in Private Practice." Presented at Annual Meeting Amer. Psychiat. Assn., Atlantic City, May, 1966.

3. Balint, A., and Balint, M. (1939). "On Transference and Counter-Transference." Int. J. Psa., Vol. 20.
4. Berman, L. (1949). "Counter-Transferences and Attitudes of the Analyst in the Therapeutic Process." Psychiatry, Vol. 12.
5. Bonime, W. (1957). "The Liking and Disliking of One's Patients." *Schizophrenia in Psychoanalytic Office Practice*. New York: Grune & Stratton.
6. Cohen, M. (1952). "Counter-Transference and Anxiety." Psychiatry, Vol. 15.
7. English, O. and Pearson, G. (1937). *Common Neuroses of Children and Adults*. New York: W. W. Norton, p. 303.
8. Freud, S. (1910). "The Future Prospects of Psycho-Analytic Therapy." *Collected Papers*, Vol. 2. London: Hogarth Press, 1946.
9. Frosch, J., *et al.* (eds.) (1950). *The Annual Survey of Psychoanalysis*, Vol. 1. New York: Int. Univ. Press.
10. Gitelson, M. (1952). "The Emotional Position of the Analyst in the Psycho-Analytic Situation." Int. J. Psa., Vol. 33.
11. Glover, E. (1927). "Lectures on Technique in Psychoanalysis." Int. J. Psa., Vol. 8.
12. Haley, J. (1963). *Strategies of Psychotherapy*. New York: Grune & Stratton.
13. Helman, P. (1950). "On Counter-Transference." Int. J. Psa., Vol. 31.
14. Hogan, P. and Alger, I. "The Use of Videotape Recording in Family Therapy." Presented at Annual Meeting Amer. Orthopsychiat. Assn., San Francisco, April 1966.
15. Little, M. (1951). "Counter-Transference and Patient's Response to It." Int. J. Psa., Vol. 32.
16. Orr, D. (1954). "Transference and Counter-Transference: A Historical Survey." J. Amer. Psa. Assn., Vol. 2.
17. Reich, W. (1933). *Character Analysis*. New York: Orgone Inst. Press, 1945.
18. Rioch, J. (1943). "The Transference Phenomenon in Psychoanalytic Therapy." Psychiatry, Vol. 6.
19. Tauber, E. (1964). "Exploring the Therapeutic Use of the Counter-Transference Data." Psychiatry, Vol. 17.
20. Winnicott, D. (1949). "Hate in the Counter-Transference." Int. J. Psa., Vol. 30.
21. Wolstein, B. (1959). *Counter-Transference*. New York: Grune & Stratton.

500 East 77th Street
New York, New York 10021

Discussant

Samuel D. Lipton, M.D.
Chicago, Illinois

Dr. Alger's thesis, supported by references to Freud and the literature, states there was a period in the development of analysis (which may indeed persist) when the analyst considered himself merely a mirror, detached from and uninvolved with the patient. The analyst dealt with the patient's responses "by denying that they were really directed at him." Alger argues for the importance of recognizing the actual responses of the analyst and openly exposing what was "once taboo."

The concept of the "detached analyst" has gained so much support from analysts that it might even be called conventional. Nevertheless I take issue with Dr. Alger and his supporters.

First, I submit there is not a single advocate of the detached analyst to be found either in the literature or on personal investigation. The detached analyst is mentioned in the literature only to be castigated and is never anything but an unnamed figure. I was once informed, by a presumably reliable source, of one such analyst, allegedly a model of detachment and, from my own experience, discovered it was not so. Subsequently I learned this sort of information is invariably unreliable.

I have seen detachment in students who believed they were acting correctly, and no doubt it occurs (as the result of error) in experienced analysts, but this is not theoretical espousal.

To summarize, I think the detached analyst, who is detached on the basis of theoretical conviction, is a mythical figure. He exists only as a result of personal behavior error or because patient complaints are misconstrued.

My second reason for disagreement lies in a

different interpretation of Freud's work, which Dr. Alger advances to support his contention. I do not believe Freud meant detachment in Dr. Alger's sense. I think ample support for this can be found in Freud's writings. If one reads the sparkling interchange with Dora, the fascinating explanations to the Rat Man (as well as Freud's disclosure that he gave the Rat Man a meal, revealing the associational repercussions), the interchanges of the Forsyth incident in the *New Introductory Lectures*, or any of a mass of other clinical data Freud recorded, one must conclude he was anything but detached in his work.

Then what of the mirror, screen, and surgeon analogies? What of the intense emotional relationship which arises without the physician's agency and is not accounted for by the actual situation? What I cited above is valid: did Freud preach what he did not practice? I think not. Rather, he used these analogies to describe the work of analysis proper, not the personal relationship on which it was based. He was attempting to describe the juxtaposition of the analyst's neutrality and evenly-hovering attention to the patient's free association. Freud realized this had to be based on a personal relationship, referring to it as the irreducible, unobjectionable element of the positive transference. He distinguished this from the work of analysis proper, taking the personal element for granted with scant explicit attention. When he referred to the inability of schizophrenics to develop a transference he meant the transference on which the analytic work is based, not the irrational elements which he recognized might develop.

Concerning the independence of the intense relationship from the actual situation, I believe Freud meant the analyst confined his efforts to the analytic work and did not attempt to instigate or provoke responses. Certainly such responses have an objective basis in some perception, but equally certainly their full explanation is not hereby elucidated. To use Dr. Alger's clinical illustration as an example—certainly the patient responded to him, yet it was not Alger's purpose, I presume, to influence her by his spontaneous response to an amenity, and it seems clear her reaction was unduly intense. Surely we can assume that some historically significant determinants lay behind the importance that his nuance of behavior had to her.

As Dr. Alger does not belabor the point of his approach as interpersonal, I will not belabor my adherence to the approach which emphasizes more genetic determinants. I would conceptualize the example as the beginning of a piece of analytic work. While I would not dispute that the explicit acknowledgment of the response of the analyst can be useful occasionally, I think it is not regularly so and can lead to a sort of *mutual adjustment* rather than an analysis of the patient. I find that under favorable conditions, granting that the analyst is not defensive, the patient learns to place reliance on his associations as having psychic reality, valid for him, whether the analyst explicitly affirms them or not, and learns to use them as a basis for deepening self-knowledge.

Dr. Alger has presented his observations and clinical data in an accurate manner which should lead to productive controversy.

Discussant

D. W. Winnicott, M.D., F.R.C.P.
London, England

Personally I welcome this trend in psychoanalysis. I have said that in psychotherapy nothing happens until two people "bump up against" each other. In psychoanalysis we strive to maintain an orderly procedure towards these situations in the transference where the "bumps" can be interpreted significantly, or mutatively.

It is not possible for me to criticize frankly because I am at one with Dr. Alger. However, there are three problems:

(*a*) It is necessary for students of psychoanalysis to proceed cautiously until they acquire the ability to include the analyst's feelings and behavior. Much that the young or inexperienced analyst feels will have more to do with his own state than that of the patient. The patient must not be involved in the analyst's personal state if it can be avoided. The beginning analyst must first learn in terms of the patient's inner conflicts and the projection of aspects of these on to the objects around, including the analyst. I think psychoanalysis will always have to be learned that way.

(*b*) I think Ian Alger has not gone as far as he will one day in his study of what the analyst may do by recognizing and pointing out his own feelings and behavior. But the beginning is the important thing.

(*c*) There is the matter of diagnosis; some patients have been distorted in their development by continuing pathologic environmental factors. It is these patients who force us to repeat the environmental factors and to hurt again. The most painful is when we must fail, repeating early failure on the mother's (or father's) part. In such cases it is only when we fail that we succeed—the patient having made us fail when we could have succeeded and when we only wished to do well.

There are many psychoneurotic and depressive patients whose troubles arise inside themselves and for whom a comment or interpretation relative to our own feelings and reactions must be inapposite or actually intrusive.

With these brief warnings I repeat that I wish to see the study to which Dr. Alger's paper points widened in its scope.

Discussant

Joseph M. Natterson, M.D.
Beverly Hills, California

Dr. Alger's brief paper is pertinent to so many important psychotherapeutic issues that a brief discussion must be selective and incomplete.

The author's emphasis on the need for self-honesty in the therapist about his own reactions in the therapeutic situation is quite valid. The usefulness of the therapist's monitoring of his emotional and cognitive responses to the patient is generally accepted. Dr. Alger's clinical example demonstrates the value of alertness to the transactions between patient and psychotherapist, even when the transactions are fortuitous and realistically unimportant.

It is with the author's basic point, viz., the therapist should *regularly* discuss his own reactions to the patient with the patient, that I cannot agree. While the therapist is more important in the field of therapeutic interaction than, say, his receptionist, I still regard the patient as the center of field. It seems to be that Dr. Alger argues for the equivalence of patient and therapist and may, in fact, be removing the patient from the center of the field of action.

Certainly, as Dr. Alger points out, the patient will respond to the therapist's conscious and unconscious reactions and communications, and the patient's discussion of these should be facilitated so he can develop an increasingly accurate awareness of his problem areas in their cross-sectional and longitudinal dimensions. However, does discussion by the therapist of his reactions invariably promote such expression by the patient? I think not.

As a patient develops an intense transference reaction, for example, he can readily find neurotic qualities in the therapist which he can effectively use as rationalizations for the transference reaction. He can once more, then, avoid the important, unrecognized causative factors. If the therapist readily acknowledges his contribution, he may truncate the transference reaction, reinforce the comforting rationalization and, by relieving immediate tension, actually retard the progress of therapy. It is my impression that therapists tend to be more self-revealing later in therapy, because the patient is then less likely to use such knowledge for resistive purposes.

Dr. Alger's method of treatment, with its emphasis on thorough explication of the therapist's involvement, may well provide us with further useful information about this factor in psychotherapy. Perhaps as he proceeds in his investigative approach he will offer specific recommendations about the types of cases and the kinds of problems for which his method is indicated.

Discussant

Gerald Aronson, M.D.
Beverly Hills, California

Dr. Alger speaks for a method (cooperative exploration) of dealing with certain kinds of resistances in the patient which are created, in part, by the analyst's emotional life. Several assumptions are made, some explicit and some covert: (*a*) Some aspect of the analyst's emotional life will be discerned by the patient; (*b*) the patient will react to his perception of the analyst's response; (*c*) the patient's reaction will constitute a continuing resistance in the analysis; (*d*) the method of handling this resistance is by mutually cooperative exploration.

Questions immediately arise. Is the method advised by Dr. Alger to be applied to those situations where the patient does not discern the analyst's responses or does not react to them? If the patient's reaction to the analyst's responses does not constitute a resistance, does the attempt of the analyst to handle the nonexistent resistance aid or hinder the analysis?

It may be that, in idealizing a tactic initially designed to handle an accident in the treatment into a cardinal therapeutic strategy, Dr. Alger is introducing a method (a repeated and insistent parameter) which creates a more powerful resistance than the one he hopes to dispel. That Dr. Alger does not consider his technique simply as one to deal with accidents or artifacts but rather as a pivotal method of therapy is suggested by his recommendation that the analyst encourage the patient to express his feelings towards the therapist as a person when the patient has not introduced such material. Might it not be wiser at such a point to attempt to interpret the absence of expression of such feelings toward the therapist in terms of other material already furnished by the patient? Otherwise one risks leapfrogging important transference resistances in favor of pushing, or seducing, the patient into a placatory attempt to produce feelings.

Dr. Alger raises an important point—involvement, living the analytic experience, the issue of psychologic distance. The optimum analytic situation is constructed to produce just enough nurture and intimacy to support an arduous procedure but not so much as to permit the anxiety-free state of infantile inertia or to stimulate its defensive twin, the anxiety-ridden state of being smothered, manipulated, and controlled. What we wish to produce in the analytic chamber is, to be sure, an encounter, but it is an analytic encounter—not simply a human encounter or a mutually cooperative experience. Without the human encounter, the surgeon, radiologist, or internist would be less effective but the very humanness of the encounter is "what to do until the healer comes" with the specific instruments of his art. Our specific instrument is interpretation; our general attitude is one of readiness to be empathic and understanding.

To wield the instrument without precision is not often fatal; to falter in our general attitude is sometimes to produce confusion and dismay, which may be rectified by Dr. Alger's technique sparingly applied. But to confound instrument and attitude, to take the one for the other is to idealize a philosophy rather than to carry out a treatment.

Author's Response

Ian Alger, M.D.

New York, New York

I am pleased there is controversy. And I am glad that Drs. Natterson and Winnicott encourage me to pursue these studies further. There is one issue which runs through all the discussions and is related to the fact that I am attempting to understand the reactions of both the patient and the analyst in the light of a different theoretical framework; namely, that of communicational field theory, whereas many points in the discussions relate to another theoretical model.

In the therapeutic session I believe that no reaction of either the doctor or the patient can be understood apart from the behavior of the other. In this understanding there is no separate "emotional life" of the analyst as talked about by Dr. Aronson. The analyst has emotional responses which are communicated to the patient. The problem for the patient arises not because of this, but only if such communication is in some way denied by the analyst. It is this kind of double yet contradictory message which leads to symptomatic behavior and "resistance." The helpful aspect of the analyst's confirming the patient's perception is that this clarifies the contradictions. It is true that this is not all there is to it, and as Dr. Lipton points out, there are historical determinants in the patient's past which indeed may now become more available for analytic understanding.

Dr. Natterson also mentions the importance of the causative factors and expresses concern that the method advocated might lead to the patient's using it as a rationalizing resistance. This kind of reaction is, of course, possible, but could also be dealt with by dynamic interaction and understanding in the therapy session.

Dr. Natterson also touches on the basic theoretical issue when he speaks of the patient being more the center of the field than the analyst. Actually, it is true that the reason for the analysis itself is based on the patient's complaint about the way his life is going; but it is necessary to distinguish this main *purpose* from the *method* itself. In the method, I believe it is the relationship between the doctor and patient in the session which is the center of the field, and not the patient alone, nor the analyst alone. Dr. Winnicott also draws on a different theoretical base when he talks of the patient's "inner conflicts." In my frame of reference, conflicts which the patient has in the session are related to what is actually going on in that session between him and his analyst. The problems are indeed related to his own past, but are not, I believe, projections without any relationship to the current stimulus situation.

Dr. Aronson discusses the important human factors in therapy and notes that these exist in any situation where one person tries to help another. I think that in psychotherapy this factor of human involvement and cooperativeness has a very specific role in determining the nature of change which will occur. In this manner the humanness is indeed a specific therapeutic instrument in a way that it is not in an encounter with a surgeon. But I am not just advocating humanness and cooperative exploration. I am saying that clarification and confirmation of the actual human interactions in the analytic situation are helpful. This is interpretation also, but not interpretation of the patient as an isolate, but rather as part of a dynamic and ongoing human situation.

I agree with Dr. Lipton that it is myth to think of an analyst who is detached on the basis of theoretical conviction. In the paper I referred to the fact that kindly human traits were not objected to as a rule, but it is those responses considered "irrational" which give therapists difficulty. It is common for an analyst not to reveal openly such reactions; perhaps the hoped-for goal is greater objectivity, or a desire not to interfere with the patient's productions. The result need not be analytic detachment. Actually, the analyst may be empathic and warm. But by not revealing his reactions clearly he may be strengthening the very confusions and binds which were originally experienced by the patient during his earlier life.

Dr. Natterson disagrees with the extent to which I advocate inclusion of the analyst's responses. It is true that the patient may use the analyst's admissions as a means of rationalizing his own behavior. But this does not mean that patients recognize the impact of their own behavior on others, or take responsibility for it in those cases where the analyst implicitly denies the nature of his own involvement. In fact, it is precisely because this does not happen often enough that I have attempted to discover ways of breaking through such an impasse.

Dr. Winnicott cautions that the patient must not be involved in the analyst's personal states if it can be avoided. The issue as I see it is that because this can not be avoided there is therapeutic merit in bringing the entire matter into the open as much as possible. Self-defeating reactions of the patient to the analyst's responses can then be more readily identified and evaluated, and the human and therapeutic value of such an intimate and cooperative exchange can be experienced.

I am most grateful to all the discussants for their interesting and thoughtful commentary, and I have found personal confirmation of Dr. Lipton's prediction that the controversy can be productive.

The Forum

Title — **Psychiatry Education Today**[1]

Author — **Ives Hendrick, M.D.**

Professor of Clinical Psychiatry Emeritus at Harvard Medical School and Chief of Massachusetts Mental Health Center (formerly Boston Psychopathic Hospital) for over twenty years. He has been President of the American Psychoanalytic Association and Chairman of its Board of Professional Standards. Dr. Hendrick has been interested in the development and educational problems of psychoanalytic training and of general psychiatry as well as a contributor to the scientific development of these specialties. He is the author of *Facts and Theories of Psychoanalysis*, *Birth of an Institute* and *Psychiatry Education Today*.

Discussants

Allen J. Enelow, M.D.

Professor of Psychiatry at the University of Southern California where he is Director of the Psychosomatic Service and of the Postgraduate Division of the Department of Psychiatry. He is concerned with problems of psychiatric education as well as studying the nature of the psychotherapeutic process. Dr. Enelow has had numerous papers published and one book is now in press.

Norman Q. Brill, M.D.

Professor and Chairman of the Department of Psychiatry at the University of California at Los Angeles and Medical Director of the Neuropsychiatric Institute. He is a member of the Los Angeles Psychoanalytic Society and has been involved in teaching of psychiatry at the undergraduate and graduate levels for many years. The author of two books and over seventy articles, Dr. Brill has had a longstanding interest in the field of psychotherapy with its central role in any psychiatric educational program.

Stephen Abrahamson, PH.D

Director of the Division of Research in Medical Education and Professor of Education in the School of Medicine and the School of Education at University of Southern California. Dr. Abrahamson has served as educational consultant to more than twenty American medical schools. He is one of the pioneers who explored possible contributions of education to medical education and is co-author of *Teaching and Learning in Medical Schools*.

[1]*Psychiatry Education Today* (Hendrick, Ives [1965], New York: Int. Univ. Press) is here critically reviewed by three educators to whom the author responds.

Discussant

Allen J. Enelow, M.D.
Los Angeles, California

When an elder statesman of psychiatry speaks, we may wonder if the past seems more attractive to him than the present, but we should all listen. Certainly, Ives Hendrick is an elder statesman of psychiatry and of psychoanalysis. He comes from that pioneering era when American psychiatrists trained in the Meyerian tradition were exposed to psychoanalysis, and excited by its promise of making behavior understandable and treatment possible, enthusiastically integrated their new-found psychoanalytic understanding into their background of careful and systematic investigations of behavior. Now, some forty years after his beginnings in the field, Ives Hendrick, with characteristic modesty and a refreshing absence of pomposity and pontification, gives us the benefit of his thinking about present-day psychiatry education.

In Hendrick's definition of dynamic psychiatry, one sees the shortcomings of the era from which he springs. He refers to the understanding of behavior only in terms of genetic dynamics with no reference to interactional dynamics. He proposes defining psychiatry as a basic science, but then, to my disappointment, defines psychology, physiology, and sociology as adjunctive areas and states that their ideas are "very different from the primary clinical facts of basic psychiatry."

Nonetheless, Hendrick makes an excellent proposal to which insufficient attention is paid today: that the basis of psychiatric theory is clinical observation and that one might, therefore, do very well to expose medical students to patients right away. His proposal that first-year medical students should do psychiatric interviewing makes good sense.

Hendrick proposes that insufficient attention is being paid to the beginning resident's unpreparedness for clinical and administrative ward responsibility in psychiatry. He raises the question: Must young residents go through the same stages as their senior teachers (analysts trained in the 1920's who came out of the Meyerian tradition)? Evidently Hendrick thinks they must. He states that psychiatry is still mostly art and it is not sound pedagogy to jump from the preclinical state of the young psychiatric resident into what he terms "free-association-derived long-term psychotherapy." He proposes, instead, more clinical experience to begin with and less early exposure to abstract concepts, utilizing intensive and careful case studies from which the first year resident should be taught to make low-level inferences adequately supported by their observations. He stresses attention to content and deplores the great deal of focus on defenses without studying that which is defended against.

Hendrick believes free association has altered the face of case study as well as that of psychotherapy and considers this regrettable. He feels there should be less structured "psychotherapy" with a programmed hour and programmed supervision and more of a spontaneous, less formalized "working with patients" in its place. He considers this kind of exposure to patients leads to a much deeper understanding of the behavioral phenomena that underlie psychodynamic theory than can come from conducting psychotherapy directly derived from the model of psychoanalysis. Hendrick feels it is lamentable that psychiatrist and therapist have become emotional synonyms, and believes that long-term therapy should come later in residency training than it does now.

Hendrick emphasizes the very first learning experiences in determining the accessibility of residents to new ideas. He does not approve borrowing the model of the "supervisor" from psychoanalytic training, and believes that residents can learn better in groups of three than in one-to-one supervision. He complains, with justice, that many mature clinicians are no longer interested in any service in a teaching program other than supervision of psychotherapy. Thus, the teaching requiring the greatest maturity is delegated to junior teachers while the senior teachers do what they are already very comfortable with doing in their psychoanalytic training programs.

Finally, Hendrick describes "the architecture of a training program." He makes the strong point that the chief purpose of a psychiatric training program is to produce personality growth as well as intellectual growth, and that it takes about five years to reach professional maturity. New residents arrive with high motivation, but this is badly stunted by the overemphasis on formalized therapy, the undue organization of their time, and the ritualizing of the externals of psychotherapy and of supervision. It is important for the residents to have inpatient as well as outpatient experience in the first year with less attention to long-term psychotherapy and more to admissions work and detailed histories of patients. He makes a cogent and convincing argument for the traditional case-study type of work-up at first, but permitting an increasing number of therapy cases based on the individual resident's ability and maturation to handle them. These long-term cases are thoroughly discussed in small groups rather than in individual supervision. Training in psychosomatic medicine, the management of chronic psychoses, the aged and the senile, and other special groups, group therapy, and child psychiatry is optional and used to meet the needs of each resident rather than uniformly taught to all.

He deplores the overscheduling and lack of unprogrammed time in residency training and regrets that informal talks, bull sessions, and thinking time are vanishing while off-duty jobs (moonlighting) have become a malignancy in professional education. He deplores the early personal analysis many residents undertake which promotes "moonlighting" to earn money to pay for it and argues for the restoration of the *full-time* character of the residency years. Finally, Hendrick states the foundation of psychiatry is the expert study of mental content, conscious and unconscious, and stresses that the young resident should not need to substitute prefabricated formulations for true discovery.

I could not be more in sympathy with the points Hendrick makes. Nonetheless, Hendrick's background betrays him. He is unaware of the consultative role of the psychiatrist of today with community agencies and with non-psychiatrists. His definition of modern psychiatry as the expert study of mental content is dated since psychiatry has as much to do with the interaction between people as with the mental content of any given individual. However, these are minor complaints and do not detract from the cogency and the relevance of Hendrick's arguments. It may well be that too many young third and fourth generation analysts, substituting prefabricated formulations for observation, are having too dominant an effect on residency training. Every director of a residency training program today would do well to heed Hendrick's sermon, even while allowing for some of the shortcomings of his understanding about the role of the modern psychiatrist.

Discussant

Norman Q. Brill, M.D.

Los Angeles, California

This book should be read and carefully considered by all those engaged in teaching psychiatry. Dr. Hendrick's experience, gained from many years of teaching at the undergraduate and graduate levels in the Harvard Teaching Unit of the Boston Psychopathic Hospital, is clearly and interestingly summarized.

There should be no argument with: "We seek to provide maximal opportunities for each student to learn from intensive work with a few patients that psychiatry is first of all concerned with what the patient feels and thinks and talks about, not what the dynamic psychiatrist or psychoanalyst supposedly talks and thinks about."

Dr. Hendrick very appropriately is concerned about the increasing tendency to downgrade the importance of teaching basic clinical psychiatry, in favor of "indoctrinating [trainees] in the high-power promotion and techniques of 'mental health' for the many. To do so is to emphasize the superficial application to much wider social objectives of what we already know, or hope we know, before residents have assimilated their fundamental training." He feels that the beginner should first learn how to "tackle honestly the difficult fact-seeking problems with each patient before he applies what he knows on a mass-production scale."

He points out that the beginning psychiatric resident has had relatively little preparation for assuming early in his career responsibility for treating the severely ill hospitalized psychiatric patient. Any program which ignores the fact that deep and unexpressed reactions of the patient are decisive for understanding the true meaning of a home visit, weekend privileges, etc., is in danger of producing a cleavage between knowledge of psychodynamics and its application to the treatment of a patient.

There will be little disagreement with the observation that "not only is psychotherapy offered the resident as an essential part of his work with patients, it is *demanded* by the resident; it is usually regarded by him as his most important and interesting clinical function, for which other work is sometimes sacrificed and more traditional techniques are ignored." The resident today, as different from his counterpart of the past, starts out with an acceptance (to some degree) of the existence of an unconscious, and a knowledge of mental mechanisms and instead of having to be taught the intent of free association (which he already knows) he must learn how to use the material therapeutically. The focus on psychoanalytic methods and principles often results in a downgrading of the importance of obtaining factual data, etc., and "is now disregarded by many younger psychiatrists in good clinics. Residents may not know the immediate reason for a patient's hospitalization, the details of sibling relationships, the details of the patient's symptoms, etc., and may confuse a summary of the patient's free associations with a summary of the case."

It is pointed out that "working with a patient," as was more often done in the past than now, involved more than just psychotherapy —and often accomplished more. It was not highly structured, formal and scheduled. It permitted a more flexible and relaxed interchange and attention to important events in the patient's daily life than "modern" treatment permits when the resident sees himself as "the therapist" and there is a tendency to sharply demarcate between therapist and administrator. "Psychotherapist" and "psychiatrist" are too often used as synonyms, and techniques of psychotherapy which are applicable and appropriate for certain outpatients are often used for inpatients whose illnesses and situations are totally different.

Dr. Hendrick points to the tendency of the "therapist" to isolate himself by a heavy schedule of treatment hours and the sanctity with which these hours are so often invested by the resident. Interruptions are not permitted and one price of such overemphasis is de-emphasis of psychiatric thinking and learning.

Supervision has tended to replace teaching with interpretation as its goal in lieu of basic clinical instruction. Good supervisory instruction involves good teaching—including such things as history taking, mental examinations, unprogrammed interviews, clinical work-ups, as well as analysis of free associations. Small group teaching is suggested as one way of achieving this broader objective. Good students learn from other students and from their cases. Personal problems of an individual resident can be handled at special conferences with him.

There is recognition of the conflict of trying to provide a well-rounded experience with chronic psychotics, the aged and senile, the mentally retarded, juvenile delinquents, criminals, drug addicts, alcoholics, etc., and the need to maintain the highest possible quality of training. "Too dilute and cluttered a program becomes more like training for community service or rehabilitation than the best training in basic psychiatry."

In contrast to the opinions of many others, Dr. Hendrick does not give group therapy a very high priority, while child psychiatry is looked upon as "a sibling to adult psychiatry . . . which deepens and supplements their basic knowledge of the personality problems, childhood residuals, and development of adult patients; it is much more than another area to which acquired skills in basic psychiatry may or may not be applied."

Social workers are quite mistakenly viewed as thoroughly trained in the non-medical knowledge and techniques of psychiatry itself—and as partners in clinical work rather than as adjuncts or assistants from an allied profession.

Psychologists are seen primarily as testers who provide additions to the psychiatrist's clinical data as well as test results and interpretations. No mention is made of the psychologist's increasing insistence that his first function is to provide psychotherapy.

Sociological approaches are seen much too much as threats to understanding and analysis of individual personalities.

Little mention is made of the place of the basic neurological sciences in psychiatric education. It is almost as if disciplines like neuropharmacology, neurochemistry, neurophysiology and clinical neurology have no relationship to psychiatry and that research in these areas is not really the responsibility of the psychiatrist. If there is any strong exception anyone can take to Dr. Hendrick's otherwise excellent summation it is his almost exclusive reliance on an understanding of personality development and unconscious mechanisms as the basis for clinical training in psychiatry. While there would be no disagreement about the fundamental importance of this, there is much that analytic approaches do not explain and it would be shortsighted to deny to possibility that the other basic sciences of human behavior may make very significant contributions to the understanding and treatment of mental and emotional illnesses as even Freud himself predicted.

It is quite likely that some of the greatest advances that occur in the next twenty years may result from neurophysiological studies which show every prospect of revealing the nature and location of the impairment of brain function that occurs with mental illness and is probably the result of emotional conflict which individuals, either because of faulty inheritance or upbringing, are not capable of coping with constructively. We are still in the dark about why different people react differently to similar environmental stress. It is quite likely that the explanation for this may involve more than psychology.

There are cycles and fashions in the advance of a science and medical disciplines. Freud's contributions provided the stimuli for the wave of emphasis on individual psychology and the role of unconscious factors in behavior and emotional illnesses. There are many who believe this cycle is past its zenith and that new advances in the understanding of human behavior may well come from the study of biochemical and neurophysiological concomitants.

While it is true that basic training in psychiatry should not be sacrificed or compromised, some time devoted to research can add a dimension and result in overall better preparation.

Dr. Hendrick very properly discusses the problem of moonlighting and its possible adverse effects on training programs. It precludes the optimal use of time during the training period and, perhaps more important, acts to siphon off libido from the main task at hand. The change in culture which Dr. Hendrick describes is quite obvious to those who had their training thirty and forty years ago and who lived through the depression. Doctors used to be content with exciting work and a modest living during their early years in practice, particularly in a specialty. It was not even thought of as a sacrifice "for the simple reason that one's own attitude was shared by all whose professional interests were genuine." Now things which were luxuries have become necessities and there is a greater importance to achieve the kind of financial success which previously came only with long application to the job. Dr. Hendrick's elaboration of this point is well worth reading although I suspect it will do little toward changing a trend in the culture which is getting progressively more pronounced.

Dr. Hendrick warns against gearing a training program to serve community needs and social improvement instead of acquiring basic knowledge and skills. We should, however, not be unmindful of the unmet needs and should make serious efforts through research to devise methods and techniques that will spread the base of psychiatric care through more careful delineation of indications for brief therapy, group therapy and crisis therapy so that there may be flexibility in our treatment approaches rather than a blind adherence to a goal of always uncovering the forces that contribute to each illness even when such uncovering is unnecessary or even contra-indicated.

Discussant

Stephen Abrahamson, PH.D.

Los Angeles, California

One of the important considerations in Ives Hendrick's book is his stressing the problem of choosing appropriate learning experiences for the beginning student of psychiatry. He expresses concern that theoretic material may be learned too early and may indeed hinder later learning. He pleads for "more gradual introduction" for the beginning resident with "graded teaching and responsibilities."

A similar brief could be made for most medical students (interns, and/or residents) in any clinical discipline. All too often, the beginner is expected to perform on the same level as those at a later stage. Indeed, the difficulty or complexity of clinical case material is seldom considered in assigning cases in the learning experience. Most formal education seems to involve a graduated structuring of the material to be learned. Surely, the processes to be mastered in clinical psychiatry warrant systematic analysis as well.

Dr. Hendrick asks whether the learner can be encouraged to "pick-up where we leave-off." In his words: "To what extent can a senior teacher of dynamic psychiatry start out to teach what he now knows, what is now the summation of what he has learned at various stages of his own development, in so rapidly evolving a profession; or is it that the younger resident, at least in part, must of necessity go through the same sequence of phases in his own professional development as we did, so that his later advanced experience in using free association and in thinking dynamically evolves from more traditional experience?"

The answer to this question must depend upon a careful analysis of (a) knowledge to be acquired, (b) cognitive processes to be mastered, (c) basic skills to be achieved, and (d) general professional behavior to be assimilated. At the same time, we must ascertain the kinds of learnings which take place in the phases referred to above. We must know, then, whether similar learning can take place with a less expensive commitment of time and money. Once we have determined precisely what is to be learned, we can more intelligently make decisions concerning the means by which such goals might be achieved.

While we look forward to ways of shortening the education of the psychiatry resident, a certain degree of pessimism should prevail. As Dr. Hendrick points out: "A beginning student of chemistry does not need to duplicate the chemistry courses of 1900 in order to learn well the fundamentals as understood today." But learning psychiatry is indeed "more than adding new information" to an established science. Pessimism grows when one considers the possibility that the complex cognitive processes can neither be mastered nor practiced competently until certain high levels of emotional maturity and self-understanding are achieved; it is well known this is attained through a developmental process. Perhaps the test (and the challenge) facing psychiatry educators today is the definition of learning experiences which might shorten the time necessary for the developmental process.

With all due respect to Dr. Hendrick, the challenge for curriculum development remains enormous and unanswered. In "The Architecture of a Teaching Program" there is no proposal for reform, only a restatement of the realistic limitation impinging upon the teaching of psychiatry today. What remains is the application of imagination and ingenuity—hopefully to take place *following* the careful analysis of desired learning outcome and necessary developmental experiences.

Author's Response

Ives Hendrick, M.D.
Boston, Massachusetts

It has been my pleasure (not always the privilege of an author) to enjoy these reviews of my recent monograph on psychiatry education today and to benefit. In part this is due to the discussants' clear summaries of my meaning, as well as their own criticisms. The direct quotations they select are particularly gratifying, for these do add up to an excellent index of my strongest motivations for writing this book. These interests are enhanced by the four variations of professional experience the reviewers and this author each represent.

Stephen Abrahamson brings us the catalyzing effect of a scholar who studies medical education as a whole. His observation that training in all clinical specialties, as well as ours, could benefit from a "more graduated introduction" is of special interest. But the difference should not be overlooked between minimal hours and years of preparation of the psychiatrist for his specialty and the years of medical training for the other clinical specialties. I am not entirely clear how well Dr. Abrahamson recognizes psychiatric teaching aims not only at intellectual knowledge and professional growth, as he reminds us, but especially at a sensitiveness to the patient's feelings. The full development of this sensitivity, regardless of talent, always requires long, intensive experience. His pessimism that the training years can be shortened much today (except by more training prior to residency) is well grounded.

All discussants sense the weighting of my convictions by my experience in long-past decades and my age; Dr. Enelow even suspects "the past seems more attractive than the present." In some ways yes—definitely. Yet I devoutly trust this is not entirely a disadvantage, due chiefly to early fossilization, or else to a frozen philosophical viewpoint of bygone decades, but that it also contributes a perspective on what could be improved today. Dr. Enelow speaks of my attitude as the "Meyerian tradition"; that may be true if he means good histories, good factual data, good records, are important for good training; it is not true if he means I limit the resident to what was taught forty years ago.

It is most natural, perhaps desirable, that my discussants' opinions about planning teaching should focus particularly on the adjunctive sciences. Dr. Brill agrees that clinical psychiatry is fundamental for professional training. But it is difficult for both him and Dr. Enelow to accept my opinion that they are overemphasized today in early resident training of the psychiatrist, partly because they offer the beginner too many facile alternatives to the difficulties of clinical thinking, and partly because limiting adjunctive training during the first two years is the best means available to reduce the clutter of many sadly overloaded and unfocused programs. Professional psychologists are not just "testers" as Dr. Brill implies I regard them; they are at best experts in methods and objectives of research in psychological areas peculiarly their own. Similarly, neurology and neurophysiology, and chemistry and pharmacology, are all sciences making exciting advances in their own fields, but I cannot agree with those who think their future discoveries will replace the psychiatric study of the mind.

With Dr. Brill's observation, "there are fashions in the advance of a science and medical disciplines," I heartily concur that they are too often overlooked, but the popularity, in the psychiatric culture of today, of the activist-minded, of the efficient time-saver, the grant-tracking bloodhounds (poor Eliza on the ice-floes)—these stylists decree this year's psychiatric hemline and its color. They affect the use of our technical language; psychiatrists unwittingly use traditional words in quite new ways, and in new semantic contexts whose present connotations would have been strange ten years ago. I do know too well no mere book is likely to stem this tide, but I like to write it anyway.

I do not agree that Freud's contribution started a "cycle" which is "past its zenith," nor concur with Dr. Enelow's opinion, "the study of mental content is dated." Truly, the promotion of community psychiatry, professionally and publicly, and its financial Niagara, tends to subordinate the advance of psychiatric knowledge; it creates pressures which are affecting the residents' interest in critical learning and fact-testing very early in their training. The unimpeachable social objectives of extending psychiatric help to the many depend on very short methods of treatment, but I deplore the beclouding of the logical boundaries between doing the best we can for mental health and the honest and wisest use of our best critical faculties. The fond hope that exploration of the mind—especially its non-rational areas—may be rendered unnecessary by the physical sciences is much older than Freud and has been activated in every generation. Public health techniques for dealing with typhoid fever and diphtheria are not considered a reason for erasing bacteriology from our medical students' education. I therefore urge the early training of the "modern psychiatrist" be similarly based on what contributes most to knowledge of the patient. The psychiatrist of the future may later choose his own priority interest in applying this training to one of many special fields our profession is filling.

Summaries of Scientific Meetings

Southern California Psychoanalytic Society

Contributing Editor:
Jerome L. Saperstein, M.D.

"Internal Object Relations"
J. O. Wisdom, PH.D
December 21, 1965 Meeting

Object relations theory springs from Freud's original theory of the superego that neurosis depended upon relations to an internal representation of a parent. Object relations first appearing in Freud's theory of the Oedipus complex were further emphasized by Klein and Fairbairn. Most of Klein's ideas are seen in Freud's work, but with Klein there is a greater emphasis on certain points. In technique she stressed transference interpretation in terms of both analyst and internal objects. As regards theory she emphasized introjection and projective identification—mechanisms also described by Freud; however, one new idea found in Klein's work is that of "depressive guilt." The concept of internal objects forms a neutral means of describing old and new theories and enables one to focus sharply on problems.

Professor Wisdom then described the world of internal objects using a model he has found useful in formulating problems and possible solutions. He divided the inner world into a nucleus of the self and surrounding inner objects (orbitals) with which the nucleus has relations. Freud's "remorse" is, thus, an attack of the nucleus by the orbitals. In Klein's theory of depression, the attack is from the nucleus to the orbitals; this difference should be testable by appropriate interpretations. This model of the inner world could help in understanding the resolution of the Oedipus complex which is unclear in classical theory. The boy could identify with the father in projective identification. Internally, there is paternal nuclear identification with destruction of sexual elements of the internal mother. In homosexuality, there may be a maternal nuclear identification and orbital identification with father. Here, the question can be raised as to where identifications go and whether they are interchangeable. Professor Wisdom believes that they are interchangeable.

In psychosis, the nucleus is under strain and projects to orbitals or to the outside—losing part of the personality. In neurosis there is ambivalence toward the orbitals. Also, there is the problem of the origin of internal objects. The idea that they originate by introjection is circular, because it implies a preexisting recognition of a boundary between inside and outside. The development of the awareness of external objects and the differentiation of self might go as follows: hunger is felt first as a sensation of being pinched or torn, giving rise to a sense of "hunger-hole," which would thus be the first internal object, a bad object. It would be an orbital. After feeding, the bad object is projected out as the first external object; since it no longer persecutes, it may be felt as a good object which can be introjected. Using this model, it becomes possible to give some account of early object formation through more generalized projections and introjections.

Finally, it is possible to develop some idea of normal development through the concept of interchange between the orbitals and the nucleus. If the mother and her breast only were nuclear introjects, then, one would see not only female personality in boys but also no possibility of reparation for oral attacks on the mother. If the introjection of the father can become nuclear and that of the mother orbital, the boy can break the destructive oral cycle and make reparation to the mother, as can be seen in normal growth patterns.

Discussion: Dr. Carroll Carlson pointed out that, in the theory of internal objects, the clinician feels left out—being only a transference figure. Perhaps the therapist won't expose his real self because of a lack of place in Kleinian theory. However, he believes that he is introjected as a real person, and that this reality of the clinician is important in therapy.

Dr. Bernard Brandchaft considered that Professor Wisdom has provided a scientific basis for a not-yet developed metapsychology of object relations. Although Freud laid the foundation for an object relations psychology, his work was encumbered by its origins in instinctual theory. Mrs. Klein pioneered in the increased importance of internal objects. Dr. Wisdom is extending her work and has opened up baffling problems of identification and identity formation. Much of the classical criticism of Klein's formulations has to do with their incompatibility with Freud's concept of primary narcissism and his hypothesis about schizophrenia being a regression to an objectless state or a state of undifferentiated fusion. Such observations that schizophrenics are incapable of object relations and transference has been shown to be faulty. Professor Wisdom's work indicates the direction of further advance from Freud's hypotheses.

Dr. Robert Litman stated that, in South America, the transference-countertransference field, itself, was considered introjected and reprojected. He also asked if orbital identifications can seize control of motility in suicide. Dr. John Lindon commented on the use of Kleinian concepts by modern classical analysts and yet the persistence of the critical divergence. Dr. Arthur Malin said Dr. Wisdom's model gives practical help in studying identification. Dr. Nemeth suggested the difference in the two schools parallels a maternal versus a paternal nuclear identification. He asked how verbal interpretations can affect such preverbal material. Dr. Richard Alexander stated that internal objects must be present soon after birth since instincts are object-directed and the inner world is the psychic representation of instincts.

In reply, Professor Wisdom thought that orbitals could not control action although they might trigger off processes which could disrupt the nucleus. He considered that one could get at preverbal structures through words, and also that early infantile processes, although preverbal, take place in terms of ideas. Freud's paper "On Narcissism" has been factually accepted although presented by him as speculative; it was based on incorrect facts about schizophrenics. Furthermore, the paper was based on the libido theory, which is non-object-relational. Klein never adjusted the libido theory with that of object relations.

Joint Meeting: Southern California Psychoanalytic Society and Los Angeles Psychoanalytic Society

Contributing Editor:
Jerome L. Saperstein, M.D.

"An Introduction to the Kleinian Technique in Psychoanalysis"

Hanna Segal, M.B.CH.B.

January 10, 1966 Meeting

Kleinian technique is psychoanalytical and is carried out according to the principles laid down by Freud. The interpretations are centered on the transference situation—the level determined by the patient's maximum unconscious anxiety. Kleinian technique is the same in dealing with psychotic or prepsychotic patients, in contrast with the parameters used by classical Freudian analysts in such cases. Changes in the nature of the interpretations and of emphasis show an evolution from classical interpretations.

As a result of her work with children, Klein felt the roots of the oedipal complex and the superego reached back to the second oral stage. Early development was influenced greatly by introjection, projection and splitting (preceding repression). These primitive levels of experience could be understood in the adult through the conceptualization of unconscious fantasy. Unconscious fantasy is the "psychic equivalent of instincts"—always active, experienced somatically and mentally, coloring reality, and developing derivatives as do instincts. Furthermore, fantasties are the subjective experiencing of mental mechanisms including those used for defense. Interpretation of fantasies is thus interpretation of defense and anxiety-ladened content.

The structure of ego and superego, partly determined by unconscious fantasies in the past, can be made accessible in the analytic situation. This view of unconscious fantasy affects the technique in that unconscious fantasy in the transference situation is interpreted from the start—both to lessen the unconscious anxiety and to focus the patient's attention on the central role of the analyst in his unconscious. Fantasy interpretations involve analyses of the original sources, defensive aspects, and the relation to external past and present realities.

Dr. Segal then described Klein's paranoid-schizoid and depressive positions. The first is preambivalent, corresponding roughly to the first oral stage, with persecutory anxiety and splitting, introjection, projection, as active mechanisms of defense. Projective identification is an important mechanism here. The depressive position occurs with integration of the self and object and with the anxiety of destroying the external mother and good internal object. These anxieties are part of normal integration and are reawakened by subsequent losses. Depressive anxiety may be dealt with by regression to schizoid mechanisms organized in a system of manic defenses in which there is denial of the value of the object, control, contempt and devaluation. Manic defense increases underlying depression by its attacks on the object. Depressive anxiety is worked out through reparation, the source of mental growth and creativity. There is constant oscillation between the paranoid-schizoid and depressive positions throughout life. The analysis of the Oedipus complex is central, but the technique is affected by the fact that the Oedipus complex begins in the depressive position; analyzing the depressive defenses is essential in liberation of the complex from omnipotent fantasies.

Discussion: Dr. Richard Alexander spoke of qualitative differences, e.g., the early origins of the Oedipus complex, the superego, and splitting, and the greater use of fantasy in transference interpretations of impulse-anxiety-defense. Kleinian theory clarifies dependency and the denial of the value of the object. "Genitality" is better understood through its connection with the working through of the depressive position. The negative therapeutic reaction is elucidated through the concept of envy. Finally, the Kleinian point of view gives a greater dynamic and living quality to psychoanalysis.

Dr. James S. Grotstein felt the presentation was lucid and internally consistent. He stated that American objections to Kleinian theory are largely mitigated by our newer understanding of the concept of unconscious fantasy, which, if it holds up, provides a unified field theory for all psychopathology. The issue of early emergence of such well-defined ego states is not yet clarified. Although the paper is consistent, we still do not know if the theoretical assumptions are valid. He questioned if the depressive position rather than the oedipal complex is the constellating force. He considered the therapeutic implications of projective identification and manic defenses to be very important.

Dr. Blumstein asked about the use of psychic energy in Kleinian theory. Dr. Call asked if affective and cognitive aspects of fantasies are differentiated and if infant observations are used. Dr. Wisdom suggested that for interpretation of defense and motive a topological model might be constructed—using vertical differentiation (splitting) instead of the horizontal layering of the classical topography.

In reply, Dr. Segal stated there is a regression in dependency conflicts to symbiosis and there may be a denial of the real dependence on the analyst. Regarding the question of validation, there are no criteria for validation of any total analytic theory. It is not known what determines introjection into either the early ego or superego. The Oedipus complex is not in the central position unless one also includes its early pregenital roots. Infant observation is very important but can't be used alone as validation for any analytic theory.

Joint Meeting: Los Angeles Psychoanalytic Society and Southern California Psychoanalytic Society

Contributing Editor:
Jerome L. Saperstein, M.D.

Panel Discussion: "Transference and Countertransference"
February 17, 1966 Meeting

Dr. Gerald J. Aronson presented a paper, "Some Types of Transference and Countertransference." There is a tradition in psychoanalysis to turn obstacles into major instruments of treatment. Freud stated in 1912 that transference manifestations are both the greatest hindrance and yet of indispensable help to the treatment. This same kind of jiu-jitsu flourishes to the present, being applied to mechanisms of defense, acting out, negative therapeutic reactions and early persistent object relations. When Freud writes of transference he is referring to emotions, actions and fears pertaining to oedipally held, incestuously cathected family members of early life, i.e., whole objects. Transferences springing from this period carry with them the appurtenances of secondary process thinking, thus enabling the patient to understand he is reacting to us *as if* we were father or mother. We will call these reactions *normal transferences*. In other kinds of reactions toward us the ratio between transference reaction and sense of reality is grossly tilted; the analyst is considered not a surrogate but the object itself. This is an *erotized transference*. In psychosis, a third type is noted, *the archaic transference*, in which the analyst is seen as either dehumanized, a part of the patient's body or a score of cut-up, monstrously reconstructed percepts.

These three types of transference have not been equally valued by us, though all types probably coexist and comingle in the same patient. We must include understanding and interpretation of all three to consider treatment to be complete. Dr. Harvey D. Strassman questioned the use of "normal" in referring to transference. Dr. Aronson amended it then to "classical" to avoid confusion.

Dr. Saul L. Brown presented his paper on "Regressive Crisis and Transference." Transference is a phenomenological construct through which the regressive components of a current object relationship can be ordered and understood. Transference reenactment requires a reciprocal partner. Ego crisis may occur when the object fails to comply with the expectant regressive impulse, with the danger of object loss and serious ego anxiety. In the family, failure of reciprocal response is resolved through splitting of the regressive longings among several others. In the psychoanalytic situation, the analyst tries confrontation, clarification and interpretation to appeal to the patient's ego to acknowledge the unrealizability of the expectations. Occasionally, and if well timed, acknowledgment of his own affect can be a reassuring substitute for the sense of imminent object loss when the analyst fails to become enmeshed in mutual regression. Merely a statement by the analyst of what is going on *within the patient* may not be enough; the inclusion of the analyst's own self as experiencing object makes the internal object loss tolerable. Several sample interpretations followed, which illustrated how the analyst communicates how he has been reached by the patient at a time of ego crisis over fantasied object loss, e.g., "I must admit I'm tempted to shout you down—that would be orgiastic, wouldn't it?"

Dr. Melvin Mandel followed with a paper on countertransference noting the difficulties in exposing oneself to public view that this subject brings with it. Always associated with failure and fault, the study of countertransference must emerge from purely pathological considerations to find its rightful place as an aspect of psychoanalysis proper, properly performed. The analysis of many disturbed patients requires the awareness on the part of the analyst of affects that have been triggered by the patient, *without ever interpreting this directly to the patient*; there is rarely need for this. Searles says, "the analyst's own inner awareness is the main thing here; when one recommends . . . *overtly expressing* such feelings to the patient, one is on dubious and shaky ground." There are points in the course of any analysis when the analyst must feel feelings with some strength in relation to his patient before the work can be meaningfully resolved. Returning to Dr. Aronson's paper, Dr. Mandel commented that countertransference, a potential obstacle, can be converted to a therapeutic tool.

Dr. Harvey Strassman completed the panel with some remarks on transference difficulties in character analysis, with special reference to shame. This arises from a conflict between the adult ego ideal and the regressed child ego. The transference toward the analyst as a pregenital parental object brings forth defenses against wishes to receive love, e.g.: conscious deception, projection of the parental (superego) imago, erotization of tender pregenital wishes, or avoiding the transference by escaping into considerations of external reality. To prevent the latter the analyst must *direct* the analysis toward the transference by seizing on reality experience, not contrived, which involves the analyst. This will eventually lead to the emergence of transference wishes, including feelings of shame arising from such wishes.

Dr. Brown questioned the usefulness of Dr. Aronson's classification, wondering if it was pseudo-objective. Dr. Aronson replied such classifications are useful if they hold up under the test of time. So far, he said, his classification has lasted three days. Dr. Mandel agreed with Dr. Brown that we are limited by our identity as analysts, but said we need to explore these limits and, within ourselves, unfreeze. Dr. David Brunswick asked if Dr. Aronson's classification was not related to stages of psychological development. Dr. Aronson agreed, without at this time feeling he could properly make the correlation.

Dr. Sheldon Selesnick wished to differentiate between real or genuine attitudes and countertransference attitudes. He cited a clinical example in which he felt a slip that revealed his sexual interest in his patient to be a non-countertransference reaction and a normal response to her as a woman, and told her so.

Dr. Lawrence J. Friedman stressed the *artificiality* of the analytic situation. Our job is to arrange conditions wherein the patient is free to express what he is otherwise reluctant to admit. When we reveal our own feelings, we put a tremendous burden upon the patient which should be carried by the analyst. It is unnecessary to interpret every level of transference; some very regressed levels do not require interpretation at all. Dr. Leo Rangell said though transference and countertransference occur regularly they are handled differently. We do not impose our understanding of ourselves onto the patient, but rather by self-analysis get them out of the way of the patient's analysis. We try to understand instead of react to our patients. It is *not* refreshing to be met by an analyst who reacts like everyone else. Empathy, not sympathy, is called for. Dr. Leavitt added that understanding is the one best thing an analyst has to give to his patient.

Southern California Psychoanalytic Society

Contributing Editor:
Jerome L. Saperstein, M.D.

"Theoretical Considerations of Ego Regression and Ego Functions in Creativity"

Phillip Weissman, M.D.

March 3, 1966 Meeting

Dr. Weissman's thesis is that Kris' concept of controlled regression in the service of the ego, in creativity, may be replaced more definitively by the concept of a dissociative function acting in the service of the synthetic function of the ego.

Creativity has been considered mainly in terms of its inspirational phase—leaving out the necessary elaboration; this fact contributes to controlled regressions being considered the hallmark of creativity. However, even in creative inspirational activity, the passive entry of drive cathexis into consciousness need not be accompanied by a concomitant regression of the ego—as may be seen in the phenomenon of the return of the repressed without ego regression. The availability of id derivatives for creative purposes, without the implication of regression, may be ascribed to a dissociative function of the ego, which may be viewed as the ego's capacity to dissociate itself from established (1) object relationships, (2) responses to specific id derivatives, (3) superego demands. Genetically this function develops in the early conflict between the pleasure and reality principles—to permit new patterns to be established; it reemerges in development to disrupt the established order to make way for maturer integrations. In creativity, it permits emerging drive cathexes to original treatment by the ego and probably is conducive to the emergence of such id-derived cathexis. The appearance of the dissociative function, as a precondition for more mature development, distinguishes it from regression, which restricts the ego to earlier stages of functioning. In creativity, it leads to increased availability of drive cathexis to the ego—not necessarily primary process discharge which can become regressively available through ego weakening.

In a non-creative mind, the dissociative function aids integrating new undertakings. Without the service of the synthetic function, the dissociative function may lead to pathological states such as fugues or depersonalization. Dissociation and synthesis are utilized in both inspirational and elaborative phases of creativity; the latter phase also aims at original solutions, in contrast to ordinary work, where synthesis without dissociation reaches already existing solutions. In creative persons, combined dissociation and synthesis can suspend established self representations and object relations and create new ones such as the creative self and the collective object.

Discussion: Dr. Samuel Futterman considered that the return of the repressed in creativity implied some regression—although not to the extent of unneutralized drive discharge and ego weakening that Kris implies. The time involved in creative processes also differentiates them from transient regressions as in humor, play, and sexual relations. He was in agreement with the author's desire to define more precisely two of the ego functions in creativity.

Dr. Martin Grotjahn stated that as a clinician, he is closer to the id than to the ego. However, the concept of the dissociative function in the service of integration has value in understanding original symbol formation, youthful aspects of creative people, and such phenomena as creative anxiety (unpleasantness in allowing the ego to dissociate). This is a different but not contradictory approach to his own ideas of creativity as deriving from the early attempts to restore the destroyed mother with the identification help of the father.

Mr. Donald Freed considered that Dr. Weissman didn't go far enough in ridding the artist from the stigma of being deviant instead of being essential for the survival of himself and his audience. Dr. Samuel Sperling believed dissociation was still too global for the description of creativity. Transformations of psychic energy, and differentiation between long-abiding creative concern and the shorter-lived creative process must be described. He also pointed out the presence of defense and control even in the dissociation of creativity. Dr. Walter Briehl suggested "reassociation" to avoid confusion with pathology.

Dr. Weissman replied by pointing out that he was not portraying the artist as a deviant—only trying to describe some of the processes in creativity. His treatment of the subject is still unfinished. He believes that defenses are present in the creative process, but they operate in new variations so as to allow new themes to be written. He speaks of dissociation as an ego function and not as a pathological process to avoid the confusion to which Dr. Briehl alluded.

Seattle Psychoanalytic Society

Contributing Editor:
Eugene Goforth, M.D.

"Psychoanalysis and the Family Life in India"

Dr. Tarun Chandra Sinha
Calcutta, India
January 27, 1966 Meeting

Family life in many sections of India is changing rapidly as a result of a great acceleration in urbanization and industrialization. The "old family" structure is prevalent in rural areas but newly-married couples are leaving their family homes, moving to cities, and starting their own homes. This is similar to the situation existing in many parts of the United States.

The "old family" structure is dependent and based on many members of the same family living together. Fathers, mothers, aunts, uncles, sons, daughters, cousins and grandparents all live in the same home—marriage and births bring new additions. The dominant person is the oldest, whether male or female, and all family members defer to this person for judgments and monetary decisions. A new baby arriving on the scene has "many mothers." He is rarely, if ever, alone (although the infant is separated from the biological mother for the first ten days of life), and for the first two years there is much bodily contact with adults. At about this age the older children take over most of the care of their siblings and cousins.

There is much bickering amongst the children but absolute obedience and submission is demanded from and accorded to all adults in the family. Infant feeding is either on schedule or by demand, forced feeding is sometimes practiced, although in general food supplies for all are meager. Most families are tolerant in toilet training practices. Dirt, of all sorts, is everywhere and uncleanliness is widely acceptable. Nakedness of children is common but becoming less so. In infants genital stimulation occurs from being carried astride the mother's waist and from the dangling of coins and sticks from a waist band. Castration anxiety is generally less intense and Dr. Sinha related this to early and persistent sexual stimulation, nakedness, and frequent exposure to the primal scene. In rural areas, and unless the family is wealthy, all living, eating, and sleeping is done in one or, at the most, two rooms.

Individuals are, for the most part, "fixated at an oral sucking phase," and according to Dr. Sinha, one encounters a "special type of personality structure." Those who leave their family homes for urban life generally find many frustrations and the majority lead unhappy, unsuccessful existences. Some turn to drink and many become increasingly passive, waiting for guidance and help which in the past they had received from the older adults in the family; others become chronically depressed.

Dr. Sinha spoke of a general attitude of submissiveness which characterizes many Indians, in his opinion more so than in most other countries; however, this is slowly changing, again due to the rapid social and economic changes. He felt that Gandhi promoted widespread passive-aggressiveness with his doctrine of non-violence.

In closing, he told of a recent survey he conducted in villages contained in an area of 5,000 square miles. He interviewed village leaders, persons in authority, and many individual villagers, but he could not find evidence of any person who might be considered psychotic. He estimated that he learned of only two or three persons who might be considered psychotic in the total memories of all those interviewed.

Discussion: Dr. Robert Forman, of Portland, Oregon, was the formal discussant. He pointed out that far-reaching changes can be expected in today's children of India as the result of their parents' reactions to the marked social and economic change that they are experiencing and have experienced in the past twenty years.

He felt learning more about the fantasy life of Indian children would give the greatest insights into the effect of today's social upheaval. In this regard he pointed to the work of Melanie Klein and the value she placed on understanding childhood fantasy in relation to character development. He hypothesized that the Indian infants' persistent exposure to nakedness and parental intercourse results in "some specific effect on the character of the Indian." He said that the degree of permanence on the character is greatly dependent on the infant's fantasy understanding of what he sees.

Seattle Psychoanalytic Society

Contributing Editor:
Eugene Goforth, M.D.

"Regulatory Mechanisms of the Perceptual Apparatus on Involuntary Physiological Actions"

T. L. Dorpat, M.D.
Seattle, Washington
February 14, 1966 Meeting

Psychological processes mediated by the perceptual system control the central nervous system pathways of those somatic reflexes that have central sensory connections. Regulatory mechanisms of the perceptual apparatus on these involuntary physiological actions are first described and then explained with a psychoanalytic theory. The positive hallucinatory sensation regulatory mechanism involves the initiation of involuntary motor and secretory actions by somatic hallucinatory sensations. Several investigations showed that somatic hallucinatory sensations brought about involuntary motor and secretory actions in conversion symptoms. Hallucinatory somatic sensations preceded motor and secretory actions occurring during states of instinctual drive arousal. At times of erotic excitement hallucinatory genital sensations led to erections. In thirsty subjects hallucinatory taste sensations led to salivary secretion.

The fact that the involuntary physiological actions did not occur without prior hallucinatory sensations led to the conclusion that the physiological actions were caused by the hallucinatory sensations. They were termed somatic hallucinatory sensations because they occurred in the absence of any peripheral stimulation. The psychoanalytic theory advanced to explain this regulatory mechanism is as follows: In the absence of a stimulating object, the drive for sensory stimulation with the object revives memories of previous sensory stimulation in the form of hallucinatory sensations. The hallucinatory sensation causes the involuntary physiological action. The theory advanced is identical with Freud's theory of the primary process and of dream formation. The only addition to Freud's theory is that the somatic hallucinatory sensations have a regulatory effect upon physiological actions. The functioning of the primary process model is extended to include the sensory memory traces of all sensory systems.

The negative hallucination regulatory mechanism involves the inhibition of physiological responses to peripheral stimuli by negative hallucinations. This regulatory mechanism occurs in conversion reactions and in normal adaptive behavior. An example of the latter is the function of negative hallucinations in the process of shutting out peripheral stimuli when going to sleep. Clinical and experimental studies indicate that negative hallucinatory phenomena are associated with decreased involuntary motor and secretory responses to peripheral stimuli. The lack of taste and hunger sensations in depressed patients accounts for their decreased salivary and gastric secretory response to food intake. The psychoanalytic explanatory hypothesis for this mechanism is adapted from Freud's concepts of the stimulus barrier. In a situation where the sensory stimulation is unpleasant, the ego brings about a counter-cathexis against the sensory system's memory traces. This leads to suppression of sensation formation. The negative hallucination, i.e., the absence of sensation, inhibits involuntary physiological responses to peripheral stimuli.

The data presented indicate a continuum of sensory responsivity with negative hallucinatory phenomena on one end of the scale and positive hallucinations on the other. In between these extremes, different degrees of cathexis or counter-cathexis of a sensory system's memory traces provide a dynamic variable threshold for the formation of sensations and consequent physiological activity.

Discussion: Dr. Arnold Katz was the formal discussant of Dr. Dorpat's paper. He commented that the theorizing was simple and encompassed many facts.

In speaking of the author's use of the term "felt" sensations, the awareness needs more detailed consideration in this study, acknowledging that it is an enormously complex, although important issue. To illustrate this point, Dr. Katz discussed the problems inherent in studies of awareness including: what cues initiate awareness; can subjects remember these cues, or might they need a sort of complex catalog; a system would have to be devised so that confidence could be gained in reported awareness; and finally, the clarity of experience and its relation to states of consciousness.

His next item was a criticism of the use of sensation which he thought was used in a too elementary way "as if they are in a pure form."

Graham's work on relating different specific attitudes to specific psychosomatic diseases was reviewed, particularly that portion in which Graham, through hypnosis, induced specific attitudes in experimental subjects. He then demonstrated in these subjects predicted autonomic nervous system and other physiological changes. He made the point that cognitive attitudes and sets, as well as perceptual functions, regulate involuntary physiological activity.

The Continuing Forum

The Continuing Forum is open to all readers so that they may send their reactions, suggestions, criticism and contributions to the topics which are presented in The Psychoanalytic Forum.

Sigmund Freud on Suicide

(Dr. Simon's discussion was received as Volume I, Number 2 went to press. Dr. Litman, the author, now responds.)

To the Editors: In my paper I criticized clinicians who isolate certain of Freud's formulations and use them as a justification for an "overemphasis on aggression and guilt as components of suicide with underemphasis of the helplessness, dependency and erotic elements."

Dr. Simon commented that in comprehensively reviewing Freud's work, we touch the "epistomological philosophical frontier of psychoanalytic theory which is the death instinct; but in his role as original contributor he [Litman] focuses so sharply upon the therapeutic-prophylactic issues as to blur the main province of psychoanalysis which lies between psychotherapy and philosophy."

In a psychoanalytic patient studied under research conditions, Dr. Simon observed that significant death responses occurred only when specific transference frustrations reactivated powerful aggressive impulses against both parents about which the patient felt guilty and turned back upon herself. Dr. Simon states that "while it may be therapeutically valuable to deemphasize aggression in the suicidal patient, the metapsychological validity of that shift has yet to be demonstrated."

To this I can only comment, Dr. Simon is right. I do not see how a metapsychological theory of suicide can overlook the death instinct and its clinical derivatives, destruction turned inward and aggression turned outward. Intuitively I agree with Freud and Simon that there is a death instinct which operates with terrifying intensity in human affairs, but this concept belongs to the half-acre of metapsychology called the "Economic Aspect" in which we struggle fruitlessly, probably because we lack suitable tools.

Recently, however, there have been exciting developments involving instinctual drives and psychic economics. I refer to the discovery in the brain of various metabolites (notably catecholamines) which are intimately associated with effective reactions. These chemicals may be a substrate for death instinct! We now have possibilities for directly influencing instincts with drugs, and an expanded theory of instincts could well be the vehicle for correlating neurophysiology with psychology. Ostow has pioneered in this direction.

It seems to me that various aspects of metapsychology which seem to be divergent (for example, instinct theory, structural viewpoints, adaptation dynamics) are actually complementary formulations which say the same thing in somewhat different language.

Physicists have become accustomed to learning that formulations which appear entirely dissimilar are actually identical statements with a mathematical transformation. The following quotation is from a Nobel Prize Acceptance Speech by R. P. Feynman (Science, 153:699-707, Aug. 12, 1966). "We are struck by the very large number of different physical viewpoints and widely different mathematical formulations that are all equivalent to one another. Theories of the known which are described by different physical ideas may be equivalent in all their predictions, and hence scientifically indistinguishable. However, they are not psychologically identical when one is trying to move from that base into the unknown. For different views suggest different modifications which might be made and hence are not equivalent in the hypotheses one generates from them in one's attempt to understand what is not yet understood."

I believe the moral is this: For clinical application in a crisis center, ego adaptation theory and the loss-abandonment, helplessness, hopelessness and regression aspects of suicide psychodynamics provide a good working model for the therapist; but in different situations, for example, in psychoanalytic research on depression, or in understanding the psychological effects of drugs, other models will have as much or more to offer.

Robert E. Litman, M.D.
Beverly Hills, California

A Patient and Her Cats

To the Editors: I want first to convey my appreciation to the editors for the opportunity of expressing thoughts stimulated by reading this journal. The idea of a Continuing Forum is delightful because its freedom and informality spare one the necessity of rigidly formalizing his concepts. A light approach to our formulations may be a hopeful beginning to better worked out principles and spare us the tediousness that often accompanies scientific clarification.

However, a discussant's freedom here to express himself in an impressionistic fashion (there may be considerable value to an impressionistic discussion) does not mean that what he is discussing is necessarily an artistic, although clinical, creation with little scientific meaning. Mrs. Sandford's article, "A Patient and Her Cats," is a case in point. Most of the discussants agreed that it was a charming paper and that the author displayed a sensitivity toward the patient that could be found only in a skillful therapist, which she obviously is. Her theoretical formulations, on the other hand, were to a large measure considered unjustified or irrelevant, and one discussant (Dr. Rosow) believed that therapeutic success was solely dependent upon the relationship aspects of the treatment rather than upon the integrative effects of her interpretations.

I choose to discuss this situation because it is commonly encountered in clinical psychoanalytic presentations. I agree also that warmth and empathy were important factors in the relatively successful outcome of her treatment. But I seriously doubt that Mrs. Sandford went to the trouble and labor of writing a paper simply to display her intuitive skills.

Some of the discussants extended her clinical formulations and this is always helpful. Others requested more data in order to feel convinced of the plausibility of her formulations.

Still it is difficult, if not impossible, to determine when one has presented enough data "to justify the conclusions" and whether the data are relevant.

Leaving aside further methodological issues, the value of any formulation rests upon its clinical usefulness, i.e., how it can be applied to our own cases. Mrs. Sandford believed she had to visit her patient and see "for herself" the patient's ego state as she had projected it into her cats and rooms. Is stepping outside of the analytic situation by seeing and responding necessary for therapeutic resolution? Can one integrate such a parameter with the theoretical formulations?

Apparently Mrs. Sandford believes it was necessary to visit her patient. A previous "classical" analysis was not sufficient and the patient showed improvement which seems to be more than just symptomatic. However, the author believes that her initial interpretations served as stepping stones for the resolution that followed the crisis of Spooty's death.

I wish to raise a rhetorical question based upon Mrs. Sandford's theory as to whether this case could have been handled exclusively in the consulting room. The question has to be rhetorical because no two cases are alike and obviously one cannot handle the same case in two different ways. Furthermore, therapeutic success is not necessarily a criteria as to whether one's approach is, at least, theoretically justified (*post hoc ergo propter hoc*).

This patient finally felt understood. Patients suffering from severe psychopathology have never felt understood in terms of their needs and feelings of helplessness and vulnerability; their guardians have been too narcissistically involved in their own needs and treat the child as an extension of the self. Mrs. Sandford's paper illustrates this point brilliantly.

At first her patient equated each interpretation with an assault, an impingement, upon a precariously held together self-representation. One can deduce from this reaction that the patient's early introjects were destructive and attacking, a situation that the patient was reliving when demanding that the analyst stop interpreting. The past history corroborated this point, but because the patient was experiencing anxiety about her early introjects in the consulting room, she therefore must have projected considerably upon the therapist. This would constitute a transference projection, and Elsie's reactions could perhaps be considered defenses against the transference.

I wonder whether bringing the cat to her hour was a reaction to the mounting anxiety of having converted Mrs. Sandford into a destructive image and she had to dilute the transference, so to speak, by reinforcing her projection on to the cat. The tea parties also might have been designed to further dilute so she could manage her anxiety and protect herself from projecting too much on to the therapist. At the same time she would be protecting her analyst from her destructiveness.

I realize that I, too, am making an alternative and incomplete formulation, but I believe it is within the same theoretical frame of reference as the author's (as is Dr. Searle's). If my surmise is, to some extent, correct, then it might be possible in such cases to keep the treatment in the consulting room. Interpreting defenses against the transference and the inability to dilute further after Spooty's death may have led to unmanageable anxiety and possibly to discontinuing treatment. I doubt, however, whether it would have been a permanent interruption because patients also experience considerable relief in being able to focalize their disruptive feelings on to the analyst.

Finally, it is not difficult to make retrospective formulations, especially when one is at a comfortable distance from the live patient! Still, the value of presentations as excellent as Mrs. Sandford's is in the stimulus they supply for reformulating our own clinical experiences. As we are able to incorporate theoretical principles such as she expounds, our vista about the applicability of the psychoanalytic method widens.

Peter L. Giovacchini, M.D.
Chicago, Illinois

Conjoint Therapy

To the Editors: Our understanding of interminable analysis is deepened by studying Dr. Rogawski's material. He describes patients who were unable to separate from the analyst—whom they perceived as an idealized source of all happiness in life—while devaluating and denigrating their spouses. Dr. Rogawski focuses on the use of conjoint therapy for ending the analyses of patients whose transference reactions were characterized by this primitive kind of splitting of the ego and the objects.

Dr. Rogawski says this split could not be resolved by interpretation within the transference. If we were to contend that these transference reactions *could* have been resolved by interpretation, our discussion would lead to polemics, or could proceed only on the basis of different data than that which Dr. Rogawski presents.[1]

So, for purposes of discussion it is important that we accept Dr. Rogawski's observation that the transference reactions could not be resolved by interpretation. It now becomes appropriate for us to wonder why this was true and to turn to the rest of Dr. Rogawski's data for an answer.

When we do this, we find that the question must be considered from a broader standpoint than is implied in the choice of individual or conjoint therapy for the ending of the analysis: we need to consider the formation of the transference in the first place.

Usually, when we offer a setting designed to provide the greatest possible opportunity for the spontaneous development of the transference, there is a continuity between the positive loving transference and whatever loved and loving objects the patient has been able to incorporate, maintain, or create in the past. To the degree that the patient can perceive that the transference is his own creation, the feelings it includes can enrich his relations with others rather than keep him defensively attached to the person of the analyst.

Dr. Rogawski, on the other hand, describes many ways in which he takes one side or another in the conflicts of his patient and thus structures the patient's reaction toward himself. The way which is most relevant to this paper, of course, is that he has "always met with the spouse of [his] patients once or several times during the course of their analysis." He observed that "Even the possibility of a meeting with the spouse reduced much acting out in the family. . . ."

The patient and his family may, of course, project an archaic superego image onto the analyst. But seeing the spouse gave Dr. Rogawski an actual disciplinary role in the family. Such action gives reality to projection and in this way tends to create an unresolvable dependent transference. "Even the possibility of a meeting" between the analyst and the spouse is thus a sufficient explanation of the development of transference reactions that cannot be resolved.

I would like to make one other comment on this description of conjoint therapy: Distorted perception of the analyst by the spouse is given as another reason for seeing the couple together, ". . . a face to face meeting with the spouse reduced my image from a parasitic, threatening monster to a more realistic perception. After the meeting I often felt that the spouse had turned from a foe into an ally of the therapeutic process."

The spouse's impression of the analyst comes primarily from the patient. Therefore, such a meeting with the spouse would seem to me to run a risk of wasting the capacity of the patient to organize and to project the image of a parasitic threatening monster and of provoking the spouse into making this image manifest.

Alfred Flarsheim, M.D.
Chicago, Illinois

To the Editors: It takes considerable courage or utter security to expose tentative, new modes of approach for one's colleagues' certain criticisms, particularly when, as with Dr.

[1]Giovacchini, P. *Methodological Aspects of Psychoanalytic Discussion.* To be published.

Rogawski's use of conjoint interviews, this represents a departure from the usual parameters of psychoanalysis.

As a contributor to *The Forum*, an open-minded innovator must welcome the challenges thrown at him when readers' own critical faculties are stimulated. So we have here a partial safeguard against embracing too rapidly those departures which might require further shoring-up to be on sound bases or which might introduce more problems than they solve. On the other hand, we also have a much-needed antidote to the tendency to regard methodology in a ritualistic fashion and to see any modification from previous forms as evidence of heresy. The panorama of views enables one to gain perspective both on the conservative and the adventuresome in the profession—and in oneself.

If psychoanalysis is to be viable, in theory and in practice, it must not only be open to, but must encompass, findings from related fields. Among the most important studies of recent years have been those which shed new light on the family as it contributes both to pathology and to health; it is evident that analysts are making use of these additions to our knowledge, and in many ways. I particularly applaud Dr. Grotjahn's comment that each therapist must be free to develop his own "style." There is nothing so stifling to creativity as the presumption that there is but one way to do psychotherapy.

Therapists differ—and Dr. Rogawski can, out of his own personality and particular experiences, comfortably and successfully use conjoint interviews in the finishing phase. Perhaps others would not find themselves at ease with this and should not, therefore, do it.

Among the experiences which encouraged Dr. Rogawski to dare "bringing the patient's reality to the treatment" were perhaps his extensive consultations with social workers who have a long heritage of family interviewing and of working close to what Redl once called "the foxholes of human behavior"—on the scenes where behavior happens.

To work on these fronts one must indeed give up the "exalted role" and settle for being human, too, for omnipotence is difficult to demonstrate in such "bright sunlight." To maintain it requires a kind of magic which involves not allowing the patient to observe too closely lest he see too clearly. Of course the patient, also, must give up his illusions that all his problems will be solved by his all-powerful patient, also, must give up his illusions that all (at least in part) that he is, with responsible relationships with other human beings. Both sacrifice fantasy. But then the discovery of reality may not always be totally painful; there is considerable pleasure in the mastery of it.

Jean Livermore, ACSW
Los Angeles, California

To the Editors: This symposium opens many areas for profitable discussion, foremost that of the break-away from the traditional analytic procedure of avoiding encounters with members of the family other than the nuclear patient. Seasoned analysts have long been unbound by ironclad rules in this regard. But many younger analysts, because of their fears of being considered deviant or unorthodox, are reluctant to see other family members.

It must be remembered that the goal of therapy is not that the patient become adjusted to the analyst, but rather that the microcosm of the physician-patient relationship carry over to the macrocosm of the patient's outside world. It happens too often that the therapeutic relationship acts as a device for closing off communications with other pertinent individuals in his life. Let me cite a case:

I had a young man in analysis who presented many problems. His family felt his main difficulty was inability to carry out a consistent school program. In therapy he brought out many other symptoms, such as fear of death from heart disease, guilt for masturbation and for stealing, and inordinate fear of his father. He had an older sister in analysis with another analyst and a brother in analysis with a third analyst. Since the husband of the older sister and both parents had never been permitted to see the other analysts, they were in complete ignorance of what was going on with the patients.

My patient agreed when I told him there was no communication in his family, and he described the deadly dinners at his home where no pertinent conversation ever took place. I suggested some family meetings. Fortunately, the other analysts offered no objections. These meetings, held at monthly intervals for two-hour sessions, did more to bring about the resolution of the intra-familial conflicts than had been accomplished by years of individual personal analysis.

But this is not conjoint therapy which must not be confused with the occasional interview of a mate or even with the sporadic meeting with both marital partners during the analytic process. Nor is it the kind of work which has been called "marriage counseling."

It is a specific form of therapy, psychoanalytically bound, which emphasizes conflictual value systems, ego defenses and adaptive devices of the two marital partners in a therapeutic setting in which both parties are active participants and in which the faltering marriage is treated as the presenting symptom.

It operates on the assumption that two individuals who had regarded each other sufficiently to get married should be able to work out their problems of adjustment to each other. The therapist is called upon to help convert the original romantic relationship into a workable and prolonged conjugal relationship.

When one or both partners are not sufficiently adult to be able to form a lasting conjugal tie, then either or both should undertake a full-scale personal analysis. In some cases, it reveals that the marriage had been so deeply rooted in neurotic mechanisms that no mature object relationship or mate cathexis was possible: in others, freeing oneself from infantile fixations releases new energy for intensifying the marital bond. Keeping the mate within the scope of the analysis helps encourage this marital investment.

Joseph C. Solomon, M.D.
San Francisco, California

Author's Response

To the Editors: I have said what I wanted in the paper, and I listened with great interest to all varied responses.

Alexander S. Rogawski, M.D.
Beverly Hills, California

Death Instinct

(Dr. Hanna Segal, a training analyst in the London Institute of Psychoanalysis, is a well-known exponent of Melanie Klein's work. Dr. Friedman questioned the validity of the death instinct in his paper "From Gradiva to the Death Instinct," and Dr. Segal was invited to discuss the paper. [The Psychoanalytic Forum, Vol. I, No. 1.] Inadvertently, part of her discussion was omitted. We present here her original and thought-provoking comments.)

Dr. Friedman's interesting article traces the genesis of the concept of the death instinct in Freud's own psychological preoccupations. His thesis is: (*a*) that Freud arrived at the concept of the death instinct as a way of mastering his own anxiety about death, stimulated by his cancer—"Thus man overcomes death, which in thought he has acknowledged.

No greater triumph of wish fulfillment is conceivable;" (*b*) that the concept of the death instinct is a defense against guilt about aggression, the denial of destructive impulses in relation to his mother being characteristic of Freud and often reflected in his psychological formulations; (*c*) that the anxiety about his own death may have led to a regression with a reactivation of his original ambivalence toward his mother, thus necessitating the formation of the concept of the death instinct as a defense.

I should like to examine these contentions separately. It seems to me quite likely that Freud's anxiety about his own death, as well as his preoccupation with death in the broader context of the 1914-18 war, was a contributory factor in his wish to tackle the problem of life and death and the psychological meaning of death. Such a preoccupation, however, is not itself pathological: indeed, coming to terms with the finiteness of life in general and the idea of one's own personal death in particular seems to be a fundamental psychological task in middle age.

Elliot Jaques, in a paper entitled "The Mid-Life Crisis,"[1] on the basis of his analysis of middle-aged patients and his study of the mid-life crisis in the life of artists, arrived at the conclusion that the basic problem of middle age is the acceptance of the idea of one's personal death. He also suggests that this task is particularly in the foreground in the creative artist whose capacity to work breaks down if he cannot deal with this problem. When he can deal with it and come to terms with death, his work achieves a new richness and maturity. In my paper, "The Psycho-Analytic Approach to Aesthetics,"[2] I also came to the conclusion that the artist must come to terms with death as a precondition for truly creative activity.

I quote in this paper the following dream of a middle-aged patient, a writer. "She was in a nursing home and the matron of this home, dressed in black, was going to kill a man and a woman. She herself was going to a fancy dress ball. She kept running out of the nursing home in various fancy disguises, but somehow something always went wrong, and she had to come back to the nursing home, and to meet the matron. At some point of the dream she was with her friend Joan."

Her friend, Joan, was for my patient the embodiment of mental health and stability. After telling me the dream, she said, "Joan was not in a fancy dress, she was undisguised, and I felt her to be so much more vulnerable than me." Then she immediately corrected herself, "Oh, of course I meant she was so much *less* vulnerable than me."

This slip of the patient gave us the key to the dream. The mentally healthy person is more vulnerable than my patient, she wears no disguises and she is vulnerable to illness and death. My patient herself escapes death, represented by the matron, by using various disguises. Her associations to this dream led us to a review of some of her leading symptoms in terms of her fear of, and attempted escape from, death. The disguises in the dream represented personifications, projective and introjective identifications, all three used by her as means of not living her own life and—in the light of the dream—not dying her own death.

In the following sessions, we had material indicating that she was inhibited in writing, because using words was "making things finite and separate." To free her creative writing, she had to accept not only the idea of the separateness and loss of her object and agression toward it, but also the idea of her own finiteness.

Thus, to my mind, not only is Freud's

[1]Read in the British Psycho-Analytic Society and shortly to be published in the International Journal of Psycho-Analysis.

[2]Segal, H. (1956). "The Psycho-Analytic Approach to Aesthetics." Int. J. Psa., Vol. 33.

anxiety about his own death part of a normal process of maturing, but his dealing with it by expanding his work and introducing a new concept is a further proof of his creative genius. "Thus man overcomes death, which in thought he has acknowledged" may be not the great achievement of wish fulfillment, but just a great achievement.

Anxiety about death is neither the prerogative of middle age nor that of the artist. It is the successful overcoming of this anxiety that characterizes the latter. Fear of death, and the struggle with it, seems to be an inseparable companion of life. It is a curious inconsistency of Freud that he never altered his original view that in the unconscious and in the mind of the child there is no concept of death, except by extension of castration anxiety. This seems a direct contradiction of his concept of the death instinct and his hypothesis that, under the stimulation of the anxiety provoked by the death instinct, the organism deflects it outwards. Surely this anxiety would not be an extension of the castration fear, but a more primitive anxiety of being annihilated by the death instinct; and, indeed, observation of small children shows that death, their own as well as their object's, is often on their minds and is frequently both acted out and verbalized.

The analysis of small children reveals fears more primitive than castration anxiety and pertaining to phantasies of death, such as fears of disappearance, dissolution, fragmentation, disintegration, etc. Dead babies often appear in play and phantasies which seem to represent a child's perception of part of itself as dead. The wished-for state of fusion with the mother can be experienced also as a dread of "not being." Again, small children suffer the fear of dying at the hand of persecutors, of being devoured, poisoned, cut to bits, burnt, etc.

What is the instinctual source of this anxiety? In her analysis of children, Melanie Klein discovered an inner world in the child's mind containing phantastical, threatening and death-bringing figures, early aspects of a superego, terrifying in their lethal power. The analysis of the child's phantasy life soon revealed that the primitive terrifying aspects of these internal figures sprang from the child's projected destructiveness. When the projections were analyzed, the internal figures lost their terrifying power. She was confirmed in her belief in the importance of the child's destructive drives by his depressive anxieties about the omnipotence of his destructiveness. Melanie Klein has given as much weight to the destructive impulses as to the libido and worked out the vicissitudes of the destructive drives parallel to and in conflict with the libidinal ones.

However, could not all these phenomena be accounted for by primary destructive drives? Is it necessary to postulate that the destructive drives themselves are due to the deflection of the death instinct? This leads to Dr. Friedman's second point, that the concept of the death instinct may be a defense against the admission of aggression.

If he were right about this, it would, to my mind, invalidate the concept as being a defense against a true realization. It is indeed true that aggression is a concept which does not get easy acceptance. The concept of the libido may be resisted in the world at large, but it is fully accepted by all psychoanalysts. As has been noted many times, aggression is a poor relative, often ignored or explained away even by psychoanalysts. If the concept of the death instinct were such a good defense against the acceptance of aggression, why has it not been more universally accepted? On the contrary, the concept of the libido has the widest acceptance, that of aggression comes second, and the death instinct is the most strongly resisted of all. Furthermore, it is precisely those analysts, e.g., followers of Melanie Klein, who attach most importance to the conflict between libido and aggression, who are more inclined to accept the concept of the death instinct.

Could it be that the idea of aggression, however painful, is in fact more tolerable than the idea of containing within oneself a permanent source of self-destruction? A 13-year-old patient showed her preference for aggression in the following way: She had missed a session because of a cold, and, in the next session, she described herself lying in bed with a cold, staring out of the window.[3] She thought of various activities she was looking forward to next week and said that, as she was lying in bed, she was wondering whether her "morbid spirit" would stop her doing any of it. Her "morbid spirit" was her expression for her tendency to get ill on the eve of any important event, and also her preference, which she often consciously experienced, for lying in bed and staring. She suddenly cheered up greatly at the thought that she might just have got this cold from her father, and she brought in a number of associations linking with the familiar context of her death wishes and hostility toward her father, followed by the introjection of a cold and hostile father (a relation having antecedents in her relation to her mother). It seemed that the persecution and depression due to the turning of hostility against her father was experienced as a positive relief from the thought of having this "morbid spirit" as a permanent part of herself directed against herself.

A concept, such as the one of life and death instincts, cannot be viewed as true or false. It can only be validated as useful or useless. If all clinical phenomena could be explained by the conflict between libidinal and destructive drives, the concept of the death instinct would not be useful and could be misused for defensive purposes, so the validation of this concept must lie in the clinical field.

Are there phenomena, not fully covered by using the concept of aggression towards an object, which are more adequately covered by using the concept of the death instinct? Freud himself thought that this was the case with masochism. It is, however, in work with schizoid and schizophrenic patients that Kleinian analysts find the clearest clinical evidence of the operation of the death instinct.

In contrast to Freud's statement that the death instinct is mute and can be observed only in its derivatives, in the schizophrenic it can often be observed operating directly and violently. One example of such an operation of the death instinct is "pathological projective identification."[4] In this form of projective identification, the primary attack is on the self. Whenever the ego experiences anxiety or pain, the part of the ego which experiences it is destructively splintered and projected into the object. The aim of this splintering and projection is to get rid of awareness. Here the aggression is directed primarily against the self; the aim is not to experience, that is, not to live. In a paper entitled "Some Schizoid Mechanisms Underlying Phobia Formation," I described a patient who wakes from a dream saying "I scatter, I splatter and I sink." In the session it became clear that her reaction to any stimulus of pain was a wish to disintegrate and abolish awareness. Interestingly enough, this was the same patient whose dream about the nursing home I quoted earlier in connection with coming to terms with death. The great difficulties she had in that area were due to the enormous anxiety stirred up by the operation of her death instinct in the "scattering, splattering and sinking."

Severe anorexias also often reveal anxieties related to a direct operation of the death in-

[3]She could remember the time when she stared at the sky from her pram. Such staring is characteristic of schizoid babies.

[4]Bion, W. (1956). "Development of Schizophrenic Thought." Int. J. Psa., Vol. 37.

stinct. A little girl patient had from birth refused first the breast, then the bottle, when she was weaned in despair of making her accept the breast and then solid foods. At the time when she started her analysis, at age 4, she still fed exclusively on tins of baby food. Her typical reaction to any form of separation from the analyst was a feeling of falling to pieces. For instance, she would cut out a paper doll, representing herself, cut it to pieces and then beg the analyst either to tie the child herself with string or to tie the paper doll. Like the older patient, her primary reaction to frustration was to "scatter."

Another method was to immobilize herself and make herself into a doll. In her play, dolls would represent her, and in her looks and appearance she was extremely doll-like. A frequent game was to arrange a situation in which the analyst was to play the mother of the doll and then be unable to reach her, the child saying "Mum cannot reach her, she will die." She constantly emphasized the point that, unless Mum could reach her and bring her to life, she would fall into pieces or become an inanimate doll.

Her material also contained, as would be expected, a great deal of persecution: the breast was cold and "smelly," and it was clear from the beginning she could not feed because of her fears of being poisoned. This paranoia was, however, not only a projection onto her mother of her aggression toward mother, but also of her self-destructive wishes. If she wanted to die or to fall to pieces, the mother who did not reach her or save her was felt as the person wishing her death.

In an adult anorexic schizoid patient, the hatred and contempt of the part of her that wished to live was very much in evidence. The image of the dying baby played a large part in her analysis. She had a perception of a part of herself as a dying baby and a constant fear of death. In the analysis it appeared that the baby was dying because someone hated the baby feeding at the mother's breast.

There was always a third, interfering, death-bringing factor between the breast and the baby. It appeared first as an older brother, felt as a personification of hatred, who interfered between her and the feeding breast. Then it became clear that the brother was used as a vehicle for projection and that the third party was perceived as an aspect of the breast hating her or of herself hating the breast. The third party, interfering between the baby and the breast, was the part of herself hating herself as the feeding baby. She had an utter hatred and contempt for, and a wish to annihilate, the baby part of herself—felt as the part containing the life instinct, the part that wanted to feed and live. The hatred of this part was due to the fact that it was that part of her which could experience pain. It is the baby wanting to live and feed that has to experience need, pain, envy, anger, jealousy, aggression, etc., and the hating part of her wanted to annihilate this source of pain. Withdrawal into sleep—this brother of death—was a frequent way of dealing with this troublesome baby. It was not the normal sleep, she often emphasized, but something she described as "more related to not being or being dead."

Another schizophrenic phenomenon happening under the aegis of the death instinct is the evacuation taking the place of introjection. In *Learning from Experience*, Bion[5] describes a method of functioning in which the mind responds to any stimulus, external or internal, by evacuation. Basically, when the infant experiences hunger, it rids itself of the hunger by projecting it and experiences no need to take in the food or introject the breast. Ultimately, the aim of such functioning is to get rid of all sensation and achieve peace.

---

[5]Bion, W. (1962). *Learning From Experience.* New York: Basic Books.

The concept of the death instinct is an inevitable corollary of the pleasure-pain principle. Freud's idea of the motor discharge in order to "disemburden the psyche from stimuli" could be seen as the operation of the death instinct. In terms of the pleasure-pain functioning, whenever life does not offer pleasure and pain arises, the quickest way of getting rid of the pain is death. The point was very succinctly made by a schizoid patient who was a corset fetishist. His fetishistic ritual represented a return to the womb and union with mother as a painless state.

This patient was extremely intolerant of frustration. He once propounded quite seriously that, if he ever had sciatica, he would painlessly commit suicide. He saw no reason why he should suffer pain. Probably at the primitive level there is a part of everyone which feels the same way, and only when the wish to live is strong enough, and objects are invested with libido, can the wish to die rather than experience pain be overcome.

In the last few pages of *Martin Eden*, Jack London describes the hero committing suicide by drowning. The passage conveys something of the basic struggle between the life and death instinct. Martin Eden finds himself trying to swim: "It was the automatic instinct to live. He ceased swimming, but the moment he felt the water rising above his mouth, his hands struck out sharply with a lifting movement. 'The will to live,' he thought, and the thought was accompanied by a sneer."

The contempt for the part wishing to live, similar to the contempt I described in the patient above, is strongly brought out. " 'The will to live,' he thought disdainfully." All the pain in drowning he attributes to this will to live. " 'This hurt was not death,' was the thought that oscillated through his reeling consciousness. It was life, the pangs of life, this awful suffocating feeling. It was the last blow life could deal him."

Melanie Klein accepts the concept of the life and death instincts as a basic metapsychological concept, and she bases her ideas of the early object relations and ego structure on the polarity of instincts. In her view, there is sufficient ego at birth to experience anxiety and to use primitive mechanisms of defense. It is the ego, therefore, which responds to the anxiety stirred by the death instinct by deflecting it.

Freud saw this deflection as a conversion into aggression. In Melanie Klein's view, this deflection consists partly of a projection into an object and partly of a conversion into the aggression against the now threatening object. In deflecting the death instinct, the ego produces the first splitting within itself between the life and death instinct, and in the object, between the ideal object to which the infant's libido is directed and the persecutory object, toward which hate is directed. The introjection of these early objects forms the basis of ego and superego structure.

It has been argued that this emphasis on the polarity of instincts does not allow for the importance of environment. This does not at all follow. Mother's handling of the baby is vital for the outcome of the instinctual conflict. She must not only provide sufficient love and care to help the infant's libido to develop and grow—she must also be able to contain and deal with the infant's projection of the death instinct. The little girl, whose material I quoted, emphasizes that the baby will die if "Mum" does not reach it. The way in which that particular mother failed to reach her baby had to do with her inability to contain her daughter's projections. She was, in fact, a loving and devoted mother, not failing the infant in that way, but she was unable to tolerate either anxiety or aggression in the baby—she could not contain the deflected death instinct.

Hanna Segal, M.B.CH.B.
London, England

The Psychoanalytic

FORUM

Table of Contents Vol. 1, No. 4, Winter, 1966

continued

The Forum

Title **Office Treatment of Schizophrenic Patients by Psychoanalysis**

Author **L. Bryce Boyer, M.D.**

Co-Chairman of the Research Committee of the San Francisco Psychoanalytic Society and Institute, and former Research Psychiatrist with the Departments of Anthropology of the Universities of California (Berkeley) and New Mexico. He is concerned mainly with the therapy of schizophrenics, his research of 17 years with the applicability of psychoanalysis to the treatment of psychotics and with cross-disciplinary studies. He has published some 40 papers pertaining to entomology, medicine, psychiatry, psychoanalysis and combined anthropology and psychoanalysis.

Discussants

Charles Brenner, M.D.
Has published widely in his 20 years as a practicing psychoanalyst. "The Psychopathology of the Psychoses" is a chapter in his second book, *Psychoanalytic Concepts and the Structural Theory*, co-authored with Dr. Jacob Arlow. Dr. Brenner is President-Elect of the American Psychoanalytic Association.

Milton Wexler, PH.D.
Member of the Scientific Advisory Board of the Foundation for Research in Psychoanalysis and practicing psychoanalyst. Recipient in 1948 of a Menninger Foundation research grant to investigate the problem of psychoanalytic therapy of schizophrenia, Dr. Wexler has since maintained special interest and has written, taught and researched in this area.

Gustav Bychowski, M.D.
Clinical Professor of Psychiatry and Training Analyst at the State University of New York, Downstate Medical Center, and Preceptor at the Institute of Psychiatry at Mount Sinai Hospital. *Psychotherapy of Psychosis*, one of his many published works, is the first book dealing comprehensively with the application of psychoanalysis to the treatment of psychosis.

John N. Rosen, M.D.
The Institute for Direct Analysis at Temple University, where he is Clinical Professor of Psychiatry, studies the techniques and results of work with psychotics in which Dr. Rosen pioneered and continues to investigate. With others, he has contributed nearly 200 publications on the subject.

Herbert A. Rosenfeld, M.D.
Has been engaged in training analysts and lecturing at the Institute of Psychoanalysis in London since 1949. In his private practice he has treated many psychotic and borderline patients by psychoanalysis. He has written several papers on narcissistic, schizophrenic and depressed patients whose analyses present difficult technical problems. Some of his work has recently been published in the book, *Psychotic States*.

Office Treatment of Schizophrenic Patients by Psychoanalysis[1]

L. Bryce Boyer, M.D.
Berkeley, California

Introduction

During more than 17 years, I have conducted a study directed toward evaluating the efficacy of psychoanalytic therapy with few parameters in the office treatment of schizophrenic individuals. All prospective patients under the age of 50 years who suffered from borderline or overt schizophrenia or schizoaffective psychoses were included. The 17 patients who supply the data for this report exclude chronically regressed, "back ward" individuals, and all had average or superior intelligence. Some were seen at reduced rates. No waiting list was kept; patients were accepted when they were referred and therapeutic hours were open.

In the present series, the psychotic core has been altered fundamentally within two years, as a rule. All but three of the patients developed transference neuroses which were usually resolved.

Under the term "psychotic core" Bychowski(5) subsumed three points of special interest for the understanding of future psychotic development: (*a*) persistence and prevalence of archaic forms of functioning such as magic thinking and thinking on the original concrete level; (*b*) persistence and prevalence of such primitive mechanisms as introjection, primary identification and projection, though of universal significance for every mental functioning, assume the leading role and culminate in paranoid formations in individuals under consideration; and (*c*) splitting of the ego, occurring according to the original highly ambivalent attitudes of the child toward essential figures of his environment.

I submit that psychoanalysis can be used for the successful treatment of borderline and schizophrenic patients of the types included in this study, and that countertransference problems may constitute the *major obstacle* to the psychoanalytic treatment of such patients. It remains moot whether successful outcome depends upon special qualifications of the therapist. My data suggest that the professional and theoretical orientation of the analyst is a major determining factor.

Theoretical Orientation

The roots of all functional psychoses have been traced to the qualities of the symbiotic and separation-individuation phases described by Mahler and her co-workers. The structure of the ego and superego results from the interaction of inborn and socialization factors, which determine the nature of their introjects. Deprivation in infancy alone—whether due predominantly to hereditary and/or constitutional defects within the babies or to psychological defects within their mothering figures—does not produce all of the group of schizophrenias. The schizophrenic has traversed to some degree all phases of psychosexual and psychosocial development, has manifold areas of developmental failure and fixations and uneven levels of ego and superego development, and the various ego functions are affected differently from patient to patient. As observed by Arlow and Brenner(1) and Glover,(8) defensive regression

[1]This paper is extracted from *Psychoanalytic Treatment of the Characterological and Schizophrenic Disorders*, by L. Bryce Boyer, M.D. and Peter L. Giovacchini, M.D., soon to be published by International Science Press. A number of extensive references to clinical material and relevant literature had to be omitted in this context.

typically transpires in response to adolescent or postadolescent stresses which reawaken unresolved oedipal conflicts.

No human action can be conceptualized to be free of hereditary factors. The hypothesis that schizophrenia is due especially to environmental influences has led to many investigations of schizophrenic patients and their families. Research has shown that schizophrenic behavior serves various functions in particular kinds of family organizations and cultural groups and that serious impairment of ego functioning may be related to the failure of the parents to transmit properly the usual communicational tools of the society. The families of schizophrenic patients have discouraged the learning of methods of communication which are based predominantly on secondary process logic and include generally understood, rather than idiosyncratic, symbolic connotations. Individuals who have been reared in such unfavorable milieux do not learn to exchange information well in extrafamilial or cross-cultural situations. It seems likely that they regress defensively when confrontation with their message-sending-and-receiving difficulties are superimposed upon already existent intrapsychic conflicts.

Consistent with this bias regarding the origins of schizophrenia is the notion that the primary therapeutic task is to restore and/or develop a reasonable ego and superego. Theoretically this can be accomplished by modifying or replacing cold, unloving, and archaic ego and superego introjects. Therapy must be directed toward the growth of intrapsychic and interpersonal communication techniques.

Methodology

First let me tell you of my procedure with prospective patients who came to my office. All individuals of the groups mentioned above were accepted for treatment except those for whom there was not time or who could not pay minimal fees. Once the diagnosis was made, the patient was told that the object of therapy was to make him comfortable with himself, that treatment was to be of an experimental nature and that an indefinite period might be spent in our collaborative work. During the vis-à-vis hour or hours, I explained the analytic procedure as one does with neurotics. In addition, I set clear criteria regarding vacation periods, interview attendance and payment arrangements. (3)

Couch treatment started after the patient had been seen no more than four times—usually after one or two face to face interviews. Free association techniques were used from the beginning. Once couch therapy was instituted, few parameters were employed, and they were—with one exception—of the ordinary varieties used in the analyses of neurotics, such as the arbitrary setting of a termination date in one instance, the demand bills be paid on time in two cases, and the instruction to face a phobic object in several analyses. (3) None of the 17 patients who are included in this series was given medicine at any time while being seen in the office. Telephone contacts were discouraged and occurred rarely, except in two of the three cases with whom failures resulted. Direct communication with relatives was rare and almost nonexistent after office treatment began. Patients were not called by their first names. They were seen four times weekly, except for one of the two women whose treatment failed. (She was seen five or six times weekly during some months of treatment.) As Searles (14) has noted, the techniques employed in the care of the patients included in this study have more nearly approached orthodox psychoanalytic treatment than has been reported previously in any detail in the literature.

Five of the six patients who were first interviewed in hospital were under the care of other psychiatrists at the time. With one exception, I did not involve myself in the physical or drug therapy of any of those patients. I restricted my activities to observation and interpretations. All of these cases then came to the office for therapy and, although they were still actively psychotic, were begun in analysis after having been given the conditions of therapy while still in hospital. Only two of the 17 patients were hospitalized during treatment with me.

For purposes of amplification, the treatment of these patients can be divided conceptually into two phases. In the first phase, reasonably stable, loving introjects appear to be established within the patient, and psychotic thinking patterns and behavior are removed or their cathexes are markedly diminished. At the end of this artificially divided first period, a transference neurosis has developed, replacing the transference psychosis. The second phase constitutes the analysis of the transference neurosis.

Psychotics, too, develop transference reactions to the therapist. They have been called transference psychosis (13) or delusional transference. (10) Searles (14) has written: "The difficulty of discerning the transference aspects of one's relationship with the [chronically schizophrenic] patient can be traced to his having regressed to a state of ego-functioning which is marked by severe impairment in his capacity either to differentiate among, or to integrate, his experiences. He is so incompletely differentiated in his ego-functioning that he tends to feel not that the therapist reminds him of or is like, his mother or father . . . but rather his functioning toward the therapist is couched in the unscrutinized assumption that the therapist *is* the mother or father."

The matter is further complicated by the fragmented nature of the patient's introjects which are projected onto the therapist, so that the analyst may during the course of even a few minutes be reacted to as though he were an actualization of a mental representation of a part of first this person and then that. Additionally, under the influence of the primary process, cathexes are sometimes loose and easily displaceable, so that an intense reaction which is present at one moment may be misjudged by the therapist to indicate a more serious involvement (than later analysis will indicate to be the case) with the introjected and usually distorted aspect of the person represented.

The psychotic patients in this study had at all times areas in which their regressions were similar to the regressive level of neurotics. Thus, intermixed with the use of transferences and the presence of the transference psychosis which developed during the treatment of each, elements of transference neurosis were present simultaneously. A very complicated transference relationship was the rule. Some patients who had been hospitalized immediately before entering analysis quickly projected fragmented introjects onto me. At the same time, their relationships with other individuals had varying degrees of objectivity. Others, who appeared to be less psychotic, first developed a relationship in which a transference neurosis was evident and only later were transference psychosis elements obvious. Since those individuals functioned better in their everyday lives by that time, I considered it a sign of progress when they began to focus their reexperienced infantile emotions onto me, rather than to maintain them in their previously generalized state.

Psychotherapists have sought usually to avoid states of further regression in the treatment of psychotic patients. I think the patient's ability to regress in a controlled manner in the therapeutic situation is a sign of development of trust and psychic structuralization. If no psychotic transference develops to be analyzed, there is little likelihood of cure; the most one can hope for is isolation or encapsulation of the psychotic process.

The course of treatment, then, constituted a continuum which can be viewed from the side of changing transference relationships.

After there had been more or less controlled regression to a stage where psychotic transference elements were obvious and these had been effectively analyzed, a neurotic transference relationship ensued. Sometimes this neurotic transference seemed to have the same content as that which had developed before the regression to the psychotic transference state, but the bases of the initial neurotic transference had been cleared of parts of their meanings and could be analyzed meaningfully from the standpoint of a more advanced period of psychosexual development.

To state the case slightly differently: The second phase of the arbitrarily divided continuum constituted the analysis of the neurotic character disorder and its attendant symptomatology. Most therapists of psychotics have not sought to continue treatment to the resolution of these elements. However, the patients included here gave no indication of a desire to discontinue therapy after they had lost their psychotic symptomatology and thinking patterns. I wished to continue because of the possibility that neurotic elements might be masking further psychotic mechanisms or process, inasmuch as a goal of this study was to test the hypothesis that psychoses can be cured by the use of psychoanalysis.

My remarks in this paper are directed to the first of the artificially divided phases, however, since there appeared to be little to distinguish the second phase from the usual analyses of neurotics. Nevertheless, during the second phase, in times of stress, the patients sometimes defensively recathected psychotic thinking and behavioral patterns for short periods, but the intensity of such recathexis was less than that observed during the first phase; when the reasons for the regressions were determined, they quickly abated.

As the result of more than two decades of work with schizophrenics, I believe that few, if any, patients are truly inaccessible. Of my patients, seven had been hospitalized just before they began treatment with me; they believed in the reality of their hallucinations and/or delusions. Four had received courses of electroplexy and one had undergone insulin shock therapy. Seven cases were borderline schizophrenics whose psychotic thinking became obvious only after they lay on the couch.

Therapy during the first phase is directed toward the replacement or modification of undesirable introjects—that is, to restoration and/or development of a reasonable ego and superego. Clearly, the first step in preparing the patient to accomplish such goals is to establish meaningful and lasting contact with him. I strive to do this in an atmosphere of abstinence and through the use of interpretation. I believe that such a technique is most apt to offer true ego support, through the integrative and structuralizing effects of interpretation and through the immediate establishment for the patient of an atmosphere in which symptoms are treated calmly and as subjects for investigation.

Throughout this research project, I have considered the primary initial goal of therapy to be to enable the patient to develop altered introjects. At the same time, I have attempted to use interpretations as the ultimate therapeutic tool. The patient is taught consistently to regard his conflicts as subjects for study and to develop a working alliance with the analyst. Thus, treatment begins with steady but gentle confrontations with distortions, contradictions and other abandonments of reality, coincident with interpretations which are, as a rule, of the defensive functions of the products of his psychotic thinking.

Many years ago, I responded rather indiscriminately to the patient's productions, interpreting defensive products of the derivatives of both sexual and aggressive drives. Now, I tend initially to restrict my interpretations to the aggressive aspects of whatever material is presented and to ignore material stemming from sexual drives per se unless an erotized transference which may prove to be unwieldy threatens to develop. Of course, at the same time, such interpretations are made through the technique of stressing the object relationship aspects of the utilization of such aggressive drive derivatives.

Another shift in my technique over the years has been in the direction of choosing to deal with depressive material when possible in preference to persistently pursuing the products of paranoid ideation.

Both changes in technique reflect my growing conviction that ego introjects cannot be altered efficiently unless simultaneous changes take place in the superego introjects, in the direction of reducing the archaic, sadistic nature of that psychical structure. However, in contrast to Wexler (15) and others, I do not give direct superego support. I stress the patient's anxiety when he factually has transgressed morality, and I label asocial and antisocial actions by their common names. When his "sins" have been moral infringements in thought only, I ask him to consider whether his thoughts have harmed anyone. Within the framework of the therapeutic situation, such support is not limited to the prohibitive functions of the superego.

I have called the initial period of treatment the "noisy phase." It is unusual that such patients can tolerate my silence for long periods. When they seem to be developing too-great anxiety, I make noncommittal noises or request amplification. Almost any sound seems to reassure the patient that he has neither been deserted nor has he magically committed murder.

In general, an interpretation of content emphasizing forbidden or frightening wishes arouses feelings of guilt, whereas one concerning defense gives the patient the sense that the therapist—whom he perceives to a large degree as a superego figure—appreciates how much he struggles against his impulses. However, content interpretation can at times serve as a means of regaining contact with the patient when it becomes necessary to demonstrate to him that the therapist does not understand some small part of what he tries to communicate.

Numerous writers have called attention to the fact that in the presence of inadequate differentiation of id and ego, tensions are frequently fixed to physical phenomena. In the treatment of psychotics, the analysis of the meanings of phenomena that result from automatic actions of bodily systems innervated by the voluntary and involuntary nervous systems is sometimes mandatory before further differentiation of id and ego can transpire. Such analysis is usually necessary during the period while the patient is psychotic; like Searles, (14) I have found it to be an essential step during the resolution of the transference psychosis. Subsequently, the defensive regression to the utilization of such phenomena must be repeatedly analyzed.

It is a noteworthy and mysterious fact that no patient to whom treatment was offered has refused. A potentially favorable transference relationship existed from the beginning. Those patients who have spoken to this point stated that they interpreted my not having been upset by their recitations of material which seemed extremely dangerous to them to signify that I was too strong and wise to be made anxious.

Although various authors have discussed the importance of accurate interpretations in dealing with the schizophrenic, what constitutes an accurate or a wrong interpretation presents a most complex problem. In general, in my experience, *accurate* interpretations are more detrimental to the course of treatment than are totally inaccurate or partially wrong statements and explanations, *when the correct statements are faulty as to timing*—that is, when they pertain to phenomena which are not near enough to the conscious, economic or dynamic agenda, to paraphrase Loewenstein.

Fromm-Reichmann has also written of the dangers of pretense of understanding. I cannot speak to this because when I think I have failed to understand, I let the patient know my lack of comprehension and invite him to amplify and clarify. Additionally, I never consciously play a role.

It is obvious that I disagree with those who advocate nonanalytical and parametric methods of fostering a "positive transference" as a means of establishing contact. The schizophrenic is terrified of the potential destructiveness of his impulses and when the emergence of hatred of former love objects is discouraged, he thinks the therapist fears his own or the patient's hostility. I refer to hostility which is expressed in words or symbolically and not to that which shows itself in assault. No patient has ever attacked me in the office. When I have been attacked or threatened with attack by a hospitalized patient, and have been unable to mollify the patient's panic or rage by interpretative means, I have commanded cessation or directed attendants to calm the patient physically. When hostility is expressed in words or symbols, they are interpreted from the standpoint of their defensive or testing functions. The appearance of hostility is not discouraged, but the rate and intensity of its emergence are slaked by the timing of interpretations.

Above all, I wish to emphasize the importance of consistency in attitude and technique; my attitude and technique can best be described by the terms calmness, indirectly-communicated optimism, and scientific detachment. All of these phenomena are superimposed, obviously, on a capacity to understand productions which are influenced heavily by primary process thinking and some knowledge of why they are used at the times they are employed.

I periodically remind patients that interpretations are made tentatively and solicit their active cooperation in validation and modifications of answers to enigmas. This procedure enhances the development of at least the observing and synthesizing functions and reduces the severity of the patient's primitive superego introjects by permitting him to view his new parent-model as fallible.

Results

The treatment of this series of 17 patients was terminated at least two years ago, except for one patient who took his life. Fourteen appear thus far to have outcomes which can be classified as satisfactory or, in some cases, most encouraging. The number of cases involved and the short time which has elapsed since their termination of treatment make this an interim report.

It has been noted regularly that psychotic states which include overt anxiety and mood changes, particularly depressive manifestations (8) have a better likelihood of therapeutic success. All of the patients in this series manifested overt anxiety and the majority could well have been labeled to suffer from schizo-affective psychoses, with depressive aspects prevailing over manic, although several patients experienced periodic hypomanic episodes. All evidenced extremely punitive superegos.

Authors have discouraged regularly (since about 1908) the use of analytic therapy for paranoid schizophrenics. In this series, two patients, both male, had systematized persecutory delusions. One had had hallucinations during a period of late adolescence and early adulthood (symptoms which reappeared during one phase of his selective analytic regression), but the other man never experienced hallucinations and in previous years might well have been labeled a paranoiac. Both recovered from their paranoid states although they both remained hampered by obsessive-compulsive character disorders. Each man had been psychotic for many years before analysis; neither has regressed since termination of analysis.

The treatment of one man lasted six years and ended ten years ago; that of the other lasted five years and was terminated eight years ago. Each reentered analysis at a later time for relief of depressive symptomatology and received further assistance in overcoming obsessive-compulsive rigidity.

Three cases of this series ended in outright failure. The lack of success with two of them appeared to have been related more to my problems than theirs; I believe the third failed because of faulty judgment on my part.

Discussion

When a psychotic takes the couch, certain facets of his ego and superego are already in a deeper state of regression than we usually expect the neurotic to reach in his therapy. He reenacts the early mother-child relationship, although the areas of ego and superego regression which permit such a reliving differ from patient to patient. We recall that the unfolding of conflict-free ego spheres is dependent upon the mother-infant relationship. In the treatment situation, identification with the actual frustrator is enhanced and there exists a danger of the patient's becoming too like the therapist and being unable to develop subsequently in a manner optimal to his personal potential. The therapist appears for a time to become a variant of Winnicott's (16) transitional object or Balint's (2) ocnophilic object. Empirically, the second phase of treatment has been found to eradicate this danger.

The psychotic patient wishes consciously to validate his auditory perceptions through other perceptual experience, notably visual and tactile, and sometimes presses to be allowed to sit. When he is met with questions concerning his desire to sit, he develops anxiety which stimulates the emergence of data, serving the analytic purpose. Patients have verbalized subsequently their gratitude that they had not been encouraged to face or touch me.

As an example, during the third year of the analysis of a borderline schizophrenic who had used every technique I have ever witnessed in her attempts to seduce me to abandon following rigorously the analytic technique, she suddenly blocked in her associations and had an intense desire to sit and look at me. I asked her to tell me what her wish to see me brought to her mind. She became furious and hurled the following words at me, the transition in her vocal expression mirroring the change in the content of the sentence. First she shouted a few words, then her tone became scathingly sarcastic, then softer and ultimately loving. She said: "You God-damned rat fink, you buddy, you pal, you dear, sweet, kind man. Do you know that if you had not been incorruptible throughout my analysis, I'd have been dead long ago? I used to be afraid, too, that you'd grate off like a potato. I'm so glad you're ungratable and haven't been destroyed."

Patients have commonly said that their remaining on the couch had made them aware of the magical nature of their fears of being destroyed by me or of their destruction of me which at times they sought to achieve through fusion via tactile or visual contact. It is my impression that the notion that visual and/or tactile contact are of primary importance in the treatment of psychotics has been overstressed.

In infants, such contact abets the differentiation of id and ego. In certain acute episodes of psychotic regression, such contact is also mandatory for the reestablishment of some degree of autonomy, as is evident by the terror expressed by patients at some times when they are deprived of the sight or touch of the therapist.

It is my opinion that the helplessness of the psychotic is exaggerated in the minds of many therapists who, by their attitudes, encourage patients to remain deeply regressed at times by rewarding them for such infantile behavior—that is, by supplying the secondary gains sought by the patients.

In order to develop a working alliance with psychotics, it behooves us to appeal to the more mature aspects of the patient's ego whenever possible. Clearly, in the presence of too-great anxiety, no analysis can take place. I am suggesting that in the analysis of psychotics, especially during periods of acute regression, too little importance has been placed on the value of words and that therapists have underestimated the resiliency of their patients. They appear to have forgotten sometimes that the psychotic patient is not *all* psychotic and that he has both normal and neurotic aspects which can be called into service by directing attention to them.

The analyst is both a superego and witness to the patient; these roles are of inestimable importance in the treatment of the psychotic. As witness, he serves as an accessory, reminding memory—an autonomous ego. When the patient has verbalized data, those data become more real and more easily remembered, possibly a partial result of auditory perception. The analyst stores previously imparted data and recalls them to the patient at appropriate times. Communicated private data become objective and social data, especially if they are not allowed to become repressed.

Many analysts have stressed the role of the superego in schizophrenia.(9,11,15) I have spoken of my means of affording superego support. In general I communicate indirectly my philosophy that guilt is appropriate when one's behavior, without rational cause, jeopardizes the rights and comforts of others.

I believe revision of faulty ego and superego structures in psychotic patients of the types included can be accomplished by the analytic process. The success of that process is dependent upon two main phenomena: (*a*) In a controlled situation, qualities of the new parent-model, the therapist, can be introjected and such introjection can alter unhealthy nuclei(7) of the patient's ego and superego; (*b*) Interpretation has a structuralizing effect.(4)

Schizophrenic patients worry that their aggressive tendencies will destroy the object or, projected onto the object, result in their own destruction. Psychic structuralization is dependent upon neutralization of the aggressive drive and its internalization into the ego and superego for which it supplies motor power. It is probable that interpretation is the principal tool which leads to neutralization of the aggressive drive and to its being made available for such internalization. I suggest that, in contrast to the prevailing attitude of psychoanalysts regarding the therapeutic procedure of choice for such patients, the analytic method, modified as little as possible, may be not only preferable *but mandatory* if the psychotic processes of the patients are not to be merely masked or isolated.

Clearly the internal security of the therapist is of signal importance. I would assume that most properly trained psychoanalysts could become relatively free of anxiety while dealing with psychotic patients and proficient at treating them.

A number of therapists have stressed that the role of countertransference is of great importance for the successful outcome of treatment of schizophrenics.(6,12) I learned that when dealing with patients whose conflicts struck literally too close to home, I developed a countertransference neurosis. Further personal analysis enabled me to treat successfully two patients with whom I had previously failed.

Summary

For 17 years I have treated borderline and overtly schizophrenic patients by the analytic method ordinarily reserved for the treatment of neurotics. In seminar groups, colleagues have remarked that I was more strictly and consistently analytical while treating psychotics than they were with neurotics.

The patients were all of average to superior intelligence; the symptom picture of almost all included strong depressive tendencies. No chronically regressed, withdrawn patients were studied.

In the time elapsed since termination, 14 of the 17 cases have achieved satisfactory or striking improvements. There has been no psychotic or serious neurotic regression among them during periods which range from two to ten years. The data suggest that, with patients such as those included, therapists have used more parametric and extra-analytic procedures than have been necessary or, perhaps, advisable.

I suggest that the psychotic process is reversible in some patients and that we, as analysts, might aim not at encapsulation of at least some psychoses, but at their cure. I believe the role of genetic interpretations is as important in the treatment of psychotics as it is with neurotics and that the likelihood of successful therapy will be enhanced by the therapist's taking only such actions as do not jeopardize subsequent use of interpretations.

Bibliography

1. Arlow, J. and Brenner, C. (1964). *Psychoanalytic Concepts and the Structural Theory*. New York: Int. Univ. Press.
2. Balint, M. (1959). *Thrills and Regressions*. London: Hogarth Press.
3. Boyer, L. (1961). "Provisional Evaluation of Psycho-Analysis With Few Parameters Employed in the Treatment of Schizophrenia." Int. J. Psa., Vol. 42.
4. Boyer, L. and Giovacchini, P. *Psychoanalytic Treatment of the Characterological and Schizophrenic Disorders*. (To be published.)
5. Bychowski, G. (1957). "From Latent to Manifest Schizophrenia." Congress Report of the Second Int. Congress for Psychiatry, Vol. 3. (Zurich).
6. Fromm-Reichmann, F. (1950). *Principles of Intensive Psychotherapy*. Chicago: Univ. of Chicago Press.
7. Glover, E. (1930). "Grades of Ego-Differentiation." Int. J. Psa., Vol. 11.
8. ———. (1955). *The Technique of Psychoanalysis*. New York: Int. Univ. Press.
9. Hoedemaker, E. (1955). "The Therapeutic Process in the Treatment of Schizophrenia." J. Amer. Psa. Assn., Vol. 3.
10. Little, M. (1958). "On Delusional Transference (Transference Psychosis)." Int. J. Psa., Vol. 39.
11. Pious, W. (1949). "The Pathogenic Process in Schizophrenia." Bull. of the Menninger Clinic, Vol. 13.
12. Rosenfeld, H. (1952). "Transference Phenomena and Transference Analysis in an Acute Catatonic Schizophrenic Patient." Int. J. Psa., Vol. 33.
13. ———. (1954). "Considerations Regarding the Psycho-Analytic Approach to Acute and Chronic Schizophrenia." *Ibid.*, Vol. 35.
14. Searles, H. (1963). "Transference Psychosis in the Psychotherapy of Chronic Schizophrenia." Int. J. Psa., Vol. 44.
15. Wexler, M. (1951). "The Structural Problem in Schizophrenia: Therapeutic Implications." Int. J. Psa., Vol. 37.
16. Winnicott, D. (1953). "Transitional Objects and Transitional Phenomena." Int. J. Psa., Vol. 34.

3021 Telegraph Avenue
Berkeley 5, California

Discussant

Charles Brenner, M.D.
New York, New York

As Dr. Boyer emphasized, his report is an interim one. As experience with analyzing psychotic patients accumulates, some details of his current views may change. What seems to me important to emphasize at present is that many patients who could be helped by analysis are denied the opportunity because of the mistaken idea that a patient who is psychotic is *ipso facto* unanalyzable. In my opinion, some are analyzable and some are not, as is the case with neurotic patients.

My own experience in analyzing psychotic patients has been less extensive than Dr. Boyer's. Moreover, the ones whom I have treated were less disturbed than were the sickest of his when their analyses began. Perhaps for these reasons I have been less impressed than has Dr. Boyer by evidences of prompt and considerable improvement.

The only patient I recall who had begun to hallucinate (auditorily) just before starting analysis did in fact enjoy a prompt cessation of his hallucinations after treatment began and was able to resume his university studies after the first year of analysis. Other patients, with less ominous initial symptoms, showed much less in the way of rapid improvement. Indeed, I have come to expect considerably slower progress in the analyses of psychotic patients than in those of neurotic ones.

I am in agreement with Dr. Boyer's main points as outlined in his summary. My experience with treating psychotic patients in an office setting has convinced me, too, that they may be successfully treated by psychoanalysis. Arlow and I have suggested on the basis of our pooled experience with the psychoanalytic treatment of psychotic patients that the psychopathology of the psychoses is more like that of the neuroses than has been generally believed by analytic authors until now (Arlow and Brenner, 1965). The differences, we believe, are of degree rather than of kind.

Discussant

Milton Wexler, PH.D
Beverly Hills, California

More than two years ago I had the opportunity to discuss a somewhat expanded version of the Boyer presentation now under consideration. The final paragraph of that discussion still seems pertinent:

"Finally I must say that Dr. Boyer's mode of presentation has left us no way to be fair to him. He has tried to encompass too much in too limited a space. He has dealt with a theory of psychotic illness, the theory of his technique, specific but minimal clinical data, broad generalizations about results that surpass our most optimistic expectations, and in the same breath has given us a challenge not only to our expectations and the beliefs of many analysts but also a challenge to their specific and repetitive experience. Under these circumstances nothing less than the most detailed factual reporting of a great many cases or clinical experiences could really be considered as a methodologically sound approach to reporting this research. It is my sincere hope that Dr. Boyer will soon undertake the more extensive but certainly much needed task."

Such large claims for success, even if inadequately supported by data, should at least have the virtue of clarity and consistency. I miss these qualities in the presentation. The reporting confuses me.

For example, the title of the paper suggests that we are dealing with schizophrenic patients. Yet when the patients are categorized, seven of them are merely defined as people who were hospitalized and who believed in the reality of their hallucinations or delusions. This is purely descriptive. Seven additional patients are termed "borderline." At best this is a doubtful diagnostic category. Three of the 17 cases dealt with are undefined, undiagnosed, even unmentioned.

At a later point it is said that the "majority [of patients] could well have been labeled to suffer from schizoaffective psychoses with depressive affects prevailing over manic." At which point I find myself really troubled. We have difficulty enough defining schizophrenia but we are in an even deeper morass communicating with each other about "schizoaffective psychoses." It would be enormously helpful if Dr. Boyer would clearly define his research population.

Even the theoretical issues are not well defined nor consistently stated. Boyer believes that the primary therapeutic task is to restore or develop a reasonable ego and superego. He wishes to modify or replace cold, unloving, and archaic ego and superego introjects. Therapy must be directed toward the growth of intrapsychic and interpersonal communication techniques.

And how is all this to be accomplished? By sitting out of sight behind a prone patient and interpreting in the classic psychoanalytic mode! Contact and communication are apparently of central importance but it is suggested that we reduce and narrow rather than maximize the avenues and tactics by which relationships, attachments, and identifications develop. It is no wonder then that we find the following opposite tendencies of thought in the Boyer presentation:

"It is my impression that the notion that visual and/or tactile contact are of primary importance in the treatment of psychotics has been overstressed."

And then:

"In certain acute episodes of psychotic regression, such [visual, tactile] contact is also mandatory for the reestablishment of some degree of autonomy, as is evident by the tensions expressed by some patients at some times when they are deprived of a sight or touch of the therapist."

It seems to me that Dr. Boyer wishes to accomplish the impossible task of reconciling the views of Freud with those of Arlow and Brenner. The former viewed schizophrenia as an ego defect involving the loss of internal object representation. The latter viewed schizophrenia as an extension and deepening of the conflicts involved in neurosis but fundamentally requiring the same therapeutic operations. In my view these ideas are not reconcilable either at the theoretical level or at the technical level. The most valuable issue that lies before us is the determination as to which position is more nearly correct. If we accept Freud, then every means to foster the development of internal representations, introjections, and identifications becomes of paramount importance and the interpretation of conflict takes on a secondary role. If Arlow and Brenner are correct, then it may well be that there is some hope for a technique based in the classical psychoanalytic model with interpretation of resistance and transference at the core.

Nevertheless we cannot ignore the claim made in this paper for considerable therapeutic success with a sizable population of quite ill patients. Similar claims have appeared with increasing frequency in our literature and must be dealt with sympathetically and with greatest interest. I hope that Dr. Boyer's research can be formalized, given adequate research safeguards, and then generalized beyond his own individual experience. He could not be involved in a more challenging, more potentially rewarding and more difficult problem.

Discussant

Gustav Bychowski, M.D.

New York, New York

This discussant finds himself in a somewhat difficult situation when asked to discuss Dr. Boyer's contribution because I am in agreement with most points he has raised. However, I am happy for this opportunity to emphasize certain aspects of a problem to which I have dedicated much of my research and my psychotherapeutic activity.

I am happy to see that Dr. Boyer speaks clearly of psychoanalysis and not of psychotherapy of schizophrenia. I concur with Freud who said that any therapy which is based on the concepts of the unconscious, resistance, transference, and interpretation deserves the name of psychoanalysis.

I fully agree with the points Dr. Boyer makes in his theoretical orientation, particullarly with his comprehensive view of all the etiological, psychological, and genetic factors. I do take exception to his emphasizing the "reawakening of unresolved oedipal conflicts." I think that in a great number of our patients, deeper analysis reveals that preoedipal conflicts play a predominant role. This is especially true for the symbiotic background so important in the psychopathology of many of our patients.

Since Dr. Boyer gives an excellent formulation of the defensive regression of the patients when they become "confronted with their message-sending-and-receiving difficulties," I would not agree with his describing this theoretical premise as a "bias."

I am glad Dr. Boyer emphasizes the importance of pathological nonintegrated introjects and their replacement by more adequate mental contents. I have devoted a number of studies to this special topic.

The problem of controlled aggression is one of the most arduous in psychoanalysis of the psychotic. The therapist must deal with this sufficiently firmly and skillfully so as not to allow regression which will enable the patient to slip beyond his control.

The psychotic transference presents special difficulties which can be handled successfully only when the analyst is not frightened by the psychotic potential. I agree that this can be handled but I do not concur with his optimism that it can be handled always in the office, without the use of such parameters as medication or hospitalization. On the other hand, exaggerated fear of psychotic regression leads in many instances to a protracted treatment which is at best supportive or symptomatic treatment and thus does not attack the psychotic core.

In dealing with the psychotic core, Dr. Boyer emphasizes correctly the importance of interpreting and correcting the basic psychotic mechanisms and distortions. I, too, feel that aggression should be dealt with constantly, since it threatens to engulf the ego and leads to regressive defenses. Thus, the substitution of a nonpunitive realistic superego for what I have called the primitive superego remains one of the most important goals of analysis of the psychotic.

Some points of technique deserve more detailed discussion:

My experience has taught me to be more flexible than Dr. Boyer seems to advocate. I am in agreement on the general rule of abstinence, but I feel we cannot maintain it with rigidity. There are moments in the analysis of a psychotic when his anxiety, his existential dread or his despair at his loneliness are such that it might be of inestimable help to hold his hand or even stroke his hair. The same holds true, I feel, for accepting an occasional small gift or lending him a book, or even — horrible dictu— offering him a flower from a bunch of daffodils on my desk.

Also, I would be much less absolute in keeping the patient in the classic reclining position. There are situations which warrant a temporary change of position, a change whose duration must be left to our clinical and psychological judgment. I found that rigid maintenance of the classic position might encourage regression, produce blocking, increase anxiety and even stimulate paranoid ideation. Time and again I found it useful to have the patient sit up in the last 10-15 minutes of the session to allow him to emerge from his distorted world and to be prepared to face the metropolis with its crowds and subways or even his own family and place of work. This change of position helps the confrontation between the world of archaic objects and the world of actual reality.

In principle, I, too, am against contact with the family. Yet, I cannot advocate this rule as absolute. The patient's weak ego might be constantly traumatized by a symbiotic parent or spouse and his anxiety or his suspicions be continually aroused by certain elements of behavior in his environment. In such cases a rare conference or simply a telephone conversation with a member of the family might bring about a significant change. It could be possible to elicit in this way a piece of information concerning the patient's behavior of which he is completely unaware and which could contribute important material to our work. All these communications should be approved by the patient.

These modifications of classic psychoanalytic attitude should be limited to what we are convinced is beneficial for therapy.

The author does not do justice to the personality of the analyst and to his own personal assets. It is not a "mysterious fact that no patient has refused the treatment when it was offered." Conversely, we know that certain analysts are ill-suited to treat psychotics.

In describing his technique, Dr. Boyer again emphasizes correctly his lack of anxiety, consistency in attitude, calmness and indirectly-communicated optimism. Anyone who, like this discussant, has the pleasure of knowing Dr. Boyer will appreciate the importance of these qualities. However, I disagree with his expression "scientific detachment" and think "objectivity" is the proper term for describing an attitude which remains human, sympathetic, and strives toward the maximum of understanding.

I fully agree with the ambitious goals of this treatment which aims at the elimination of the psychotic nucleus and reconstruction of personality. On the basis of long experience I, too, am convinced this is possible. Much research remains to be done; in particular we would like to know more about the cause of failures. Of this, unfortunately, the author was unable or unwilling to give us more data.

Discussant

John N. Rosen, M.D.
Doylestown, Pennsylvania

Dr. Boyer has independently arrived at many of the conclusions which I reached, and began to publish, during the 1940's. For instance, he, too, has concluded that psychosis reflects the individual's early familial relationships; that the ego, and especially the superego, are inadequately developed; that analytic treatment can be used to redevelop them; more specifically, that aspects of the analyst himself can be introjected; that psychotic transference permits these therapeutic introjections; that further regression may be necessary in the course of treatment; that recovery is possible, without institutional procedures, in many cases; and that proper treatment extends into the post-psychotic phase, which I have designated as the "neo-neurosis."

Indeed, most of Dr. Boyer's discoveries are so familiar to me that I can only encourage him to go further along these lines and to move beyond the limits of our current knowledge. Surely it is no longer necessary to "suggest that the psychotic process is reversible in some patients," as if that were news.

The question of interest now, in 1966, is what constitutes the optimal way of achieving these results—taking into account such considerations as the huge number of people who need to be treated, the small number of psychotherapists who are prepared to treat them, the insistent clamor from the pharmaceutical lobby, and so on.

The real novelty in Dr. Boyer's paper is his claim of strict adherence to so-called "classical" procedures in the treatment of psychotics. "In seminar groups," he says, "colleagues have remarked that I was more strictly and consistently analytical while treating psychotics than they were with neurotics." As far as I am aware, this is news.

Freud and many of his followers have stated flatly that classical psychoanalysis does not work with psychotics. In my own experience—originally with the "chronically regressed, withdrawn patients" whom Dr. Boyer does not treat—it has been necessary to introduce a number of technical modifications, or "parameters" as Dr. Boyer calls them, in order to make any therapeutic use of Freudian psychology. With relatively less psychotic individuals, with "neo-neurotic" individuals who have recovered from psychosis, and more recently with neurotic individuals who have never been psychotic, I find that the same technical modifications, collectively known as "direct psychoanalysis," are still appropriate, assuming that the goal of treatment is recovery rather than analytic sophistication or self-knowledge.

While I have been gradually encroaching on the traditional preserves of classical or "indirect" psychoanalysis to the extent that I question its therapeutic effectiveness even with mildly neurotic individuals, Dr. Boyer has evidently been moving in the opposite direction. Perhaps the two of us should get together to discuss our differences.

In the meantime, I would like to have a much more explicit and detailed description of the analytic situation, as he sees it, with psychotics. He says: "I restricted my activities to observation and interpretations." But how does he bring about a "controlled regression"? How does he "enable the patient to develop altered introjects"? Why is it that "no patient has ever attacked me [Boyer] in the office," and what will he do when a patient does attack him?

These are a few of the therapeutic problems which I have encountered in the treatment of psychotics and for which I believe I have found a variety of effective, humane solutions. If Dr. Boyer has discovered any better solutions, and if he is willing to reveal them now or later, I, for one, am eager to learn more about his work.

Discussant

Herbert A. Rosenfeld, M.D.
London, England

Dr. Boyer's paper is of particular interest to me as he uses the psychoanalytic approach to schizophrenia without any alteration of his usual technique. He disagrees with all seductiveness and fostering of the positive transference; he avoids role playing and resists all attempts of the schizophrenic patient to make him change his analytic role by manipulation.

I have in my own work with acute and chronic schizophrenic patients adhered to a technique where the essential features of psychoanalysis are retained, namely, detailed interpretations of the transference neurosis or psychosis in all its negative and positive aspects without the use of reassuring or educative methods. What the schizophrenic patient seems to value most as the analysis progresses is the analyst's capacity to convey what he understands from the patient's verbal and nonverbal communications in interpretations and not by action.

It is, of course, typical for the psychotic, particularly the schizophrenic patient, to attack what he needs most. So he constantly seems to attack the analyst's state of mind, his sanity and capacity to function, because he envies it and because it makes him aware of his own madness.

It is here valuable to differentiate the behavior of the nonpsychotic and psychotic part of the patient's personality. One may say it is the sane part of the patient which values the capacity of the analyst to function, while the psychotic part hates the analyst's sanity and tries by manipulation and confusion to force him into collusion. I believe this desire for collusion is often mistaken by psychotherapists as a need for symbiosis and therefore is not resisted. I have often found that the patient's psychotic excitement increases when he believes he has forced the analyst out of his analytic role. The excitement implies that the psychotic parts of the patient have experienced this as a triumph not only over the analyst but over his own saner personality. This is one of the reasons why it is so important for the analyst to remain in the analytic interpretive role.

So far I have stressed only my agreement with Dr. Boyer and want now to discuss some disagreements.

It is interesting that Dr. Boyer believes that accurate interpretations are more detrimental to the course of treatment than are totally wrong or partially wrong statements. I have myself found that some wrong interpretations need not interfere with the course of the analysis and can be corrected afterwards, but there is no doubt in my mind that persistently faulty interpretations make the patient feel rejected, not understood, and increase his feelings that he is too mad to be understood by anybody.

Accurate interpretations are, of course, often painful to the patient who is fighting against insight, but in the long run they form the basis for good experiences with the analyst who becomes a reliable object with whom the patient can develop his feelings of dependency. Since a schizophrenic patient often has parents who have considerable difficulties themselves or who were unable to understand and cope with their child's problems, I would regard the analyst's capacity to understand and verbalize accurately to his patient as quite basic.

I am surprised Dr. Boyer found that the psychotic core of his patients altered within two years of treatment and I would be interested to study his material in greater detail. In my own case material, and also in the cases which I have supervised, the deeper psychotic structures of the schizophrenic patient take many more years to be modified. Of course, even though the psychotic or schizophrenic patient may improve greatly during analysis and may show no overt psychotic behavior in outside life, or even in the transference, the deeper psychotic structure seems to be retained in a split-off form and comes to the surface again in the later part of the treatment, whereas in the successfully treated cases, it is modified.

Concluding, I would like to say a few words about the choice of interpretations. It is interesting that Dr. Boyer has found it more valuable to concentrate his interpretations on aggressive drives rather than libidinal ones, particularly in the beginning of treatment. I find it contraindicated to interpret apparent oedipal material on a libidinal level to the schizophrenic patient, as it is almost always misunderstood by the patient as a seductive invitation from the analyst and stirs up acute psychotic excitement. I have always paid a great deal of attention to the patient's massive projective identifications, but during the last few years I have also been concentrating on helping the patient to differentiate between the various parts of his personality. It is particularly important to interpret the struggle between the more psychotic omnipotent parts of the patient's personality which attempt to keep him in the psychotic state and the saner infantile parts of the patient which try to find an object in the analysis—generally on an early infantile level—where the patient can develop his dependent needs.

Author's Response

L. Bryce Boyer, M.D.

Berkeley, California

I am deeply grateful to the discussants for their thoughtful comments and penetrating questions. Their choice is happy, since they encompass a group who have widely varying theoretical viewpoints concerning, and employ vastly divergent technical procedures in, the treatment of borderline and psychotic patients. Their selection accurately emphasizes that there is as yet no psychoanalytic concensus concerning either theory or technique and that all avenues must be explored rigorously.

Before I respond to the individual discussants, I wish to stress that this interim report presents the theoretical orientation, methodology and, perhaps in a too-condensed form, the results of an empirical study. It is submitted that those results indicate that psychoanalysis conducted with techniques consistent with adherence to the structural hypothesis, including use of the couch, benefits some schizophrenic patients and may indeed be the treatment of choice for them.

I have not, of course, claimed that any patient has been "cured." I have not had the opportunity to use the same methodology in the treatment of patients who have been long and continuously confined to institutions. Whether psychoanalytic treatment as defined by Freud and stated above by Dr. Bychowski could be used exclusively in their care remains a moot point, since, to my knowledge, no systematic and rigorous study has been done to test the hypothesis. The work of Fromm-Reichmann and Searles and some of their followers and of a few Kleinians, such as Dr. Rosenfeld, seems to me to suggest that such a study *might* show that psychoanalytic treatment could be used effectively in their therapy.

Obviously I claim no originality because of

my adherence to the "so-called 'classical' procedures" in the treatment of psychotics. As I have noted elsewhere,[1] many other analysts—some of whom practiced during the period when the topographical theory represented the furthest advance of psychoanalytic thought—have cleaved to psychoanalytic methods consonant with their theoretical orientations in the treatment of such patients. The sole claim to novelty which I might make is that I conducted a systematic study in which psychoanalysis was employed almost exclusively and with the technical procedures which are implied by adherence to structural hypothesis.

Dr. Rosen's own technical procedures indicate that he operates almost entirely within the framework of the topographical theory. This I infer from his preference in the majority of cases to interpret from the side of the id rather than that of the ego and from his responses to patients' productions in id language and from his concepts of transference and working through. I have found in his many writings no clear revocation of his 1947 position in which he stated that, using "direct psychoanalysis," cures of psychotics were effected in 3 days to 11 months and "transference is as completely worked out as we aim to do in ordinary analytic procedures," presumably with neurotics.

Before the introduction of the structural hypothesis, other psychoanalysts developed "original" methods of therapy because they, too, found analytic therapy to lead frequently to "analytic sophistication" and not to recovery. I believe Dr. Rosen and I view very differently psychoanalytic concepts and techniques.

Detailed case reports might have spelled out more clearly the answers to Dr. Rosen's first two questions than does the terse synthesis of methodology which was offered, but those answers are implicit in the presentation. I would remind the reader that the communication submitted here is an abstract of a longer article, but Dr. Lindon's synthesis meets with my approval.

My teleological explanation for the fact that no patient has attacked me in the office (acutely disturbed patients have, in the hospital) is that, subjected to the outlined methodology, my patients *did* develop altered introjects and controlled regression which included a degree of mastery over their hostile impulses and despair. I attribute this to my relative calm and inactivity and to my using interpretations from the side of the ego, stressing initially the derivatives of the aggressive drive.

Not a small aspect of my clinical approach is my chariness of comments and my giving patients much time to work through their conflicts. On two occasions, patients in treatment other than psychoanalytic have threatened me with loaded revolvers. I was able to state with more apparent calmness than I felt that they had come to me for help and that I would be of little assistance to them were I dead. After this statement directed to their egos, I offered interpretations of their needs to express their despair and hatred in such a manner.

Dr. Bychowski and I have even more areas of agreement than would appear to exist from his remarks. My stressing the importance of the reawakening of oedipal conflicts was based on clinical observations and the established fact that schizophrenic regressions have been known to begin frequently with adolescence, childbirth and climacterium. That the position to which patients regress is schizophrenoid clearly depends upon faulty resolution of preoedipal fixations and areas of faulty id-ego differentiation.

No implication was intended that the psychotic transference or aggressive drive derivatives can be handled always without the use of hospitalizations or medications. However, in the series reported here, none was hospitalized while in analysis, and only one continued taking sedatives for more than a few weeks after

---

[1]Boyer, L. B. and Giovacchini, P. (In Press). *Psychoanalytic Treatment of the Characterological and Schizophrenic Disorders*. New York: Int. Science Press.

analysis began. During the past eight years, two of Giovacchini's patients required brief hospitalization. *He* did not hospitalize them. The therapeutic function was split; a colleague assumed the managerial functions and the transference remained relatively uncontaminated.

Regarding the use of abstinence, I believe that the actual giving of presents tends to complicate the transference. When I have had the impulse to bestow something, I have striven to investigate my countertransferential reactions and usually thereby learned more about both the patient and myself. Changes in voice tone reflect my sympathy or concern and are perceived as gifts. Perhaps the form of giving of presents is a matter of individual style. I know of no relevant documented empirical study.

I have not forbidden patients to sit and have found it unusual that patients wish to do so after the first interviews. When patients have asked to or have done so, I have investigated their wish or action. The exposure of the anxiety and often-present paranoid ideation has proved to be valuable and the patients have later been grateful.

The important point about all of this is the preservation of the analytic setting. If the therapist maintains his analytic intent and attitude, minor deviations are unimportant. If that intent is affected by the analyst's internal needs to behave in manners reminiscent of actual "good" parents, the preservation of unconscious delusion results and the analysis and rectification of ego defects are seriously hampered.

Dr. Rosenfeld's comments are so lucid and wise as to warrant only applause. Concerning our areas of apparent disagreement, I shall make brief remarks.

When I indicated that "correct" interpretations can be more detrimental than incorrect ones, I did not make my position clear. A specific statement or symptom can, as we know, have many meanings. If an accurate interpretation is made which applies to a meaning which is repressed and incomprehensible to the patient, or if he *almost* understands its meaning and has made appropriate adaptive or defensive steps—that is, if the interpretation is timely—no adverse effects can be expected. However, when the interpretation is made relating to a meaning which is almost within his ken but for which he has not yet prepared himself, it is ill-timed and can lead to severe regression of one form or another.

I, too, have been suspicious of my observation that the psychotic core is as a rule modified deeply within two years, even though projective psychological tests and clinical observation have suggested this to be true. Since this paper was written, two patients who appeared to have made such fundamental changes have returned for analysis of what appeared to be neurotic depression. Each of them briefly used the old psychotic mechanisms for defensive purposes. The fact that they could suggests that the deeper psychotic structure may have been retained and split off, but their responses to interpretations suggest that they had but briefly recathected old behavior defensively.

Dr. Rosenfeld's last paragraph struck a vibrant chord within me. It was as though I heard a voice state, "You have done the same thing, in addition to what you stressed in your report." Briefly reviewing in my mind my changed techniques over the years, I think this to be true. Fortunately, I have kept detailed notes of all interviews and shall have a chance to validate this subjective response.

I can only thank Dr. Brenner for his pithy and pertinent remarks.

Dr. Wexler's comments are of a different order than those of the other discussants. He seems to have attempted to discredit my work through the use of distortion and ridicule and by inferring that I am either naive or dishonest.

He has been aware previously that the extent of my "claims" has been much more modest than he infers, and he has known that the diagnoses of these patients were established independently by other clinicians and affirmed by psychological testing. We all know of the difficulties involved in diagnosis. Obviously, these were severely ill patients, regardless of what rigid labels we might attach to them. I believe Dr. Wexler would agree that because he sees the views of Arlow and Brenner as being irreconcilable with those of Freud does not make them so. Dr. Wexler was aware formerly that I, and many others, had reached the same views as Arlow and Brenner before the publication of their book.

He refers to Freud's 1911 and 1914 position concerning psychosis, during the time when Freud was working within the framework of the topographical theory and attempting to elucidate his theory of narcissism through exploitation of the Schreber case, as though these were Freud's last and irrevocable words on the subject. This, of course, is false.

However, let us turn to the content of Dr. Wexler's discussion. He forwards five points: (*a*) My data are insufficient. (*b*) My diagnoses are unreliable. (*c*) His experiences with patients have been different. (The implication here is that data similar to mine lead to different phenomena.) (*d*) Analysis reduces and narrows, whereas these patients need expansion and broadening; therefore the analytic method is inappropriate. (*e*) Analysis can be used successfully solely for rectification of intrapsychic conflict, not for treatment of ego defects.

(*a*) Dr. Wexler does not perform the discussant's obligation to spell out in what way the data do not support the conclusions.

(*b*) Regardless of diagnostic labels, these were obviously sick patients. It would have been condescending of me to have spelled out all details of my thinking and approach, and since Dr. Wexler seems not to credit me with sophistication or honesty, it is unlikely he would have believed my reporting of details. The audience is expected to accept condensation and conclusions and to proceed from there to determine whether they are internally consistent. If the discussant is unwilling to accept such condensation, he must delineate clearly where my statements are not possible and do so in terms of theoretical processes. Dr. Wexler did not do this.

(*c*) His experience *has* to be different from mine. Although he *starts* with the same data (similar cases), the therapeutic interaction which results from our different approaches changes all subsequent data. It is my impression that Wexler's and Rosen's patients act out because Wexler and Rosen respond to their patients' primary process data in implied primary process terms. While our *patients* constitute an independent variable, *we* constitute dependent variables, and subsequent data are not comparable. A significant difference between us is to be found in the next point.

(*d*) Wexler states as though his pronouncement were a dogma that analysis "reduces and . . . narrows." I hold that if one has such a deprecatory view of psychoanalysis, he cannot function in a psychoanalytic setting; then the patient cannot function in such a setting because it has been withheld from him. I feel comfortable while my seriously ill patients use the couch, and problems rarely arise; we both work better.

(*e*) To discuss this point at length would require another paper. However, briefly stated, it is my view that the patient's selective and controlled regression to stages preceding the formation of disruptive introjects and the gradual acquisition of the "analytic" introject *are* analysis and are characteristic of the therapeutic course of cases with severe ego defects. Lastly, there is no case of ego defect without intrapsychic conflict.

The Forum

Title

A Psychoanalytic Contribution to the Theory of Cyclicity of the Financial Economy

Author

Henry Krystal, M.D.

Practicing psychoanalyst, Clinical Associate Professor of Psychiatry in Charge of Postgraduate Education at Wayne State University, Detroit, where he has conducted the workshops on social and individual aftereffects of social stresses. A book, *Massive Psychic Trauma*, concerning these studies, will soon add to his published works which include papers on the effects of migration and Nazi persecution. Social problems producing individual and resultant social pathology are among Dr. Krystal's research interests.

Discussants

Arnold A. Rogow, PH.D.

Former Professor of Political Science at Stanford University, he has recently joined the Graduate Faculty of the City University of New York. Dr. Rogow has published five books and more than 40 articles, his current research being in the direction of building intellectual and training bridges between psychiatry and the social sciences.

Gordon Saver, M.D.

Member of the Southern California Psychoanalytic Society and Assistant Clinical Professor of Psychiatry at the University of Southern California. He has been especially interested in group psychology and analysis and is the author of the recent article, "Migration and Psychiatric Help-Seeking."

John W. Higgins, M.D.

Associate Professor of Clinical Psychiatry at St. Louis University and a psychoanalyst in private practice. His principal research interest concerns the problem of values and the determinants of guilt.

David L. Grove, PH.D.

Chief Economist of the International Business Machines Corporation. Before joining IBM in 1966, he was Vice President and Chief Economist at Blyth & Company, an investment banking firm, and has held similar positions at the Bank of America and the Federal Reserve Bank of San Francisco. Dr. Grove has published a number of papers in economics, including the article on central banking in the *Encyclopaedia Britannica*. He is on the Editorial Board of the "Financial Analysts Journal."

Leonard J. Comess, M.D.

Assistant Clinical Professor of Psychiatry at the University of Southern California; Director, Extension Division, Southern California Psychoanalytic Institute; Consultant to Mount Sinai Hospital and to Jewish Family Service of Los Angeles, and (according to the editors and his broker) a genius at winning in the stock market.

A Psychoanalytic Contribution to the Theory of Cyclicity of the Financial Economy[1]

Henry Krystal, M.D.
Detroit, Michigan

Economics and the Business Cycle

Classical economic theory chooses to concern itself with the movements of goods and capital and to ignore the psychology of the "movers." The occasional mention of psychological factors has been shallow and behavioristic. (6, 11,30)

Katona provides the introduction to our interest in economics as a manifestation of individual and group psychology, as opposed to the basic assumption of Keynesian economists that there was "a fundamental psychological rule of any modern community that when its real income is increased, it will not increase its consumption by an equal absolute amount, so that a greater amount must be saved." (23) Lord Keynes predicted that in economically mature (i.e., industrialized) countries, the capital becomes accumulated, investment opportunities decrease, and eventually the economy goes into a state of chronic depression or "stagnation."

Keynesian economists view spending as passively tied to, though lagging behind, the income of an economic unit (usually a family). (12) This assumption is contradicted by Katona (15) who produced survey evidence to the effect that the saving and spending functions have separate, complex sociological and psychological determinants. (13,14,16,18)

A serious limitation of Katona's viewpoint is his assumption that the consumer's behavior is in the main rational, and any irrational factors in our economic life can be ignored because they will cancel each other out. Yet, the development of the "consumer" school of economics by Katona and his followers indicated that the "mood" prevalent among the consumers was the prime moving force in our economy. (19) Because of this change in emphasis and object of study, economics has become a behavioral science.

Psychoanalysis, having access to the greatest depth and breadth of understanding of the human mind, can and must make a contribution to this aspect of economics, and we are directed to the study of the psychological factor of "changes in the American people's optimism or pessimism, in their feelings of security or insecurity, in their degree of confidence or mistrust and uncertainty." (17)

This paper, then, will highlight some aspects of the psychological foundation of the cyclicity of the financial economy and correlate clinical observations derived from individual analyses to group behavior.

The Reflections of the Public Mood in the Stock Market Prices

Our first focus of observation is the public mood in a period preceding a stock market crash. Poignant is this description of the mood of the predepression period: ". . . before the stock market crash of October, 1929, a kind of nervous dissatisfaction and apprehension had begun to manifest itself in American intellectual life. The liberating movement of the twenties had by that time accomplished its work in discrediting gentility and Puritanism of the latter nineteenth century; the orgy of spending of the boom was becoming more and more grotesque, and the Jazz Age was ending in hysteria." (35)

[1] This paper is a slightly revised edition of one read at the American Psychoanalytic Association Meeting, December, 1963.

Katona's surveys taken during the periods of great prosperity revealed what he called "The Psychology of Prosperity." People were in a state of boundless optimism, expecting that constant increases in earnings and profits would be guaranteed by the government. (20) Katona described opposite attitudes for the "Psychology of Recession" without appreciation that he was dealing with a typical swing in mood from boundless oral optimism and greed to an emotional depression preceding its economic counterpart.

As examples of group psychological reactions, consider the following:

In the thirties, the public was so preoccupied with reactions to their "era of excess" that "not until the reformers got rid of the problem of prohibition, could they concentrate on the other urgent social problems of the time." (31)

During the great depression, the ascetic propaganda machine of the prohibitionists named the alcoholic excesses of the twenties as its cause. Historically there has been described in the United States a "prohibition cycle" which paralleled in time the business cycle, with prohibition activities at the peak before the onset of each depression. (32)

Before the crash of 1962 there was a widely prevalent feeling of guilt over the excesses and overindulgences of the "good life." (2,4,22)

In May, 1962, a fall in the stock market prices surprised the economic and political leaders in the United States. Without apparent economic cause, the stock market experienced its greatest decline since September, 1930. Despite repeated assurances from authorities, a persistent panic and selling caused losses estimated at over 100 billion dollars, (3,8,34) and "the severe decline in the stock market reflected a massive swing in investor psychology from unreasoned optimism to undisciplined pessimism." (26)

In the ensuing two years, prosperity continued, but the climbing stock prices made the investors anxious and jittery. The market responded to emotional shocks with remarkable regularity—the assassination of the late President Kennedy produced a panic on Wall Street; Lyndon Johnson's orderly takeover of the presidency caused a recovery so precipitous that on Monday, October 25, 1963, only the "insiders'" early orders could be filled, and prices recovered in a day.

In June of 1965, after prices had declined mildly for a couple of weeks, William McChesney Martin, Jr., Chairman of the Federal Reserve Board, cautioned against excessive inflationary policies and "perpetual prosperity psychology." Misinterpreting—and panicked by—his speech, the public saw his comparison of the present situation with the twenties as a prophecy of depression. (28) There was immediate panic selling, with a precipitous drop in prices, and a rumor swept Wall Street that President Johnson was seriously ill. This rumor, an expression of investors' anxiety, produced another wave of panic selling with "paper losses of nearly 10 billion dollars, thus rivaling the losses sustained in the twenty minute flurry of trading following President Kennedy's assassination." (27)

We note that investor and consumer anxiety produce a prime moving force in stock market prices. Since we can assume that similar forces operate in the economy as a whole, what is our knowledge of the psychology of the people involved?

Psychoanalytic Contributions and Group Reactions

A transference relation exists between the economic leaders (regardless of the nature and extent of their psychopathology) and the investor, worker and consumer. Many investors have an incurable trust in the omniscience of the brokers and counselors. Confidence in "name brands," in service and transportation companies is a faith in which modern man often must entrust his life. Betrayal of such confidence may have severe repercussions on the entire economy, as did the discovery of "serious irregularities" in certain stock exchanges preceding the crash of 1962.(1,5,7)

But for clues to the psychological causes of the depression, recession or panic, we turn to the study of such pathological phenomena as the gambler's psychological need to lose(10) and emphasize the problems of guilt over success and acquisition, just as we emphasize the historical study of crashes and depressions rather than prosperity. Our interest in pathological economic "giants" is not only because of their direct influence on the economy, but also because they reflect, in magnification, the emotional influences in the economic behavior of all.

One such "giant" was S. Rubenstein, whose psychopathology involved spectacular economic success, and in whose rise and fall thousands of people became involved.(33) The biography of Rubenstein shows some of the problems reflected in the psychopathology of economic behavior. He was a phallic-aggressive character who used his money as a source of power. He purchased not only things but people, especially women, whom he had to own and use for a variety of perversions. His avarice was matched by his gluttony, and his sexuality was dominated by greed and sadism. Despite temporary successes, unconscious guilt and self-destructive tendencies drove him to get himself labeled as a draft-dodger (unnecessarily), to lose most of his money, and finally to get himself killed. At the police investigation of his murder, thousands of people confessed motives to kill him, and the police never determined his assassin. Notwithstanding his arrogant, cruel and repeatedly dishonest behavior, there were always people willing to give him money to invest.

Case Illustration

The unique psychoanalytic contribution in this field of psychopathology comes from studies of these phenomena in individuals. The following is a clinical vignette:

This patient presented himself for analysis because of family and financial difficulties, depression, and ejaculatio/retardata. Among his conspicuous problems had been a cyclicity involving both his mood and financial dealings. During his "high" moods he invariably involved himself in reckless investments in which he would overestimate anticipated earnings and borrow further and invest more, thus "snowballing" until he had completely overreached himself. Then the "bubble would burst"—he would be in bankruptcy and have to turn to his father and plead to be bailed out. He had been through this pattern twice before, and it occurred twice in the course of the analysis. The investments involved a variety of business enterprises, including the most reckless kind of speculation in commodities. Each time, they involved a great deal of capital and a variety of people whom he picked up during his high period and who often turned against him when things got rough. He always had an employee or partner who made "shady" deals which the patient later claimed to have had no knowledge of.

Involved in this behavior was the patient's relationship with his father who was a man of great wealth, acquired by daring and shrewd operations. Having made his large fortune, he became exceedingly conservative. He had endowed his son, upon marriage, with capital which the latter intended to multiply—and felt he had "almost come close to multiplying it 100,000 fold" a number of times; but always "something went wrong," he lost it all and had to return to his father pleading for help. The father would berate him cruelly, predicting that the money would go "down the drain" and calling the patient an idiot and the like. Eventually, however, he would come through with the minimum cash to keep his son going—but only after prolonged sadomasochistic abuse during which the patient was usually severely depressed and berated himself with the kind of abuse which in analysis was transparently more appropriate to his father's attitude.

In the course of the patient's analysis, many other symptoms appeared: his orgastic impotence was accompanied by pruritus ani; preoccupation with keeping his anus dry led to prolonged "wiping," amounting to anal masturbation. He was the first child of his parents, and all evidence pointed to the fact that his mother was severely depressed and possibly even psychotic post-partum. The patient was told he was a "difficult baby who could not be comforted." As a child he was a "fussy eater," particularly aggravating his mother by chewing his food but refusing to swallow it.

In the patient's present behavior, there were two outstanding characteristics: (*a*) He seemed to be very calm and easygoing, but, repeatedly, his family and business associates would get "furious" at him—with some of the close relatives actually "blowing their tops" and even developing "nervous breakdowns" requiring prolonged psychiatric treatment. Despite repeated explanations by many relatives and psychiatrists, the patient would look on these developments with complete bafflement, utterly unable to comprehend that he was the cause. His acting out behavior in family life and social intercourse created countertransference problems because he was able to make the analyst angry as well. The patient moved through the turmoil with the feeling and facial expression of childish innocence, while things—and angry people—were literally falling apart all around him; (*b*) He had a constant need to "fish in muddy waters"—it was impossible for him to make a factual financial statement or actually to straighten out the facts in his life or the figures in his financial dealings. One obtained only estimates, colored by his moods, about his financial status which was too confused and complex to assess accurately. Other areas of his life were equally unclear.

On the eve of the second major price drop in the stock market slide of 1962, the patient was overextended in a variety of areas, yet estimated that he was doing very well. In the previous days and weeks, he reported: "Today I made $50,000 or $100,000, or more" on this or that operation, investment or stock market speculation. All these figures were, of course, paper profits.

On July 6, 1962, the night preceding the greatest fall in prices of stocks and commodities, he had the following dream: He was in a cafeteria piling up various dishes on his tray. The tray was overfilled and overflowing; he seemed unable to carry it. Yet, he felt he must take all of the food because he had to feed "this little boy." When he came to the cashier, he realized he had lost his wallet and couldn't pay. He woke up with an urge to go to the toilet. After bowel evacuation, he had an intense burning of his perianal area which he proceeded to pat dry, and at last he returned to bed with a premoistened medicated tissue between his buttocks. He was quite uncomfortable and could not fall asleep.

His Associations: The patient had a quarrel with his wife and ate supper at his club where he was deeply in debt. This reminded him of various charities to which he was several years behind in payment of pledges, yet kept making large ones in expectation of getting rich "any day." He thought that if he moved to another city, perhaps he would not have to "keep up" with his family and live beyond his means. He was driven to give the appearance of great financial success.

He recalled that his mother was a penny-pincher (also chronically constipated) who was especially stingy in regard to food and a "fanatic" about not wasting any. She strictly controlled the consumption of some foods, such as meat and sweets, so that he felt chronic deprivation in the "midst of plenty." The parents seemed to have hidden their actual affluence and denied it for years, especially during the depression.

During his early adolescence, he was mystified by his sisters' talk when they made fun of boys—calling them "drips" and joking about how they frustrated their sexual advances. He experienced his adolescent sexual tensions as deprivation in oral terms and carried this over into his marriage. Women were always controlling and depriving him.

After an inquiry about the boy in the dream to which the patient ventured that it might be his little boy, it was suggested that possibly the boy represented the patient himself as perpetually deprived. This opened the subject of the patient's greed which had been under discussion for some time prior to this hour because of his "pyramiding" investments. He then volunteered that his unsuccessful attempt to get away with the full tray represented his past experiences of losing his investments. His wallet brought up the fear (really expectation) that the current "bubble" would burst again and that he would lose his money. He admitted that, despite his very precarious financial position, he had acted on a "tip" and had made a large investment in the stock market, buying on margin and using the funds he should have covered some of his debts with. Had the tip been accurate, he would have taken advantage of a misfortune affecting a large group of people.

The reaction of the dream acted out after awakening was related to his anticipated reaction to the loss. He realized that by overreaching himself he obtained a certain relief from his mounting tensions. The later reaction—of financial embarrassment and having to return to his father with a new defeat—was somehow separated in his mind. He rationalized it as the necessary price to pay for chancing operations which would lead to his "liberation" from the father.

The impression gained by the analyst, however, was that the anal stimulation and excitement on awakening suggested that he yearned, not for "liberation" from the father, but for submission to having his "ass reamed." In the patient's ideation, the oral themes were often combined in various patterns. The dream about the loss of money brought up homosexual longings. Thus, his financial dealings had been disturbed by his oral and anal fixations. Although anxiety attended this dream, one is impressed with the anticipation of a "crash" dictated by guilt over the oral overindulgence and with the aggression toward the father involved both in making money and even (passively) in losing it. Attempts to act out identification with his father were frustrated by the fear of the ambivalence, especially of the aggression involved.

Concentrating on the patient's reaction to his financial dealings, one can restate that at the peak of his acquisitive activities and elation, when he was "stuffed with paper profits," he experienced anxiety, yearned to lose the hoard and to assume a passive homosexual position, and to submit to a "rape." He was actually hoping that a market failure would fulfill his "neurosis of destiny" so that he could avoid confronting himself with his own aggressive and self-destructive needs.

Such individual manifestations must be considered in light of the fact that, at the same time, many other people shared his need to lose money and to "tighten their belts." Many investors who took significant paper losses on the market were showing a remarkable indifference to this untoward event. The prevalent mood affected decisions regarding capital investment, new business formation and—first of all—consumer spending and saving.

The stock market crisis lent itself to integrating the material derived from psychoanalytic work with a group reaction. The stock market is notably the part of our economy most sensitive to mood swings of the investors, quickly responding to and even magnifying them. The reason the stock market especially reflects the mood swings is that the investors utilize it for their fantasies of reaching the fulfillment of their ambitions for power. In their work and business affairs, an ever increasing majority are bound by rigid rules and fairly precise limitation for their ambitions; but the salaried person who saves some money and invests it in the stock market thereby removes the lid to his aspirations and may engage in such expectations of success as his psychic freedom allows him.

Thus, the investors' expectations of the stock market performance may vary from limitless optimism to profoundest depression. Fantasies deriving from all levels of libidinal interest may find fulfillment here: greed, a need to hoard, ambition, and the conflicts over indulgence or success on every level can and do become involved in setting a trend in stock prices. Finally, the stock market has been selected as a reflection of our economic condition because, as the brokers fondly say: "It is the only barometer which not only predicts, but is also capable of making its predictions come true."

Discussion

My thesis is that an important factor in economic cyclicity is an emotional cyclicity in the lives of the consumers, manufacturers, distributors and financiers. Cyclothymic mood fluctuation is a universal phenomenon. Booms in the economy generally come in times of a great demand for goods. These times have followed periods of deprivation. The very same periods, however, have been periods of guilt-free consumption, resulting from a feeling of sufficient expiation that follows wars or other major catastrophies. In the United States, there was a Mexican War prosperity in the 1840's, a Civil War prosperity during and after the Civil War, and so on, after each war and disaster,[2] this despite the fact that the economic forces in postwar periods are of a generally retarding kind. F. D. Roosevelt tried to "cure" the general depression by letting the people feel they had suffered enough, and therefore "better days are here again." President Kennedy's victory over the greed of the steel industry had the opposite effect.

The fears, forebodings and guilts which people fail to dissipate in religious activities, illnesses, accidents and mishaps culminate in a general feeling of pessimism which periodically makes us *"pay the price" of the main motivator in our society: greed.* Kubie pointed out that greed has been for a long time and now remains the prime motivating force in our society and is, in his estimate, the best motivation mankind has yet devised. (36) But, as Judge Bazelon indicated, greed as a motivator functions best under scarcity, and scarcity has become obsolete. (25) With the removal of deprivation, the psychic motivating forces derived from displaced instinctual needs have assumed new importance. The economic behavior of individuals in this country now seems less under the influence of bare need for survival and closer to wish-fulfillment fantasies and conflicts.

Psychoanalysis teaches us that whenever a fairly neutral activity serves as displacement for libidinal striving, that activity must become the stage for intersystemic conflict. Some observers attribute the American tendency to depression to the influence of the "Protestant Ethic." However, guilt over economic aggression and acquisitiveness is not an American monopoly but can be traced through history. The biblical tradition reflects the need to appease God with offerings of food, first-born animals, first fruit, and money. The reapers

[2]Wm. G. Niederland has described how the loss of one's homeland may produce reckless gambling which also warded off depression in refugees. Besides the need to force fate, they felt entitled to be "lucky" after their loss of the homeland. (29) We have previously reported the suspension of superego, extreme recklessness and aggressiveness of concentration camp survivors after liberation. (24)

had to leave the fallen ears of corn for the poor gleaners. The prophets were forever attacking the rich and preaching charity. This tradition was continued in the teaching of Christ and his apostles. Freud pointed out: "The sense of guilt was the most important problem in the development of civilization . . ." and maintained that "The price we pay for our advance in civilization is a loss of happiness through the heightening of the sense of guilt." (9)

In a capitalist society, the profit motive in work is acknowledged, and the society as a whole, as well as each person individually, bears the guilt over the unequal distribution of goods over the world. It would seem that this guilt accumulates and contributes to the cyclicity of the economy. In a socialist society, state planning can buffer to some extent such needs of the people. Their apparent immunity to economic depressions may be due not to the planned economy but to the fact that the state assumes the guilt for profit-making as the major, if not the sole, entrepreneur, and does so in the name of abolishing capitalism.

Summary

In this attempt to understand the psychological factors in the stock market crash of spring, 1962, no claim is made that psychological factors were the only ones active. Psychoanalytic observations and those of general psychologic reactions suggest that an important role in the business cycle can be attributed to the vicissitudes of anal and oral partial-instincts in individuals related to the business world. Our economy is based on individual initiative and profits. The generation and amassing of wealth tend to create guilt. When this guilt is not dissipated in other ways, it may become reflected in market trends in terms of a group feeling of depression, anxiety, or—to use a financial term—a "fall in the level of confidence."

Bibliography

1. Bedingfield, R. "S.E.C. Finds Many Abuses in the American Exchange." N.Y. Times, Jan. 6, 1962.
2. Clark, J., Jr. "The Prohibition Cycle." N. Amer. Rev., May, 1933.
3. Crane, H. N.Y. Times, June 3, 1962.
4. Editorial. Time, June 1, 1962.
5. ———. *Ibid.*
6. Estey, T. (1956). *Business Cycles.* Englewood: Prentice Hall, p. 185.
7. Excerpts from S.E.C. Report on the American Exchange. N.Y. Times, Jan. 6, 1962.
8. Financial Correspondent (no name given). Christian Sci. Mon., June 1, 1962.
9. Freud, S. "Civilization and Its Discontent." *Standard Edition.* London: Hogarth Press, 1961, Vol. 21, p. 134.
10. Greenson, R. (1947). "On Gambling." Amer. Imago, Vol. 4.
11. Hald, E. (1954). *Business Cycles.* Boston: Houghton Mifflin Co., p. 113.
12. Hamberg, D. (1951). *Business Cycles.* New York: Macmillan.
13. Katona, G. (1949). "Analysis of Dissaving." Amer. Econ. Rev., Vol. 34.
14. ———. (1949). "Effect of Income Changes on the Rate of Saving." Rev. Econ. & Stat., Vol. 31.
15. ———. (1951). *Psychological Analysis of Economic Behavior.* New York: McGraw Hill.
16. ———. *Ibid.*
17. ———. *Ibid.*
18. ———. (1960). *The Powerful Consumer.* New York: McGraw Hill.
19. ———. *Ibid.*
20. ———. *Ibid.*
21. ———. *Ibid.*
22. Kendal, E. "A Timely Tale of Trading Stamps." Reporter, July 19, 1962.
23. Keynes, T. (1936). *General Theory of Employment, Interest and Money.* London: Harcourt, Brace & Co., p. 97.
24. Krystal, H. and Petty, T. (1963). "The Dynamics of the Adjustment to Migration." Proceedings 3rd World Cong. of Psychiat. and Psa. Quart Suppl., Vol. 37.
25. Kubie, L. (1961). "The Eagle and the Ostrich." Arch. Gen. Psychiat., Vol. 5.
26. Merrill, Lynch, Pierce, Fenner & Smith, Inc. *Guide for Investors,* Sept., 1962.

27. Metz, R. "$5 Billion Loss Batters Market," N.Y. Times, June 9, 1965.
28. Mullaney, T. "Martin's Expression of Concern Upsets Wall Street." N.Y. Times, June 6, 1965.
29. Niederland, W. "A Contribution to the Psychology of Gambling." Presented at Fall Meeting of Amer. Psa. Assn., Dec., 1965.
30. Pigou, A. (1927). *Industrial Fluctuations.* London: Macmillan.
31. Sinclair, A. (1962). *Prohibition, the Era of Excess.* Boston: Little, Brown & Co.
32. ——. *Ibid.*
33. Smith, G. (1962). *The Life and Death of Serge Rubenstein.* Garden City, N.Y.: Doubleday.
34. Stront, R. "Steel Slide Alerts U.S." Christian Sci. Mon., May 29, 1962.
35. Wilson, E. (1952). *The Shores of Light.* New York: Farrar, Straus & Young, p. 492.
36. ———. *Ibid.*

19210 Coyle
Detroit, Michigan

Discussant

Arnold A. Rogow, PH.D.

Palo Alto, California

As one who welcomes efforts to apply psychoanalytic insights to social and political problems, I read Dr. Krystal's article with great interest and, I think, a sympathetic feeling for the difficulties involved. Certainly he is correct in arguing that the psychological side of economic behavior has been neglected, or, rather, subsumed in the classical model of economic man as rational man. (Incidentally, prevailing behavioral models in political science also tend to be rationalistic.) And it is clear that all kinds of psychologies influence stock market behavior, including those characterizing relations between brokers and clients, economic consultants and corporate leaders, Johnson and DeGaulle, etc. No doubt much more needs to be known about these psychologies if we are to understand adequately why the economy is so sensitive to rumors that the President, for example, is in ill health, or that there are new troubles in Kashmir.

But an important question is whether substantial insight into stock market behavior can be gained from the case history presented by Dr. Krystal, or from any single case history. To what extent is his patient typical of investors and speculators, and even if typical, to what degree do such individuals significantly affect trends as against the influence of institutional investors, Federal Reserve Board, and so forth? What evidence is there for the "fact" that "many other people shared his need to lose money and to 'tighten their belts.'"? While it is probably true that in America making and spending money arouses guilt as a consequence of the Puritan ethic, I should have thought that this factor in our national character had considerably diminished in the last three decades as a consequence, at least in part, of rising affluence and the advertising insistence on the good life. Does anyone doubt that *losing* money arouses much more anxiety and guilt than making it, notwithstanding our absolute conviction as a religious nation that the poor enter heaven more easily and in far greater number than the rich!

Here and there I must also question a detail. Do we really know that before the 1962 crash "there was a widely prevalent feeling of guilt over the excesses and overindulgences of the 'good life'"? "Time" magazine editorials hardly establish the existence of such a feeling, much less an article published in 1933. Too, I was rather surprised to read that Serge Rubenstein was an "economic giant."

Despite these queries and criticisms, I want to emphasize that more and not less attention needs to be paid to psychological factors in economic behavior, and surely psychoanalysts and psychiatrists have much to contribute. If, however, their efforts are to be significant and not merely suggestive, the case approach will have to be reinforced by other types of data that will enable us to identify all of the factors that determine buying and selling patterns. The very least that can be demanded is a presentation of a variety of cases drawn from clinical practice. After all, people undergoing analysis are, in general, drawn from the higher income bracket, and it follows that almost every analyst has patients whose psychopathologies and market behaviors he can compare with the material supplied by Dr. Krystal.

Discussant

Gordon Saver, M.D.

Los Angeles, California

Dr. Krystal has offered a psychoanalytic explanation of stock market crashes and depression in the financial economy—by extrapolation from the study of *one* very masochistic patient.

This is the sort of psychoanalytic impressionism that fills me with dismay. To jump from the analysis of one man to conclusions about a highly complex set of variables (i.e., the economy) is patently unscientific. We simply are not entitled to make assumptions about the dynamic interaction in a *dyadic* relationship and thence make that the basis of conclusions about modular groups of 10, 100, 1,000, etc. Therefore, the basic experimental model and methodology from which he works is unacceptable to me.

I would refer him to Naylor and Gianturco's recent article on "Computer Simulation in Psychiatry"[1] which deals with the difficulties in setting up such basic models upon which to test hypothetical psychologic assumptions.

There are other aspects of Krystal's interesting paper that additionally arouse contention. He postulates that economic aggression, acquisitiveness and prosperity produce unconscious guilt and a need for expiation, with resultant self-punishing economic cycles of depression. I am not as willing to ascribe postwar prosperity to guilt-free consumption after the expiatory suffering of war. Might it not, more importantly, be a reaction to prolonged deprivation and to a renewed pleasure-life cathexis?

Contrary to what the author suggests, social-

[1]Naylor, T. and Gianturco, D. (Sept., 1966). Arch. Gen. Psychiat., Vol. 15.

ist states are not all immune to economic depression. They have frequently been much less prosperous than capitalist societies and are often chaotically bureaucratic and depressing cultures where the opportunity for independence and attainment of personal ambition (whether it be oral or genital) is distinctly limited or frustrated.

As for the patient cited, I am most impressed with the great denial of reality, which in effect appears to be his psychotic defense against acknowledgment of the absence of a good breast. His stock market speculation is certainly a pregenital search for Lady Luck and a nourishing mother. But interestingly, his symbiotic retaliative tie to the post-partum psychotic mother reflects itself in his oral rage and need to drive her and his relatives crazy with his particular brand of financial ineptitude (a greedy orality for the maternal breast which he both longs for and destroys).

The author makes some reference to the patient making him angry too. How did he try to inflict his craziness on the analyst? I was quite curious about whether the analyst was being paid his fee. The dream material hints at such a difficulty in the transference.

Searles's paper on "The Effort to Drive the Other Person Crazy"[2] is germane to the understanding of Krystal's case.

Discussant

John W. Higgins, M.D.
St. Louis, Missouri

We know how difficult it sometimes is in the treatment situation to judge whether or not a proffered interpretation is "correct." Glover, for instance, long ago formulated for us that inexact interpretations may, although making a patient "feel better," strengthen defenses and impede rather than promote the work of analysis. Ordinarily, we look for some "advance" in the patient as proof: evidence of further insight, synthesis, productive action, and so on. This bears on the general form of the problem of appraising Dr. Krystal's thesis that an important factor in economic cyclicity is an emotional cyclicity in the lives of the people participating in the economy. How can we know his interpretation is correct? I am assuming that it could be generally agreed that he is in fact making an interpretation—that he is not simply observing, but that in offering an explanation of a phenomenon, he is interested in its verification, and hopeful of its being influential.

As a friendly reader, and a psychoanalyst to boot, *I* think he is probably correct. He is certainly most interesting; and furthermore, within me, his interpretation has the sense of correctness, particularly in that he stimulates curiosity about and understanding of my own fiscal behavior. In addition, within the framework of psychoanalysis, his thesis is plausibly developed. On these grounds, I would like to leave no doubt that my reaction is a positive one, as individual and therapist. In connection with the latter, my surmise is that at least for a time, I will hear the vicissitudes of my patients' financial interests more acutely. That is, as a contribution to clinical theory, the paper is eminently respectable.

Yet, Dr. Krystal is writing about more than our patients. He is writing about our society. Despite the brevity of the paper in proportion to the topic, its thesis and the questions it raises are of a very large order. If he is right, then certain implications of his ideas require considerable appraisal and reappraisal. For example, Krystal refers to Kubie's notion that "greed" is the best motivation mankind has yet devised." If "greed" could be read "intense

[2]Searles, H. (1959). British J. Med. Psychiat., Vol. 32.

motivation," its value might be indisputable. However, "greed" suggests the primitive and impetuous, and in this way could be instrumental in the guilt provoking the unwanted and harmful cyclicity with which this paper is concerned. In this event, those who really grasp and agree with Dr. Krystal's thesis are seeing something which they would properly wish to put to societal therapeutic use. As psychoanalysts, this may be none of our business; as citizens, it would be. Therefore, I return to the large problem of knowing whether or not the interpretation is correct (other than through agreeing with it); and if correct, how is it to be effectively proffered?

There may be others, but the only instance I know in which the effect on a population of a psychoanalytic interpretation has been appraised is Eissler's comment[1] on Freud's *Moses*, where he suggested that this interpretation of the meaning of Judaism freed the Jews to establish the Republic of Israel. Eissler's view is, of course, open to argument. But it reminds us that the wealth of knowledge we glean about *an* individual's behavior informs us about universal problems. Despite having this information we remain novices in knowing what to do with it. Whatever effect or lack of effect Krystal's interpretation has, I applaud its being offered. It will be interesting to see the response of some of the executors and principals in the world of economics.

[1]Eissler, K. (1963). "Freud and the Psychoanalysis of History." J. Amer. Psa. Assn., Vol. 11.

Discussant

David L. Grove, PH.D.
Armonk, New York

If an author tries to bridge two disciplines but is qualified in only one, he runs the risk of being charged with ignorance in the other. I regret that I must level such a charge against Dr. Krystal's knowledge of economics. I shall try to limit my criticisms to those issues which are pertinent to his theme.

Dr. Krystal does not accurately present the contemporary view of economists concerning the determinants of consumption. For such a view I recommend Paul A. Samuelson's deservedly famous *Economics: An Introductory Analysis.*[1] Nor does he do justice to Lord Keynes.

When Keynes refers to a "fundamental psychological rule," it is clear from the context that he means a general behavioral pattern verified by experience. On pages 96 and 97 of his *General Theory* he says, "The fundamental psychological law, upon which we are entitled to depend with great confidence both a priori from our knowledge of human nature and from the detailed facts of experience, is that men are disposed, *as a rule and on the average* [italics mine] to increase their consumption as their income increases, but not by as much as the increase in their income. . . . This is especially the case where we have short periods in view, as in the case of the so-called cyclical fluctuations of employment during which habits, as distinct from more permanent psychological propensities, are not given time enough to adapt themselves to changed objective circumstances. For a man's habitual standard of life usually has the first claim on

[1]New York: McGraw Hill, 6th Edition, 1964.

his income, and he is apt to save the difference which discovers itself between his actual income and the expense of his habitual standard; or, if he does adjust his expenditure to changes in his income, he will over short periods do so imperfectly. Thus a rising income will often be accompanied by increased saving, and a falling income by decreased saving, on a greater scale at first than subsequently."

In the *General Theory*, Keynes was trying to show that, as incomes in a country rise, savings will rise, and that, unless investment opportunities also rise at a sufficiently rapid rate, the rise in national income may not be sustainable. He was fearful that, in mature economies, profitable investment opportunities might not be sufficient to absorb the amount of savings the economy would generate at full employment levels of income; hence, the economy might stumble along at an equilibrium level of national income that would be so low that substantial unemployment would be a chronic condition. He recommended that Government fiscal policy be used to combat such a tendency.

It is true that Keynes underestimated the growth of investment opportunities in the decades following the publication of his great book in 1936. But, how *could* he have anticipated World War II, the Cold War, and the Space Race, all of which have spurred technological advances and thereby created investment opportunities? Nor could he have been expected to anticipate how widely his policy recommendations would have been embraced by governments, or how urgently many governments have sought to make high levels of private investment an important objective of national economic policy.

It is also true that Keynes believed consumption to be *primarily* a function of income. Economists still think this to be the case, and Katona has not disproved it. For example, Samuelson, on pages 216 and 217 of his textbook, says, "While aggregate income is not the only factor determining aggregate consumption, common sense and statistical experience tell us that it is one of the most important factors. Note in Figure 4 how closely consumption seems to follow yearly disposable income; the only exceptional period is that of the war when goods were scarce and rationed and people were urged to save." While Katona correctly emphasizes the importance of consumers' attitudes, statistical studies make it quite clear that changes in consumption are largely explainable in terms of changes in income; changes in attitudes play a secondary role. In fact, it is likely that changes in consumer attitudes are to a greater extent a function of changes in income than the reverse.

Why do I go into so much detail about the relationship of consumption to income? It is not that income is the *only* determinant; certainly we can forecast more effectively if we know a number of other factors, including the results of attitudinal surveys, but it simply is not true that Katona and the "consumer school of economics" (to use Dr. Krystal's term) have changed the "emphasis and object" of economic analysis. For example, in Samuelson's textbook, the index gives 14 references to Keynes and not a single one to Katona. This is not to undercut Katona's useful work; it is merely to put the issues in perspective.

Now to proceed to Dr. Krystal's observations on the potential contributions of psychoanalysis to economics. Economists generally are concerned with the economic behavior patterns of large groups of people rather than of individuals. Thus, while the consumption and savings patterns of some individuals may be erratic, experience confirms that erratic individual behavior tends to cancel out or be submerged by more predictable behavior by the majority of the members of the group. Economists, moreover, are interested in *how* people react to changes in economic variables (i.e., income, prices, interest rates, etc.) rather than in deep-seated *reasons* behind the behavior. Nevertheless, the more we know about *why* people act as they do, the better should be our capability to predict *how* they will act. This is why I read Dr. Krystal's paper with keen anticipation. I have regretfully come to the conclusion that his efforts have not been successful.

Let us suppose for the sake of argument that *individuals* do react in the way Dr. Krystal says they do. Would this explain cyclicity? I think not, *unless he can explain why these psychological reactions should cluster together and not be more or less uniformly spread over time.* I cannot stress this point too strongly. In short, *why should a predominating number of investors get the same reactions at the same time?* There are always "phallic aggressive characters as Rubenstein" about, and there are always investors with guilt complexes. But one cannot leap to a conclusion that cyclical movements of *individual* behavior explain the cyclical movements of such a broad statistical aggregate as the stock market. A "timing" bridge needs to be constructed between individual and group behavior.

No one would dispute that "investor and consumer anxiety produce a prime moving force in stock market forces." But what causes the anxiety? If it is caused by the fact that the President has hinted that taxes will be increased (and corporate profits thereby reduced), or that continued rapid growth of business sales and profits is becoming increasingly dependent on the Vietnam situation (which could suddenly change for the better and remove the principal prop from under the current prosperity), or that current rates of return on bonds are so high that bonds appear to be a better investment than stocks, or that some of the key economic indicators seem to be warning that the current expansion is becoming old and tired, then the anxiety is explainable without reference to independent psychological elements. The problem is to discover the relative importance of such "real" factors and the ways in which they interact.

Much useful work needs to be done in this area, but it must be done in a scientific manner and be susceptible to quantitative testing. Unfortunately, Dr. Krystal has not followed such an approach. One way in which analysts might contribute is to keep an "index of anxiety" based on sessions with their patients. After several years of scientific collection of data, movements in the index could be charted alongside movements in stock prices in order to observe possible relationships between them.

Dr. Krystal emphasizes the widely prevalent feelings of guilt over the excesses of the "good life," and he quotes periodicals as his source. But one can always find such expressions of alarm over the nation's indulgences and over its "moral fiber," even in recessions. What Dr. Krystal needs to demonstrate is that these preachments are *particularly* widespread prior to stock market breaks, and that basic economic factors do not call for a downward adjustment. He fails to do this. Perhaps a systematic count of such expressions of concern could be collected over a period of years and compared with stock prices. Then we would have some evidence.

A few additional comments: His explanation of postwar booms as "resulting from a feeling of sufficient expiation that follows wars" is less convincing than the customary explanation, to wit: In times of war, governments spend enormous sums and commandeer real resources. The public is left with lots of money (whose purchasing power is declining) and few goods. Once consumer goods become available again, the public endeavors to restore a more "rational" or more "normal" (historically) relationship between holdings of money and holdings of goods. The result is heavy spending.

Finally, in view of Dr. Krystal's feeling about the role of the stock market as an outlet for the "greed complex" of individuals, it would be interesting to have his interpretation of the following figures, bearing in mind that we have had unprecedented prosperity for several years.

Change in Individuals' Holding of Common and Preferred Stock (billions of dollars)

Year	Held Directly	Held in Form of Investment Company Shares (i.e. mutual funds)	Total Holdings of Individuals
1962	—3.4	+2.0	—1.4
1963	—4.3	+1.6	—2.7
1964	—2.5	+2.0	—0.5
1965	—4.4	+2.1	—2.3

Source: Securities and Exchange Commission, Washington, D.C., *Statistical Bulletin*, September 1966, p. 24, Table, "Saving by Individuals in the United States."

Why is it that *individuals* (in contrast to pension funds, insurance companies, etc.) were *net sellers* of stocks, in dollar terms, during the years shown? According to the Krystal thesis, the *public* should have been in the "bullish" phase after recovering from the guilt-ridden feeling which produced the market break in the first half of 1962.

Discussant

Leonard J. Comess, M.D.
Beverly Hills, California

Dr. Krystal presents an interesting and thought-provoking thesis. His statement that psychological factors play an important role in the swings of the stock market is, of course, true, as any broker empirically knows. He states that the problem has never been seriously investigated by psychoanalysts, and here, too, I agree with him. I disagree with him as to the importance he gives to the cyclic aspect, i.e., that guilt over accumulation and excesses produces an economic recession. Selling stocks at a profit is not necessarily a guilt reaction, yet it is overselling that produces a market decline. Excessive profit-taking begins the change in market direction, and then the small investor, who cannot financially or psychologically stand too great a loss, joins in and the Bull becomes a Bear.

Krystal's concept of greed and oral optimism deserves serious consideration. I believe these are the essential forces operating with the unsophisticated investor and that they largely determine his attitudes and behavior. Lord Rothschild, when questioned as to his formula for success in the stock market, responded, "I sell too soon." The small investor buys too late and is unwilling to accept a small profit. He hopes to double or triple his money. He seldom buys when the market is low—only when the market is strong and he hears of great profits being made; then he greedily plunges in, hoping to achieve similar gains. Fate, the silent handmaiden of the parental image, beckons and says, "You can get your share and maybe even more." Unfortunately, this is usually too late and at a time when the market has almost peaked. The large investors, i.e., institutions and mutual funds, are already shifting their portfolios into high yield bonds because of the high price/earning ratio and low dividend yields. Then, as the market turns, the small investor clings optimistically to the hope that this is only a temporary setback. Finally he loses hope—Fate has denied him again. It is with this rejection that the emotional depression occurs and affects his economic choices. He sells his stocks and accepts his loss.

It is a Wall Street axiom that the small investor buys at the high and sells at the low. Many sophisticated investors gauge their buying and selling primarily on this barometer—selling when odd-lot purchases become high, indicating a flood of small investors, and buying when the situation is reversed. It is as if they understand the psychology of the small investor only too well.

I think the connection Dr. Krystal makes between the small investor and the compulsive gambler is unfortunate, for, although there are some similarities, there are also many differences.

At this time when institutions and mutual funds form a major background for the market, it might be important to investigate the psychology of those "dispassionate" men who manage huge sums. An understanding of their motivation might give us additional insight into the psychology of the market. I look forward to a paper by Dr. Krystal on this subject.

Author's Response

Henry Krystal, M.D.
Detroit, Michigan

I wish to thank the discussants for their interesting comments, helpful criticism and suggestions. From the onset, I want to voice my wholehearted agreement with two points made by some of the discussants forcefully, and by others very subtly and kindly. I agree completely that with this paper, my amateur standing as a student of economics is not at all jeopardized.

In addition, while I do call for a psychoanalytic study of the behavioral aspects of economics, I have not claimed to have accomplished such a study. The case illustrations (as well as the three cases which I eliminated for the sake of brevity) were offered only as a reminder that in our everyday work we observe that emotional forces invade and modify the economic behavior of all the people with whom we come in contact. Dr. Saver is correct that observations made in a dyadic situation cannot be translated into inferences about group behavior. However, in our work we gain information about our patients' economic behavior, their behavior within groups, and the behavior of their groups. Group studies cannot be made by behavioristic observation of the entire group. After all, a group has no mind, no more than it has a torso.(1) Social scientists, students of group dynamics, and economists have to do their research as we do: mostly by studying one individual at a time, even in a group setting.

My point is that the studies of economic behavior of groups should be enriched in the manner that Freud enriched the "group psychology" of LeBonn.(2) The present concepts of psychological economics of the interaction within families and groups concerned with economic decisions are naive and simplistic. Katona's consideration of intra-family and intra-group financial influences is limited to such statements as "The husband and wife appear to be aware of each other's buying plans." There is an inattention to the effect of family dynamics on economic behavior. All forces other than the rational decision-making are expected "to cancel themselves out." (5)

I maintain that many a fluctuation in the economy of capitalistic countries is caused by the summation of the spread of feelings and attitudes resulting from irrational and unconscious sources within individuals. The simplest example of family dynamics is the annual cyclicity culminating in the Christmas economic boom. Sterba has been among the psychoanalysts who have dealt with the dynamics of the annual shopping spree. (7) Katona and his school shy away from dealing with irrational, unconscious motivation in human behavior; he seems to consider them unmeasurable, unassayable, perhaps even unfathomable.

The economists' consideration of the effect of individual and group psychodynamics on economic behavior are naive and glib. Dr. Grove gives us a good example of it: "... erratic individual behavior tends to cancel out or be submerged by more predictable behavior by the majority members of the group." The unconscious forces are *judged* to be erratic.

I wish to reassert the principle of psychic determinism. Irrational moods and tendencies often snowball and spread in an infectious way. Given a shared latent predisposition within the group, any development may evoke the feeling for which they are ready. That is why the saying is that the public reaction to any news is "*unpredictable*." Unpredictable? Only so long as the latent mood is considered unfathomable. History records not just episodes but ages of irrational economic behavior by nations. Peoples driven by guilt, fear, self-subjugated to their unconscious (self) oppressors, have expanded all their economic potential upon building temples or other projects which served only to exhaust them, spread disease, weaken and finally bankrupt them as a society. During the *Kristall-nacht*, when dominated by their aggression, Germans indulged in looting and destruction which had to be paid by their own (non-Jewish) insurance companies—that is, in the end, by themselves. (3) We recall that during panics such as the great depression, the reassuring and reasonable voices of the political and economic leaders were useless to stem the onslaught of irrational terror.

The opposite effect was demonstrated in postwar Germany: when the confidence of the people in their own resources and values was established, the economy developed to a high level without regard for the absence of a "gold standard." Considering the complexity of the psychological factors in postwar Germany, I agree with Dr. Saver that to call such economic buoyancy "guilt-free consumption" is a gross oversimplification.

It must be granted that developing measurements and indexes of the latent emotional forces of society cannot be without some effects of their own. Any structuralization, organization and publication of data does produce effects of its own. For instance, as the Dow-Jones index neared the "1000" level in 1966, people seemed frightened. Had the latent feelings been of boundless optimism, however, that factor could have been used to further boost the level.

I am convinced that the behavioral approach to economics is going to prove itself (at least for capitalist societies) a radical advance. When perfected, survey-based theories of economics will be as superior to Keynesian economics as modern weather forecasting is to the farmer's almanac.

If, as Dr. Grove says, Samuelson's important textbook on economics has no appreciation of this development as yet, that is sad but not unique in the history of science and the arts. Katona and other writers have proven quite adequately that Keynesian economics are erroneous in the matter of the relationship of earnings and spending, and inadequate to deal with the cyclicity of the economy (references 12,15,18 in the paper). Lekachman (6) seems to relate Keynesian economics to the history of the decline of the British Empire.

Since, however, the consumer-oriented economists have inherited the rationalistic and phenomenological tendencies of the older schools, they limit their scope and usefulness. And so it seems to me that the question is not *whether* psychoanalytic thinking can be applied to the study of economics, but *how* it can be done. I have therefore decided to list a few possibilities for the application of psychoanalysis. In order to be able to do so, I will not be able to discuss some of the points raised by the discussants, for which I do humbly apologize.

These, then, are some ideas about how we psychoanalysts could be involved in multidisciplinary studies of economics:

1. *Investigation of the unconscious motivations of groups*: The essential subject of the study would be the latent affect and its ideational concomitants in reference to finances. In addition, we need to study the circumstances under which unconscious forces become widespread and set future trends. In order to get a background to the relationship of latent affects to their conscious outcropping or to their influencing the economy *without becoming conscious*, a certain amount of background study and "calibration" will be necessary, as follows:

(*a*) The development of psychological testing and interview techniques which enable the researchers to go beyond what people know about their feelings to the preconscious level, with special attention to the influence of repressed impulses. The utilization of psychoanalytic understanding of productions and projective technique is available for this reason. These studies could be augmented by questionnaires which also check the internal consistency of responses.

(*b*) Similarly, techniques can be applied to study the relationship between what people think they want and like, and the motivations on which they will act. There is a complex interaction of yearnings, inhibitions, influences of superego function, self-representation and group influences. Experiences show that if the automobile industry makes cars as the consumers *say* they want them, the cars do not sell. Conversely, a newspaper which conducted an advertising campaign implying that its readers were financially successful got excellent results despite the general scorn for the silliness of the approach.

(*c*) To provide the background for a more comprehensive evaluation of forces within the society or the economic climate, we must make preliminary studies of the interaction of certain key groupings within our economy. E. Jácques' study of the effect of ritualized aggression in the labor-management crisis in Britain illustrates the possibilities. (4)

The family has to be investigated from the point of view of the interrelationship between the generations. The handling of money and goods is the common means of control, substitute for love, expression of aggression, etc. Since such forces exist in all families, how can we ignore them? Even the matter of identification or the need to distinguish oneself has been of great effect on selected aspects of the economy. Along with the family, the self-image of the community is of great impact. The feedback between the community and an individual on matters of ego-ideal, life-goals and aspirations of an economic nature cannot be ignored.

(*d*) Finally, the effect of the non-human environment has to be investigated. (In our society, this would relate to such diverse influences as the effect of automation, the residuals of "frontier psychology" replaced by crowding, air and water pollution, and other factors such as war, international and local politics, which all contribute to our feelings about our place in this world and its future.)

2. *An investigation of the freedom to make economic decisions, and the effects of the deprivation of such freedom*, and an investigation of various means of influencing and controlling economic behavior—from suggestion (advertising), exploitation of drives and anxieties, to more overt impositions such as price-and-wage controls, planned economies or outright *economic* dictatorship: We are concerned here with the individual and group psychopathology produced by economic oppression. We know, for instance, that in Stalin's forced collectivization of Soviet farming, millions of people died in the process of a generalized resistance to an economic change. As Dr. Saver points out, the socialist states are not immune to economic difficulties, but theirs, because of the limitation of expression of the feelings of investors and consumers, are not analogous to the "business cycle." Their problems come close to the observation made by Dr. Comess, namely, that "dispassionate managers" of investment funds, and of entire economies as well, are subject to psychological influences.

The opposite side of the coin is represented in credit buying—in it one can give great play to his emotional needs without limitations set by one's present capital, as long as one is willing and able to mortgage his future economic potential. In our own buoyant, mildly inflationary economy, the consumer indebtedness has probably reflected more faithfully than any other indicator the unconscious and irrational influences hitherto ignored by academic economists. The computerization of the credit card system, with the proposed universal credit card—Wilmouth's "PIP" (Personal Identification Project)—will represent the possibility of a revolution in the monetary function in this country.[1] No longer will one have to consider his resources; he will have only to pay an interest on his purchases. Those people whose impulse control will exceed their earning potential may find themselves "blacklisted . . . developing a two-class society. . ." If these developments come true, will the bank find it necessary in establishing the credit rating of a young person to require psychological testing of some applicants?

3. *The application of psychoanalysis to economic behavior*: Despite Dr. Saver's fears of applying observations from psychoanalysis to group economic behavior, I believe that there is much room for psychoanalysts to contribute to our knowledge of economics. The physiologist or pathologist, upon examining a few cells in high magnification, can tell about the function of the entire organism. Because of the intensity and attention to detail inherent in our work, it is possible to form hypotheses and inferences which no survey or questionnaire can make. The fact that such hypotheses may require validation by other approaches need not discourage us. Significant contribution in the study of human history, and especially of the genesis of war and other outcropping of instinctual derivatives, have already been made.

Thank you, Professors Rogow and Grove, Drs. Saver, Higgins and Comess. It is gratifying to feel that we all agree on the basic point which I have tried to make: that an important area of economics is a behavioral science which can be enriched by the efforts and thinking of psychoanalysts.

---

[1]Robert K. Wilmouth, Chairman of the American Banking Association Automation Committee, predicts a "single credit card with a single number for each person" in which all financial transactions of a person may be "amalgamated into one financial form." (8)

Bibliography

1. Dorsey, J. Personal Communication.
2. Freud, S. (1921). "Group Psychology and the Analysis of the Ego." *Standard Edition: Collected Works.* London: Hogarth Press, 1955.
3. Hillberg, R. (1963). *The Destruction of European Jewry.* Chicago: Quadrangle Press.
4. Jacques, E. (1959). "Psychoanalysis and the Current Economic Crisis." *Psychoanalysis and Contemporary Thought* (ed. J. D. Sutherland). New York: Grove Press.
5. Katona, G. (1960). *The Powerful Consumer.* New York: McGraw Hill.
6. Lekachman, R. (1966). *The Age of Keynes.* New York: Random House.
7. Sterba, R. (1944). "On Christmas." Psa. Quart., Vol. 13.
8. "The Reporter Notes: 'The New Proletariat.'" The Reporter, Dec., 1966.

The Forum

Title — **The Psychodynamic Formulation of Agoraphobia**

Author — **Edoardo Weiss, M.D.**

Dr. Weiss was the founder of the Italian Psychoanalytic Society and Institute in 1931. He is now in private practice in Chicago and is Staff Member Emeritus of the Chicago Institute for Psychoanalysis and former Visiting Professor at the Psychiatric Clinic of the Marquette University of Milwaukee.

Discussants

Carlos Nuñez-Saavedra, M.D.
President and Professor of Chilean Psychoanalytic Association and former Ordinary Professor of Psychiatry at the Catholic University of Chile. He has presented numerous psychoanalytic papers on disturbances of consciousness and many other topics at different national and international meetings.

Raymond H. Gehl, M.D.
President of the New Jersey Psychoanalytic Society; member of the Executive Council, American Psychoanalytic Association, 1964-65, and developer of a projective test, "The Graphomotor Projection Technique." Since publication of his paper "Claustrophobia and Depression" in 1964, Dr. Gehl has been called upon frequently to discuss other papers concerning phobia. His latest, "Providing a Therapeutic Climate by Pairing Patients," describes a new approach to the treatment of hospitalized patients.

Samuel Novey, M.D.
Director of Training at The Sheppard & Enoch Pratt Hospital; Associate Professor of Psychiatry at Johns Hopkins University, and Training Analyst at The Baltimore Psychoanalytic Institute. He has published about 20 papers in the general areas of ego psychology, affect theory, and the relevance of history to psychiatry and psychoanalytic therapy.

Mortimer Ostow, M.D.
Practicing psychoanalyst who has written some 70 papers and two books on theoretical and clinical aspects of psychoanalytic psychiatry. His general approach is to attempt to isolate clinical phenomena, and, within the framework of psychoanalytic theory, to attempt to discover some biologic mechanisms to which the phenomena can be related.

I. Peter Glauber, M.D.
His 25 years of psychoanalytic treating and investigating functional speech problems as ego disorders have led to more recent study of other ego disturbances, particularly the automatisms and the schizoid state, with the focus on changes of cathexis. Dr. Glauber has written also on linguistics, anhedonia, homosexuality, deterrents in the study and practice of medicine, and on Federn's ego psychology, and has abstracted and reviewed some of Edoardo Weiss's writings.

The Psychodynamic Formulation of Agoraphobia[1]

Edoardo Weiss, M.D.

Chicago, Illinois

In over 50 years of psychoanalytic practice I have had the opportunity to study very many cases of agoraphobia. Some were not very accessible to treatment, but in several cases I obtained a good and lasting therapeutic result. However, I have gained a deeper insight into the psychodynamics of this neurosis only in recent years.

As I mentioned in my book, there is a voluminous pre-Freudian literature on this particular neurosis. French, German, Swedish, and Italian neurologists and psychiatrists described its various clinical aspects and the physiological manifestations of agoraphobic anxiety. However, none suspected the psychological nature of this phobia. Only in the light of psychoanalysis were unconscious conflicts recognized as the determining factors.

In the psychoanalytical literature there is no accurate description of this neurosis. Furthermore, some of the concepts of agoraphobia are confusing. Phobias which in their manifestations and psychodynamic aspects are quite different from agoraphobia are often considered agoraphobias by some psychoanalysts. In the classical—but not the most frequent type of—agoraphobia, the patient is afraid to cross a wide open space, a square, or a broad street. (In 1872 the German neurologist, Westphal, (8) introduced the term "agoraphobia" for this fear. He considered it to be a neurological disease.) Why is the patient afraid to cross such a wide open space? He will tell us that he is afraid to fall or that he feels dizzy. A more accurate investigation of his conscious experience is that he does not trust his ability to walk into a wide open space.

One of my patients said that he lost the sensation of his own body when he had to cross a wide open space, and that he could do so only when he shielded his eyes, thereby excluding from his sight the expanse of space which lay before him. So it would seem that the classical type of agoraphobia is due to some physiological sensory disturbance. In fact, in this type the patient becomes unable to gauge the bodily result of his motor impulses in walking, as if he were unable to coordinate his movements properly. In Federn's terminology, the patient's "bodily ego feeling" is impaired when he faces a wide open space. (I do not know whether Federn had ever analyzed agoraphobic patients—at least, he never mentioned agoraphobia in his writings—but I gained a psychodynamic understanding of this phobia in the light of his concepts of ego psychology.)

What kind of unconscious conflicts, if any, could lead to the classical type of agoraphobia, for which the *neurologist*, Westphal, had chosen this term? To my knowledge, this type has not been psychologically interpreted with any precision. The patient's need to lean on another person in order to be able to cross such a space is the consequence of his incapacity to do so unaided.

Later, the term agoraphobia was extended to designate all anxiety reactions to abandoning a fixed point of support, e.g., the anxiety reaction to venturing some distance from home. Such a fear was illustrated by the

[1]After the publication of my monograph (7) on agoraphobia, I was asked by the Chicago Institute for Psychoanalysis to present my basic ideas on the psychodynamics of this neurosis. This paper, which I read on February 10, 1965, contains a more concise formulation of agoraphobia.

French neurologist, Leuret, in 1834, long before Westphal introduced the term "agoraphobia" for the classical type of this disease. Leuret (4) described the severe anxiety of a patient who did not dare to leave home, often for as long as six months at a time, and then only in a carriage and accompanied by some person who could assist him in case of emergency. All cases such as this were later called agoraphobia, and for this type we find various psychoanalytical interpretations with which the reader is certainly well acquainted. Let me mention here only the most important ones.

A very popular interpretation of this kind of agoraphobic anxiety is that it is due to a fixation or regression of the adult patient to an infantile dependency on the mother. Agoraphobia, however, can be found also in children who *ipso facto* are dependent on the mother. Abraham (1) wrote about an agoraphobic child who said, "I want to be a mother's boy, not a boy of the street."

In recent years many psychoanalysts have elaborated on the symbiotic attachment of the child to the mother and on the concept of symbiotic neurosis and psychosis. The feeling of being enclosed in some place can be related to intrauterine and postnatal symbiotic states in which the child's ego is not yet completely differentiated from that of the mother. Pollock (5) has published the most exhaustive article in the literature concerning symbiosis and symbiotic neurosis.

Another popular interpretation of agoraphobia is that it is due to an unconscious sexual temptation. The populated street offers, particularly to women with exhibitionistic and unconscious prostitution fantasies, the possibility of forbidden sexual gratification. They are afraid to become, as it were, "women of the street."

Deutsch (3) found in agoraphobic women a pronounced identification with the mother, toward whom they felt strongly ambivalent. They wished her not to return home but to die. Through their identification with her they feared that they themselves would die on the street. In Deutsch's opinion, the effect of this identification is analogous to that of melancholic patients: accusations against the object are turned into self-accusations. Deutsch also mentions that because the unconscious death-wish against the mother arouses in the patient an exaggerated fear that the mother may die, the patient cannot separate from her and therefore must always keep her close by. As Deutsch says, the mother becomes a "protected protector."

We may now ask: What do such cases have in common with the classical type of agoraphobia to justify the extension of this term to them, namely, to all phobic fears about leaving home and venturing on the street?

All cases which should be called agoraphobia are characterized by two factors: (*a*) an anxiety reaction to a danger which is consciously sensed as an internal one; (*b*) the situation from which it ensues, namely, by the patient's leaving home and venturing some distance from it. This feeling of internal insecurity can, of course, also be experienced in other situations, but it is always provoked by the patient's leaving a place of support and venturing some distance from it. All types of real agoraphobia are characterized by such a depletion of the ego sensation and/or of the confidence in the ability to function in an adequate manner.

In order to clarify this point, let us compare agoraphobia with other phobias. Patients who have a phobic fear of dogs, of being struck by lightning or of being run over, fear an *external* danger to an exaggerated and irrational degree, whereas agoraphobic patients are *actually* exposed to a danger which is consciously perceived as an *internal* one. They fear to be trapped by a feeling of ill-being which incapacitates them from functioning in a rational and integrated manner.

At the time when Freud treated neurotic

patients through hypnotic suggestions, he once hypnotized a young agoraphobic woman, suggesting to her that from then on she would be able to walk on the street without anxiety. The hypnotic suggestion worked—the patient could actually leave home and walk some distance from it without anxiety. But soon Freud learned that she was behaving in a psychotic manner. He went to her, hypnotized her again and gave her the suggestion that she should become agoraphobic again. With the return of her agoraphobia she was cured of her psychotic breakdown. She was thankful to Freud for having given her back the agoraphobia, since it was the minor evil.

Many analysts include under the term agoraphobia all kinds of phobic fears related to the street. Therefore, I avoid the term "street-phobia." Thus, for instance, Bergler (2) reports the case of an agoraphobic man who looked in the newspapers every day to find out how many people were struck by passing cars. But such patients are not necessarily agoraphobic, particularly not when they can walk on the street and cross open places without anxiety where there are no passing cars.

Agoraphobic anxiety is always a reaction to a feeling of mental ill-being which is experienced in different ways by different patients. Yet this feeling of ill-being always impairs the patient's capacity to function independently. Some patients complain of feelings of confusion or disorientation, some feel the external world to be estranged or unreal, some are afraid to lose the feeling of their identity, and some lose the sensation of their legs while walking. One of my patients said that his ego faded progressively away the further he ventured from his home.

In all these cases the patient feels unable to act properly and feels the need to be taken care of by somebody. This need is analogous to that of patients suffering from the classical type of agoraphobia, who must lean on the person who accompanies them when they have to cross a wide open space. (Symbiotic security?) Often agoraphobic patients say they are afraid to be trapped in a situation in which they would feel completely helpless.

In all cases of agoraphobia we find several characteristic features, though I will mention only a few of them here. We always find in agoraphobic patients what I call the "claustrophobic syndrome." These patients cannot tolerate the sensation of being enclosed somewhere. They must feel free to leave a place whenever they wish. They are intolerant of any kind of restriction. (Could this be fear of regression to the womb?) I illustrated this syndrome in my book with various examples. (7) While every agoraphobic patient has the claustrophobic syndrome, not all claustrophobic patients are agoraphobic.

Another always present condition in agoraphobic patients is a strong, repressed sexual tension which is blocked from a satisfactory outlet. The study of such a blockage and of the patient's orgastic experiences upon its therapeutic removal drew my attention to a phase of sexual outlet which has not been described in psychoanalysis. I called this phase the "post-climactic efflux of libido."

In sexual activity we considered the phase of forepleasure and the explosive orgastic outlet of the libido in the act of intercourse. But we must pay attention also to the individual's emotional states which follow his orgastic experience. It has been observed that sometimes an individual reacts with depression or even with disgust to an orgastic experience. Such a pathological reaction was expressed in the Latin phrase of unknown origin, *Post coitum omne animal triste est.* Normally, however, the individual feels a pleasurable relief of tension after he has reached a sexual climax. He may feel a pleasant need to sleep near his sexual partner. But the intense libidinal tension is not yet completely relieved through the explosive orgastic experience. The remaining libidinal tension is then discharged in prolonged feelings of happiness and loving closeness to the sexual partner. Sometimes some sublimated desires are enhanced, as we can observe in artists. It is this phase of libidinal outlet which I call "post-climactic efflux of libido."

In cases of sexual conflicts and feelings of guilt the patient may be able to reach a sexual climax; but then the post-climactic efflux is blocked and the patient feels depressed and disgusted with his sexual partner. One of my patients said that he feels the desire to throw the woman into the waste basket after he has reached a sexual orgasm with her. Analogous feelings are expressed by women who have the post-climactic efflux of the libido blocked.

Agoraphobic patients often have negative feelings about sexuality. Sometimes they are impotent or frigid, and sometimes their repressed sexual instincts have a perverted character. And those patients who can reach sexual orgasm have the post-climactic efflux of the libido blocked. They react to sexual orgasm—even if in itself it was enjoyable to them—with depression, feelings of guilt or disgust. We find such reactions also in promiscuous women.

We realize that such conditions are very frequent in all kinds of neuroses, particularly in hysterical patients. We may wonder why a strong sexual conflict and an inhibited sexual outlet lead sometimes to agoraphobia and sometimes to other neurotic symptoms, mostly to hysterical conversion symptoms. If we consider the interpretations of agoraphobia given by the previously-mentioned analysts, we understand that agoraphobic patients feel more anxious in situations which arouse their repressed sexual instincts. But their anxiety is always consciously related to the feelings of ill-being, which, as I have mentioned, ensue from their walking or riding to some distance from home, even when external situations do not stimulate their repressed sexual instincts. If we consider the equation of mother and home, we may relate the agoraphobic feeling of ill-being to separation anxiety. But we may then ask what makes the patient regress to such infantile dependency on the mother.

I came nearer to the understanding of agoraphobia in the analysis of some particular patients whom I discussed in my monograph. (7) The patient whom I called Michael was afraid to lose the feeling of his identity. Another patient, David, then 25 years old, regressed at a certain stage of his analysis to a childhood ego state while walking on the street. In this ego state he recaptured some daydreams he had had at the age of two or three. The contents of these daydreams were of a kind which he could not possibly have conceived at an adult ego stage. He was so astonished about the nature of his childhood wishes that he exclaimed at the analytic session: "How on earth can an adult person ever understand children!"

The erotic daydreams of that early childhood were that he was held naked in the arms of his mother who was surrounded by her women friends, all of whom admired his beautiful body and even played with his penis. In his fantasy he enjoyed his own passive abandonment to the care and manipulations of his mother and all the other women, feeling secure in his mother's protective arms.

What came to this patient's consciousness was not merely a single repressed memory but also that ego stage where the remembered fantasy belonged. The affect adhering to those daydreams was integrated with the ego as it was in the patient's early childhood. There those daydreams were ego syntonic.

In the obsessional neuroses, however, some impulses pertaining to a repressed ego stage isolate themselves from that ego stage and intrude themselves, in a more or less disguised form, into the adult ego. There they are felt as ego alien. But when a repressed ego state in toto, which contains these impulses, threatens to replace the adult ego, then the thus threatened ego loses the sensation of its stability. Furthermore, the patient's conscious ego is weakened because much ego cathexis is invested in the regressed ego stage. It is this sensation which is responsible for the agoraphobic feeling of ill-being.

It is an interesting observation that ensuing obsessional thoughts in an agoraphobic patient lessen the feeling of ill-being to which he reacts with anxiety. Through an obsessional outlet of impulses which become detached from the pertinent ego stage, the tension of that ego stage decreases. Obsessional as well as hysterical symptoms may alternate with agoraphobic anxiety; they do not usually coincide with it.

For a better understanding of the integrative difficulties caused by strongly cathected, repressed ego states, let us now consider the psychological condition called "ego dissociation."

The agoraphobic anxiety of the patient whom I call Ethel in my book started with a severe hysterical seizure. Exactly nine months after her first menstruation, this 13-year-old girl had the following experience after she had left her classroom during the recreation period: She felt very ill at ease and then had the strong sensation that she was turning into another person. It is evident that she felt her conscious ego weakening, since much ego cathexis was absorbed by the ego state which represented the other person. Therefore she struggled with all her might to retain her identity. Then she lost consciousness, and, upon coming to, heard herself desperately screaming. The screaming was not produced by the already awake portion of her ego: first she heard the screams and then she realized that it was she herself who was screaming. She had then the impression of having expelled something from her interior through her mouth by means of her screams. After this seizure she felt relieved.

The analysis revealed that in these seizures she had identified herself with her mother in the act of giving birth to a child—she felt turned into her mother. When she was six years old her brother was born and she had wished her mother to die during childbirth. Through her identification with her mother she feared that she herself would die. This reminds us of Deutsch's interpretation of the agoraphobia of some of her women patients. The death-wish against their mothers, with whom they identified themselves, aroused in them the fear that they themselves would die. A severe agoraphobia became then the substitute for Ethel's seizures.

From this and other examples we learn that repressed ego states are not only ego stages of childhood but are also repressed states of identification with another person. We speak of ego dissociation when two or more strongly cathected ego portions cannot be integrated into a unit. Ego dissociation can lead to various psychological conditions. It can lead to a double personality, so magnificently illustrated in Stevenson's story *Dr. Jekyll and Mr. Hyde*.

But apart from real double personalities, we find some individuals who alternately have satisfaction from two dissociated portions of their ego. For instance, a married man who most of the time lived with his family and had normal sexual relationships with his wife, occasionally left his family for a few weeks to satisfy his homosexual desires. His bisexuality was of an alternative nature. In his heterosexual state he was not afraid of an intrusion into his ego of his homosexual state because the latter could find from time to time an emotional outlet.

Another vicissitude of an ego dissociation is the paranoic projection in which the repressed ego state is projected into the external world. A paranoic patient may become afraid of being killed by somebody instead of being conscious of his own homicidal ego state. Such a projection is a defense against total ego disintegration. In the Schreber case, for example, the completely disintegrated, catatonic patient progressively regained ego integration as he developed a delusional system.

In dreams, very often a dissociated portion of the dreamer appears as a dream person. And it is inexact to interpret such a dream person simply as the dreamer himself, since this dream person represents only a dissociated portion of him. When a dissociated ego state which is strongly cathected by an included instinct alternates with the other ego portion, it obtains from time to time emotional relief, and thus it never reaches a strong intensity. Therefore it is not sensed as an internal threat. But we never find a double or alternating personality in agoraphobic patients. They stick firmly to the conscious ego state which they have reached in their development.

We now understand the source of the agoraphobic feeling of ill-being. We also understand why the ego sensation is disturbed and weakened in those patients who fall easily into a state of panicky helplessness and possibly why they regress to an infantile dependency on the mother. In my opinion the regression to this dependency, and the related separation anxiety, is not the cause of agoraphobic anxiety but rather the consequence of the ego disturbance. (Perhaps the patient has never completely abandoned his symbiotic tie to the mother.)

We may also ask whether the fear of leaving home and of going some distance from it is due only to a regression to an infantile dependency on the mother. Venturing some distance from home or abandoning a familiar place is sensed by the patient as a withdrawal from his conscious familiar ego state.

I would like now to illustrate with another example the emerging of a repressed ego state in an agoraphobic patient. The analysis of Frank[2] revealed that he suffered from a severe castration anxiety. He was 23 years old when he started his analysis to be cured from a moderate form of agoraphobia. He revealed that he had never masturbated because touching his penis had always been meaningless to him. He had very early repressed any erotic sensation of his penis, and he had never experienced an ejaculation in waking life and only rarely in dreams. He was sexually interested only in women who could not possibly remind him of his mother. He was amazed when he read Freud's statement that a child's first sexual interest is directed towards his mother. He had quite opposite feelings. He had been enuretic until his fifth year, and his mother used to tell him that she would cut off his penis if he wet the bed again. But he never took her threats seriously.

He had very strong sublimated interests, and therefore, I think, his agoraphobia did not reach great intensity. His main interest was in ancient history, and he studied the life and cultural conditions of the people of ancient times. He was interested in their housing conditions, their social organizations, the way they dressed, and what they ate. He imagined how thrilling it would be to walk on the streets of ancient Rome or Athens, or of Egypt and the biblical Palestine. He spent many hours in the archeological sections of the museums. He started teaching history and obtained his Ph.D. degree while he was still under treatment.

Soon the analysis was concentrated on conflict-solving issues related to the Oedipus complex. He was 26 when he succeeded in reaching a sexual orgasm for the first time, during intercourse with a girl. For the first time he began to experience erotic sensations

---

[2]This analysis, which lasted over three years (six sessions a week), is described at greater length in my book.(7) Some episodes from the analysis were published shortly after its termination,(6) but I was not permitted to publish it *in extenso* until 30 years later.

in his penis, sensations which increased rapidly to an enormous intensity and invested his whole personality. In his words, his "whole ego became flooded with the most enjoyable erotism." As he approached orgasm, he felt an extremely pleasurable urge to urinate which he tried instinctively to control, but without success. And he experienced his ejaculation as a violent, uncontrollable urination. And in this state he had the almost hallucinatory sensation of being a child in his mother's bed and urinating on her nightgown. This experience was followed by an intense post-climactic efflux of libido.

When after this fantastic experience he went out with his girl, he felt his whole personality invigorated and rejuvenated. He enjoyed all his perceptions with great intensity and remembered that in his early childhood all his visual and acoustic perceptions had a much greater vividness and conveyed to him a very pleasant feeling tone. On the street he enjoyed looking at the shop windows, at the trees and flowers, and at the people who passed by. He enjoyed hearing people's voices and the horns of cars. And he recognized that this was not a new experience—he had felt the same way in his childhood when his mother would take him out for a walk. He had been much more alive then than in later life. He came to the conclusion that the feeling of one's existence is much more vivid in childhood than in later years and remarked that old people must feel almost dead.

What interests us now is his sensation that such a vivid feeling of his existence was incompatible with agoraphobic anxiety. It is evident that this was due to the strengthening of his ego. In such a spirit he could go out alone, during the day or night, without the slightest feeling of ill-being.

One year after the termination of his analysis he visited me and told me that his return to the repressed ego stage of childhood had been as fascinating to him as if he had been transported to some ancient city of antiquity which he had imagined in his fantasies.

The repressed ego stage of childhood which contained a strong sexual tension came to this patient's consciousness through the emotional outlet of that sexual tension. In this case, the experienced orgastic discharge could then be integrated within the adult ego stage because the original conflict in which that sexual urge was involved and the castration fear had been progressively overcome in the treatment. And once that sexual tension could find an outlet, the early ego state itself could be integrated and adjusted to that of adulthood.

We now may wonder whether every agoraphobic patient would lose his anxiety when he became able to reach a complete orgastic experience with the post-climactic discharge In taking clinical histories we find sometimes that patients who do not suffer from agoraphobia at the time of the interview have experienced some type of agoraphobia in the past. In these cases we learn that they have lost their agoraphobic anxiety once they have experienced a sexual satisfaction or upon experiencing a more intense one than ever before. But transitory agoraphobias are rather rare. Usually an agoraphobic condition does not subside without treatment, and in many cases the patients remain agoraphobic for most of their lives. The prognosis of agoraphobia in older patients is not favorable.

There are cases who after 10 or 15 years of analysis improve very slightly or not at all. There are also cases, however, which improve after a relatively short treatment. Such improvements are mostly due to the relief of tension which the patients find in the transference relation with the analyst. The case of Gertrude may illustrate this point.

This young married woman, who was sexually frigid, reacted with anxiety to very strange sensations, which she described as the loss of the exact feeling of her own size. She became anxious when shop windows and doors of buildings seemed larger than they actually were. She felt that either her own size was reduced or that that of the buildings was magnified. The streets also seemed broader than they actually were.

Gertrude was not very productive in her treatment. She dwelt with greater detail than necessary on many conscious memories and on her relationships to people. After more than a year of analysis she developed a sexual transference to me (because I was a forbidden sexual object), and it soon became clear that her desire to get closer to me was more important to her than to understand the psychological reasons for her neurosis. I explained to her the transference phenomenon and enlightened her about the Oedipus complex—explanations she understood only intellectually. Eventually I decided to discontinue treatment before the summer vacation. As long as she could indulge in the positive transference feelings, she felt freer of anxiety; but, when the summer vacation approached, her anxiety state increased and she also manifested negative feelings toward me. She felt rejected.

After summer vacation she phoned to tell me that something astonishing had happened which freed her of her agoraphobic anxiety. When I saw her again, she told me that her husband had taken her to a health resort in Austria and had left her there in the care of friends while he was away on a 10-day business trip. During his absence she was seduced by a pianist.

She remarked to me that now she understood very well what transference meant. She felt as safe with the pianist as she did with me. Because I had rejected her, she felt great consolation in being accepted with open arms by him. In her opinion she had developed a transference from me to the pianist. His approach was so thrilling that she could not resist him, and in his embrace she experienced for the first time a strong sexual orgasm. Her description of the intensity of her sexual experience with him was similar to that of Frank's, not only with regard to the climax but also with regard to the post-climactic libidinal efflux. After this experience she felt her surroundings were more real and enjoyable than before. She felt guilty not toward her husband for her behavior, but toward her mother, who would have been horrified by it. Gertrude lost her agoraphobic anxiety after this experience.

When her husband returned to the resort, she was able to reach a sexual orgasm with him, while thinking of the pianist. Her husband, very happy about it, remarked that the health resort had done much more for her than the analysis.

Gertrude asked me if it had ever occurred to me that sometimes an extra-marital experience could improve one's marital relationship. My answer was that something must have been basically wrong either with the person or with the marriage if the marital relationship needed such a therapeutic device. I advised her to resume analysis, explaining to her that an improvement obtained by such means is fraught with serious dangers. (In the subsequent analytical treatment, Gertrude eventually recaptured the frame of mind of her childhood and remembered having been sexually aroused by her father.)

With these cases I wanted to illustrate various developments in the analysis of agoraphobic patients in which a repressed, dissociated portion of the ego becomes integrated within the adult ego organization. When this goal is achieved, the patient is freed from that feeling of ill-being to which he reacts with agoraphobic anxiety. But in many cases it is very difficult to achieve this goal, particularly in the older patient.

I wish now to say only a few words about the claustrophobic syndrome of agoraphobia, which is based on a projection of an internal psychological mechanism. On the one hand, the patient's ego feels an urge to remove the internal barrier of counter-cathexes in order to obtain relief of a steadily increasing drive tension; on the other hand, the ego does not dare to have this barrier removed, for it secures the defensive repression of unacceptable drives. I called such a conflict an intra-ego conflict, since both the defense against the drive and the urge to relieve the increasing tension are ego-invested concerns. The more agoraphobic a patient is, the more he senses the absence of an external confinement as the absence of an internal protective barrier against dangerous drive tensions. The more claustrophobic a patient is, the greater is his need to find relief of a drive tension, and thus he cannot endure restrictions. In accordance with this view, we find that the agoraphobic patient can more easily adapt himself to renunciation of satisfactions, while the claustrophobic patient cannot easily renounce satisfaction of his instinctive wishes.

The agoraphobic and claustrophobic syndrome may have a deeper determinant in a conflict between symbiotic union with the mother and the need for separation from her in order to establish one's own autonomous ego.

Bibliography

1. Abraham, K. (1913). "On the Psychogenesis of Agoraphobia in Children." In *Clinical Papers and Essays on Psycho-Analysis.* London: Hogarth Press; New York: Basic Books, 1955.
2. Bergler, E. (1935). "Psychoanalysis of a Case of Agoraphobia." Psa. Rev., Vol. 22.
3. Deutsch, H. (1929). "The Genesis of Agoraphobia." Int. J. Psa., Vol. 10.
4. Leuret, F. (1834). "Hypochondrie sans lésion préalable de la santé physique de l'intelligence." In *Fragments Psychologiques sur la folie.* Paris: Crochard.
5. Pollock, G. (1964). "On Symbiosis and Symbiotic Neurosis." Int. J. Psa., Vol. 45.
6. Weiss, E. (1934). "Agoraphobia and its Relation to Hysterical Attacks and to Traumas." Int. Z. Psa., Vol. 20; Int. J. Psa., Vol. 16, 1935.
7. ———. (1964). *Agoraphobia in the Light of Ego Psychology.* New York and London: Grune & Stratton.
8. Westphal, C. (1871-1873). "Die Agoraphobie eine neuropathische Erscheinung." Arch. Psychiat., pp. 138-61.

737 North Michigan Avenue
Chicago, Illinois 60611

Discussant

Carlos Nuñez-Saavedra, M.D.
Santiago, Chile

Dr. Weiss regards agoraphobia from the psychodynamic point of view as an anxiety reaction, originating from a feeling of ill-being, which corresponds to impulses pertaining to a repressed and dissociated portion of the ego which has become a part of the organized adult ego.

This statement conveys a defense mechanism of the agoraphobic patient, which Freud, as Dr. Weiss comments, had pointed out, and which has stimulated several thoughts which in my opinion may contribute to emphasize certain aspects of the concepts of the author.

First, it should be pointed out that while agoraphobia defends the patient from a repressed and dissociated portion of the adult ego which is the cause of the ego disturbance, a manifestation in which there is no genetic difference with other neurotic symptoms, agoraphobia implies the fear of disintegration in a specific situation, i.e., the feeling of loneliness and abandonment in an open space, felt in fantasy as frightfully dangerous.

That repressed and dissociated portion, in my opinion, contains strong aggressive impulses which stimulate paranoic and depressive anxiety. The sadomasochist characteristics of the agoraphobic, as well as his inhibitions, sexual deviations, persecution and depressive guilt feelings, should not be disregarded—all of which points to the paranoic and depressive background common to all agoraphobic patients. The symptom practically reaches the limit of a delirious rapture of the schizoid type even though a sense of reality subsists.

When protected, the agoraphobic adult may display executive, aggressive, domineering and even abusive behavior; unaided, he experiences the fear of the disintegration menace.

The sexual life of the agoraphobic is always confused. Occasional orgastic satisfaction, as in the patients described by Dr. Weiss, is followed by temporary relief of the phobic reaction. In such cases the analysis of the selected object and the emotional evaluation of the erotic relationship are the clues which permit a comparison of the orgasm and an abreaction.

Discussant

Raymond H. Gehl, M.D.
Maplewood, New Jersey

The subject of phobias has absorbed my interest for the past several years. I have particularly attempted to gain insights into them by studying the relationships of phobic patients in areas not directly concerned with the phobic symptom itself. It is important to study the characterology of the phobic patient as well as other affective states which seem to coincide or alternate with the acuteness of the phobic involvement. The relationship of claustrophobia to depression is one such area.

What I most appreciated about Dr. Weiss's paper was his emphasis on the phenomenology of the phobic state itself rather than on the particular fantasies involved. I would have preferred even more of this emphasis, since nothing is so confusing as to attempt to understand so complicated a symptom as agoraphobia without underlining the basic ego states involved.

The literature on agoraphobia shows us what a host of fantasies can be expressed in the street fear. A partial listing, which includes the case reports of Weiss, Deutsch, Lewin, Bergler, Abraham, Katan and others, would delineate fantasies of birth, death, pregnancy, sexual temptations such as prostitution, exhibitionism and fellatio, aggressive wishes, outbursts or attacks, as well as oral wishes and fears of separation, fusion and annihilation. These fantasies run the gamut from oral to oedipal wishes and fears. Of course the case material is important, because only from such reports can we derive the information to help us formulate and classify the position of such states as agoraphobia in our schemata of the psychology of the neurosis. Helene Deutsch attempted to do this when she found the phobias to be midway between the hysterias and obsessional neuroses.

The essence of Dr. Weiss's presentation seems to be contained in the following quote: "When a repressed ego state in toto, which contains these impulses, threatens to replace the adult ego, then the thus threatened ego loses the sensation of its stability. Furthermore the patient's conscious ego is weakened because much ego cathexis is invested in the regressed ego stage. It is this sensation which is responsible for the agoraphobic feeling of ill-being. It is an interesting observation that ensuing obsessional thoughts in an agoraphobic patient lessen the feeling of ill-being to which he reacts with anxiety."

Dr. Weiss's thoughts about a dissociative type of process occurring in agoraphobia help explain some of the symptoms which the patient experiences. It seems to me convincing that in agoraphobia and claustrophobia there is a struggle in identification. Regressive infantile identifications seem to be easily mobilized in these narcissistic individuals, and the struggle between the two opposing self representations, the adult and the infantile, sets off the alarm. To deal with the regressive tendencies, the ego resorts to primitive defensive devices which involve feelings of depersonalization, derealization, estrangement and *déjà vu* as well as other somatic feelings such as dizziness, faintness, and blurring of vision. However, Dr. Weiss attributes the agoraphobe's anxiety entirely to a reaction to the feeling of ill-being with first the loss of stability, and then the anxiety. I would agree that the ego can and does react to altered ego states with anxiety, but can we attribute the entire agoraphobic pattern to this phenomenon? Can we say that the agoraphobic anxieties are only the pathological result of a conflict within the ego?

I saw a striking example of the agoraphobic syndrome occur frequently in the analysis of a classical agoraphobic patient while she was on the couch. Whenever she would approach sexual or aggressive feelings in the transference she would develop nausea, dizziness, blurring of vision, a feeling of falling and a desire to run out of the room. She could admit to her feelings and thoughts only by dissociating and attributing them to "her" or "she" or "it" or "the head." The dissociation into the "good" and "bad" self let her deal in some measure with the conflict but in itself produced anxiety. She would describe, along with the dissociation, a feeling of floating as if she were decapitated or disembodied.

This 38-year-old woman had a constant wish for symbiotic union with the mother and made use of a hired female companion for her travels. She would say that she was lying in the couch rather than on it. For her the street was not only a place for sexual temptation but also for death. When she was small, her mother would warn her of the dangerous men outside and would slap her or take away her shoes to punish her and prevent and discourage any tendencies to find freedom. A firehouse driveway had to be passed on the way to school, and the mother, in her fear, insisted that the child be accompanied across it. The patient's identification with the mother whom she wished dead, as in the cases of Dr. Weiss and Dr. Deutsch, seems present also in this illustration.

Some aspects of Dr. Weiss's formulation concerning the agoraphobic feeling of ill-being are difficult to conceptualize. He states that the regression to a dependent state and the separation anxiety are not the cause of agoraphobic anxiety, but rather the consequence of the ego disturbance. However, he parenthesizes that perhaps the patient has never abandoned his symbiotic ties to the mother. In the last paragraph of the paper he also states that the agoraphobic and claustrophobic syndrome may have a deeper determinant in the conflict between one's symbiotic union with the mother and the need for separation from her in order to establish one's own autonomous ego.

My findings indicate that this wish and fear of symbiosis is a constant factor in these phobias. If the patient never abandoned his symbiotic ties, how can the separation anxiety be viewed only as a consequence of the ego disturbance? Perhaps it's the other way around; perhaps the potential ego disturbance had its causation in part due to the early mother-child relationship which did not foster separation and individuation. Dr. Weiss seems to evidence some similar question in his last paragraph. My patient, in addition to the sexual temptations (exhibitionistic, prostitution, and masturbatory) and aggressive death wishes, also saw the street and open places as huge devouring mouths waiting for her, and the ocean threatened as "a great big empty" calling to suck her in.

It seems to me that we must look to more than one explanation of these complex processes. Although I agree with Dr. Weiss's formulation of repressed ego state or repressed self representations, I do not feel that this is the only process active and that it explains everything.

In these patients, the oral triad of wishes and fears seems to predominate, and the street or the claustrum can act as stimulant in the arousal of these preoedipal fantasies along with the oedipal wishes and castration fears. Too, the frequency in which depressive states are seen in these phobias would indicate the functioning of a sadistic type of superego producing severe guilt feelings whenever sexual or aggressive thoughts interpose themselves, accounting for the sexual blocking that Dr. Weiss describes. Although anxiety and ill-feelings are aroused by the threat of the replacement by a repressed ego state, there is also an attempt to defend against superego anxiety and instinctual anxiety through regression, dissociation, denial, displacement and projection. I suggest that we are dealing with three types of anxiety: signal anxiety in the form of castration fears, traumatic anxiety in the reexperiencing of separation anxiety, and secondary anxiety which seems to accompany the ego's experiences of dissociation, depersonalization or estrangement.

To summarize, I think that Dr. Weiss's paper is extremely interesting and stimulating. He has focused our attention on the ego side of the agoraphobic process, and this is very helpful in understanding certain symptomatic aspects of the agoraphobic experience. His researches on the agoraphobic syndrome are doing much to clarify a very complicated clinical entity.

Discussant

Samuel Novey, M.D.
Baltimore, Maryland

I have had only a limited amount of experience with true agoraphobia patients as compared with Dr. Weiss's very extensive experience and considerable success with them. I am thankful to him for emphasizing the often neglected difference between agoraphobia and other common phobias, namely, the emphasis in the former on the experience of inner disorganization as the primary source of the fear, and in the latter, on some externally perceived threat as the primary source of it.

Since, however, I disagree with the theoretical position taken, and this is primarily a theoretical paper, I will limit my discussion to the elaboration of those questions in the areas of my disagreement.

My first remarks will be addressed to the limitations of the proposition that there are "conscious ego states" and, at least in the patients under discussion, "repressed ego states" which "threaten to replace the adult ego." No issue is being taken with the disorganizing influence of conflict upon the organization of the ego, including the sense of personal identity. As Dr. Weiss states, this may eventuate in the threat or actuality of identity diffusion, depersonalization and derealization among other things. The "repressed ego state" as an organized entity is too gross an invitation to reify an internal state of affairs rather than to describe it in terms of its dynamics. In addition, in suggesting that this "repressed ego state" takes cathexis away from the "conscious ego state" and thereby "weakens" it, the use of economic postulates is subject to no evident consideration other than the fact that the psychologically ill person is said to have a "weak" ego. Just so, in connection with the achieving of sexual gratification and what Dr. Weiss describes as the "post-climactic efflux of libido," one of the patients described is said to have had a "strengthing of the ego" with a resultant reemergence of repressed ego states and, I would assume, a reduction of his symptomatology.

Much of the theoretical argument is based upon the thesis that the phenomenon of ego dissociation makes for a conflict between these two strongly cathected parts of the ego. The resultants, but not the cause of which, are felt to be by Dr. Weiss the commonly held sources of agoraphobia. These are: fixations or regressions to an infantile dependency on mother, symptomatic attachments of the child to mother, unconscious sexual temptations, and unconscious identifications with an ambivalently-experienced mother with reaction against the wish to destroy her. Surely, however, the dissociated portion of the ego as a theoretical proposition would of necessity not be a first cause but must rest upon prior disruptions of infantile relationships of one kind or another.

One has the impression that what is being considered in this paper in the name of agoraphobia are certain sweeping general propositions relating to the neurosis and the psychosis: that repression of early ego states maintain a high level of organization and that they are disruptive of ordinary ego functioning, and that sexual gratification, based on a loving relationship to the sexual partner, is a necessary condition for full ego functioning. What is less clear is whether such highly organized states do in fact exist in the fashion stated, whether the "conscious ego states" are threatened by such repressed states, and not, for instance, by anxiety deriving from the threats to identity based in separation anxiety or other such reasons. Dr. Weiss infers a high level of unconscious organization and integration rather than diffuse, chaotic inner states which may attain organization only in the process of translating them into consciousness and into words. Finally it is not at all clear whether sexual maturity is to be seen, in the context suggested, as the cause or as the result of therapeutic success.

Discussant

Mortimer Ostow, M.D.
Riverdale, New York

Dr. Weiss mentions four types of etiologic explanation of agoraphobia: the classical psychodynamic formulations; the idea that an ego state from early childhood, poorly repressed and unassimilated into the adult ego, usurps control over the latter; the idea that the agoraphobe is a person who cannot tolerate the absence of intra-ego barriers against instinctual discharge; and the idea that agoraphobia may arise from the need to separate from the mother in the interest of establishing one's own autonomy.

The body of this paper consists of the development of the second theory; the first, third, and fourth are merely noted.

It is evident that in by far the largest number of instances of illness, a predominant, discrete cause cannot be discerned in the sense that one can attribute pneumonia to the pneumococcus or a laceration to a trauma. In this same sense, then, explanation four (maturational need), explanation one (conflict resolution), and explanations two and three (specific kinds of ego weakness) may all be considered etiologic agents which synergistically participate in the pathogenic process. In the paradigmatic case, a striving will originate from inner need; it will engage the ego to find a suitable discharge path for it; the particular discharge pattern selected by the ego will depend upon the constraints and opportunities of reality, the pressures of the superego, the weaknesses and strengths of the ego itself, and the various conflicting dynamic needs. To this point what I have said is conventional wisdom which has by now become textbook cliché.

One may acknowledge that in certain instances one of these several etiologic factors may be so pronounced that minimal cooperation by the others is required. For example, in the case of schizophrenia, there are some individuals who are born with such weak egos that the normal frustrations and stresses of daily life suffice to precipitate full ego fracture. There are others, though, whose ego weakness is so slight that it does not become evident until the individual is confronted with a castastrophic frustration. However, in discussing the pathogenesis of agoraphobia, I believe that one may venture at least slightly beyond mentioning the mutually complementary roles of the several different etiologic factors. I would say that the agoraphobe is a person who has not succeeded in establishing his instinctual and emotional independence from his mother. He is continually motivated to do so during the early decades of adult life.

This motivation seems to arise from two sources: First, the anaclitic relation with the maternal object generates instinctual needs which become frighteningly powerful. The proximity to the object intensifies the impulse and thereby contributes to the creation of a claustrophobia, a fear of closeness. Second, the maturational impulse itself continues to strive against the indissoluble tie to the mother which has thwarted it and thus created a fixation. In fact, it is possible that the first of these factors acts as a normal reinforcer for the second. The individual in any case is motivated time and again to cut himself off from his mother. He sees this maturational step as a kind of rebirth which he has not yet been able to achieve. The proposed advance to independence will create anxiety for any of a number of familiar reasons. When the patient makes the effort once more to take this step, the separation from mother generates anxiety which presents itself to him in topographic imagery. He seems to be frightened of spatial and temporal isolation. In the conscious image of the cause of his fear, mother does not appear. He is usually, however, aware of his anxiety, though some patients deny even that.

I have one patient, for example, who behaves exactly like an agoraphobe but will not admit that he is frightened to be alone, only that "I just don't like it." At this point he does something to bring about a reunion with mother. He may retreat from his effort to establish independence, both on the street and in the emotional relation. His ego may fracture so that we see a hysterical type of dissociation. However, the fantasy associated with this hysterical dissociation is frequently an obvious reunion with mother.

In Dr. Weiss's patient, Ethel, the menarche presents a challenge to the hitherto retarded psychic maturational process. The child is motivated to make a heroic effort really to get away from mother. Yet, at a given point, after nine menstrual periods, all she can do is establish once more her identity with mother in a simulated act of giving birth to a baby. However, she must be identical with mother; she cannot be the baby who must go away. This mental dissociation itself creates anxiety, though its *purpose* was to alleviate the separation anxiety. I would not go along with Dr. Weiss in stating that the agoraphobic anxiety is primarily the result of the ego dissociation. I believe that the agoraphobic anxiety is a secondary anxiety caused by a miscarried defense against the separation anxiety. One can often find rebirth tendencies in the efforts of dependent patients to break away from their anaclitic objects. In Dr. Weiss's other example, one can easily interpret Frank's subjective state after his first orgastic intercourse as an experience of rebirth which the young man contrasts with death.

To recapitulate, I would suggest that the agoraphobic episode is initiated by a renewed maturational drive which expresses itself as a desire to achieve a rebirth experience, that is, separation from mother. Once this effort to establish the separation gets under way, separation anxiety which becomes manifest in a topographic fantasy sets in. In many individuals this anxiety, the humiliation at having to retreat because of it, and the shame and guilt bring about a hysterical dissociation, the content of which ordinarily displays the desired reunion with mother and frequently the rebirth drive, too. This dissociated state itself may generate anxiety.

I should like to add a word about the postorgastic reactions Dr. Weiss describes. I, too, believe that these are important phenomena which have not received the attention they deserve in psychoanalytic literature. As Dr. Weiss says, there is nothing specific for agoraphobia about these reactions. However, agoraphobic patients share with others whose object relations are unsound the propensity to abnormality in this fragment of behavior. In my experience the abnormal postcoital reaction may be seen in men as well as in women, but the forms are not the same. Both men and women may experience the sensation of letdown, depression, guilt, disgust. However, some women's sexual desire is so increased by the orgasm that they want to repeat the experience as soon as possible. I have never encountered this phenomenon among men. The difference seems to correlate well with the observation that women are capable of several orgasms within a brief period of time, while male capacity is far more limited. Some women weep after orgasm, but I have never heard of men who do. What is even more interesting is that these women may also weep after their partners' orgasms.

It is my impression that in these cases of abnormal postcoital behavior, the genital mechanism is used in the pursuit of oral desires. The act of coitus is undertaken out of a need to combat either the loneliness of isolation or the loneliness associated with depression. During the period of precoital foreplay, the intense sensations and excitement engendered actually succeed in dissipating the unhappiness of the solitude. However, the orgasm represents the termination of pleasure rather than its climax. One of my patients used to say to his partner after a relatively long period of coital union, "Let's die." The depression which then follows the orgasm is not something caused by the orgasm but is rather the original depression which the coital experience was called upon to dissipate. That is why some women respond to orgasm only with a desire to repeat the experience. For a woman, the partner's orgasm is just as definitive a termination of the coital excitement as is her own. That is why she may weep in either case. The man's sensual pleasure, however, is terminated only by his own orgasm.

Finally, Dr. Weiss mentions instances in which the achievement of orgastic competence terminates the agoraphobia more or less permanently. I can understand that, when psychoanalysis enables the patient to overcome phallic and oedipal anxieties so that he can consummate intercourse successfully, he will be able to see himself as reborn and lose his fear of leaving mother. However, I have seen one agoraphobic patient who became capable of full orgastic satisfaction on only two occasions. After each, she awoke the next morning seriously depressed. I surmise that in her case, in her attempt to struggle against the impending depression, oral needs took a genital form and so overcame the usual genital inhibition. But the relief brought about by the excitement was shortlived, and so the patient soon lapsed into the definitive depression which she had been struggling to evade. An increase in genital drive and in apparent orgastic competence may indeed represent improvement in capacity for object relations. However, in other cases it may indicate a more desperate effort to overcome isolation from objects.

Discussant

I. Peter Glauber, M.D.

White Plains, New York

In my review in the "Psychoanalytic Quarterly" of Edoardo Weiss's monograph on agoraphobia, I addressed myself directly to some of its component elements including aspects of anxiety and of the ego. Here I wish to discuss some implications of Weiss's contribution for our psychoanalytic metapsychology.

His base of operation, the special dimension he emphasizes, is the economic level; more precisely, the economic variations within the cathexis of the ego. In practice the economic plane which deals with the quantities of energy is frequently considered jointly with the topographic plane which deals with the qualities of energy. Both of these levels stand in a more direct relation to the clinical phenomenology than do the structural-dynamic levels which encompass the theoretical concepts.

Weiss's orientation has special significance at this time because it can serve as a corrective against a current tendency to employ, somewhat imperialistically, the structural-dynamic levels beyond their legitimate scope. One effect of this tendency is the lessened utilization of the economic-topographic levels with a resultant constriction of insight, as I will attempt to demonstrate. Perhaps such a developmental phase is the fate of all scientific theories which undergo vicissitudes of expansion, contraction, distortion, reconstruction, replacement, etc.

Our psychoanalytic metapsychology is, I believe, an excellent example of Niels Bohr's principle of complementarity. He stated that when a complex of phenomena is observed by means of two or more instruments, one gets two or more sets of findings, each finding having a relation to the others in the same set but not to those in the other set. The sets are mutually exclusive. As our definitions of the various metapsychologic levels determine our instruments, they invoke this law of mutual exclusiveness: one level cannot be equated with another.

Weiss has shown that anxiety in the agora is the reaction to the ill-feeling stemming from alterations in the cathexis of the preconscious automatisms of locomotion, equilibration, etc.; it is a feeling of imminent dissolution of the ego. The economic shifts in the ego cathexis and the anxiety they induce have the characteristics of the actual and traumatic neuroses and their associated anxiety which is massive and disorganizing. Together they constitute an existential phenomenon of functional breakdown in the here and now, one which represents an echo or a resonance of conflicts on the dynamic-structural level. On the other hand, it is from these same conflicts, but more directly, that the agoraphobe, on getting ready to leave the house, experiences anticipatory or signal anxiety. This type is induced defensively or teleologically; the former, causally.

Thus there are two related and distinctive types of anxiety in agoraphobia: one *intra*-systemic and economically determined, the other *inter*systemic and determined structurally and dynamically. The current tendency is not to differentiate the two but to lump both under the structural-dynamic heading. As a result, significant phenomena explicable on the economic level are missed or misunderstood.

Another example occurs to me from the realm of the affects. It is the definition of depression as it is usually given exclusively in structural-dynamic terms: the introversion by the superego of aggression upon the self. While this explanation is correct, it is only partial. Depressive affect is associated with other painful affects such as shame and self-derogatory feelings, each having different structural-dynamic meanings. What they have in common with depression rests on the economic plane, namely, libidinal depletion as affected by the superego (depression), by the ego ideal (shame), or by identification with the aggressor (rejecting parent) on the basis of self-defense (self-derogatory feelings). Further, other aspects of depression such as psychomotor retardation are explicable only on the economic-topographic base. We owe these additional insights to the work of Edoardo Weiss and Paul Federn who define the ego as the core of the personality and as a phenomenon that can be experienced by means of the ego feelings.

A third example: Some analysts deny the striking symptoms of the actual neurosis as a distinctive entity. In my opinion, they thereby perform *the* impermissible act in a scientific discipline, namely, denying a phenomenon because they cannot explicate it in terms of a concept to which they have a prior commitment. That concept seems to be that all psychopathologic formations serve the sole aim of defense. Inasmuch as the actual neurosis, and the depersonalization which I believe is a species of actual neurosis, are in essence forms of breakdown—resonance phenomena having a causal explanation (hence, also having no psychic content)—they do not fit into the theory of symptoms as universal defense. What is called for instead of denial of clinical facts are modifications in this theory.

Variations in ego cathexes produce significant clinical phenomena which are part of the data upon which our theories are based. The economic level is broad in the sense that it is a kind of final, common ground of phenomena of similar qualities of cathexis but of diverse dynamic-structural origins. Perhaps the resistance to recognizing its importance may stem from a concern about obscuring the dynamic factors. But if we recognize that the two levels are mutually exclusive, and that the economic vicissitudes follow almost invariably on the heels of structural-dynamic conflicts but with few exceptions have no independent standing, this fear would be eliminated.

This comes close to saying that there may be no such thing as intrasystemic conflicts, only intersystemic. Whether this is completely true or largely true, or whether the concept of conflict is not applicable to the economic-topographic in the same way as it is to the structural-dynamic levels (perhaps "disturbed cathectic homeostasis" would be a more appropriate designation), are questions beyond the scope of this discussion. At any rate, the place of the dynamic-structural plane of our metapsychology has been established. But as its limits are defined more sharply, both the dynamic-structural *and* the economic-topographic levels will become more useful and contribute more to the enrichment of the whole metapsychology.

Author's Response

Edoardo Weiss, M.D.
Chicago, Illinois

I was very much interested in the discussants' remarks to my paper. Before revealing my reactions to their stimulating thoughts, I would like to clarify some of my findings in the study of the agoraphobic and claustrophobic afflictions.

In each case we find some individual features in the patient's anxiety experiences, in his defense mechanisms and in the kind of instinctive drives which threaten to break through into his consciousness. In all cases, however, the deepest source of the patient's conflict is rooted in his sexual fixation to the parent of the opposite sex and his panic fear of being abandoned or rejected by the mother. Such abandonment is felt by the patient as an annihilation of his ego. In male patients the castration fear is mostly related to the mother. I agree with Dr. Gehl that the agoraphobic patient has never completely abandoned his symbiotic attachment to the mother.

In some cases the deeply repressed Oedipus conflict leads to various developments of the original instinctive drives, giving rise to homosexual, sadistic and masochistic urges. Satisfaction of such derivative urges, however, does not free the patient from his agoraphobic anxiety. Only the acquired capacity to reach heterosexual satisfaction upon resolution, in the analysis, of his Oedipus conflict can free him from his phobia. Besides, I found in every case of agoraphobia those ego-psychological difficulties on which I elaborated in my monograph and in my paper.

I would also like to mention here that there are some rare cases of agoraphobia which we may call "malignant," because in them the ego weakness is more pronounced, and the symbiotic attachment to the mother too tenacious to be overcome through classical treatment. We may say that their ego has not been completely "born," i.e., separated from the ego of the mother. Such conditions may lead to a schizophrenic breakdown. In these cases the orthodox psychoanalytical technique should be modified in the sense of Federn's procedure in the treatment of weak egos and of the psychoses.

Dr. Nuñez-Saavedra mentions that the dissociated, repressed portion of the ego contains strong aggressive impulses which stimulate paranoic and depressive anxiety. He also mentions masochistic characteristics and sexual deviations of agoraphobic patients. As I have said before, such impulses are not at the root of the agoraphobic anxiety, but they are rather the result of vicissitudes of the basic oedipal conflict. When sadistic impulses gain the upper hand, then the patient may become more obsessional than agoraphobic. Satisfaction of drives derivative from the basic Oedipus constellation does not free the patient from his agoraphobia. One of my female agoraphobic patients could freely satisfy her lesbian urges but developed a symbiotic attachment to her female sexual partner. Only the uncovering of her sexual fixation on her father and the solution of the oedipal conflict freed her from her agoraphobic anxiety.

I was very pleased that Dr. Gehl confirmed my findings that, in agoraphobia, conflicting ego states are involved. He also mentions that agoraphobic patients have many fantasies of sexual deviations. These fantasies, I repeat, are due to a secondary elaboration of the oedipal conflict.

Dr. Gehl agrees with me that in agoraphobia ego states are repressed in toto. It was Federn's finding that ego states are repressed and stratified in the unconscious. I have experienced, as Dr. Gehl did, that some female agoraphobic patients became anxious on the couch as a reaction to their sexual transference feelings toward the analyst. In such a state one of my patients wanted to run away from my office. Another female patient had started her analysis with another analyst. She told me why she suddenly refused to see him again. When she had developed a sexual transference to him, he tried to reassure her by saying, "Don't be afraid, I can control myself." She got up immediately from the couch, left his office and did not want to see him again. In her childhood she had been afraid that her seductive father would not have been able to control himself.

I am glad that Dr. Novey, also, acknowledges that in agoraphobia the patient fears an inner disorganization. I think, however, that he misunderstood me when he says that my paper is primarily theoretical. The contrary is true. I avoided theory as much as possible and tried to describe accurately the patient's actual experiences. The existence of conscious and repressed ego states is an important discovery of Federn's and this is recognized by an increasing number of analysts. The observation that alternating ego states never lead to agoraphobic fears confirms my interpretation of this anxiety.

I disagree with Dr. Novey who says that a repressed ego state taking cathexis away from the conscious ego state is the same as saying that such an ego is simply "weak." An ego can become weak also because of unexplored organic and endocrinologic deficiencies and for various other reasons. To use an analogy, we cannot disregard the reasons why a person became physically weak. He could have become weak because of too great physical exertion, or because of lack of food, because of old age or because of a long-lasting physical disease. And so the ego weakness of the conscious ego state of the agoraphobic patient is due to the absorption of ego cathexis by a repressed ego state. I would like to emphasize that I consider in all cases not only the resultants but also the sources of specific weaknesses of the ego. And, as in every neurotic and psychotic disease, I keep in mind Freud's concept of the "complementary series." Some agoraphobic patients are constitutionally strongly fixed to an infantile ego state.

I agree with Dr. Ostow that agoraphobic patients did not succeed in establishing an instinctual and emotional independence from the mother. He observed, too, that the patient's anaclitic relation to the mother generates instinctual needs which become frighteningly powerful. We all agree with him that the proximity of the object intensifies the impulse and thereby contributes to the creation of a claustrophobic anxiety. However, the fear of being enclosed in a space is also felt by the patient's ego as a blockage of any possible emotional outlet for his drives. This I made clear in my paper.

I would like to clarify Dr. Ostow's idea of rebirth which he conceives as a process of maturation, representing a step toward complete emancipation from the mother, of cutting oneself off from his mother. In my opinion, the process of being born is not terminated with the physical detachment of the child from his mother after the umbilical cord is severed. The ego is completely born after its maturation and complete abandonment of the symbiotic and anaclitic attachment to the mother. In this connection I would like to clarify the cases of Ethel and Frank which Dr. Ostow mentions in his discussion.

Ethel had been seen by Freud before her recovery. Freud himself had interpreted her hysterical seizures as her identification with her mother in the act of giving birth to a child. And, since she had wished her mother to die in the act of giving birth to a child, she was afraid that this may happen to her. She wanted to replace her mother in relation to her father. Her seizure started with the feeling of losing her own identity and being turned into another person. The analysis revealed that this other person was her dying mother. This conflictual identification with her mother in the oedipal constellation was certainly not a successful attempt at emancipation from her. Besides, as I pointed out in my monograph, Ethel identified herself also with the child who was being born.

I am glad that Dr. Ostow recognizes the importance of the post-climactic emotional reaction. The clearest case of this experience was that of Frank. I disagree with Dr. Ostow in his interpretation of Frank's subjective state after his first orgastic relief of his sexual tension. I cannot conceive Frank's experience as that of a rebirth which this young patient contrasts with death. I described accurately his ego state without any theoretical implication. Frank experienced very intensively that he felt again the way in which he had felt in early childhood. His ego feeling of childhood had been reawakened; all his sensory perceptions acquired a much stronger reality sensation; they became more enjoyable than they were in later years, prior to his orgastic experience. He concluded that old people do not feel so vividly alive as he himself had felt in his childhood. So, I would say, the accurate description of his experience was actually a reliving of an ego state of childhood. This cannot be interpreted as the feeling of being reborn.

I read with great interest Dr. Glauber's discussion. He wrote an excellent review of my monograph in the "Psychoanalytic Quarterly," and he participated in Federn's study group. In contrast with Dr. Novey, he emphasizes the importance of the economic variations within the cathexis of the ego, in addition to the consideration of the quantity of energy from a topographical point of view, between the id, ego and superego. I agree with him that it is still "a current tendency to employ, somewhat imperialistically, the structural-dynamic levels beyond their legitimate scope." I found his discussion of this issue very interesting and clarifying, not only in the study of agoraphobia, but also of many other manifestations of ego impairment, particularly of some depressive states. He expressed most clearly his view by saying "... there may be no such thing as intrasystemic conflicts, only intersystemic."

The Forum

Title — **Little Red Riding Hoods on the Couch**

Author — **Lilla Veszy-Wagner, PH.D.**

Member of the British Psychoanalytical Society and in private practice in London. In addition to a book on psychological anthropology and several papers in Hungarian, she has authored many papers, both theoretical and clinical, on psychoanalysis as applied to anthropology, sociology, mythology and literature. Her present contribution adds to Dr. Veszy-Wagner's published studies on mythologic figures whose behavior we may rediscover in patients today.

Discussants

Herbert Fingarette, PH.D.

Professor of Philosophy at the University of California, Santa Barbara. He has in the past 16 years written extensively on relationships between psychoanalysis and philosophy. In addition to a book, *The Self in Transformation*, he has published numerous papers and addressed psychiatric congresses on philosophical-psychoanalytical aspects of literature, law, religion, and psychiatric theory. He is an Advisory Editor of "The Psychoanalytic Review."

Mark Kanzer, M.D.

Clinical Professor of Psychiatry at the State University of New York, Downstate Medical College, where he is a member of the psychoanalytic faculty. He has long been a contributor to the analytic literature on mythology, most recently in a study, "On Interpreting the Oedipus Plays," in *The Psychoanalytic Study of Psychiatry*.

Thomas Mintz, M.D.

Both a Child and Adult Psychiatrist in private practice, he also serves as a Supervisor at the Reiss-Davis Child Study Center. Dr. Mintz has a special interest in children's literature and has recently had published a paper on nursery rhymes.

John W. Markson, M.D.

Assistant Clinical Professor of Psychiatry at Marquette University and in private practice of psychoanalysis. Evidently unafraid of Virginia Woolf, he has written a paper on "The Plays of Edward Albee" and has had published an article on Edward Albee's play "Tiny Alice." His paper on "Creativity" is part of a symposium published by "American Imago" in Winter, 1966.

Little Red Riding Hoods on the Couch[1]

Lilla Veszy-Wagner, PH.D.

London, England

Through the cases of a few self-styled Little Red Riding Hoods (subsequently referred to as LRRH) who were in analysis with me, I became interested in the analytical implications of this widespread motif in folklore. There seems to be no particularly relevant folkloristic material available to this story outside Europe so we may infer that problems pertaining to this tale seem to be more connected with the unconscious of the European mind.

In analytic practice, I soon learned that LRRH is an important story often referred to in dreams, memories or associations; yet analysts seem to have given thoughts only to three of its many psychologically important facets.

The first is the motif of the *filling the wolf's belly with stones*, after LRRH and grannie are removed. Freud's relevant passage (1) on infantile sexual theories refers to it pointblank: "... the abdomen is slit up and the baby taken out—which was what happened to the wolf in the story of LRRH." One may add that the wolf in the LRRH story suffers a "caesarean" and her twins are respectively LRRH *and* her grannie. M. Wulff (8) mentions a girl of eight who, afraid her abdomen will be slit open, nonetheless hopes the huntsman will shoot the aggressor eventually.

E. Fromm (5) contends that the wolf "attempted to play the role of a pregnant woman ... Stones are a symbol of sterility, they mock his usurpation of the pregnant woman's role. The huntsman at the end is the conventional father figure without real weight ... it is a story of triumph by man-hating women." I will later return to this point.

The second important facet mentioned by analysts is Freud's theory about the *Angsttiere* (anxiety animals), but he nowhere states that the wolf, as one, should be given special relevance, and he deals only with that one feature of the wolf in the infantile fantasy—that it *is* an anxiety animal representing the child's fear of the father. Any other aggressive male or masculine-looking animal would do.

The third feature is aptly described by Funk and Wagnall (6) as a "deliciously horrible series of climactic questions about the ears, eyes, nose, teeth, and mouth of the 'grandma,'" i.e., the wolf. It was again Freud who drew attention in connection with the Wolfman's (2,3) case, to the phenomenon of *zärtliches Schimpfen* (affectionate abuse) (4) which may arouse anxiety because of the facetious threat of being oral-cannibalistically devoured by the adult.

Neither Freud nor others have, however, dealt with the intrinsic meaning of the "climactic questions" themselves. In my view, they represent the horror of the child who, when asking the classical questions to satisfy his sexual curiosity and not getting answers, slowly, and in increasing measure, starts to dread the possible, although illusioned and fantastic, answers. He feels they must point to unspeakable, awful and annihilating things, corresponding to his fearsome and cruel fantasies about the "sadistic intercourse."

My experience with patients has, on the whole, corroborated these psychologically important facets but with two main differences: (*a*) The LRRH fantasies are much more complex than would seem at first sight. (*b*) *The wolf does not represent an unequivocally male aggressor in these fantasies.*

[1]This paper is an abbreviated version of a larger study. Many extensive references to clinical material and relevant literature had to be omitted.

The stones in the belly make it clear that the wolf is a mother figure, however distorted, and not a mere male impersonator of her, since the infantile theory pertains to the baby's being cut out from the mother's, not the father's, body. The anxiety animals of Thompson's Eskimo tale (7)—in which no other rapacious, ferocious animal could be equally represented—are clearly a parental couple, with the formidable mother figure, the wolverine, beside the father. Nor should we forget that the first person on whose part a child would experience the "affectionate abuse" is not father but mother.

These facts would indicate that, under the *oedipal* layer, there is also a *preoedipal* one present in the LRRH-type story. In fact, it is the preoedipal fear of the mother which has manifested itself in the fantasy material of those cases which I want to present.

Before describing them, I would like to note that Fromm's theory, inasmuch as he thinks that the LRRH story is exclusively born from the feminine mind, is most certainly false. Male patients—and not only the homosexual ones—have also referred to this story. I think the normal reader or listener will primarily identify with the *first nice protagonist*, whether male or female. Certainly, the bisexual component of an author may determine the protagonist's sex, and only rarely would a male creator of a tale choose a female in the leading role in order to express his latent bisexual, or even homosexual, self.

Hence, it is likely that folktales in general, as told by mummies, nannies, and grannies, should owe more to feminine than to masculine invention and bias. On the genital level, LRRH is a cautionary tale, invented by anxious nannies against the girl-child's liveliness and sexual precocity, with the usual effect of intimidating the child. This contrasts with Fromm's idea that LRRH is a "story of triumph by man-hating women." The rescue-fantasy at the end seems to stem either from a male rescue-fantasy or from male-worshipping females' pious good wishes for the little girl. However, even the nannies' ample preoedipal fantasies—for the nannies were once little girls—will not fail to seep through and even take over at certain junctures of the story.

I do not agree with all Fromm's inferences of "female-directedness" in LRRH. "The little cap of red velvet" as "a symbol of menstruation" seems doubtful, for the small girl's normal knowledge of menstruation is scanty. Encountering it by chance, she is filled with the anticipated horror of a sadistic injury, fantasied masochistically as a punishment for her oedipal covetousness as regards the primal scene, or for a preoedipal sadistic desire to scoop out mother's body. In several primitive tribes, it is believed that the menarche is caused through such a punishing sexual violation by the ancestral spirit. In other words, the little girl may have a vague notion of the possibility of defloration earlier than that of menstruation.

Also, I certainly have not encountered the equation red = menstrual blood in any case in which patients referred to the LRRH motif. Although her red garment certainly attracts the attention of the wolf, it is more a distinctive characteristic of her gay, bonny self. In this respect, the color would represent her self-confident femininity—crudely speaking, her erogenous mucous membranes—just as her posy of flowers does, and not her loss of blood. After all, she *is* a little girl, and little girls can be violated but cannot menstruate. Yet even violation does not occur in the story; she is swallowed, not torn open, by the wolf.

Fromm contends that "the male is portrayed as a ruthless and cunning animal and the sexual act as a cannibalistic act" and that this story "is an expression of a deep antagonism against men and sex." However, the "good" male, the rescuing huntsman, is equally represented in the tale and rescues both LRRH and her grannie. Finally, the wolf is not necessarily a male. Oedipally, for the girl, he is, but preoedipally, he seems to represent not one, but several, frightening aspects of the early *mother figure.*

Although the distinctly sexual allusions to the wolf's character in LRRH seem genuinely authentic in the oedipal version, the story has aspects other than oedipal. In the cases of my patients presented below, the sex of the wolf is rather equivocal and not essentially masculine as Fromm has postulated. Each of the patients spontaneously associated to LRRH with no guidance from me.

Clinical Illustrations

1. Miss A. is a student of 20, very dependent on her beloved-and-hated mother and on her boyfriend. After a visit home, she dreamt that her mother was ill, in bed, fat, angry, and red in the face, her hair in curlers and wearing a white cap. She glared angrily as the patient entered the bedroom. Miss A. noticed that her father was also in the bed but looked small and insignificant. She felt afraid for him—that enormous angry woman would smother him. (The primal-scene significance, but in the reverse, was unmistakable.) The angry red woman clutched the spouse and pulled the bedclothes over his head. Miss A. screamed, with the agonizing feeling that she now will murder both of us! She woke up in terror, feeling that father and mother are now punished "for their sins against her."

In her associations, she reported her mother's suspicion that the father had had intercourse over the weekend with his mistress. Miss A. then remembered her own suspicion that her father's "analyst" had made passes at her mother. This alleged analyst visited in her parents' house when she was 16, concurrent with a visit by another person with whom she had talked about the LRRH story and had imagined grannie to have worn a white bonnet. I asked whether in the dream it was perhaps the wolf in bed with the grandmother? She emphatically said no, adding that she remembered her own "grandma" well, who did not, however, resemble her *father*. "In which case," I said, "the indication was that it was mother in bonnet and curlers who represented the wolf?" She almost enthusiastically agreed.

A week after, Miss A., who was amenable to the primal-scene interpretation of the dream, had a nightmare remembering only that the locality was reminiscent of the former dream and that she was attacked and about to be killed. This was a repetitive dream to which she associated that as a child she had thought Germans ate children and that she had been afraid when she saw an uncle remove his false teeth.

About a year later, for reasons unconnected with her neurosis, she read the story of LRRH in German. Soon after, she worried how to reply should the porter at my address ask why she visits me. She decided, in that eventuality, to say she comes to visit her grandmother. I asked whether she would not be embarrassed if I would then disavow her as my granddaughter. She immediately protested that this had been only a fantasy. Next day, when the porter did ask whether Miss A. was my daughter, I did not question him, but my impression was that she had introduced herself to him as a relative of mine.

The following day, Miss A. volunteered that she knew she would make me older by announcing herself as my granddaughter but she always wanted a kindly grandmother and thought I could be one. She added that her mother never told her age. I remarked that to appear younger herself, perhaps she decided to make herself once removed, a granddaughter rather than a daughter. She was silent, but then referred to my curtain which she did not dare to look at because it was similar to one in her parents' bedroom and reminded her of the bedroom scene in her LRRH dream.

Then she associated "I can't accept the death of other people." I asked whether I had died in her fantasy of me as a mother-grandmother and whether I was killed by the wolf? She said no, but admitted that she felt guilt, as if she had been responsible for something, perhaps for having murdered my husband, and that she will never be happy again. If she felt guilty, I asked, was she then the wolf? She was confused about this and suddenly remembered that once a German visitor and she had had a linguistic argument with her father about something being unsuitable for translation because it would have the meaning of "being in bed." I reminded her of her original LRRH dream—her father in the bed, and her mother's accusation of his infidelity—and of her own dream panic. She said she felt her mother had wanted to squash her father. Mother-grandmother's face was flushed and red in the dream. Suddenly she recalled that as a child she had identified with LRRH, because she, herself, had red hair.

After that, the LRRH fantasy unfolded to the full. In the primal-scene setting of the dream she seems to have represented LRRH who, owing to infantile curiosity, arrived earlier than expected and saw the wolf eat the mother-grandmother. At the same time, it is also the moment *after* the devourment that she arrives, i.e., when the wolf poses, in bonnet and curlers, as grannie. The dominant, fatter mother seems to have squashed and devoured the father who represents also grandmother. The denial of his resemblance to grandmother would prove it. Mother is, therefore, the wolf who punished the gallivanting father identified with the little girl naughtily gallivanting in the wood, picking flowers. (This is Miss A. herself, who in fantasy leads a rather promiscuous sex life.) She is simultaneously also a kind of she "wolf," a man-eater. Hence the child's panic, seeing mother-wolf devouring father. Her guilt feeling—that she herself devours him and has also murdered both my husband and her own father because of greed and jealousy— persecutes her. She fears the retaliating mother-wolf who now will devour her. I, the analyst, am the kind grandmother, to whom she comes but with murder in her heart. Through projection of her own guilt, I also become the wolf, and "my kind features become distorted into the wolf's grin." This grin becomes even more ominous in Miss A.'s case, since she herself usually sports a semi-schizophrenic grin which embarrasses her. She explains this grin with her shyness and desire to capture people's benevolence by displaying a childish trust and helplessness. The analyst is both the wicked wolf and the good grannie. She is not allowed to be the mother, that is, a powerful competitor in the fight for father. *The grandmother as a symbol in a dream represents the mother once removed, either more benevolent, or less dangerous, with whom the erotic love-hate involvement has become more distant*. The patient herself is the poor, innocent LRRH, to be devoured by the wicked analyst-wolf, and also a devouring she-wolf, coming to the unsuspecting mother-grandmother whose husband she also wants to devour. Finally, she is, in a lesbian fantasy, also father.

The transformation of the good grandmother into the wicked wolf is the key to the LRRH fantasy. The love-hatred toward mother become transferred to grannie, while the undiluted, hostile feelings to mother undergo a massive repression because they are unbearable. After all, she is the originator of LRRH's misfortunes, because it is she who sent her on a dangerous errand and who expects the little girl to behave sensibly and as if she were a grownup. Mother must be neutralized into an innocuous person, a non-entity, compared with the little heroine; her suppressed good and bad sides thus cannot avoid displacement and splitting. The child, rebelling against the maternal demand to grow up, procrastinates "in the wood" with the result of the split; she has practically no "mother" anymore, but a good grannie and a bad wolf. The mother, to remain good, must become a grandmother, old and ill, and no competitor sexually or in any other respect. The analyst cannot be tolerated as a mother figure either—she must become a grandmother figure.

LRRH has no grandfather. Obviously, grannie is a woman who can live without a man; hence, the patient is not compelled to remember that she, in a fantasy, has already owned up to having "killed" the analyst's husband. Yet, for the robbing of her womanliness, her being made old and ill by the patient, the analyst must also be transmogrified from the benevolent grannie into the wolf who is both the projection of the guilty patient who harmed the analyst and the personification of the ensuing punishment. By becoming old and ill through the patient's bad wishes, the analyst thus becomes also bad and revengeful, the wolf, who will devour LRRH. The porter represents for Miss A. the huntsman. She feels a compulsion to tell him that she visits her mother-grandmother in the house in case she might need him for protection against the wolf.

Miss A. now began carrying to the session a bulky basket which she said was more feminine and housewifely than a carrier or a handbag. With it, she felt she was a country-maiden carrying a basketful of flowers. A fantasy followed which she thought was a Goethe poem about a flower-girl whom a prince carries off after buying up everything. I pointed out her LRRH pose and that she was thinking of bringing flowers to grannie, but that in her fantasy the wolf seemed to have mellowed into the form of a prince. After recalling another poem in which a prince had seduced a girl but left her, Miss A. remembered a young male acquaintance whom she had chatted with on her way to me, although she was anxious to come. I drew her attention to the LRRH analogy and also reminded her that at the beginning of her analysis, she had brought me flowers from her parents' garden, characteristically informing me that her mother had told her to. The LRRH story applied and she eagerly accepted the interpretation.

Now Miss A. revealed the books in her basket—books she said she had often brought but had forgotten about—to show me how many she had read and how her attitude toward working had improved. Soon after, she passed an exam she had feared even to take.

I cannot help feeling that the analysis of the LRRH might have been instrumental in the improvement.

2. Mrs. B., 29 years old, had a puerperal depression after the birth of her second child, now a lively girl of five whom she dislikes and is aggravated by. The child, while being undressed, once teasingly told her: "I am a boy." That night, the patient dreamed of a pack of unruly little she-devils, tumbling down a hill. She was afraid of being attacked by them and felt relieved when they leapt past her. As their little hooves clattered, her daughter came into her mind; then, that the little she-devils must have escaped from somewhere. She, herself, was recently in Rome. How awful it would be if the wolves under the capitol would escape! The Roman she-wolf had suckled two children which were not hers, but they were at least boys, whereas she, herself, also had two children but had never breast-fed them. A play was then being performed in London, entitled "Who's Afraid of Virginia Woolf?" "I am," she was tempted to reply and was reminded that Virginia Woolf meant a virgin she-wolf. She felt her mother would not approve of a home she planned to buy. "Virginia Woolf would puff and blow?" I asked. She felt the interpretation was sensible enough but objected to my referring to her house. "The grandmother of LRRH has also got a house," Mrs. B. said. (Here I must remark that she often commiserates with me on my having lost a house where she fantasied visiting me.) "LRRH wants to visit her grannie?" I asked her. She eagerly said yes, and that she also would like to bring me provisions.

About two months later, Mrs. B. reported an "odd dream." The day before, she had a fantasy that she would get me a small house, like that of LRRH's grannie, perhaps a kind of woodcutter's cottage, on her estate. "Would it not be the huntsman's?" I asked. "Oh, no," she said, "on second thought, it must be something independent."

In dream after dream, Mrs. B.'s daughter, with whom the relationship had not improved, was disposed of, lost, or put into one or another dangerous situation. In a recent dream, Mrs. B. and the child were riding with a male acquaintance whose reckless driving made her fear for their lives. She remarked that she sometimes felt I drove her mercilessly. The evening before this dream her fingers felt like claws as she switched off a T.V. program with much shooting in it, and she felt that she, in a way, had killed it. The claws of the wolf, masquerading as grandmother, came into her mind. She wanted to keep me safe from the claws as she switched off a T.V. program with her in the cottage, always at her disposal but "in my place, not above her." She would provide for me, bring me books and tea on a tray. The issue got somewhat confused when it came to the question of who should serve whom.

Session after session, she expressed the desire that we meet socially and I should bring her a cup of tea. She wanted to provide for me just as LRRH and her mother had catered for grannie. But I should be confined to my woodcutter's cottage. Her daughter, when grown, should stay with her and attend to her needs when she grows old, never leaving her house.

As we analyzed her thirst for tea by me, she felt, besides its meaning of milk, there was something heavy in her stomach. Perhaps a baby, but no, it was dead and cold as stone, and she would feel relieved if only she could get a drink. I reminded her that the wolf in the LRRH story, after having been stuffed with stones, had also felt a terrible thirst. No, she said, it was more the desire to feed a baby-stone or a stone-baby inside her, but it ought to be fed from the outside. And it is I who should do it! Then she recalled her reluctance to feed her babies once they were born. I said the baby is a stone-baby because it weighs heavily on her conscience. Had she, as the she-wolf, not have gobbled up both grannie and LRRH, she would not feel her stomach so heavy. "Yes," she replied earnestly, "Both you and my own little daughter." She wondered why the wolf cannot get at LRRH's mother as well. "That is," I said, "because for the unconscious, mothers seem to be indestructible. They must be first divided into innocuous, good grannies and stray or naughty little girls." She said: "It is a heavy punishment to get drowned in the well, only because one is thirsty."

The night before this session, she dreamt that the buyers of her old house were dissatisfied with it. I suggested she was afraid I would be dissatisfied by her arrangements of the woodcutter's cottage for me and that I had retaliated by sending her to the wolf into the trap. She agreed and said that thus also mother seems to be divided into two wolves, one who sends LRRH on her errand, and one who becomes the wolf awaiting her there in the trap. I said that in a way, she is that she-wolf-mother herself who, in her series of bad dreams about her own daughter, is trying to send LRRH to the wolf. She sadly replied that she still does not seem to be reconciled with her own sex and with that of her daughter.

The latest of her LRRH fantasies was a daydream while coming for her last session before the summer holiday break. She would leave her family at their holiday spot, and, equipped with a large basket full of good things, she would come up to London to pay me a surprise call. The basket, in her associations, held her good products—no, her babies, which she would then bring me. She felt I wanted her to be pregnant again and have babies. The hamper was an offering to pacify me. "So you felt I was a Moloch, or the wolf itself, eating babies?" I asked. Her pious mood promptly vanished and she said that in her fantasy I wasn't really the wolf itself but that I was just about to entertain the wolf, and that she has caught us red-handed—the suspicious grannie gallivanting with the wolf—a fearful situation for the good and unsuspecting LRRH to find. She recalled that, on the bus to today's session, she had been in a dozing state, like a despondent baby waiting for food. She added that when the feed comes, she's just past enjoyment. It seems she had originally wanted to feed the analyst-grandmother in order to get even more miraculous food in return. Now, her homosexual feelings toward mother once more broke through in the disguise of her having wanted to gang up with grandmother. She had wanted grannie to forget that it was mother and LRRH herself who had made the cakes and is the provider. But almost before my eyes, this was followed by an oedipal feeling, the first I remember, and her jealousy of the man-(wolf) in the primal scene appeared. For the first time her interest turned now toward the sadistic he-wolf, then toward a good one, and he was promptly equated with her husband.

3. Mr. O., in his 30's, is an emotionally infantile, overt homosexual and a habitual drinker who, for years, was suspected to have diabetes. After eating, especially when it includes drinking, he feels as if he has stones in his abdomen. Once complaining of it, he thought of the wolf in LRRH who met his death in the known way. On this day, he had an attack of hayfever. He had picked some flowers in the country the day before and felt perhaps they had caused it. "Like LRRH?" I asked, and he replied that one could say so, adding facetiously that he would have preferred to meet the wolf himself, meaning an active homosexual, and been swallowed up by him.

Mr. O. is passive and masochistic. He said he had very little to drink the previous day but felt bloated around the midriff. He had a pregnancy fantasy and said he could not resist eating starchy food—meat would be better but for that he is not masculine enough. I asked whether he thought the wolf was masculine enough. He thought so but then became noncommittal, adding only that he promised to stay for dinner with his mother next day but would have preferred to see "fresh faces" instead. He also complained that he seemed to be in my consulting room all the time. The topic petered out.

On a subsequent occasion, he reported disappointment with a friend and having drunk out of sheer impatience. He then told of waking fantasies about another friend he was about to visit in Rome: He was afraid of the she-wolf there: what if she were to escape? Bats, vampires, wolves and other night-predators— he's afraid of them all. His father's second name was Lopez. He felt himself to be a wayward LRRH. Next, he thought of Virginia Woolf and of the play using her name. In this, a so-called exorcism happens and the last act is called "exorcism." He then said the three little pigs in the story were triplets and really LRRH's twins. He always wanted to have a twin. The cutting open of the wolf's belly was also an exorcism.

Mr. O. had an earlier LRRH dream in which he referred to the same friend as "the wolf," to himself as LRRH, and to the place they were to meet as "grandmother." Both grandmother and I and his working place were somehow out to trap him for the wolf. He had liked but neglected his own grandmother and had not visited her in her terminal illness. I commented that his father's name resembled that of the wolf and that, as a child, he was perhaps afraid that mother would hand him over to the wolf, the father. He said this was very likely because, when his parents separated, there had been a squabble as to whom the boy should belong. It seems that his unconscious interpreted LRRH's story as a primal scene. His parents had always quarrelled in his presence. He got the strange fantasy that maybe they didn't quarrel when he was absent. If LRRH had not gone to visit the grandmother, maybe the wolf would not have gobbled up the old lady. Maybe that also kept him from visiting grandmother. He would have liked to sacrifice himself for the grandmother; there was such a story in Amica's *Il Cuore* which both fascinated and repelled him.

To sum up, I would say that these patients (and others I have not reported) resemble each other in using the LRRH story to express their persecutory fantasies both in the negative transference and otherwise. I could not trace the scene in the grannie's cottage in all cases back to primal-scene reminiscences, but they all possessed this potential. Each patient mentioned the story spontaneously but used it in differing ways and with different intensity. Both men and women identified with both the female child-heroine, and also the enemy, the wolf, who usually combined both the paternal and the maternal characteristics of the more sinister order. The grandmother—that is, the mother once removed—represented the mother's more benevolent or less dangerous aspects.

To repeat, the wolf does not represent an unequivocally male aggressor in these fantasies. The wolf is also a mother figure, but not only on an oedipal level. Under this, there is a preoedipal layer in which there are several frightening aspects of the mother present in the fantasy material.

For Fromm, the pilgrimage of LRRH from her mother's house to her grandmother's seems to represent a life-pilgrimage of the girl's ages, from childhood, through menstruation and defloration to childbirth. I regard the pilgrimage as a dream-fantasy which represents the advancing schizoid tendency of the patient, starting in the child's desire to disobey mother and acquire a pseudo-independence from her. This results in a guilty fear of the consequences, manifested in splitting processes both of the self, projected into the several characters of the story, and of mother. In the story, mother is more or less an integrated and benevolent figure who develops into several emerging bad and sinister mother figures. In short, there is the process of regression after an almost normal but frustrated attempt at a "peaceful" separation or weaning from the protecting mother figure.

I regard the emerging of both grannie and the little girl alive from the wolf's (mother-grandmother) body, aside from its implication of an infantile sexual theory, as a narcissistic twin-fantasy in which the good ones emerge from the bad one unhurt and lovingly united against the latter—a well-known homosexual fantasy of both male and female. The stones as a substitution for the living contents of the womb seem primarily to be only a revenge-fantasy of the child against the wicked mother-rival.

The fight of the primal-scene parents seems to be the child's narcissistic illusion that the parents contend for him. This is reassuring for the feeling of self-esteem but also gives rise to fears of cannibalistic attacks by one or both of the vicious parents. I would also emphasize here the importance of the tension which the "climactic questions" produce in the youthful listener.

I think the gruesome climax suggests that the trauma of a primal-scene experience or fantasy forms the nucleus of the LRRH story in which the child tries to understand and motivate his horror of it in retrospect.

It is interesting to note that in several variants the story ends with the cutting open of the wolf and the sewing in of the stones and without the wolf falling into the well. The *raison d'être* of the fuller variants is perhaps the desire to exonerate the new couple, the huntsman and the little girl, aided and abetted by the good grannie, of the murder. In them, the wolf dies, as it were, twice; once from the operation and once from the self-induced accident, the falling into the well.

Bibliography

1. Freud, S. (1908). "The Sexual Theories of Children." *Standard Edition*, Vol. 9. London: Hogarth Press.
2. ———. (1913). "The Occurrence in Dreams of Material from Fairy Tales." *Ibid.*, Vol. 12.
3. ———. (1914). "History of an Infantile Neurosis." *Ibid.*, Vol. 17.
4. ———. *Ibid.*
5. Fromm, E. (1951). *The Forgotten Language*, Vol. 7. New York: Rinehart.
6. Funk and Wagnall. (1950). *Standard Dictionary of Folklore, Mythology and Legend* (ed. M. Leech), Vol. 2. New York.
7. Thompson, S. (1955). *Motif-Index of Folk-Literature*, Vol. A-C. Copenhagen: Rosenkilde.
8. Wulff, M. (1912). *Beitrage z. infantilen Sexualität*, Zentralbl. 2.

12 Boyton House
Wellington Road
London, N.W. 8, England

Discussant

Herbert Fingarette, PH.D.
Santa Barbara, California

It is a distinctive merit of Dr. Veszy-Wagner's paper that she states and then demonstrates in rich detail how "the LRRH fantasies are much more complex than would seem at first sight." It is this issue of complexity of meaning in such folktales that constitutes the theme of my remarks. In this connection, Dr. Veszy-Wagner takes us, I think, further than we were, but still not far enough. She reveals complexity of meaning but still tacitly assumes that such tales have a definite pattern of meaning, however complex. This view is by no means unique to Dr. Veszy-Wagner; indeed it is a typical view, and I think it is wrong.

Dr. Veszy-Wagner notes that "each patient mentioned the story spontaneously but used it in differing ways and with different intensity." I would argue that the crucial methodological truth lies in this statement rather than in the attempt to single out *the* oedipal meaning, *the* preoedipal meaning, or *the* "nucleus" (i.e., the primal scene fantasy). I do not mean to assert that such a folktale can mean just anything at all: it would be incredible that the wolf should not represent some significant degree and kind of aggression, whatever else he might signify. But just as with elements of the manifest dream or other derivatives of the unconscious, so many additional factors enter into the picture that the contextual significance of the wolf can be quite different from person to person. For some persons, the exciting series of questions ending with the gobbling up of Red Riding Hood could be intensely erotically colored, the aggression being best understood as a mode of (passive) sexuality. For another, the erotic element will, in the particular dynamic context, be minimal. In one context the wolf as male may be significant, whereas in another—

as Dr. Veszy-Wagner shows in detail—the wolf is a mother figure. There is obvious oral imagery in the tale, but this may or may not be of special importance to a particular person: it may be that the tale takes on significance to someone by virtue of associations—viz., red cap-red hair—which have nothing to do with orality.

What folktales do, I believe, is to present a series of images whose inner meaning and whose connections are, psychologically, highly ambiguous. Yet these images nevertheless easily evoke certain very elemental and powerful themes: sex and aggression, parents and children, weakness and power, knowledge and innocence, eating up, cutting, marrying, and so on. These highly general themes are evoked by weaving the images together into a simple narrative. The power and fascination of such a narrative comes not from one single pattern of meaning, however complex, but from the fact that the story can be used to express so many different kinds of conflicts just because it has so many possible meanings; and of course each meaning is rooted in some powerful psychic dynamism. Thus, in a way, the so-called "complexity" of meaning which is so often found as one goes more deeply into the folk material is in truth multiplicity of meanings rather than complexity. To be more precise: The pattern of meaning which the story has for any one person may well be a complex unity, but the variations in meaning from person to person are not due to the complexity of some ultimately unified psychic significance in the tale itself. These variants reflect the multiplicity of possible meanings left open by the tale.

Two important and familiar facts about folktales are consistent with my view: (*a*) their universality, and (*b*) the variety of psychological interpretations to which they notoriously lend themselves. Their universality I ascribe to the universality of the themes and to the fact that these are so ambiguously woven together as to allow very different persons and groups to make of the story what they wish—what they unconsciously wish. And it is from this fact, I believe, that many differences of interpretation derive: the tale was used by different persons "in different ways and with different intensity." I believe we can isolate possible themes in any tale, but when it comes to a specific interpretation, I do not think we can say anything *a priori*. Instead, the test is this: What meaning does the tale actually have in the particular case as established by the usual evidence of associations, dreams, etc.?

There is one important addendum to the preceding remarks. My theses apply to folk materials but not to reasonably self-conscious art. I wrote a paper several years ago in which I argued that the psychological interpretation of the Orestes story in terms of homosexuality is wrong, and that the plays psychologically represent instead the complement of the Oedipus story, that is, a paradigm of the successful resolution of the oedipal conflicts.[1] I believe such a claim is methodologically defensible, for a work such as the Orestes trilogy of Aeschylus is not a folktale but a highly refined, worked through, unified drama. It is precisely the psychological mark of art—as distinguished from folktale—that many meanings are so connected as to reenforce, to express in manifold ways, a single overarching meaning. Of course the psychological distinction between art and folktale is a matter of degree. The more there is art, the more there is unity-in-complexity. As Kris and Kaplan pointed out,[2] even the ambiguities in art contribute to its unity. In the folktale, however, there is *mere* ambiguity, multiple possible meanings associated with elementary and powerful psychic themes.

---

[1]Fingarette, Herbert. (1963). "Orestes: Paradigm Hero of Contemporary Ego Psychology." Psa. Review, Vol. 50, pp. 87-111.

[2]Kris, E., and Kaplan, A. (1952). "Aesthetic Ambiguity." *Psychoanalytic Explorations in Art.* New York: Int. Univ. Press, pp. 243-264.

Discussant

Mark Kanzer, M.D.
New York, New York

LRRH, as a fairy tale, provides a natural thematic apperception test which invites and has received a wide variety of interpretations, almost any of which may claim a certain degree of validity. Nevertheless the story itself, viewed as a sequence of preconscious images, communicates its own message which we shall undertake to translate (with no great variance from other translations that have been made) as follows:

"The pubescent girl, at the time of menstruation, defies her mother's warnings and enters into conversation with a strange man who accosts her. Taken to his room [which fuses in her unconscious with the bedroom of her parents], she inspects his body and is consumed sexually [just as mother has been by father]. There follows [foreshortened in time] a pregnancy and delivery. However, a denial element is registered at this point: not the girl but the 'wolf' becomes pregnant while she is delivered from his body by a good man, the hunter. The wolf, justly enough, succumbs to the perils of the pregnancy he has engendered."

There is a great confluescence of childhood sex fantasies here, and we have little reason to cavil at diverse interpretations. That transference aspects in relation to a female analyst (Dr. Veszy-Wagner) will intensify the preoedipal and bisexual aspects of the wolf need not surprise us. I also find some support for Dr. Fromm's suggestion that there is an allusion to the inability of the male wolf to bear children. With the aid of the well-known equation, stones = feces, we find that he cannot, after all, convert his feces into children.

LRRH belongs to a group of fairy tales with similar connotations—"Snow White," "Sleeping Beauty," etc.—which are nature myths that describe death, resurrection and fertility in relation to the seasons. A female version of the Oedipus legend may be discerned in the encounter of LRRH with the wolf; however, allowing for the differences in sex, it is the heroine who discovers that it is dangerous to ask too many questions. The LRRH theme expands in tribal customs to the sacrifice of maidens to totem animals and on to less extreme initiation rites for pubescent girls. Geza Roheim, who explored the anthropology of this tale, reported as many variations of the narrative as there are analytic interpretations.[1]

Discussant

Thomas Mintz, M.D.
Beverly Hills, California

It is always a challenge to an author to develop new themes from old materials, and it is a pleasure to the reader if the author succeeds. Dr. Veszy-Wagner, using a Kleinian frame of reference to understand the three cases she presents, makes a good case for extending the ordinary clinical meanings of the Little Red Riding Hood story. Relying on her clinical data, she shows how preoedipal elements are essential to a full understanding of the story. By looking very deeply into latent meanings of the story, she points out that an exclusively oedipal interpretation is narrow. This is her main point, and one which, in this instance, seems wise.

Probably a fuller and more complete understanding of the story rests on a combination of

[1]Roheim, G. (1953). "Fairy Tale and Dream." *Psychoanalytic Study of the Child*, Vol. 8.

oedipal and preoedipal elements. Oedipal elements might include wolf = father = the sexual tempter; big eyes, ears, hands, teeth = big penis of father; and the wolf in bed with grandmother's clothes = fusion of male and female in the parental bed together. Preoedipal elements might include wolf = mother; bigness of wolf = bigness of mother when heroine was a baby; wolf dressed in the grandmother's clothes = phallic mother.

The story is very rich in symbolism and lends itself to many different interpretations. For example, if one saw the whole story as a dream and applied methods of dream interpretation (a technique which is very useful in understanding fairy tales, children's stories, etc.), one might see all the characters in the story as representing the dreamer: the wolf would represent sexual temptation and cannibalistic desires (the id) which must be killed off by the punishing huntsman (the superego) in order that the small child (the ego) will not be consumed and overwhelmed.

One might take issue with certain minor points, which I felt needed further elaboration: (*a*) The author feels the unconscious of the European mind is different from the unconscious of the non-European mind—it is perhaps more correct to say that the derivatives of the unconscious which find expression in European and non-European countries vary because of the molding role of the differing cultural values, rather than because the unconscious is basically different; (*b*) The author feels that "the small girl's normal knowledge of menstruation is scanty," and yet she also feels that the small girl has a "preoedipal sadistic desire to scoop out mother's body." If one inference is justified, why not the other?

The three cases amplify, extend, and support the author's views, and despite the fact that at times the data seem sketchy, one comes away from the cases with the feeling that with all the patients there was an abundance of preoedipal material, focused around the story, which weaved in and out of the treatment process. The fact that the analyst is a female (who has an interest in the story) might be a factor in the production of the material, since the driving force in treatment is the wish to please the analyst in order to receive his love; however, it is impossible to assess the significance of this factor. If one is theoretically very much interested in the human being's early responses to his mother, one will tend to see the material in this light. Nevertheless, in my opinion, this happens to be a valuable and illuminating light.

Whether preoedipal themes or more classical frames of reference prove useful will depend on the situation. In any event, the patient and his responses should, and will, decide the "correctness" of an interpretation. Clinically it is important to utilize as many frames of reference as are possible to help us understand a piece of human behavior; and whether that behavior be a fairy tale or a reality tale, the use of a singularly "correct" formula of interpretation to the exclusion of any other may endanger and stifle the creative process of understanding. It is in this spirit that I find Dr. Veszy-Wagner's paper most valuable.

Discussant

John W. Markson, M.D.
Milwaukee, Wisconsin

This paper is an imaginative untangling of a psychodynamic aspect of folklore. Dr. Lilla Veszy-Wagner illuminates the process of an educational mythology which is useful to the adult as a way of unconsciously discharging his own unresolved tensions, and simultaneously, by inculcating fear of punishment for those who disobey the harsh and rigid restrictions of adult law, indoctrinating permanent respect for the adult world in the "innocent" child.

I would dispute the existence of the author's conception of a specifically "European unconscious" as indicated in the opening paragraph of this paper. The validity of a universal unconscious seems well established to me, although socio-cultural differences may consciously heighten one aspect or another of pertinent myth or folklore. Wolf stories do exist in contemporary American, European, and Asian lore as well as the classical myths. The wolf appears to be one of the animals that man has used to symbolize the emotional gamut of our noble heights and base fears.

Miss Elizabeth Crawford ("American Imago," Fall, 1955) wrote on "The Wolf As Condensation" and summarizes: ". . . The wolf as symbol is manifold, multiplex, protean. Man, in his ages-long relationships with the wolf, has made him so. Onto wolf, man has projected father, mother, danger, safety and rescue, evil and good, voraciousness and nurture, and the fascination and peril of his own sexuality. Only as man knows the wolf within him will he be free."

Miss Crawford also calls attention to the excitement-fear axis of childhood sexual excitement and cites a passage from *Nightwood* by Djuna Barnes: The character Nora seeks the doctor at 3:00 A.M. and finds his room as "muscular as a boxer's training camp." However, there are feminine articles of toiletry and lacy apparel about, and the doctor, sitting up in bed, has rouged cheeks and is wearing a long blond wig. Nora thinks, "God, children know something they can't tell; they *like* Little Red Riding Hood and the wolf in bed."

Mankind's most celebrated wolf is probably the she-wolf who provided nurture for Romulus and Remus, but she, however, only nursed them. It was a bird—the *woodpecker*—which brought them food. The bird has become widely accepted as a breast symbol, but to attempt a symbol interpretation of a bird with *this* name in the context of this great classical myth is probably best left to the readers' imagination. Joseph Campbell retells the story in his *Masks of God—Occidental Mythology* (pp. 313-319).

Kipling in his *Jungle Book* tells the well-known story of Mowgli. "Wolf-mothers" of wild "wolf-children" appear as a part of universal folklore. The wolf in the Russian tale *Peter and the Wolf* is neatly dispatched by the *boy*, Peter, who has been cautioned by his *grandfather* to avoid the wolf and play safely (a similar theme but with role-reversal of LRRH). The aggressor wolf in "The Three Little Pigs" is boiled by his intended victims, and the rigid Puritan Work-Ethic is underscored for learning toddlers.

On the other hand, Nordic mythology offers Fenris, a monstrous wolf who can destroy iron chairs and shackles. Eventually he was shut up in the bowels of the earth, and at the time of the twilight of the gods, which signals the end of the world, he will break out of his prison and devour the sun. Here, the wolf is associated with the ultimate annihilation of the universe and symbolizes an epic height of oral aggressiveness.

The fact that the symbolic wolf-creature can be slaveringly inimical to the Nordic people and a symbol of valor to the Romans and Egyptians could provide much speculation.

In the case of Mrs. B., the analyst introduces a new parameter by inquiring about "Virginia Woolf puffing and blowing." It seems to me that this association properly derives from the childhood story of "The Three Little Pigs" and not from LRRH. Also, Mrs. B. may be partially identifying with the character Martha who closes the play admitting that *she* is "afraid of Virginia Woolf." If may well be that a patient (especially an English person or an intellectual from another country) could associate fear of the actual Virginia Woolf as symbolizing a fear of madness and suicide. These persons would more likely know of the real Virginia Woolf.

The fact that two of these three patients referred to Edward Albee's play was of special interest to me. The only linking referrent to the famous English authoress in the actual play is the tuneful title which is intended to be sung to the music of "Who's Afraid of the Big, Bad Wolf?" which appeared in Walt Disney's cartoon-movie of "The Three Little Pigs." Albee's explanation is that he saw the phrase "who's afraid of Virginia Woolf" scrawled on a Greenwich Village wall and that this "is when the play started." I feel there are necessarily many more highly overdetermined reasons—but that, too, is another matter.

I take exception to Dr. Veszy-Wagner's view of creativity, at least "... only rarely would a male creator of a tale choose a female in the leading role." I will cite only *Alice In Wonderland*. Drs. Martin Grotjahn, Phyllis Greenacre and others have documented the psychoanalytic biography of the Reverend Charles Dodgson. The function of the creator or audience-reader concerning *Alice* or *LRRH* is to assist in humanity's healthy homeostasis by providing a controlled regressive experience, achieving a temporarily free communication with the unconscious, discharging potential ideational pathogens and providing a useful way of maintaining the ego in its civilizing work of sublimation, etc. The work of creativity and the work of the involved audience-reader run pari passu with the goals of psychoanalytic treatment although our "treatment" is of a different nature.

Folklore, mythology and popular works of any form of art reflect the deeper unconscious aspects of humankind—the more universal the conflict, the greater the work of art. Whether "Nannies" or "Dannies" perpetuate the story, I cannot agree that "folktales ... should owe more to feminine than to masculine invention and bias." I feel that the story *becomes* classic because it reflects deep universal emotional struggle of the type that requires sublimation, repression, etc., in order to provide control and mastery over impulses.

The retelling of an inherited classic story diffuses the intensity of "personal" guilt or anxiety and serves to diminish the emotional cathexis. An individual might select a story, embellish it and reveal himself in the process. Conversely, the folktale itself can be the result of a cultural type of transgenerational collaborative authorship and of a collective approbation that utilizes the male-female motif but is not inherently "caused" more by the male or by the female.

I have one more reflective and purely rhetorical question for the author: *Does* she object to the patient's assigning her the role of grandmother, instead of the role of mother?

Author's Response

Lilla Veszy-Wagner, PH.D.
London, England

I greatly appreciate the discussants' interest in both my topic and my paper. The latter was originally 34 pages and illustrated with six instead of three cases.[1] Some differences of opinion may have arisen through the abbreviation to its outlines.

For instance, I would not say, as Professor Fingarette assumes, that there is an ultimately unified psychic significance to this (or to any) tale. Psychoanalysts are used to the fact that, since dreams, symbolic actions and fantasies are overdetermined, their interpretations must also vary accordingly and always in consideration of the different levels in whose bedrock they appear. Neither do I believe in a specifically European unconscious as Dr. Markson thinks. Owing to the lack of a more widespread material (not to wolves in general, but specifically to LRRH) outside Europe, I only postulated that "problems pertaining to it seem to be more connected with problems of the European mind's unconscious." I agree with him and with Dr. Crawford, whom he quotes, that the wolf as a symbol is protean, but I thought, in view of this topic's expanse, that I should limit myself (albeit mentioning *en passant*, the Roman she-wolf, the "Three Little Pigs," the ambivalence of the wolf's popularity in folktales, etc.) to the two essential points I wanted to emphasize: (*a*) the significance of the wolf as a mother figure, likewise, the preoedipal (oral) elements contained in this tale, and (*b*) the relevance of the sadistic primal scene in the story which, certainly, some little voyeurs would enjoy. I do not think I should have extended my paper to the Fenris and other mythological wolves.

[1]London Imago Group, July 12, 1965.

Also, the interpretation of the Orestes story in which Professor Fingarette is interested would not possibly have come within the pale of this paper, whether seen through Aeschylus' eyes or based on the original myth. Here I would remark only that although I do not know of any myth dealing with LRRH, myths and folktales frequently overlap, with folktales often deriving from myths and being told mainly to children; whereas myths form a religious, traditional store of perpetuated tales about worshipped gods, semi-gods or heroes. That is also the reason why I felt that the former owe more to nannies than to male storytellers or seers.

Dr. Mintz rightly sees that the preoedipal elements are essential to the full understanding of the story. However, in my original paper, I tried to deal also with some of the oedipal implications as well as with those of ego development. Further, I would mention that I had never been especially interested in this particular folktale until several of my patients had started to react to it.

I feel indebted to Dr. Kanzer for pointing out that the LRRH provides a natural thematic apperception test. This is exactly how I feel about it. However, he leans heavily on the oedipal material, while I tried to show that there exist, also, more angles to the understanding of this tale's symbolism than those propounded by Fromm and others.

I am also very grateful to Dr. Kanzer for having drawn my attention to Roheim's essay which, unaccountably, I had failed to read before writing mine. The "uterine-regressive" factor which Roheim pinpoints is very valid (i.e., that the tale represents a dream in which the sleeper is "in his own body"), as is his observation that "the cannibal child creates the cannibal mother," because "being eaten is the talion aspect of his aggression." His essay also corroborates my hunch that LRRH is a "cautionary tale."

Lastly, in answering two questions of Dr.

Markson, I want first to mention that in the original version, and based on Dr. Balint's observation, I said "the male creator of a tale would usually choose a male as his protagonist, and only exceptionally, mainly in order to express his latent bisexuality, a female, in the leading role and vice versa." This I said just in view of Dodgson's case, and remembering that Flaubert had said: *"Mais Mme. Bovary, c'est moi."*

Second, as to his "purely rhetorical" query, whether I "object" to the patient's assigning me the role of grandmother instead of mother: I do not object to *any* role the patient happens to assign to me. Being, besides an analyst, also a grandmother of four delightful grandchildren, I have found this question rather quaint. Usually children have a less ambivalent attitude toward grandparents than toward parents, and the affectionate side is more often to the fore (perhaps, because proverbially, grandmothers are more forebearing, and maybe also weaker to retaliate). Hence, in transference, it seems to denote a greater unconscious reluctance to bring out the aggressive, negative side of their bond with the analyst.[2] This, in both sexes, expresses a fearful distancing of the patient from the crude libidinal and/or aggressive involvement with the analyst and represents (*a*) a defensive measure (of not wanting to harm himself or the analyst), or (*b*) a false attempt at restitution by evasion.

May I finish this with a joke about LRRH I lately heard? When LRRH says: "What a big snout you've got, Granny!" the wolf gruffly replies: "Well, you can talk!"

---

[2]"The mother, in order to remain 'good,' must become a grandmother, old and ill, i.e., no competitor in the sexual or in any other respect." (Original version of my paper.)

The Continuing Forum

The Continuing Forum is open to all readers so that they may send their reactions, suggestions, criticism and contributions to the topics which are presented in The Psychoanalytic Forum.

The Poet Shelley

To the Editors: There are several occasions for surprise in the discussions of Dr. Milton Miller's paper on Shelley ["Manic Depressive Cycles of the Poet Shelley," *The Psychoanalytic Forum*, Vol. 1, No. 2]. A few of these justify comment.

While all agree on the excellence of this contribution, it is heralded in places as a new departure in understanding an author through his literary productions. The surprise lies in the absence of mention of Dr. Miller's substantial accomplishment by this method in his thorough study of Proust[1] which receives notice only in the biographical paragraph on Dr. Miller. *Nostalgia* is required reading for all interested in this approach.

Then a minor point: In the famous ode, Shelley's explicit relation with the West Wind is not simple, or even primarily, identification. More emphatic is the plea for succor and for strength:

> Oh! lift me as a wave, a leaf, a cloud!
> I fall upon the thorns of life! I bleed!
> ...
> Make me thy lyre...
> Be thou, spirit fierce,
> My spirit!...

[1]Miller, M. (1956). *Nostalgia*. Houghton Mifflin Co.

But a major point lies in the diagnosis. The description is of "mad Shelley," of wild individualism in marriage, in politics, in personal relations; of unrestrained *acting out* with strong unconscious hostility and masochism. This brings us to a fundamental of psychiatric understanding and nomenclature. This is no place to marshal the evidence, but do not most psychiatrists agree that a disorder of motivation, a disturbance in the interplay of emotional forces, a "pathodynamics," finds expression in a whole range of symptoms? In short, are not all symptoms expressions of a disturbance in the *personality*, in the feelings to others and to self, feelings which were once appropriate responses to treatment received from those responsible for the child and close to it during the earliest years?[2]

Which symptom is chosen—psychosomatic, neurotic, psychotic, perversion, addiction, behavior disorder, criminality—depends upon the balance of the emotional forces. This in turn depends upon the imprinting and upon the early conditioning of the basic motivations and reactions of the neonate, the infant, and the young child. Shelley, from Dr. Miller's description, was under almost uncontrollable tensions. These no doubt gave the intensity to his feelings, thinking, and behavior and came to expression in his poetry, where it was esthetically disciplined, and in his life which, less disciplined, was therefore so stormy.

Basically, then, his life expressed some form of behavior disorder, and the elations and the torpor were no more than the emotional reflections of his turbulent pattern of living. These turbulent feelings, reflected in his mind, he projected with breathtaking artistry in his poems. Some specific motivational pattern is basic; the mood swings are merely a result, and not a cause, not central clinically, but the

[2]Saul, L. and Wenar, S. (1965). "Early Influences on Development and Disorders of Personality." Psa. Quart., Vol. 34.

accompanying affect. The clue to the main pathodynamics, in the material presented, lies, of course, in the reaction of rebellion against the father's control, which pattern of rebellion is evident in all phases of Shelley's life as here depicted.

One cannot but wonder whether Dr. Miller found any clues whatever to what made Shelley a great *poet*. Others have the intensity, "the agony and the ecstasy," but the result is only turmoil. What was it that enabled Shelley to shape his inner tumult into so unsurpassed an artistic form as his *Ode to the West Wind?*

Leon J. Saul, M.D.
Media, Pennsylvania

Response

To the Editors: Re Shelley's *Ode to the West Wind*, for Shelley, identification, succor and strength tend to be one. His identification with the West Wind, like that with Queen Mab, or Laone, the combination of mother and self in *The Revolt of Islam*, and his merging with the beloved in *Epipsychidion*, all illustrate the engulfing, fortifying nature of love and identification, as he conceived of love.

Re the diagnosis of Shelley as manic depressive, I agree that the "clue to the main pathodynamics . . . lies, of course, in the reaction of rebellion against the father's control," as Dr. Saul points out. It was Newman Ivy White, author of the detailed *Portrait of Shelley* (Knopf, 1945), who stated that Shelley was manic depressive, and added the question: What more is there to say about it? I mentioned in my paper on Shelley in this journal that there were certain similarities between this great poet and the manic depressive patients studied by a group of Washington psychoanalysts. Frieda Fromm-Reichmann's paper on manic depressives was published in 1959. Then in 1961 Edith Weigert's paper appeared. (Previously, Lewin's work on manic depressive cycles had seemed to corroborate Shelley's cryptic messages about himself in his own writings.) Shelley's outstanding characteristic was not that he was given to moodswings but that his genius utilized his conflicting unconscious and conscious powers and, at his best, integrated their entirety. Like Proust, Shelley sensed that there was more meaning in what he wrote than he, himself, was aware of. It was Shelley's intent to impart new psychological knowledge that would improve mankind.

Freud questioned whether manic depressive swings were psychogenic or "spontaneous." He thought they might sometimes be constitutional.[1] What light can Shelley's fantasies throw on what is cause and what is effect? Which came first, the defiant acting out or the moodswing? Do conflicts cause moodswings or vice versa? Both seem inextricably involved, in Shelley, and both seem deeply ingrained. He never failed to act provocatively. He always created a milieu of megalomania and paranoid fear, and there was never any peace, only triumphant ecstacy and then once more the hostility, the martyrdom, and the involvement of others who were dependent on him—innocent, beloved victims who shared his downfall; then once again there was erotism, fusion with a supernatural lover, and triumph in spiritual rebirth. Always he renewed the cycle in life and in fantasy, refined and worked over his verbal imagery into a set of beautifully finished, integrated, esthetically satisfying symbols. This was done after long, diligent study of the great classics. Shelley's copious notebooks show that practically all of his imagery is interrelated with a core of basic fantasies.

[1]Freud, S. "Beyond the Pleasure Principle, Group Psychology and Other Works." *Standard Edition*, Vol. 18. London: Hogarth Press and Institute of Psycho-Analysis, p. 132.

The marvelous esthetic quality of his lines is not explainable by his persistent concentration alone, nor by his many years of efforts to improve his verbal gifts. He had tireless energy, when he was working, and demanded of himself the very best. He felt that he had cryptic messages about his own inner being that pressed for communication to mankind. He periodically had a sense of his own genius. His words carry the ring of truth. The aerial Shelleyan universe, neutralizing its contradictions, carries over to his readers truth, eternal reality, superior to current reality. Disciplined harmony and integration were achieved at the expense of suffering not only on his part, but on the part of those around him. The difficulties he, and they, experienced are only a background to the integration he laboriously achieved by writing.

Milton L. Miller, M.D.
Chapel Hill, North Carolina

Depressive Character

To the Editors: In his account of the "depressive character" ["Psychodynamics of the Depressive Character," *The Psychoanalytic Forum*, Vol. 1, No. 3], Dr. Berliner has introduced a "need to be loved"—an "instinctual need," as he calls it—which is clearly incompatible with the psychoanalytic theory of instincts and with the definition of "love" which derives from this theory. The whole thrust of Freud's sexual or "life instinct" theory is that an active ego relates to passive objects, not for the purpose of loving them, much less of being loved by them, but for the purpose of satisfying somatic needs. Freud's paper on "Instincts and Their Vicissitudes" makes a definitive statement: "the word 'to love' moves further and further into the sphere of the pure pleasure-relation of the ego to the object and finally becomes fixed to sexual objects in the narrower sense and to those which satisfy the needs of sublimated sexual instincts."[1] A later statement makes this point even more explicit: "Love with an inhibited aim was in fact originally fully sensual love, and it is so still in man's unconscious."[2]

While "being loved" is casually mentioned by many analysts, including Freud himself, it has no formal place in the psychoanalytic theory of sexual instincts, since it implies a situation to which the theory simply does not extend: that of a passive ego being related to active objects which are seeking somatic satisfactions of some sort. We can always overcome such problems by overlooking them, or by blurring the old distinctions so that, for instance, Freud's passive "loved" objects become "love" objects, both active and passive, in Berliner's view. Or else we can back off, reconsider the problems, and see whether they might be avoided if we take a somewhat different theoretical line.

In regard specifically to "being loved," I have shown elsewhere that Fairbairn's object-relations theory provides us with a viable alternative.[3] Fairbairn took the position that the ego's object-seeking is an end in itself, rather than a means of fulfilling any instinctual aims, inhibited or otherwise. Hence I have extended his theory to situations in which the ego may be active or passive, loving or being loved, in relation to its objects.[4]

In regard to depression, perhaps we should emphasize the difference between loss of a

---

[1]Freud, S. (1915). "Instincts and Their Vicissitudes." *Standard Edition*, Vol. 14. London: Hogarth Press, 1957, p. 137.

[2]Freud, S. (1930). "Civilization and Its Discontents." *Standard Edition*, Vol. 21. London: Hogarth Press, 1961, pp. 102-103.

[3]Sullivan, C. T. (1963). *Freud and Fairbairn: Two Theories of Ego-Psychology*. Doylestown, Pa.: Doylestown Foundation.

[4]Sullivan, C. T. (1965). "On Being Loved: A Contribution to the Psychology of Object-Relations." Psa. Rev., Vol. 52.

loved object—necessitating the withdrawal of libido by the ego, in Freud's theory—and loss of an object's love—which might involve the withdrawal of libido *from* the ego, by the object itself. This is the loss which concerns Dr. Berliner, which seems to account for the clinical picture of depression, and which Freud's theory does not contemplate.

For that matter, Freud's theory never entirely explains why the ego must withdraw libido from an object—an object being a psychical representation, after all—even if its external referent is "lost," e.g., in the death of a parent. What is to prevent the ego from continuing to "love" such an internalized object? Does "loving" necessarily stop when the external referent ceases to be available for the full satisfaction of instinctual needs?

It seems to me that depression is better understood in terms of the derivation, from Fairbairn's theory, that an object may cease to be active, i.e., "loving" toward the ego, when the object's external referent expires. Again, questions arise as to how closely the fate of a psychical object is bound up with that of its external referent. But these questions are taking us too far beyond the scope of Dr. Berliner's paper. Perhaps we can persuade him to consider them in future.

Charles T. Sullivan
NIMH Predoctoral Fellow
New York, New York

Response

To the Editors: Sullivan disagrees with calling the infant's need to be loved, including to be fed and held in warm contact with the mother's body, an instinctual need, which he thinks is incompatible with the psychoanalytic theory of instincts. For the purpose of my paper I have no objection to calling it simply a "vital need." Its connection with libido is well enough known and certainly fits the libido theory. My paper deals with the effects of frustrations of this need, the loss of love, loss of love objects and particularly the many experiences of unpleasure the child has to take from love objects and which are introjected. The ego, for self-preservation, builds up defenses in the form of denial and libidinization. The latter is the libidinal cathexis by an active ego of introjects and of the unpleasure connected with them. If this cathexis is projected or acted out with actual persons or events, we see the symptom of masochism. The sexual form of masochism has indeed the purpose of satisfying somatic needs. In nonsexual masochism the goal is the satisfaction of the need for affection. Depression, in contradistinction to ordinary unhappiness, can be understood only as a libidinal phenomenon, that is, in terms of the libido theory. The admixture of aggression, at least in the depressive character, appears to be a secondary development. This may be different in the melancholic psychosis, but this needs further study.

Fairbairn's theory may also be applicable to my work, though I cannot confirm the withdrawal of libido from the ego by the object itself. On the contrary, the ego holds on, tenaciously and with the power of the libidinal instinct, to the injurious inner objects, which, in the light of this need, appear to be still better than no object at all. There is in the depressive character (perhaps it is different in the melancholic psychosis) no withdrawal of libido; there are misplaced cathexes, self-injurious object choices, suffering-centered preoccupations which interfere with healthy object relations. But libido remains the innermost steering force. I think Freud's libido theory has in the psychology of the depressive character one of its most articulate verifications.

Bernhard Berliner, M.D., PH.D.
San Francisco, California

Omnipotence

To the Editors: Despite my inclination to avoid success and preserve my omnipotent fantasy of maternal fusion, I cannot resist making a comment on Dr. Norman Levy's discussion of Dr. Alexander's paper on "Omnipotence and the Avoidance of Pleasure" [*The Psychoanalytic Forum*, Vol. 1, No. 3].

I think the reason Dr. Levy's closing remark that the paper "does not represent an original contribution" (nothing really new) seems so gratuitous is that it is really directed to object relations theory rather than to this paper in particular. It is a denial that there is a very real divergence between libido theory and object relations theory which requires fundamental theoretical reorientation.

Thelma Strickler, ACSW
Beverly Hills, California

Conjoint Therapy

(Joachim Flescher, M.D. *is Director of the Dual Therapy Research Bureau, New York, and author of* Mental Health and Prevention of Neurosis *and* Dual Therapy and Genetic Psychoanalysis.*)*

To the Editors: My experience with conjoint therapy (since 1960) confirms fully most of Dr. Alexander S. Rogawski's observations and lines of reasoning ["Psychoanalysts View Conjoint Therapy," *The Psychoanalytic Forum*, Vol. 1, No. 2]. In a recent publication I have tried to integrate conjoint therapy into the larger framework of genetic psychoanalysis. The latter rests, in my view, on the triadic principle, that is, on the proposition that the healthy development of an individual is predicated upon a well-balanced and equidistant (from each parent) position within the original family triad. Many puzzling observations in the analytic process and many technical difficulties may find both clarification and successful solution if we use this frame of reference.

Difficulties in resolving transference are contingent upon the tendency of patients to overidealize the analyst, a tendency which to a large degree is expressive of an exacerbated ambivalence. It takes courage and honesty to admit, as Dr. Rogawski did, that innumerable interpretations and working through often fail to reduce the strength of the patient's transference attachment.

While in the process of formulating my reaction to the panelists' views on conjoint therapy as published in *The Forum*, I participated in a discussion[1] of Dr. Phyllis Greenacre's paper, "Overidealization of the Analyst and of Analysis: Manifestations in the Transference and Countertransference Relationships." This paper was precisely on the dynamics and sequelae of overidealization in transference, and I shared with my colleagues at the New York Psychoanalytic Institute an important insight relevant to that problem and even more significant to the analytic methodology. I reached this insight through a decade of concentration on the dynamics of the analytic process and especially on the transference-countertransference interplay.

I reminded the colleagues of Dr. Victor Rosen's witty remark about the analyst's tendency to pretend that he doesn't know everything. I do not think, as does Dr. Greenacre, that the god-like image of the analyst, perfect and infallible, mirroring the same idealization of parents that is at the root of man's belief in the reality of gods, is traceable exclusively to the narcissism and hostility of the analyst. Rather, at least for a certain category of patients, this defensive exaltation of the analyst's

[1]At Meeting of the New York Psychoanalytic Association, Oct. 11, 1966.

image ensues from the original design of the analytic situation which has remained unchanged since Freud bestowed it upon us.

I questioned whether occurrences reflecting the fact that each of the *two* parents in different stages of development has in different ways influenced detrimentally the child's maturation can be reconstructed, made evident, and reversed in a one-to-one relationship. How can the mother's mediation of the father's influence in the child's early years appear in the confined dyadic system of analysis, where the need for a double transference has to converge forcibly toward *one* object alone? In other words, I find that the difficulties which result from overidealization used as a defense are not due to the analyst's countertransference liabilities as such nor to the past traumatizations of the patient so much as to one inherent but not inevitable aspect of traditional analysis—its dyadic nature.

By allowing and promoting the superimposition of maternal and paternal transference on one object figure alone, we increase considerably the obstacles in tracing back processi at the root of the patient's psychopathology. Although the analyst is the object of maternal and paternal transference, his objective sexual identity, or certain defensive needs of the patient, makes one of these two roles preponderant at the expense of the other. This is equal to a symbolic separation of the parents. In other words, it is not only guilt over the unrealistic infantile privilege of being listened to endlessly in a world which seems to have less and less time for such "friendship" (Rogawski)—though actually based on unilateral communication—but the conflict rooted in the oedipal and preoedipal constellation which feeds that sense of guilt and interferes with its analytic resolution. For certain patients (specified in the chapter on indication in my book *Dual Therapy and Genetic Psychoanalysis*),[2] a triadic constellation—of which conjoint therapy is a very important and popular variation—is absolutely necessary to prevent the patient's fantasies and conflicts about having separated the parents and to maintain an exclusive infantile and monopolizing preoedipal and/or oedipal relationship with the analyst.

Because he must studiously avoid—and he is committed to this rigorously—expressing his opinion about matters where disagreement with the patient might occur (philosophy of life, politics, personal tastes, hobbies, etc.), the analyst is rarely exposed to the danger of being seen as different from the patient's idealized projection of him. Thus, his defense of denial of hostility is constantly reinforced, culminating inevitably in a dyadic bind in therapy.

The admission of Dr. Rogawski that "it becomes difficult for a therapist to give up what has become a mutual adult relationship of trust and to embark once again on a laborious process with a stranger" corresponds precisely to what I have called our tendency to build our patients into our psychic economy, which then makes us often resist the resolution of countertransference as much as, or more than, the patients resist the resolution of their transference involvement.

I hope that my remarks will not be construed as being directed against classical analysis as such. Analytic therapy, more frequently than we realize, becomes a sort of reservation of indulgence for the very irrational demands and expectations which the patient, through analysis, should be helped to relinquish. Yet, without the kind of self-honesty which Freud showed and which the use of his method requires of psychoanalysts, admissions like Dr. Rogawski's, as well as my own observations in work with patients and supervisees, would not have been possible. Without the self-discipline and self-scrutiny to which we have been conditioned through following the "fundamental rule" in our own analysis and in our daily psychoanalytic work, we would not be able to

[2]Flescher, J. New York: D.T.R.B. Editions, 1966.

overcome the resistance against discovering our unwillingness to see the patient in his "social context," that is, in relationship to his spouse, his parents, and his siblings, or to ask ourselves how much our analytic work with the patient contributes to an improvement in his extra-therapeutic relationships rather than to their deterioration. In this sense, only by continuing to stand on the shoulders of the psychological genius of the 20th century, are we able to see a little further ahead than Freud himself could.

The triadic principle which my modification of the analytic constellation follows, requires that the patient be seen alternately and occasionally jointly by *two* analysts, one of each sex. This principle allowed me to apply the conjoint therapy not only to married couples but also to a duo of relatives belonging to different generations—father and daughter, mother and son, etc. The equidistance here is somewhat different from that mentioned by Dr. Rogawski who speaks about the therapeutic alliance yielding "to an equidistant position of the therapist to both partners in the conjoint session."

Dr. Rogawski also speaks of the type of communication which, through bouncing off on to the other participant who is eavesdropping, circumvents certain resistances caused by emotional tension. This comment comes heuristically close to the theory and application of the "cross-recording" technique as a way of communication in the triadic setting of dual analysis. It agrees with my observations (and Dr. Saver's) of how often the patient provides a distorted picture of the spouse because he wants to present himself in a more positive light. Such distortions frequently remain uncorrected because of the analyst's inclination—very human, indeed, but also well-rationalized by the exigencies of the treatment process—not to arouse undue opposition in the analysand. This self-protective device which is part of a larger problem of the dependence of "screened empathy" on countertransference patterns, is, in my opinion, the primary source of the analyst's misconception of the very phenomena which he is obligated to perceive as objectively as possible in order to be able to rectify them.

In classifying the various types of countertransference involvements, I commented on the frequency with which reactive countertransference involvements, after reaching a certain intensity, change into a defensive countertransference that activates, or takes advantage of, operating defenses in the analyst. The situation cited by Grotjahn as being clearly observable in long analyses whereby the analyst and the patient develop a relationship and certain defenses which evade awareness, exactly covers this obstacle which often leads to unconquerable impasses, disruption of treatment, or aggravation of the patient's condition. Similarly, Dr. Martin Grotjahn's observation that the triangular relationship of conjoint therapy changes the therapeutic situation for the benefit of all involved supports my general view on the principles governing genetic development. In contrast to the dyadic principle which interferes with the maturation of the individual, the triadic principle safeguards that evolution to the degree that under its influence, the need to safeguard the individual's existence, as well as the need for survival of the species, is optimally blended.

Of relevance here is also Dr. Grotjahn's clinical vignette from the conjoint therapy of a patient with a past coronary occlusion whose wife "had her hands around his heart and every once in a while would squeeze it," causing him to have an angina attack. It underscores how dramatic our therapeutic intervention may be in contrast to the popular and indeed sometimes justified image of the analyst as only a tolerant listener to the patient's complaints.

In general I would say that nothing more completely proves the analyst's willingness to do something about the admitted peril of indulging in one's own narcissism than his initiative to extend the treatment relationship beyond the dyadic system. I do not know how else to put under control the hostility and narcissism which Dr. Greenacre, during the discussion of her paper, had stressed as accounting for the overidealization of and overattachment to the analyst. (The speaker had commented how often "more analysis" is considered rather than an attempt to understand why the previous analysis went wrong.)

I was not surprised to find among the *Forum* panel discussants representatives of the opposition which resists the process of opening, in the analytic situation, a window toward the patient's real life and relationships. There is, for example, the usual concern that the gold of pure analysis is adulterated and that a given therapy is not "real analysis." Similar assertions have long before made me wonder whether patients are coming to us to have "real analysis" or to get relief from their suffering. Many of them, the most adamant traditionalists are by now willing to admit, often receive the first but not the latter. Occasionally, they get even worse and have breakdowns, as Dr. G. Bychowski illustrated in his recent paper, "Psychosis Precipitated by Psychoanalysis." (Genetic psychoanalysis, as my therapeutic experience has shown, is the best preventative against such an occurrence.)

The fact that Freud once complained that it was very difficult for him to deal with the relatives of patients testifies to his having had plenty, albeit disappointing, contacts with them. Today I have the impression that we now know better how to cope with such exigencies. I am inclined to think it indicative of the skill and proper countertransference attitude of an analyst if he can have good contacts with members of the patient's environment without fearing to imperil the transference or anticipating other calamities from its "contamination."

I agree with Dr. Sigmund Gabe that it will take a long time before the specific indications for the various modalities are worked out. Yet they will never be worked out if no one proceeds to experiment with them only because he is overwhelmed by the many alternatives. I disagree, however, with Dr. Gabe that analysis is "to establish a transference relationship in which the patient projects his internal life onto the analyst and relives it with him." The patient, as I see it, identifies his analyst with a figure of his past. If any psychic part of himself (never his internal life as such!) is projected, it is only to that degree to which it reflects a relationship which led to a structural deposit. It therefore is somewhat like falling victim to a self-produced smokescreen when we speak about projection of one's internal life without specifically qualifying which experiences with which people are relived, be it involving a real situation or an imaginary one in the sense of Freud's "psychic reality."

Dr. Gabe also raises a convincing objection to the attempt to handle transference in the end-stage of analysis by the analyst's seeing the patient with his spouse. He argues that the presence of the spouse interferes precisely with the ventilation of feelings rooted in the transference neurosis, although this ventilation is indispensable in helping the patient to free himself from the emotional attachment to the analyst. In a study group at the New York Psychoanalytic Institute I had made the point that giving the patient endless opportunity to ventilate his transference feelings can be compared with the situation of an unresponsive love object who let a rejected suitor express all his passionate thwarted feelings for her. Her willingness to meet him again and again to the exclusion of all others must automatically rekindle and strengthen his hope of winning her. The dichotomization of transference which is inherent in conjoint therapy as in any other triadic setting, including dual analysis, lessens the transference involvement more radically than does the most cathartic expression of transference feelings by the patient or interpretation by the analyst. (This is why I have suggested exposing the patient in the end-stage of a prolonged analysis to the dual setting.) Besides, there is no reason, should the patient desire it, why an individual session could not be intercalated from time to time in that stage (Rogawski).

Dr. Carl A. Whitaker sees the analyst who does conjoint therapy with a married couple in the role of a mother-in-law. This observation testifies to the difficulty that analysts and psychotherapists in general have in seeing themselves alternately, and even within the same session, in the role of a father or a mother according to the material yielded by the patient. There can be no doubt, however, that ultimately beneath the most pronounced paternal transference, there is operating the historically and ontogenetically antecedent maternal transference. I was interested in Dr. Whitaker's belief that one should engage the family only with a team of two therapists. I surmise that he has in mind two therapists of opposite sex, which is just the modality of joint-conjoint therapy that is capable of being extended, as I have shown, into joint family therapy.

Dr. Grotjahn's remark regarding the feminine identification in physicians neglected even in training analysis gives me confidence that he will be open to the avenues which dual analysis opens for the clarification and consolidation of the biosyntonic sexual identity, as my therapeutic experience entitles me to believe. While a feminine identification might be an important motivating source for physicians in general, it is my belief that in psychoanalysis it complicates the transference and countertransference interplay unless we modify the analytic situation in the sense here exposed. Only in this way can we hope to break the pattern of transmission of feminine identification from analysts to analysands who then become analysts themselves, promote feminine identification, and so forth.

Dr. Don Jackson's quotation from his own life history testifies to the tradition of honest self-examination in which I think psychoanalysts excel over members of any other profession. I add to his remark only that the most frequent double bind which is so catastrophic for the mental health of our children derives from the genetic disbalance in the original family triad where, to quote Dr. Jackson, the "reality is interpreted" under its most essential aspects "in different ways by each parent."

Dr. Terry C. Rodgers' exploration of the symbiotic interaction in marriage as an extra-therapeutic source of resistance in the analysis of one marriage partner—a resistance which can only be overcome by conjoint therapy—deserves fullest consideration. We should be aware, in order to have the right attitude in the analytic process, that the dyadic aspect of the analytic situation is not an improvement on but simply competes with a symbiotic marriage unless we are willing to expand the former's confining system. Conjoint therapy and, I maintain, dual analysis are such expansions.

I closed my discussion of "Overidealization of Analysts and of Analysis" at the New York Psychoanalytic Institute with the statement that therapists who persist in expecting those results which the Freudian method theoretically should bring about, may not necessarily be "victims of omnipotence and rescue fantasies" as the speaker had suggested. We may still recover, I felt, the original therapeutic reputation of psychoanalysis if we are willing to consider it to be not a religion but a science which is liable to change and progress.

I have already expressed in private communication to the editor, but I am doing so again on this occasion, my enthusiasm and my deep appreciation for his offering those who work in our field an arena for free exchange of ideas. A journal like *The Forum* will prevent forever that a new idea in our movement be discarded before its merits and shortcomings, theoretical and practical, have been explored in an atmosphere of real freedom of thought and assurance against implicit or explicit imputation of irrational and detrimental nonconformism.

Joachim Flescher, M.D.
New York, New York

---

*(A misprint occurred on page 327 in Jean Livermore's comments on "Conjoint Therapy" [*The Psychoanalytic Forum, *Vol. 1, No. 3]. The correct paragraph follows.)*

"To work on these fronts one must indeed give up the 'exalted role' and settle for being human too, for omnipotence is difficult to demonstrate in such 'bright sunlight.' To maintain it requires a kind of magic which involves not allowing the patient to observe too closely lest he see too clearly. Of course the patient, also, must give up his illusions that all his problems will be solved by his all-powerful parent; he will have to see himself as the adult (at least in part) that he is, with responsible relationships with other human beings. Both sacrifice fantasy. But then the discovery of reality may not always be totally painful; there is considerable pleasure in the mastery of it."

Jean Livermore, ACSW
Los Angeles, California

To the Editors: In *The Forum* discussion of conjoint family therapy the question is discussed of Sigmund Freud's insight into family dynamics.

A relatively unknown and to my knowledge untranslated passage from an interview given by Heinrich Meng[1] throws some more light on Sigmund Freud and his insight into family dynamics. Here is the quotation:

"I reported to Freud about a man with severe alcoholism. Freud wanted to hear details; most of all about the 'family-constellation' and about the character of the patient. His opinion then was: 'Among other things it is the masochism of the wife—who according to your report cannot be treated for various reasons—which is one of the obstacles. Considering the character of the patient and his age of fifty-eight years you ought to terminate the analysis. The man will perish of his alcoholism. Use your time for other patients who really need analysis.' "

Freud must have known the wife's important part in the husband's drinking habits, about which we are only now learning more from recent studies.

Martin Grotjahn, M.D.
Beverly Hills, California

Sigmund Freud on Suicide

*(Several key words were omitted from Dr. Angel Garma's discussion of Dr. Litman's paper "Sigmund Freud on Suicide" [*The Psychoanalytic Forum, *Vol. 1, No. 2]. Dr. Garma's final paragraph follows with the correction in italics.)*

"Oedipus does not commit suicide, although Jocasta, whom we may consider to be a part of him, does. Oedipus blinded himself, which may be interpreted as partial suicide. Following this reasoning, and as Dr. Litman expresses it, it is very probable that 'suicidal drama often reproduces not so much guilt for the unconscious wish of the child to murder the parents but rather a reaction of abandon-

[1]Heinrich Meng: "From an Interview about Sigmund Freud." Psyche, Vol. 17, No. 5, 1963-64, p. 318.

ment on the part of the child to the parents' unconscious wish for the child's death.' However, in the case of Oedipus, his parents' filicidal wishes were *not unconscious, as were* his own parricidal desires; on the contrary, they made a very conscious attempt to carry them out."

Angel Garma, M.D.
Buenos Aires, Argentina

Analyst's Responses

*(Inadvertently, an altered copy of Dr. Samuel Lipton's discussion of Dr. Ian Alger's "The Clinical Handling of the Analyst's Responses" [*The Psychoanalytic Forum, *Vol. 1, No. 3] was published. The original version follows.)*

Dr. Alger has taken the position, supported by references to the literature, that there was a period in the development of analysis, which may indeed persist, when the analyst considered himself detached from the patient, uninvolved, and literally a blank screen or mirror. He states that the analyst dealt with the patient's responses "by denying that they were really directed at him" and argues for the importance of recognizing the actual responses of the analyst and openly exposing what was "once taboo." In addition to his general support from the literature he cites Freud as late as 1925.

For the purpose of discussion I will refer to this concept as that of the detached analyst, and I will acknowledge that this view has substantial support. More to the point, it has gained enough support from analysts of various levels of experience so that I think it might even be called conventional, and I think Dr. Alger is justified in taking it as a point of departure. Nevertheless I take issue with Dr. Alger and his numerous supporters, both those cited and those unmentioned, and I shall advance two general reasons for my difference of opinion.

First, despite all the apparently knowledgeable criticism of the concept of the detached analyst, I submit that there is not a single advocate of this position to be found either in the literature or even on personal investigation. The first point is, I think, evident. The detached analyst is mentioned in the literature only to be castigated. He is never anything but an unnamed figure. The latter point refers to my personal experience. I was once informed on a presumably reliable basis of the identity of one such analyst who was allegedly a model of detachment and learned on the basis of personal experience that this was not true. Subsequently I learned that this sort of information is regularly unreliable.

Does the fact which I believe is correct, that literally no one espouses this view, mean that the phenomenon does not exist? Is there no such person as a detached analyst? I would say that such a phenomenon exists but only as an error or only on the basis of misunderstanding. I have seen detachment in students who mistakenly believed they were acting correctly, and I have no doubt it occurs as the result of error in experienced analysts, but this is a far cry from theoretical espousal. In addition we are sometimes misled by the complaints of patients, and I am sure there are occasions when this position is attributed to another analyst on the basis of a patient's complaints. To summarize, I think the detached analyst, who is detached on the basis of theoretical conviction, is a mythical figure, and I submit that insofar as he has any existence it is on the basis of personal error or the misconstruction of the complaints of patients.

The second general basis of my disagreement lies in a different understanding of some of Freud's work, which Dr. Alger advances to support his contention. I do not believe that Freud ever meant to recommend detachment in Dr. Alger's sense, and I believe ample support for my view can be found in Freud's works. I submit that if one reads the sparkling interchanges with Dora; the fascinating explanations to the Rat Man, as well as Freud's original notes in which he discloses that he gave the Rat Man a meal and then reveals the associational repercussions; the charming and amusing interchanges of the Forsyth incident in the New Introductory Lectures; or any of a mass of other clinical data which Freud has recorded, one is forced to conclude that Freud was anything but detached in his actual work.

Then what of the mirror, screen, and surgeon analogies? What of the intense emotional relationship that arises without the physician's agency and is not accounted for by the actual situation? If my clinical citations above are valid, did Freud preach what he did not practice? I think not, but believe rather that there has been an area of misunderstanding. Freud used these analogies to describe the work of analysis proper, not the personal relationship on which it was based. He was attempting to describe the essential juxtaposition of the analyst's attitude of neutrality and evenly-hovering attention to the patient's free association. Freud recognized fully that this arrangement had to be based on a personal relationship. He referred to this as the irreducible, unobjectionable element of the positive transference. He distinguished this from the work of analysis proper, generally took it for granted, and gave it relatively little explicit attention, but I think his view is clear. When he referred to the inability of schizophrenics to develop a transference he was referring to this element of the transference on which the analytic work is based, not to the irrational elements which he recognized might develop.

In regard to the second question concerning the independence of the intense relationship from the actual situation, I believe that Freud meant that the analyst acted naturally, confined his efforts to the analytic work and did not attempt to instigate or provoke responses. Certainly such responses have an objective basis in some perception, but equally certainly their full explanation is not thereby elucidated. To use Dr. Alger's clinical illustration as an example, certainly the patient responded to him. Yet it was not his purpose, I presume, to significantly influence her by his spontaneous response to an amenity, and it seems clear that her reaction was unduly intense. Surely we can assume that some historically significant determinants lay behind the importance that his nuance of behavior had to her.

Since Dr. Alger does not belabor the point that his approach is interpersonal, I am not inclined to belabor my divergence from this view and my adherence to the approach which emphasizes more genetic determinants. I will therefore state briefly that I would conceptualize the example as the beginning of a piece of analytic work, would be inclined to place somewhat less importance on it as an accomplishment in itself, and would be inclined to assume that interchanges like this one are common in analysis. Perhaps I should say that if my assumption is not true, I think it should be. I add only one qualification. While I would not dispute that the explicit acknowledgment of the response of the analyst can be useful occasionally, I think it is not regularly so and can lead to a sort of mutual adjustment rather than to an analysis of the patient. I find that under favorable conditions, granting that the analyst is not defensive, the patient learns to place reliance on his associations as having psychic reality, valid for him, whether the analyst explicitly affirms them or not, and learns to use them as a basis for deepening self-knowledge.

In conclusion, I congratulate Dr. Alger on presenting observations and clinical data in an accurate manner, suitable for discussion, and, I hope, productive controversy.

Samuel D. Lipton, M.D.
Chicago, Illinois

he Psychoanalytic Forum
ıdex of Volume I

•rum Contributors

Forum Contents